631.52 ~~EURO~~
613.11 EUR

European Commission

COST Action 814

Crop development for the cool and wet regions of Europe

Achievements and future prospects

Proceedings of the final conference

Pordenone, Italy
10 to 13 May 2000

Edited by
G. Parente and J. Frame

Directorate-General for Research

2000   EUR 19683

A great deal of additional information on the European Union is available on the Internet.
It can be accessed through the Europa server (http://europa.eu.int).

Cataloguing data can be found at the end of this publication.

Luxembourg: Office for Official Publications of the European Communities, 2000

ISBN 92-894-0227-X

Congress Scientific Committee

CHAIRMAN	P. STAMP	ETH, ZURICH
SECRETARY	K. PITHAN	RESEARCH DG, BRUXELLES
MEMBERS	N.R. BAKER	UNIVERSITY OF ESSEX, COLCHESTER
	L. CARLIER	DEPT. CROP HUSBANDRY, MERELBEKE
	A. GUCKERT	INRA, NANCY
	T. MELA	MTT, JOKIOINEN
	G. PARENTE	SAASD, PORDENONE

Congress Organising Board

CHAIRMAN	G. PARENTE	SAASD, PORDENONE
SECRETARY	G. ZOFFI	SAASD, PORDENONE

Secretariat members

A. BOMBEN
G. MOZZON
E. PRESOT
M. SCIMONE
S. VENERUS
C. VENIER
I. ZANIN
D. ZUCCHIATTI

The Management Committee of Cost Action 814 wishes to dedicate this book to Mr. Peter Stamp, Mr. Armand Guckert and Mr. Klaus Pithan in appreciation of all their hard work and energy, not only in organising this Conference, but also throughout the duration of Cost Action 814. The success of the Action is evidence of their commitment to it.

Special thanks to Mr. John Frame for the proofreading of texts and to Ms Giovanna Zoffi and Ms Nicoletta Tonizzo for their contribution to the supervision of manuscripts.

COST 814 MANAGEMENT COMMITTEE

N. Baker	United Kingdom
D. A. Ballester	Spain
J. Christiansen	Denmark
J. Connolly	Ireland
J. P. Destain	Belgium
K. Dörffling	Germany
G. Doussinault	France
B. Frankow-Lindberg	Sweden
O. Gasparikova	Slovak Republic
A. Guckert (Vice-Chairman)	France
A. Helgadottir	Island
T. Janda	Hungary
G. Kapetanaki	Greece
T. Karyotis	Greece
M. Knezevic	Croatia
T. Mela	Finland
E. Paldi	Hungary
G. Parente	Italy
K. Pithan (Secretary)	European Commission
R. T. Samuelsen	Norway
M. Sanchez Diaz	Spain
B. Solheim	Norway
P. Sowinski	Poland
P. Stamp (Chairman)	Switzerland
F. Taube	Germany
E. van Bockstaele	Belgium
P. R. van Hasselt	The Netherlands
L. J. M. van Soest	The Netherlands

SPONSORS

Directorate General Research of the European Commission
Food and Agriculture Organisation of the United Nation
Provincia di Pordenone
Regione Autonoma Friuli-Venezia Giulia
Camera di Commercio, Industria, Artigianato e Agricoltura di Pordenone
Fondazione Cassa di Risparmio di Udine e Pordenone
Comune di Pordenone
Comune di Spilimbergo
Ministero dell'Università e della Ricerca Scientifica e Tecnologica

Foreword

As the President of the Province of Pordenone, I have the duty and honour of giving my best regards to everyone here: the authorities, the delegates from both the regional and local administrations and in particular, I wish to welcome every member of Cost 814 Action, coming from all the European regions and from many other countries of the world. I have to congratulate Cost 814 members, subdivided into five groups, on their valuable research carried out during an 8-year period. These groups will bring here the results of their research with the aim of further developing agriculture in the cool and wet regions of Europe, such as the mountain areas of the Italian Alps in our region and province. The experts present have the great merit of fostering the agriculture of these areas through scientific investigation and knowledge, enhancing production, upholding traditions and improving the natural quality of the local products.

It is the duty of the regional, national and EU politicians to help farmers and peoples from areas disadvantaged due to climate, orography and social conditions and to make their economy equal to those of the most favourable areas. This will be the object of this important European meeting, thanks to the European Community which has financially supported the researches of many leading scientists present. Politicians must put these technical results to good use in order to choose the best options.

I wish to express the Province of Pordenone's gratitude for the actuality offered by Cost of hosting the Final Convention of this European Action. The Provincial Administration considers this European Action a strategic sector for the Province's economy and, for this reason, it is growing and booming. SAASD in fact will soon have adequate and prestigious premises - Villa Carinzia.

I also wish to express our pride in hosting not only the scientists who have been working during this period, but also the delegates of the 32 European nations belonging to the Management Committee and among them, on behalf of Italy, the Head of our Agriculture Sector.

In conclusion, I trust all delegates will derive valuable benefits from their work during these four days of thriving activity. I wish to give my regards to the associate delegates too; their social and cultural programme will also be quite busy and enjoyable.

I owe a special thanks to all those who have supported this initiative: in the first place the European Community, the councillors responsible for agriculture and the environment (Mr. G. Venier Romano and Mr. P. Ciani), the mayor of Pordenone (Mr. A. Pasini), the President of the Chamber of Commerce of Pordenone (Mr. A. Antonucci), the CRUP Foundation, FAO, and all Sponsors.

Elio De Anna
President of the Province of Pordenone

Opening addresses

BY GIUSEPPE PARENTE

Chairman of the Organizing Committee

Mr Mayor of Pordenone, Mr President of the Region Friuli Venezia Giulia, Mr President of the Province of Pordenone, dear authorities, dear colleagues and friends, I would like to extend my best wishes for good and useful work during these days of the COST 814 final Conference in Pordenone.

First of all, I would like to thank the European Union, the summit leaders of the COST senior officials, the secretary of COST Action 814, the Management Committee to have allowed us to organize this important final meeting involving 32 European countries, the invited speakers, and all of you here present because your participation will make this meeting a great event.

I owe a special 'thank you' to the past and present administration: the former President Mr. A. Rossi (two years ago) and the former councillor responsible for Agriculture Mr. M. Boria, who strongly supported the idea of hosting this meeting in 2000; also the present administration i.e. the President of the Province of Pordenone, Mr. Elio De Anna, and the councillor responsible for European Policies, Mr. R. Francesconi, who believed and trusted in this event and permitted its realisation. Weekly, they went on asking me the same questions: how is the preparation for the meeting going on? Is everything settled? This Province considers Agricultural Industry as a primary activity of absolute importance. The Agricultural Industry of the Province of Pordenone represents 42% of the whole regional Gross Output of Agriculture.

Climate is very variable in this region; it includes both mediterranean and oceanic components with cool and wet conditions in the alpine areas. Mountain areas represent 45% of the regional territory. In these mountain areas rainfall records are yearly registered and more than 3,000 mm/year is the average for the last 25 years. Four localities in Europe are competing for this record: Friuli Venezia Giulia, Lombardy, Montenegro, Iceland. Temperatures near the Austrian and Slovenian border easily drop to −30°C in the bottom of the valley. These areas are depressed and underdeveloped compared with the lowlands; this determines social and economic inequalities between neighbouring populations. The Province considers it important and right to carry out experiments and researches in these cool and wet areas in order to find out the most important species and cultivars and cultivation techniques capable of producing more food of higher quality. In my opinion, COST Action 814 is a very important initiative to reach this goal. Cost Action has offered many scientists from all over Europe the chance to exchange different experience and different knowledge and to travel and undertake work in top laboratories and European Industries. For example, one of my own staff after a training period in the UK, is one of the most valuable scientists of SAASD. Furthermore, Cost Action 814, by increasing SAASD's culture and knowledge, has allowed our Province to join Europe fully. Experiments carried out in about 20 countries of Europe have produced useful results not only for the countries hosting the trials but also for the other countries in similar climatic situations. For example, trials carried out on grassland have investigated the behaviour of white clover in cool and wet conditions by studying and selecting cultivars adapted to these conditions. This species is the most important among the grassland species for cool and wet regions. The availability of overwintering, cool-adapted and long-lasting cultivars will help farmers to produce forage of better quality at lower costs. The emmer wheat, a very important species in the past, will possibly help to increase the economy of these areas by producing high quality crops, important for the diet and the health of people.

To conclude my short speech: I am proud to host here in Pordenone so many people, scientists, and so many friends. I am proud to know that the Province of Pordenone has reached Europe, but above all that Europe has reached Pordenone. Your duty as scientists is to perform high-level tasks in science producing your valuable papers and I am sure it will be so. The duty of the Province of Pordenone, of my staff, and myself is to have prepared for you a good organisation and an excellent scientific and social programme. I promise - we promise - to you to do our best. We promise you that we will leave "no stone unturned" to do our very best in order to create the atmosphere of a great and happy family - the COST family! To this COST 814 family, welcome to Europe, welcome to Italy, welcome to Pordenone.

Opening addresses

BY PETER STAMP

Chairman of the COST ACTION 814

Few people in Europe today have ever experienced a scarcity of food and the necessity to garden or farm in order to survive as scientific research has helped to triple or quadruple yields on fertile farmlands during the second half of the last century. Today's society is more concerned about the ecological problems associated with intensive farming and demands radical changes that will lead to a sustainable production; at the same time, however, it expects food prices to drop. But in countries other than Europe and North America, the population is still increasing to a greater extent than agricultural productivity. For this reason the soil of marginal areas, such as semi-arid steppes and hilly monsoon regions, is being ploughed to such an extent that the soil is being permanently degraded. In a few decades there will be several billion more mouths to feed! Now it is time to face the challenge of developing more productive agriculture, which is ecologically acceptable, for Europe's marginal areas as well.

The majority of Europe's landscapes are man-made. Ingenious farmers have found ways and means to farm marginal, cool, wet regions in northern and western Europe and mountainous regions in central and southern Europe. Shortly sightedness with respect to economic aspects leads to the view that farming in these areas can no longer compete in a free-trading world. In view of the fact that we must meet the growing demand for food and increase industrial crop productivity, it is time to build on the experience of our ancestors and make farming a rewarding business once again. This can be achieved by introducing genetically well-adapted plant material into agro-ecosystems, thus contributing to the wealth of European "agrodiversity".

With this in mind, we submitted a proposal to senior officials of COST, for an Action on "Crop Development for Cool, Wet Regions in Europe". This proposal was accepted, and the memorandum of understanding (MOU) for COST 814 was signed by eight countries on 21 February 1992. By the end of Round I, highly motivated research groups from 19 countries were participating. During this time exciting changes that were taking place in eastern Europe where new partners with complementary goals and a high level of expertise were eager to participate. After intensive discussions, it was agreed that within five working groups, the close co-operation of the participating scientists should be continued. On 26 January 1996, the COST Action 814 was approved for other four years.

COST 814 experts and external experts highlighted the achievements and the need for future research in the proceedings of this final conference. They discussed crop adaptation from the perspective of all the working groups. The contributions they have made to applied and strategic research in the countries of the participants are extremely relevant for agriculture in cool, wet regions. They have proposed new goals for crop breeding for achieving sustainable, productive agriculture in marginal regions which have been the home of people in Europe for a long time.

Comments on the communication from the Commission titled "Towards a European Research Area" by the COST Committee of Senior Officials

BY GÖSTA DIEHL

Chairman of the COST Senior Officials

GENERAL

The COST Committee of Senior Officials (CSO) welcomes the communication from the Commission concerning the European research area. The CSO agrees that there is room for improvement, and recognises many interesting initiatives in the communication. The Committee will be very glad to participate in the proposed effort to improve and increase co-operation in R&D in Europe.

Many of the activities for improvement of the ERA proposed in the communication are already going on in COST in a spontaneous bottom-up manner at an expenditure of less than 1% of the R&D-volume for central administration. The annual volume of activities co-ordinated by COST has grown to an estimated 1,500 million Euro with a yearly budget for administration, co-operation and evaluation of only 12 million. The Actions in COST range from basic research to concerted Actions of great public utility. Tens of thousands of researchers are already participating in COST Actions. COST is thus becoming an increasingly important R & D-actor in Europe and will, with adequate support, continue to grow.

The CSO forwards the following specific comments to the proposed "Possible specific themes for action" in Annex 1 of the communication. While the CSO sees many worthwhile initiatives also under other headings the committee will here concentrate only on themes that are specifically within the competence of COST.

Networking of centres of excellence and creation of virtual centres

The co-operation in COST takes the form R & D co-operation projects called COST Actions with an average participation of 15 member states. These Action networks themselves frequently constitute virtual centres of excellence, as is the case in, for instance, nanotechnology, chemistry, meteorology, agriculture, drug development, transport and telecommunication.

Many COST Actions have produced the basis for European and world standards, for instance for GSM mobile systems and other advanced terrestrial and satellite communication systems recommended by the ITU, or developed standards that have resulted in EU directives, for instance concerning safety helmets. And one of them, meteorology, has resulted in a world class centre of excellence, the centre for medium-term weather forecasting in Reading in the UK. For basic research in chemistry, COST has during the last decade emerged as a key player for European co-operation. Many of the COST networks have also resulted in key programmes or actions for the framework programmes like ESPRIT, EURAM and FLAIR or activities concerning the ageing population.

The CSO therefore suggests that COST is a very useful tool for building up more centres of excellence, both virtual and real, in Europe and would be very happy to co-operate with the Commission in efforts in this direction.

More co-ordinated implementation of national and European research programmes

COST is a spontaneous and very cost-effective way to achieve the co-ordination of national research efforts that the Commission desires. There are already many examples of national research projects that are part both of COST Actions and national research programmes. One example is the COST Action on phosphate monitoring that was specifically set up to co-ordinate several national programmes of very high environmental and EU agricultural policy relevance.

So far there has been no systematic promotion of this aspect of COST, but the CSO feels that there is a great potential to do so in the future and suggests that this could be done in co-operation between the Commission and COST.

Closer relations between European organisations for science and technology cooperation

COST has a long history of direct and close co-operation with the Framework Programme and a more recently begun co-operation with EUREKA. The CSO is very much in favour of this development and of co-operation with all other relevant bodies. The CSO is, however, a little hesitant to the idea of introducing new superstructures in the ERA. Even so it is quite clear that COST would constructively support such a body if it were deemed necessary.

The CSO proposes that alternatives to such a formal body also be considered. Necessary consultations could take place in the form of an annual forum or joint thematic event where opportunities could be identified and proposals for further co-operation could be elaborated. Alternatively the possibility of forming a completely virtual council should be considered.

Development of the research needed for political decision-making

COST has in the past generated many Actions of research needed for political decisions, for instance "Government and democracy in the information age", "Changing labour markets, welfare policies and citizenship", "Reforming social protection system", "Transport and land-use policies", "Optimal management of waste-water systems", "Urban meteorology applied to air pollution problems in Europe" and many others, and will continue to do so. Safety, environmental protection and sustainable development have always been very important themes in COST.

Many domains of COST are excellently suited for building up and running research needed for political decision-making, but because of the very nature of COST there has been no central guidance in this respect within the initiative. Nor would the CSO want to start a central top-down planning mechanism for this in the future.

Keeping in mind the usefulness of COST for such research it could, however, be interesting for the Commission and COST together to study the possibility of refining a mechanism that would make it possible for the Commission to propose subjects routinely for Actions within COST.

Greater mobility of researchers in Europe

COST as such increases the possibilities for improving mobility of researchers in Europe by creating and upholding contacts between tens of thousands of them. On a more direct level, one of the best tools in use in COST for the research activities are so-called short-term scientific missions where researchers for a predetermined period – 3 days to 3 months – can do research in laboratories in other countries participating in the same COST Action. Currently COST has been able to finance about 1,000 of these missions per year but with more funding this could be increased considerably.

Giving young people a taste for research and careers in science

The CSO very much shares the concerns expressed in this point, and would be prepared to support any action to raise the science awareness in Europe. It could be worthwhile to explore how the COST mechanism could be utilised to contribute to the development of "science weeks".

Integration of the scientific communities of Western and Eastern Europe

All evaluations show, and participants constantly confirm, that COST is a crucial network, especially for new and associated members, for forming consortia for successful bids to the Framework Programme. COST has thus for many years substantially contributed to making the Framework Programme successful and it will continue to do so. It is also evident that COST greatly helps countries associated to the FP to develop their research and integrate it into Europe as clearly shown for instance in the comments by AllChemE on the communication on ERA.

The CSO feels that at the moment there is no better mechanism than COST for the desired integration. Despite the serious strain on the financial resources of the COST Secretariat that this entails, the Committee will actively encourage the newly associated countries to use this mechanism.

Making Europe attractive to researchers from the rest of the world
COST is an open research environment with an ever larger participation in Actions from research institutes outside Europe that clearly shows that there are an increasing number of researchers that find participation in European research attractive despite the high costs involved. Either COST itself, or a COST - like mechanism, might provide a useful vehicle for co-operation with other countries or regional groupings outside of the EU. So far COST has not as an organisation actively worked in this direction, but a decision in principle has been taken to start doing so. COST would be very interested in doing this in close co-operation with the Commission services and other scientific initiatives in Europe.

*Crop Development
for Cool and Wet Regions
of Europe*

CONTENTS

OPENING SESSION

WORKING GROUP 1
ADAPTATION OF THERMOPHILIC CROPS

Invited papers

Offered papers

WORKING GROUP 2
OVERWINTERING AND SPRING GROWTH OF WHITE CLOVER

Invited papers

WORKING GROUP 3
N-USE EFFICIENCY

Invited papers

Offered papers

WORKING GROUP 4
SMALL GRAIN CEREALS AND PSEUDO CEREALS

Invited papers

Offered papers

WORKING GROUP 5
SMALL GRAIN CEREALS AND PSEUDO CEREALS

Invited papers

Offered papers

CLOSING SESSION

General Introduction

Economic and ecological perspectives for crops in cool wet regions of the World

D. PIMENTEL

Cornell University, Ithaca, New York, USA

S U M M A R Y

Currently the world population of 6 billion is suffering from a malnutrition crisis (WHO, 1996). The World Health Organization reports that more than half of the world population or more than 3 billion people are malnourished (WHO, 1996) — the largest number and proportion ever. This ominous report should focus the attention of all agriculturists on the importance of grains and tuber production, both now and for the future.

The cool wet regions of the Northern and Southern Hemispheres supply nearly 70% of the world's food as measured by grains, and grains provide an estimated 80% to 90% of the world's food nutrients. Grains, like maize and wheat, can yield 8,000 kg and 7,000 kg respectively per hectare on average in North America and Europe.

To achieve high yields, such as those above for maize and wheat, about 1,000 mm of rainfall and a temperature that ranges from 25 to 30 degrees C are needed. In addition, to achieve these high grain yields, large inputs of fertilizers and pesticides are required, both of which depend on continuing supplies of natural gas and oil.

Environmental degradation, a serious problem in Northern-Hemisphere agriculture, is emerging as a serious constraint to achieving high yields. The most serious problems are soil erosion, water runoff, depletion of soil organic matter, and loss of biodiversity in the environment. Also of importance are chemical pollution problems, especially the environmental impacts of pesticides.

Technologies are now available that would help conserve soil, water, nutrients, organic matter, and soil biota. In addition to making agriculture environmentally sound, adopting these techniques would reduce fossil energy inputs by about a half, reduce production costs about 36%, while at the same time slightly increasing crop yields. Therefore, to make agriculture environmentally sustainable and profitable, every effort should be made to develop and adopt soil and water conservation technologies. Worldwide, a balance must be found between human population numbers, food supply and the essential natural resources that make the production of adequate food possible.

Keywords: environment, grains, population growth, resource conservation, tubers

INTRODUCTION

The cool wet regions of the earth produce nearly 70% of the world's food, especially in terms of grain production (FAO, 1997). These areas are located in North America, Europe, and in some areas of South America and Asia, like Argentina and China. Grains, which currently provide from 80% to 90% of the world's food, are nutritious foods, containing calories, protein, and several vitamins. Once harvested, they can be stored for long periods with relatively little loss due to spoilage. When properly dried, the grains contain from 13% to 15% moisture, helping to prevent microbes and other pests from destroying the grain. In addition, the low moisture level of dried grain makes them relatively economical for transport. Vegetable crops, especially tubers, also flourish in these cool wet agricultural regions. In contrast to grains, tuber vegetables, like potatoes, contain about 80% water, and thus are more difficult to store for long periods and are more expensive to transport.

The ecological and economic reasons for the high productivity of food crops of the cool wet conditions of the Northern Hemisphere and parts of the Southern Hemisphere are analyzed in this paper. Given the continued expansion of the world population, the continued productivity of these regions has become extremely critical to the world food supply.

YIELDS OF GRAINS AND TUBERS

Grains and tubers dominate the food system in the cool wet areas of both the Northern Hemisphere and the Southern Hemisphere. The specific areas examined in this analysis include North America and Europe.

Grains are especially productive per hectare of land, with yields of more than 8,000 kg ha^{-1} of maize grain in North America (USDA, 1998) and more than 7,000 kg ha^{-1} of wheat in Europe (USDA, 1998). In addition to sun and moisture, the production of high yields requires deep, fertile soils, moisture, and large inputs of fertilizers and pesticides. These conditions are characteristic of exiting conditions in the Corn Belt of the United States (USDA, 1998).

In North America and Europe, the average yields of common grains are maize at 8,000 kg ha^{-1}, and wheat, barley, rye, and oats ranging from 2,000 to 7,000 kg ha^{-1} (USDA, 1998). In certain regions of the Southern Hemisphere, similar high yields are achieved (USDA, 1998). These high yields are achieved not only because of quality soils and moist conditions in some regions but, as mentioned previously, high inputs of fertilizers and pesticides. In general, nitrogen fertilizer is applied at about 145 kg ha^{-1} per year, while phosphorus and potassium are applied at about 62 kg ha^{-1} per year (Table 1).

The white potato is the major tuber crop in the cool wet regions in North America and Europe. In North America, yields range from 40,000 to 65,000 kg ha^{-1} (USDA, 1998).

As with grains, these high yields are achieved with large inputs of nitrogen, phosphorus, and potassium fertilizers and pesticides.

Under optimal conditions, yields of some crops can be much higher than average, sometimes reaching very high yields like 31,000 kg ha⁻¹ for maize, 12,000 kg ha⁻¹ for wheat, and 100,000 kg ha⁻¹ for potatoes. Although only a few farmers come close to achieving these maximum yields, most could improve their yields through better management of their resources.

ECONOMICS OF COOL WET REGION CROP PRODUCTION

In part, the high yields of grains and potatoes in the cool wet conditions of North America and Europe is due to the widespread and heavy use of fossil energy, in the forms of fertilizers, pesticides, and mechanization. These inputs increase the costs of producing the crop. The large number of inputs used to produce a hectare of maize in North America is listed in Table 1, and are generally typical for Europe. The total cost for conventional maize production is about $844.38 per hectare for a yield of nearly 8,000 kg of maize grain (Table 1).

TABLE 1. ENERGY INPUTS AND COSTS OF CORN PRODUCTION PER HECTARE IN THE UNITED STATES (PIMENTEL ET AL., 2000).

Inputs	Quantity	kcal x 1000	Costs ($)
Labour	11.4 hrs	561	114.00
Machinery	55 kg	1,018	103.21
Diesel	42.2 L	481	8.87
Gasoline	32.4 L	328	9.40
Nitrogen	144.6 kg	2,688	89.65
Phosphorus	62.8 kg	260	34.54
Potassium	54.9 kg	179	17.02
Lime	699 kg	220	139.80
Seeds	21 kg	520	74.81
Irrigation	33.7 cm	320	123.00
Herbicides	3.2 kg	320	64.00
Insecticides	0.92 kg	92	18.40
Electricity	13.2 kWh	34	2.38
Transportation	151 kg	125	45.30
TOTAL		**7,146**	**$844.38**

for a 7,965 kg yield, kcal input x 1000 = 27,758
kcal output/kcal input = 3.88

Costs of production vary with the specific crop and the location of the crop. For example, summer fallow winter wheat in the State of Washington costs about $452 per hectare, with an excellent average yield of 4,500 kg ha[-1] (Willett and Gary, 1992). This yield is higher than the average yield of 3,024 kg ha[-1] in the U.S., but still less than the wheat yield of 7,300 kg ha[-1] in Germany (USDA, 1998).

White potato production in the state of Washington is expensive, costing about $2,121 per hectare, but the potato yield there is about 61,150 kg ha[-1] (Hinman *et al.*, 1992). The Washington potato yield is nearly double the average yield of the U.S., which is about 35,000 kg ha[-1], but the costs of production are also higher (USDA, 1998). The average yields of potatoes in Germany and Russia are 46 t ha[-1] and 23 t ha[-1], respectively (Neuhoff *et al.*, 1997; Zkukov and Khairullin, 1996). In general, fertilizer and pesticide applications greatly influence both yields and economic returns.

ENVIRONMENTAL CONCERNS

Temperatures

The optimal temperatures for most grain crops range from 20 to 30 degrees C, while potatoes generally prefer cool conditions in the 15 to 20 degree C range (Table 2). These relatively cool conditions help conserve moisture by reducing the evaporation rate from the land and the crop itself.

TABLE 2. FAVORABLE TEMPERATURES (DEGREES C) FOR FIVE CROPS (PIMENTEL, 1993).

	TEMPERATURES (C)		
Crop	Optimal	Maximum	Minimum
Corn	22-25	32-34	<20
Wheat	20-25	38	5
Rice	30-33	37-40	18-22
Potato	15-20	28-34	12
Soybean	25-28	37-40	10-14

Water Resources

Ample rainfall is particularly important for successful agricultural production. Approximately 1,000 mm of rainfall per hectare are required to produce a high yield of maize, wheat, and other grain and potato crops (Table 3). For example, a maize crop that produces about 8,000 kg ha[-1] of grain evapotranspires more than 5 million litres ha[-1] of water during the growing season (Leyton, 1983). To supply this much water to the crop, approximately 1,000 mm of rainfall per hectare, or 10 million litres of irrigation water, is required during the growing season (Pimentel *et al.*, 1997a). About this much rainfall or more falls in many regions of the Northern and Southern Hemispheres where rainfall is relatively heavy.

TABLE 3. ESTIMATED LITRES OF WATER REQUIRED TO PRODUCE 1 KG OF FOOD AND FORAGE CROPS (PIMENTEL ET AL., 1997).

Crop	Litres Kg^{-1}
Potatoes	500
Wheat	900
Alfalfa	900
Sorghum	1,110
Corn	1,400
Rice	1,912
Soybeans	2,000
Broiler Chicken	3,500
Beef	100,000

Not only is a sufficient amount of rainfall imperative, it must be available at the critical times of pollination and grain formation. At both of these vital stages, the crop must have optimal growth for maximum productivity.

The greatest threat to maintaining fresh water supplies is depletion of the surface and ground water resources required to meet the agricultural needs of the rapidly growing human population and related expansion in agriculture. Surface water is frequently mismanaged, resulting in water shortages and pollution that threaten humans and aquatic biota. The Colorado River, for example, is used so heavily by Colorado, California, Arizona, and other western States, that by the time it reaches Mexico, it is but a trickle as it enters into the Sea of Cortès (Sheridan, 1983). Although no technology can double the flow of the Colorado River, or enhance other surface and ground water resources, improved environmental management and conservation of all water resources will help ensure the availability of fresh water.

A second threat to maintaining ample fresh water resources is pollution. Although considerable water pollution has been documented in the United States (USBC, 1998), this problem is of greatest concern in countries where water regulations are not rigorously enforced or do not exist. This becomes especially critical when water flows through densely-populated areas. In addition, pesticides, fertilizers, and soil sediments pollute water resources when they accompany eroded soil into water bodies. Pollution by sewage and disease organisms, as well as some 100,000 different chemicals used globally, makes water unsuitable not only for human drinking but also for application to crops (Nash, 1993).

Land Resources
More than 99% of human food worldwide comes from the terrestrial environment, with less than 1% from the oceans and other aquatic ecosystems (FAO, 1991; Pimentel and Pimentel, 1996). Thus, maintaining the quality of agricultural soils is vital for continued production.

In 1960, when the world population numbered about 3 billion, approximately 0.5 ha of cropland was available per capita worldwide. This half a hectare of cropland per capita is needed to provide a diverse, healthy, nutritious diet of plant and animal products — similar to the typical diet available in North America and Europe (Lal, 1989; Giampietro and Pimentel, 1994). The average per capita world cropland has decreased to only 0.27 ha, or about half the area needed to meet that of industrial nations' standards. In China, however, the available cropland has dropped to only 0.08 ha per capita, and is still rapidly declining because of continued population growth and extreme land degradation there (Leach, 1995). This small amount of arable land means the Chinese must rely primarily on a vegetarian diet. Overall, the decline and shortage of productive cropland is one of the underlying causes of the current worldwide food shortages, malnutrition, and poverty (Leach, 1995; Pimentel and Pimentel, 1996).

Indeed, escalating land degradation throughout the world is threatening most crop and pasture land productivity (Lal and Pierce, 1991; Pimentel *et al.*, 1995). The major types of degradation include water and wind erosion, as well as the salinization and water-logging of irrigated soils (Kendall and Pimentel, 1994).

Erosion by wind and water is the most serious cause of soil loss and degradation. Current erosion rates are greater than ever previously recorded (Pimentel *et al.*, 1995). Soil erosion on cropland ranges from an average of about 13 tons per hectare per year (t ha^{-1}yr^{-1}) in the United States to an average of about 40 t ha^{-1}yr^{-1} in China (USDA, 1994; Wen, 1993; McLaughlin, 1991).

The current high erosion rate throughout the world is a major concern for all agriculture because of the slow rate of topsoil renewal. Approximately 500 years are required for 2.5 cm (1 inch) of topsoil to form under agricultural conditions (OTA, 1982; Elwell, 1985; Troeh *et al.*, 1991; Pimentel *et al.*, 1995). Approximately 3,000 years are needed for the natural reformation of topsoil to the 150 mm depth needed for satisfactory crop production.

The cropland currently used for crop production already includes a considerable amount of marginal land and newly cleared forest land that is highly susceptible to erosion. When soil degradation occurs, the requirement for fossil energy inputs in the form of fertilizers, pesticides, and irrigation is increased to offset the losses, thus creating most costly agricultural systems and great reliance on these finite energy resources (Follett and Stewart, 1985; Pimentel, 1993; Pimentel *et al.*, 1995).

Fertilizer and Pesticide Use

Although productive land and water are essential for producing high yields of grains and other crops, the fossil-energy inputs of fertilizers, pesticides, and high-yielding crop varieties are equally critical. Maintaining sufficient levels of nitrogen, phosphorus, and potassium nutrients are essential for high crop yields. Nitrogen, for example, is lost from the soil when a crop is harvested, because approximately 33% of the nitrogen is carried away in the crop. Another 67% or more of the nitrogen is lost due to soil erosion, leaching, and denitrification by microbes (Troeh *et al.*, 1991). If these large quantities of lost nitrogen are not replaced by commercial nitrogen fertilizer or livestock manure, then crop yields may decrease as much as 80%.

Although applying fertilizers early in the season may be the most economical and easy practice for farmers, it may not provide the optimal supply of nutrients at the most critical time for crop growth. Applying the appropriate amounts of nutrients each week to meet the needs of the crop is the ideal way to fertilize crops. However, the weekly application of fertilizers to crops requires large inputs of labor and machinery. In addition, once the plants had grown significantly, like with a maize crop, special machinery would be needed to fertilize the tall crop.

High yields also can be achieved by the use of pesticides, applied to prevent major losses to insect pests, weeds, and plant pathogens (Pimentel, 1997). However, despite the use of 2.5 million tonnes of pesticides worldwide, in addition to non-chemical pest controls, more than 40% of all potential crop production is lost to pests before harvest (Pimentel, 1997). The availability of pesticides and the use of non-chemical controls depends on adequate supplies of finite energy resources like oil and natural gas (Pimentel, 1997). Of course, the serious health risks with pesticides should also be a consideration (Pimentel and Grenier, 1997).

Investigations suggest that pesticide use could be reduced by 50% or more, without any reduction in pest control and/or any change in the cosmetic standards of crops, provided that sound ecological pest controls, such as crop rotations and biological controls were carefully implemented (Pimentel, 1997).

Biological Resources

In addition to land, water resources, crops and livestock species, human life depends on the presence and functioning of approximately 10 million other plant, animal, and microbe species existing in agroecosystems and throughout nature (Pimentel et al., 1992a). Although approximately 60% of the world's food supply comes from rice, wheat, and maize species (Wilson, 1988), as many as 20,000 other plant species are used by humans for food (Vietmeyer, 1995). Humans have no technologies which can substitute for the genetic material, foods, and some medicines that plant species in wild biota contribute (Pimentel et al., 1997b).

Diverse plants, animals, and microbes carry out many activities essential for humans, including pollination of crops and wild plants. Approximately one third of the world's food supply relies either directly or indirectly on effective insect pollination (O'Toole, 1993). Honey bees and other wild bees are essential in pollinating about $40 billion worth of U.S. crops annually (Pimentel et al., 1997b). They also pollinate natural plant species. Natural biota also recycle manure and other organic wastes, degrade chemical pollutants, and purify water and soil resources (Pimentel et al., 1997b).

Some living organisms are important resources for crop protection (Waage, 1991). For example, approximately 99% of potential crop pests are controlled by diverse natural enemy species (DeBach and Rosen, 1991). Some wild plants provide genetic resources that aid agriculturists in the development of pest resistance in host plants

(Pimentel *et al.*, 1997b). Greater effort needs to be focused on the use of diverse natural enemies and the genetics of host-plant resistance for pest control (Klassen, 1988). Both of these technologies help reduce our reliance on pesticides.

SUSTAINABLE MANAGEMENT OF NATURAL RESOURCES

The major difficulties associated with conventional, high-input agriculture are: 1) serious degradation of valuable environmental resources; 2) high costs of production; 3) instability of crop yields. Numerous agricultural technologies already exist that can be implemented to make agriculture both more sustainable and ecologically sound. These technologies would reduce chemical inputs (including commercial fertilizers and pesticides), reduce soil erosion and rapid water runoff, and make more efficient use of livestock manure (Pimentel, 1993).

For example, the sound agricultural practice of the ridge-planting and crop rotation system is suggested as an alternative to conventional maize production (Pimentel, 1993). Note the high level of inputs in the conventional maize system (Table 1). The total costs of these inputs average $844.38 ha[-1] in the United States. The total energy input is 7.1 million kcal ha[-1], and the maize yield is slightly less than 8,000 kg ha[-1]yr[-1].

The environmental costs attributed to both U.S. agriculture and society as a whole when maize is produced using conventional practices are listed in Table 4. The loss of fertilizer nutrients, which total $115 ha yr[-1], is based on the estimate of Troeh *et al.* (1991) who reported that $20 billion in nutrients are lost from agriculture via erosion and water runoff each year. Other environmental damages associated with maize production include loss of water; off site manure pollution, sediment impacts, and pesticide pollution.

TABLE 4. ENVIRONMENTAL COSTS BOTH ON SITE AND OFF SITE FROM CONVENTIONAL AGRICULTURE PER HECTARE ANNUALLY (PIMENTEL, 1999).

Item	Cost (U.S. $)
Loss of soil nutrients	113.00
Loss of water	50.00
Manure pollution	5.00
Off site sediments impact	37.50
Pesticide impact	50.00
TOTAL	**280.50**

Taken together, these environmental costs total at least $231 ha yr[-1] in the United States.

The ridge-planting and crop-rotation system suggested by Pimentel (1993) utilizes readily available agricultural technologies that can make agriculture more productive, economically sound, sustainable and environmentally sound than conventional maize production. In this system, which combines ridge planting, crop rotation and a cover crop, soil erosion is reduced from approximately 15 t ha⁻¹yr⁻¹ in conventional U.S. maize production to less than 1 t ha⁻¹yr⁻¹. Note, 1 t ha⁻¹yr⁻¹ is the soil reformation rate in agriculture. In addition, such sound soil and water conservation technologies increased maize yields from 15% to 30% over maize grown in conventional systems (Pimentel, 1993).

In general, the ridge-planting and rotation system has the following advantages over the conventional maize system: 1) soil erosion and rapid water runoff are reduced; 2) mechanical cultivation is substituted for some or all herbicides; 3) the rotation eliminates the need for insecticides; 4) on-farm livestock manure substitutes for all the nitrogen and large portion of the phosphorus and potassium nutrients needed; 5) the cover crop protects the soil and conserved nutrients during the non-growing season (Pimentel, 1993).

Inclusion of all these production modifications raised the maize yield from nearly 8,000 kg ha⁻¹ in the conventional system to 8,640 kg ha⁻¹ in the low-input ridge planting and rotation system (Pimentel, 1993). Total fossil energy input for the low-input system was about 3.7 million kcal, or about half of that of the conventional system. The total cost of production, which included the added labour, was $337, or less than half of the conventional system (Pimentel, 1993). If, however, the environmental costs attributed to conventional production had been included, then production costs in the low-input system would be even less than half that of the conventional system. Another strategy is to select an appropriate crop, like soybeans, for rotation with maize to reduce maize rootworm pest, maize disease, and weed problems (Pimentel, 1993).

Furthermore, a maize and soybean rotation system is more profitable than raising either crop alone, because the maize rootworm problem is eliminated and insecticides are not needed. Average maize losses to insects for conventional, continuous maize is about 12%, compared to only 3.5% for maize grown in rotation (Pimentel *et al.*, 1993).

REFERENCES

DeBach, P. and D. Rosen, 1991. Biological Control by Natural Enemies. New York: Cambridge University Press.

Elwell, H. A., 1985. An assessment of soil erosion in Zimbabwe. Zimbabwe Sci. News, 19: 27-31.

FAO, 1991. Food Balance Sheets. Rome: Food and Agriculture Organization of the United Nations.

FAO, 1997. Quarterly Bulletin of Statistics. FAO Quarterly Bulletin of Statistics, 10, 125 pp.

Follett, R. F., and B. A. Stewart, 1985. Soil Erosion and Crop Productivity. Madison, WI: American Society of Agronomy, Crop Science Society of America.

Giampietro, M., and D. Pimentel, 1994. Energy utilization. In: C. J. Arntzen and E. M. Ritter (Eds.), Encyclopedia of Agricultural Science (pp. 73-76). San Diego, CA: Academic Press.

Hinman, H., G. Pelter, E. Kulp, E. Sorensen and W. Ford, 1992. Enterprise Budgets for Fall Potatoes, Winter Wheat, Dry Beans, and Seed Peas under Rill Irrigation, Columbia Basin,

Washington. Pullman, Washington: Washington State University.

Kendall, H. W. and D. Pimentel, 1994. Constraints on the expansion of the global food supply. Ambio, 23: 198-205.

Klassen, W. , 1988. Biological control: needs and opportunities. American Journal of Alternative Agriculture, 3: 117-122.

Lal. R. , 1989. Land degradation and its impact on food and other resources. In: D. Pimentel (Ed.), Food and Natural Resources (pp. 85-140). San Diego: Academic Press.

Lal, R. and F. J. Pierce, 1991. Soil Management for Sustainability. Ankeny, I.A.: Soil and Water Conservation Society in cooperation with the World Association of Soil and Water Conservation and the Soil Science Society of America.

Leach, G., 1995. Global Land and Food in the 21st Century. Stockholm: International Institute for Environmental Technology and Management.

Leyton, L., 1983. Crop water use: principles and some considerations for agroforestry. In: P. A. Huxley (Ed.), Plant Research and Agroforestry (pp. 379-400). Nairobi, Kenya: International Council for Research in Agroforestry.

McLaughlin, L., 1991. Soil Conservation Planning in the Peoples' Republic of China: An Alternative Approach. Ph.D. Thesis, Cornell University.

Nash, L., 1993. Water quality and health. In: P. Gleick (Ed.), Water in Crisis: A Guide to the World's Fresh Water Resources (pp. 25-39). Oxford: Oxford University Press.

Neuhoff, D., D.G. Schulz and U. Kopke, 1997. Influence of cultivar and increasing rotted manure fertilizer on yield and quality of middle early ware potatoes. Schriftenreihe – Institut fur Organischen Landbau, 4: 361-367.

OTA, 1982. Impacts of Technology on U.S. Cropland and Rangeland Productivity. Washington, DC: Office of Technology, U.S. Congress.

O'Toole, C., 1993. Diversity of native bees and agroecosystems. In: J. LaSalle and I. D. Gault (Eds.), Hymenoptera and Biodiversity. Wallingford, Oxon, U.K.: CAB International.

Pimentel, D., 1993. World Soil Erosion and Conservation. Cambridge: Cambridge University Press.

Pimentel, D., 1997. Techniques for Reducing Pesticides: Environmental and Economic Benefits. Chichester, U.K.: John Wiley & Sons.

Pimentel, D., 1999. Environmental and economic benefits of sustainable agriculture. In: J. Kohn, J. Gowdy, F. Hintenberger, and J. van der Straaten (Eds.), Sustainability in Question: The Search for a Conceptual Framework. Northhampton, MA: Edward Elgar.

Pimentel, D. and A. Greiner, 1997. Environmental and soci-economic costs of pesticide use. In D. Pimentel (Ed.), Techniques for Reducing Pesticide Use: Economic and Environmental Benefits (pp. 51-78). Chichester, UK: John Wiley & Sons.

Pimentel, D. and M. Pimentel, 1996. Food, Energy and Society. Boulder, CO: Colorado University Press.

Pimentel, D., U. Stachow, D.A. Takacs, H.W. Brubaker, A.R. Dumas, J.J. Meaney, J. O'Neil, D.E. Onsi and D.B. Corzilius 1992a. Conserving biological diversity in agricultural/forestry systems. BioScience, 42: 354-362.

Pimentel, D., N. Brown, F. Vecchio, V. La Capra, S. Hausman, O. Lee, A. Diaz, J. Williams, S. Cooper, and E. Newburger, 1992. Ethical issues concerning potential global climate change on food production. Journal of Agricultural and Environmental Ethics, 5 (2): 113-146.

Pimentel, D., L. McLaughlin, A. Zepp, B. Kakitan, T. Kraus, P. Kleinman, F. Vancini, W.J. Roach, E. Graap, W.S. Keeton and G. Selig, 1993. Environmental and economic effects of reducing pesticide use in agriculture. Agriculture, Ecosystems and Environment. 46(1-4): 273-288.

Pimentel, D., C. Harvey, P. Resosudarmo, K. Sinclair, D. Kurz, M. McNair, S. Crist, L. Sphpritz, L. Fitton, R. Saffouri and R. Blair, 1995. Environmental and economic costs of soil erosion and conservation benefits. Science, 267: 1117-1123.

Pimentel, D., J. Houser, E. Preiss, O. White, H. Fang, L. Mesnick, T. Barsky, S. Tariche, J. Schreck, and S. Alpert, 1997a. Water resources: agriculture, the environment, and society. BioScience 47 (2): 97-106.

Pimentel, D., C. Wilson, C. McCullum, R. Huang, P. Dwen, J. Flack, Q. Tran, T. Saltman and B. Cliff, 1997b. Economic and environmental benefits of biodiversity. BioScience, 47(11), 747-758.

Pimentel, D., R. Doughty, C. Carothers, S. Lamberson, N. Bora and K. Lee, 2000. Energy inputs in crop production in developing and developed countries. Manuscript.

Sheridan, D., 1983. The Colorado — an engineering wonder without enough water. Smithsonian, February, 45-54.

Troeh, F. R., J.A. Hobbs and R.L. Donahue, 1991. Soil and Water Conservation (2nd ed.). Englewood Cliffs, NJ: Prentice Hall.

USBC, 1998. Statistical Abstract of the United States 1998. Washington, DC: U.S. Bureau of the Census, U.S. Government Printing Office.

USDA, 1994. Summary Report 1992 National Reseources Inventory. Washington, DC: Soil Conservation Service, USDA.

USDA, 1998. Agricultural Statistics. Washington, DC: USDA.

Vietmeyer, N., 1995. Applying biodiversity. Journal of the Federation of American Scienctists, 48(4), 1-8.

Waage, J.K., 1991. Biodiversity as a resource for biological control. In D.L. Hawsworth (ed.). The Biodiversity of Microorganisms and Invertebrates: Its Role in Sustainable Agriculture. Proceedings of the First Workshop on the Ecological Foundation of Sustainable Agriculture. (pp. 149-163). Wallingford, U.K.: CAB International.

Wen, D., 1993. Soil erosion and conservation in China. In D. Pimentel (Ed.), Soil Erosion and Conservation (pp. 63-86). New York: Cambridge University Press.

WHO, 1996. Micronutrient Malnutrition — Half of the World's Population Affected (Pages 1-4 No. No. 78). World Health Organization.

Willet, G. S. and W. J. Gary, 1997. Economic Analysis of Alternative Irrigated Wheat Enterprizes. Farm Business Report EB 1862. Walla Walla County: Washington State University.

Wilson, E. O., 1988. Biodiversity. Washington, DC: National Academy of Sciences.

Zkukov, Y.P. and I.M. Khairullin, 1996. Effectiveness of calculated doses of fertilizers and combinations with pesticides in the fourth rotation of a cropping cycle on dernopodzolic soil. Agrokhimiya. No. 6: 52-62.

Land use perspectives in cool and wet regions of Europe

B. LEHMANN

Agricultural Economics, ETH Zurich, Switzerland

This contribution is focussed on 12 central messages (A to L).

Trends in direct and indirect relationship with land use in cool and wet regions of Europe

Global food demand
- Increase in world population
- Increase of meat consumption in developing countries

Global energy demand
- World wide consumption of non renewable energy
- Necessity to increase the share of renewable energy

New demands of a more and more urban population
- Farm land for urbanisation
- Farm land for "ecological compensation" ("more pure nature")
- Impact of agriculture on natural resources:
  - quality of water (drinking water)
  - quality of air (global)
  - diversity of flora and fauna on farmland
  - landscape design (natural and built landscape)
  - option value and existence value of fertility of natural resources

Regression of farmland and soil fertility through agricultural activities:
- losses of long range fertility (salt by irrigation)
- losses of arable land through erosion

Increase in productivity per ha (vegetal and animal production) through

- use of inputs
- use of plants & animal with higher performance (crop adaptation.....)

Significant differences between regions of the World concerning

- degree of urbanisation
- farmer's practices (direct and indirect impact on natural environment, energy intensity)
- conflict situation concerning the negative externalities of agriculture
- role of agriculture concerning the functions with public character

Significant tendency in world wide liberalisation of the agricultural markets combined with agri-environmental programmes/schemes/measures

- better effectiveness and efficiency of support in comparison with prior price support

- but the correction of market failures is not enough compensated by agri-environmental measures and general environmental measures (external effects of fossil energy use)

Characteristics of land use in cool and wet regions of Europe

Duration of vegetation: relatively short (altitude or latitude)

Climate: humidity and temperature

Topography: flat and mountainous regions

Relative best agricultural land use: grassland and fodder production

But: lack of competitiveness

The described trend can be summarised as follows:

TRENDS

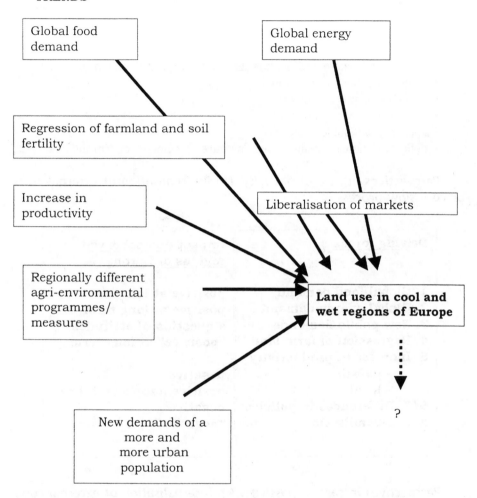

The economic concept of comparative cost advantage in the interregional or international competition

Specialisation of countries in interrelated markets brings the best common welfare
- within agricultural commodities
- within food products
- between food and non food products

- production of goods at location offering lowest costs (included opportunity costs)
- a basic principle of welfare economics

The economic concept of comparative cost advantage, limitations for the agri food sector

Limitations:
- bias through external costs in the agricultural production and the transportation
- joint production in agriculture
- if the markets are saturated we
- will have regions without production and
- therefore without joint production
- deficits in landscape maintenance, in rural employment, tourism and food safety

Perspectives in case of passivity. No internalisation of external costs or very slow process

Driving forces	Impact on cool & wet regions of Europe
1. Global food demand	positive at long term
2. Global energy demand	positive at long term
3. New public demands	a question of attitudes
4. Regression of farm land	"positive" at long term
5. Increase of productivity	
- global	negative
- local	positive (crop adaptation)
6/7. Differences in policies	negative
6/7. Liberalisation	"negative"

Perspectives in case of passivity. No internalisation of external costs or very slow process

- wrong crops, not adapted crops, wrong products
- insufficient covered costs by direct payments for restrictions and for the supply of public goods
- comparative stronger restrictions for the protection of the environment
- expensive farm structures
- high opportunity costs of the production factors

- insufficient marketing (customers value, costs, convenience, communication)
- external costs of agricultural production in competitor farms and transportation
- structural surpluses on the world markets

Protectionism, free market and internalisation of external effects

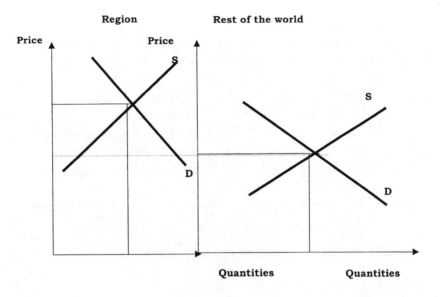

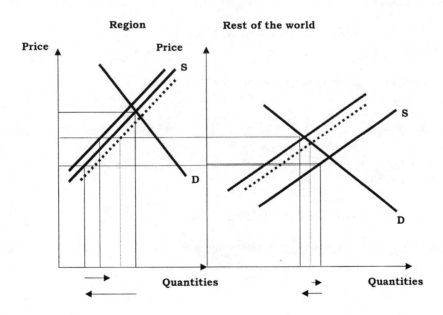

Perspectives in case pro-active attitude in internalisation of external costs (everywhere)

Driving forces	Impact on cool & wet regions of Europe
1. Global food demand (-)	
2. Global energy demand (-)	not negative...positive
3. New public demands (+)	very positive
4. Regression of farm land(-)	very positive
5. Increase of productivity	"not negative ..positive"
- global (+)	negative
- local (+)	positive (crop adaptation)
6/7. Differences /policies (-)	less negative..positive
6/7. Liberalisation (+)	less negative..positive

Private and public goods of regional agriculture

In relationship with the production of private goods agriculture modifies in a positive and also negative way natural resources, which are collective or public goods.

Competitive products (quality, price, convenience)
(food and fibre)

Farm land management   (question of property rights)
- Biodiversity
- Landscape design
- Minimal impact on resources (Water, air,........)
- Contribution to regional economy
- Option value or existence value of soil fertility & local food production (insurance, reversibility)

Maintenance on abandoned farm land

Providing of land for other uses (economy, sport,....)

Private and public goods of regional agriculture
Opportunities and expectations

Weak   Strong
demand

Competitive products

Farm land management

- **Biodiversity**

- **Landscape design**

- **Minimal impact on resources**

- **Contribution to regional economy**

- **OV, EV of fertility and production**

Maintenance on abandoned farm land

Providing of land for other uses

The demand can vary from region to region and also over time.

The role of agronomic research

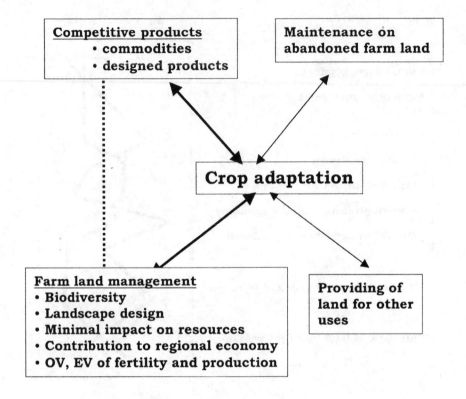

Agricultural research sustains agriculture in all its functions. Crop adaptation research has to consider this. Research has to anticipate the future challenges of the farmers, especially in the domain of the public goods.

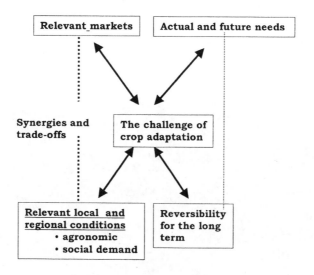

The cycle of successful management in a supply chain

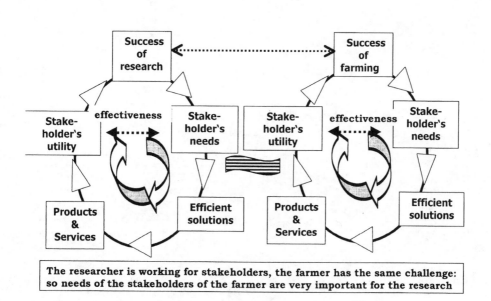

The researcher is working for stakeholders, the farmer has the same challenge: so needs of the stakeholders of the farmer are very important for the research

Adaptation of thermophilic crops
Invited papers

Impacts of chilling on photosynthesis in thermophilic plants: contrasting mechanisms

D. J. ALLEN AND D. R. ORT

Photosynthesis Research Unit of USDA/ARS and Department of Plant Biology, University of Illinois, Urbana, IL 61801-3838, USA

SUMMARY

Photosynthesis in warm-climate plants is substantially reduced by chilling temperatures. Species of tropical and sub-tropical origin offer the opportunity to study the effects of low temperature on photosynthetic processes undisguised by the myriad of protective responses observed in temperate species. In this review we highlight the primary components of photosynthesis which are impacted by chilling, both in the dark and the light, and discuss what is known of the mechanisms involved.

Keywords: carbon reduction cycle, circadian rhythm, low temperature, oxidative stress, photoinhibition, stomata

INTRODUCTION

Low temperature is one of the major stresses limiting productivity and geographical distribution of many species, including agriculturally-important crops. The formation of ice inside plant cells is devastating. Freeze-tolerant plants exhibit numerous strategies to reduce the probability of this occurring, even when air temperature drops below zero, for example by maintaining high intracellular solute concentrations and encouraging ice nucleation outside the cells. These plants also commonly exhibit xerophytic adaptations to survive the reduced water availability within the plant and the soil. Thomashow (1998) provides a comprehensive update on freezing stress and acclimation. Here we use the term chilling to refer to non-freezing temperatures (e.g. 0-12°C) that substantially compromise plant productivity and are common in temperate regions.

While temperatures of -5°C can kill an unhardened winter wheat plant, it has the genetic capacity to acclimate and thereby acquire tolerance of freezing down to -20°C (Thomashow, 1998). The same must be true for chilling tolerance in many plants native to warm climates. The cold-hardening mechanisms conferring chill tolerance have been et al., 1998) and includes changes in lipid composition, increases in active oxygen-scavenging enzymes, anthocyanin accumulation and altered growth morphology.

Many crops now being grown in temperate climates (e.g. maize, tomato, cucumber, mango) come from tropical and sub-tropical regions. Because of their evolutionary origin, these species lack the genetic information to be chilling-tolerant. These thermophilic crops thus offer the opportunity to study chill effects on photosynthesis relatively undisguised by the gamut of protective responses observed in chilling-tolerant species.

We describe below how chilling can directly disrupt all of the major components of photosynthesis including thylakoid electron transport, the carbon reduction cycle and control of stomatal apertures. One of the challenges to research in this field is identification of the primary effects in this highly interactive and regulated system. For example, stomatal closure following a chill could be a direct low temperature effect on guard cell function, or an indirect response to a rising internal CO_2 concentration (c_i) due to a chill-induced loss of Rubisco activity.

Studying the effect of chilling in the dark on subsequent photosynthesis is important partially because plants in the field experience their lowest temperatures at night. While there are specific impacts of concurrent light and low temperature, these will typically be in addition to those induced by the chilling alone. Consequently, the dark chill-induced effects described below are also likely to be true for light chills, but may be masked by larger light-induced inhibitions. Nevertheless at a specific low temperature there are substantial differences, both in the scale of the inhibition of photosynthesis and the primary mechanisms involved, between plants chilled in the light and the dark. Furthermore, while chill-sensitive species have very limited capacity to acclimate to chilling temperatures, the deleterious effects of growing at moderately cool temperatures can be quite separate from instantaneous effects of exposure to chilling temperatures (Nie and Baker, 1991; Nie et al., 1992).

Thylakoid Electron Transport
Photodamage (chronic photoinhibition) and repair

The ratio of variable to maximal chlorophyll fluorescence (F_v/F_m) in dark-adapted tissue is typically used to identify PSII photodamage, an inhibition of PSII photochemistry that is not rapidly reversible, due to the ease of measurement. The amount of ^{14}C-atrazine that can bind to the plastoquinone-reductase site of PSII in isolated thylakoids, produces a more direct assessment (Kyle et al., 1984). Excellent reviews of the mechanisms involved in photodamage are available (Aro et al., 1993; Melis, 1999). Photodamage is rarely observed following chilling of even the most extreme thermophilic species if it is undertaken in the dark (Martin et al., 1981; Flexas et al., 1999; Allen et al., 2000). In contrast, the combination of low temperature with high light has the potential to induce chronic photoinhibition of PSII. This is partly because the thermodynamic effect on reaction rates can limit the sinks for the absorbed excitation energy (light), particularly CO_2 fixation and photorespiration. Smaller sinks for absorbed excitation energy increases the potential for oxidation of PSII, notably the D1 component. Additionally, photodamage becomes apparent as low temperatures interfere with the normal rate of D1 turnover. This has been attributed to changes in the expression of psbA, the gene coding for D1, and direct temperature effects on membranes (Aro *et al.*, 1993). Low temperature stifles membrane fluidity and thus reduces the rate of D1 turnover by slowing the diffusion of D1 proteins marked for degradation, to non-appressed regions of the thylakoid. Nevertheless, photodamage of PSII is frequently not responsible for light-chill-induced inhibition of photosynthesis (e.g. Kee *et al.*, 1986; Kingston-Smith *et al.*, 1997).

Photoprotection and down regulation (dynamic photoinhibition)

Dynamic photoinhibition, the rapidly reversible down regulation of PSII quantum efficiency, occurs more often than photodamage following a chill in the dark. However, in warm-climate plants like tomato, grapevine and mango this is clearly not the primary cause of the inhibition of photosynthesis under these conditions (Martin *et al.*, 1981; Flexas *et al.*, 1999; Allen *et al.*, 2000). When chilling limits photosynthetic sinks for electrons in the light, this photoprotection is afforded by a reduction in the efficiency of energy transfer in the light harvesting complex, allowing additional absorbed light energy to be dissipated as heat. This can be observed when thermophilic crops like maize and tomato are chilled in the light (Kee *et al.*, 1986; Kingston-Smith *et al.*, 1997; Fryer *et al.*, 1998). This rapidly reversible process involves the inter-conversion of xanthophyll pigments, and is clearly a critical protective measure against the more pernicious impact of photodamage. Demmig-Adams and Adams (1992) provide a clear account of how this cycle works. Changes in the quenching of excitation energy in the antennae of PSII can easily be estimated using modulated chlorophyll fluorescence. Both F_v'/F_m', the efficiency of excitation energy transfer to open PSII reaction centres, and q_N, the coefficient of non-photochemical quenching, are widely used parameters describing the amount of down regulation of PSII electron transport.

Alternative electron sinks and oxidative stress

Analysis of the relative rates of PSII electron transport with those of CO_2 assimilation frequently reveals that chilling leads to an increase in alternative (i.e. non-CO_2) electron sinks (Fryer *et al.*, 1998; Flexas *et al.*, 1999; Allen *et al.*, 2000), although not always (Kingston-Smith *et al.*, 1997). Osmond and Grace (1995) argue that exploiting oxygen as a terminal electron acceptor, both in Rubisco oxygenase photorespiration (see later section on Rubisco) and in the Mehler-ascorbate peroxidase reaction, protects plants from photodamage in bright light.

Thylakoid electron transport is intrinsically vulnerable to producing active oxygen species. To prevent calamitous damage to component proteins and lipids, plants have many antioxidant systems. It is becoming increasingly clear that the regeneration of these antioxidants, like ascorbate (vitamin C), can be an important electron sink. The Mehler-ascorbate peroxidase (water-water) cycle has received significant attention and has been previously reviewed (Asada *et al.*, 1998). However, it does not appear likely that ascorbate regeneration is the additional sink for electrons observed following a chill, as Jahnke *et al.* (1991) demonstrated that in maize chilling temperatures substantially reduced the activities of all the enzymes involved in this cycle. In fact, interference with this process of antioxidant regeneration in response to a light chill may be a major cause of the observed inhibition of photosynthesis. In addition to the direct effects of this oxidative potential, light-chill-induced oxidative stress can lead to a change in the redox state of the stroma. This can result in a deactivation of several enzymes involved in CO_2 assimilation including FBPase, SBPase and Rubisco activase as discussed in the following section (Wise, 1995; Hutchison et al., 2000).

Photosynthetic metabolism
End-product inhibition

Soluble carbohydrates can accumulate due to low temperature inhibition of nighttime mobilization of leaf starch (Paul et al., 1992; Leegood and Edwards, 1996). As a result, end-product inhibition of photosynthesis, due to an insufficient return of inorganic phosphate (P_i) to the chloroplast, is a possible consequence of chilling. An increase in P_i limitation of photosynthesis would lead to a smaller stimulation of A in response to a switch from ambient to non-photorespiratory conditions (1-2% O_2) (Sharkey, 1985). Typically however, end-product inhibition of photosynthesis is not responsible for chill-induced declines in photosynthesis (Paul et al., 1992; Allen et al., 2000).

Stromal bisphosphatases

The widely used models of photosynthesis (e.g. von Caemmerer and Farquhar, 1981) imply that the activities of the regenerative enzymes of the Calvin cycle do not limit CO_2 uptake. RuBP regeneration is described only in terms of the maximum rate of electron transport (J_{max}), which provides the chemical energy (ATP) and reducing power (NADPH) for these reactions. Over the last decade it has become increasingly apparent that not only are several of these stromal enzymes regulated in a sophisticated manner, but also under certain conditions they can be a primary limitation to photosynthesis. In particular, the role of the stromal bisphosphatases, SBPase and FBPase, in moderating photosynthesis under stress, needs to be appreciated. Both of these stromal bisphosphatases are activated by the ferridoxin/thioredoxin system, and so under optimum conditions their activity is tightly coupled to the redox state of the thylakoid. It is clear that in tomato the primary restriction on photosynthesis imposed by a light chill, is a reduction in the activity of these two enzymes due to an impairment in their reductive activation (Sassenrath et al., 1990; Hutchison et al., 2000). Chilling maize at 4°C and 350 mmol m^{-2} s^{-1} PPFD for 24 hours, reduces the maximum FBPase activity (after incubation with the artificial reductant DTT) after rewarming by ca. 50%, indicating an actual loss of the enzyme (Kingston-Smith et al., 1997).

Rubisco

Declines in photosynthesis following a chill, both in the dark and the light, have been attributed to a loss of Rubisco activity (e.g. Kingston-Smith et al., 1997; Allen et al., 2000). Labiality of the Rubisco protein has been proposed, with disassembly of the 8 large and 8 small sub-units at low temperatures. The breakdown products of Rubisco were more abundant in maize grown at 14 rather than 20°C, concurrent with 300 mmol m^{-2} s^{-1} PPFD (Kingston-Smith *et al.*, 1999). However, recent work with mango demonstrates that the loss of Rubisco activity observed at midday of a warm photoperiod following an overnight chill is not an instantaneous low temperature effect, but rather that Rubisco activity declined during the morning. This suggests that it is some aspect of Rubisco activation that is disrupted by the chill. It is tempting to speculate that the redox regulation of the larger Rubisco activase isoform, which has just been described (Zhang and Portis, 1999), can be affected by chilling as is observed for SBPase and FBPase.

The argument that Rubisco oxygenase photorespiration, by acting as an electron sink, is a protective mechanism against photoinhibition (Osmond and Grace, 1995; Kozaki and Takeba, 1996; Streb *et al.*, 1998), does not appear plausible with respect to chill-induced photoinhibition. This is because the frequently reported concurrent loss of Rubisco carboxylase activity (Kingston-Smith *et al.*, 1997; Allen *et al.*, 2000) will inevitably be mirrored by a decline in oxygenase activity and therefore a reduction in photorespiration and its sink for electrons. For photorespiration to act as a protective sink for electrons in response to a chill, the primary limitation to CO_2 uptake has to be a reduction in stomatal conductance. An increase in stomatal limitation of photosynthesis could reduce c_i, and hence increase the relative rates of photorespiration to CO_2 assimilation (see below).

Circadian disruption

Rhythms in many cellular processes, which are maintained even when plants are held under constant (free-running) conditions, with a period of approximately 24 hours, have now been described. These circadian rhythms, by definition, have temperature compensation to maintain the same cycle period over a range of temperatures (Wilkins, 1992). However, Martino-Catt and Ort (1992) demonstrated that the circadian rhythms in cab and Rubisco activase mRNA expression in tomato appeared to be stalled by chilling in the dark. Both these enzymes are so abundant that transient changes in translation rates do not have a significant impact on activity. This work, however, raised the intriguing idea that some of the depression of photosynthesis in thermophilic plants following a chill is the result of the mistiming of multiple circadian regulated processes. This hypothesis was supported by the observation that a low-light chill of tomato disrupts the circadian rhythm in activity of two key enzymes of the carbohydrate and nitrogen metabolism pathways, sucrose phosphate synthase and nitrate reductase (Jones *et al.*, 1998).

Stomatal responses
Chill-induced water loss

Reduced air and leaf temperature will usually reduce evaporative demand. However, cool roots reduce hydraulic conductivity and substantially inhibit water uptake from the soil. Due to the high specific heat capacity of the soil, transient root chills are far less common in the field than low shoot temperatures. In addition to not reflecting a natural chill, experiments that chill whole potted plants have to be interpreted with caution because of the ease with which unrealistic drought stress can be induced. This is because the soil warms up after a chill much slower than leaves and the surrounding air, and so unless humidity is maintained close to saturation, the evaporative demand will increase faster than leaf water supply.

Direct effects of chilling on stomata

In many chilling-sensitive species, like cucumber, bean, cotton and soybean, low temperatures can lead to stomata that that appear locked open, and cannot respond normally to leaf water deficit (Bagnall *et al.*, 1983; Eamus, 1987; Guye and Wilson, 1987). Such species will quickly wilt if not re-warmed under extremely high humidities. In other thermophilic species, however, stomatal closure following a chill can be observed, even with warm roots. Attempts have been made to estimate whether this reduction in stomatal conductance is in response to an inhibition of mesophyll photosynthesis, or rather is the cause of the decline in CO_2 assimilation. These approaches typically involve determining the dependence of CO_2 uptake on the c_i. Such assessments of stomatal limitation of photosynthesis frequently attribute the chill-induced inhibition of CO_2 fixation to a combination of stomatal and non-stomatal effects (Martin *et al.*, 1981; Bongi and Long, 1987; Flexas *et al.*, 1999; Allen *et al.*, 2000). However, because interactions between components of photosynthesis appear to be mediated by c_i, identification of the extent stomata limit photosynthesis remains problematic.

Impacts on photosynthetic productivity

The impact of chill-induced inhibition of photosynthesis on crop photosynthetic productivity has been reviewed previously (Long *et al.*, 1994) and is beyond the scope of this article. However there are a couple of points that are useful to keep in mind when considering the effect of chilling on photosynthesis. Evaluation of the impact of such chill-induced effects on plant productivity is critical. For example, when integrated over the whole canopy, day and season, photosynthesis is primarily light-limited not light-saturated. Therefore chill effects on the quantum yield of CO_2 assimilation is likely to have a much greater deleterious impact on crop productivity than a similar sized decline in light-saturated photosynthesis (Baker and Ort, 1992). It is also salient to remember that plant growth and productivity is usually correlated with total leaf area and the time of canopy closure, rather than instantaneous photosynthetic rates. However, photosynthesis during early leaf and plant development is critically important in determining such performance. Therefore chill effects on the development of photosynthesis are critical.

ACKNOWLEDGEMENTS

This work was supported in part by a grant from the USA-Israel Binational Agricultural Research and Development Fund (BARD; IS-2710-96).

REFERENCES

Allen, D.J., K. Ratner, Y.E. Giller, E.E. Gussakovsky, Y. Shahak and D.R. Ort, 2000. An overnight chill induces a delayed inhibition of photosynthesis at midday in mango (*Mangifera indica L.*). Journal of Experimental Botany (in review).

Aro, E.M., I. Virgin and B. Andersson, 1993. Photoinhibition of photosystem II. Inactivation, protein damage and turnover. Biochemica et Biophysica Acta, 1143: 113-134.

Asada K., T. Endo, J. Mano and C. Miyake, 1998. Molecular mechanisms for relaxation of and protection from light stress. In: Satoh K, Murata N, (eds.) Stress Responses of Photosynthetic Organisms. Amsterdam: Elsevier, pp. 37-52.

Bagnall D., J. Wolfe and R.W. King, 1983. Chill-induced wilting and hydraulic recovery in mung bean plants. Plant, Cell and Environment, 6: 457-464.

Baker, N.R. and D.R. Ort, 1992. Light and crop photosynthetic performance. In: Baker N, Thomas H, eds. Crop Photosynthesis: Spatial and Temporal Determinants. : Elsevier Science Publishers, pp. 289-312.

Bongi, G. and S.P. Long, 1987. Light-dependent damage to photosynthesis in olive leaves during chilling and high temperature stress. Plant Cell and Environment, 10: 241-250.

Demmig-Adams, B. and W.W. Adams III, 1992. Photoprotection and other responses of plants to high light stress. Annual Review of Plant Physiology and Plant Molecular Biology, 43: 599-626.

Eamus, D., 1987. Influence of preconditioning upon the changes in leaf conductance and leaf water potential of soybean, induced by chilling, water stress and abscisic acid. Australian Journal of Plant Physiology, 14: 331-339.

Flexas, J., M. Badger, W.S. Chow, H. Medrano and C.B. Osmond, 1999. Analysis of the relative increase in photosynthetic O_2 uptake when photosynthesis in grapevine leaves is inhibited following low night temperatures and/or water stress. Plant Physiology, 121: 675-684.

Fryer, M.J., J.R. Andrews, K. Oxborough, D.A. Blowers and N.R. Baker, 1998. Relationship between CO_2 assimilation, photosynthetic electron transport, and active O_2 metabolism in leaves of maize in the field during periods of low temperature. Plant Physiology, 116: 571-580.

Guye, M.G. and J.M. Wilson, 1987. The effects of chilling and chill-hardening temperatures on stomatal behaviour in a range of chill-sensitive species and cultivars. Plant Physiology and Biochemistry, 25: 717-721.

Huner, N.P.A., G. Öquist and F. Sarhan, 1998. Energy balance and acclimation to light and cold. Trends in Plant Science, 3: 224-230.

Hurry, V.M., Å. Strand, M. Tobiæson, P. Gardeström and G. Öquist, 1995. Cold hardening of spring and winter wheat and rape results in differential effects on growth, carbon metabolism, and carbohydrate content. Plant Physiology, 109: 697-706.

Hutchison, R.S., Q. Groom and D.R. Ort, 2000. Differential effects of chilling-induced photooxidation on the redox regulation of photosynthetic enzymes. Biochemistry, 39: 6679-6688.

Jahnke, L.S., M.R. Hull and S.P. Long, 1991. Chilling stress and oxygen metabolizing enzymes in Zea mays and Zea diploperennis. Plant Cell and Environment, 14: 97-104.

Jones, T.L., D.E. Tucker and D.R. Ort, 1998. Chilling delays circadian pattern of sucrose phosphate synthase and nitrate reductase activity in tomato. Plant Physiology, 118: 149-158.

Kee, S.C., B. Martin and D.R. Ort, 1986. The effects of chilling in the dark and in the light on photosynthesis of tomato (Lycopersicon esculentum cultivar Floramerica): Electron transfer reactions. Photosynthesis Research, 8: 41-52.

Kingston-Smith, A.H., J. Harbinson and C.H. Foyer, 1999. Acclimation of photosynthesis, H_2O_2 content and antioxidants in maize (*Zea mays*) growth at sub-optimal temperatures. Plant Cell and Environment, 22: 1071-1083.

Kingston-Smith, A.H., J. Harbinson, J. Williams and C.H. Foyer, 1997. Effect of chilling on carbon assimilation, enzyme activation, and photosynthetic electron transport in the absence of photoinhibition in maize leaves. Plant Physiology, 114: 1039-1046.

Kozaki, A. and G. Takeba, 1996. Photorespiration protects C_3 plants from photooxidation. Nature, 384: 557-560.

Kyle, D.J., I. Ohad and C.J. Arntzen, 1984. Membrane protein damage and repair: selective loss of a quinone-protein function in chloroplast membranes. Proceedings of the National Academy of Sciences USA, 81: 4070-4074.

Leegood, R.C. and G.E. Edwards, 1996. Carbon metabolism and photorespiration: temperature dependence in relation to other environmental factors. In: Baker, N.R., (eds.) Photosynthesis and the Environment. Dordrecht: Kluwer Academic, pp. 191-221.

Long, S.P., S. Humphries and P.G. Falkowski, 1994. Photoinhibition of photosynthesis in nature. Annual Review of Plant Physiology and Plant Molecular Biology, 45: 633-662.

Martin, B., D.R. Ort and J.S. Boyer, 1981. Impairment of photosynthesis by chilling-temperatures in tomato (Lycopersicon esculentum cultivar Rutgers). Plant Physiology, 68: 329-334.

Martino-Catt, S. and D.R. Ort, 1992. Low temperature interrupts circadian regulation of transcriptional activity in chilling-sensitive plants. Proceedings of the National Academy of Sciences USA, 89: 3731-3735.

Melis, A., 1999. Photosystem-II damage and repair cycle in chloroplasts: what modulates the rate of photodamage in vivo? Trends in Plant Science, 4: 130-135.

Nie G.Y. and Baker N.R. (1991) Modifications to thylakoid composition during development of maize leaves at low growth temperatures. Plant Physiology, 95: 184-191.

Nie, G.Y., S.P. Long and N.R. Baker, 1992. The effects of development at sub-optimal growth temperatures on photosynthetic capacity and susceptibility to chilling-dependent photoinhibition in Zea mays. Physiologia Plantarum, 85: 554-560.

Osmond, C.B. and S.C. Grace, 1995. Perspectives on photoinhibition and photorespiration in the field: quintessential inefficiencies of the light and dark reactions of photosynthesis? Journal of Experimental Botany, 46: 1351-1362.

Paul, M.J., S.P. Driscoll and D.W. Lawlor, 1992. Sink-regulation of photosynthesis in relation to temperature in sunflower and rape. Journal of Experimental Botany, 43: 147-153.

Sassenrath, G.F., D.R. Ort and A.R. Portis Jr, 1990. Impaired reductive activation of stromal bisphosphatases in tomato leaves following low-temperature exposure at high light. Archives of Biochemistry and Biophysics, 282: 302-308.

Schöner, S. and G.H. Krause, 1990. Protective systems against active oxygen species in spinach: response to cold acclimation in excess light. Planta, 180: 383-389.

Sharkey, T.D., 1985. Oxygen-insensitive photosynthesis in 3-carbon pathway plants: Its occurrence and a possible explanation. Plant Physiology, 78: 71-75.

Streb, P., W. Shang, J. Feierabend and R. Bligny, 1998. Divergent strategies of photoprotection in high-mountain plants. Planta, 207: 313-324.

Thomashow, M., 1998. Role of cold-responsive genes in plant freezing tolerance. Plant Physiology, 117: 1-7.

Von Caemmerer, S. and G. Farquhar, 1981. Some relationships between the biochemistry of photosynthesis and the gas exchange of leaves. Planta, 153: 376-387.

Wilkins, M.B., 1992. Circadian rhythms: Their origin and control. New Phytologist, 121: 347-375.

Wise, R.R., 1995. Chilling-enhanced photooxidation: The production, action and study of reactive oxygen species produced during chilling in the light. Photosynthesis Research, 45: 79-97.

Zhang, N. and A.R. Portis Jr, 1999. Mechanisms of light regulation of Rubisco: A specific role for the larger Rubisco activase isoform involving reductive activation by thioredoxin-f. Proceedings of the National Academy of Sciences USA, 96: 9438-9443.

Adaptation of thermophilic crops
Offered papers

Some structural and functional characteristics of maize root tolerance to chilling

O. GAŠPARÍKOVÁ, M. CIAMPOROVÁ, K. DEKÁNKOVÁ AND M. LUXOVÁ

Institute of Botany, Slovak Academy of Sciences, 842 23 Bratislava, Slovak Republic

SUMMARY

The chilling-tolerant Z 7 and chilling-sensitive Penjalinan maize genotypes differ in their attributes for adaptation to chilling stress. Seedlings of the tolerant Z 7 are able to withstand even severe chilling stress 6°C. At this temperature root growth was not completely inhibited. Higher number and length of laterals, and higher number of Z7 seminal adventitious roots may partially compensate for a decreased root absorption area. The larger primary root diameter due to larger area of cortical and stelar tissues including xylem-conducting area are intrinsic characteristics of the Z 7 plants. This may contribute to adaptation because only the primary root is functional in transport processes in the early seedling stages when spring chilling usually occurs. Unlike primary roots, the quantitative anatomical parameters of the 1st node roots are higher in the sensitive Penjalinan. However, under chilling, their appearance is delayed and vascular tissues are reduced to a greater extent than in the tolerant Z 7. A superior early vigour and better growth performance of 27 roots during chilling are accompanied with higher rate of respiration caused exclusively by an increase of the capacity and activity of the cyanide-resistant, alternative-respiration pathway. The protective role of alternative oxidase and some other enzymes involved in scavenging active-oxygen species is suggested.

Keywords: adaptation, chilling, genotype, maize, physiological response, roots

INTRODUCTION

The productivity of maize crops in temperate regions can be severely reduced due to low temperatures experienced during the early growing season. Although chilling has many effects on the physiology of the developing maize plant most attention is paid to growth and development of the leaves and their photosynthetic competence. Recently, it has been shown that photosynthesis may not be the only limiting factor for maize growth at low temperatures. Responses of shoot growth depend to a large extent on root growth and activity. Accordingly, co-ordinated growth processes at the whole-plant level are regarded as crucial for the adaptation of maize to low temperature (Stamp, 1984).

Therefore, we tried to find some morphological and physiological root traits contributing to chilling tolerance. We studied the effects of severe chilling stress (6 °C) on shoot and root growth and development, on morphology and anatomy of different types of roots of chilling-tolerant and chilling-sensitive genotypes. Attention was also devoted to the root respiration and participation of an alternative, non-phosphorylating pathway that might play a role in chilling tolerance.

MATERIALS AND METHODS

Seeds of the chilling-tolerant Z7 and chilling-sensitive Penjalinan maize genotypes were germinated in the dark at 24°C for 3 days, then transferred to aerated Hoagland nutrient solution (1/2 strength), and grown at 24°C, 12 h photoperiod (250 mmol m^{-2}s^{-1} photon flux density) until 3-leaf stage. For chilling treatment the plants were transferred to the growth chamber with chilling temperature 6°C, for 6 days. The recovery phase at 24°C followed for another 5 days.

Lengths and number of the primary, adventitious seminal, mesocotyl and nodal roots, their laterals and branching density were measured manually in 10 plants. Dry weight of shoot and the whole root system were evaluated. Rate of respiration was measured polarographically as an oxygen uptake with a Clark-type electrode at 25°C on detached 2 cm tips of primary seminal and seminal adventitious roots (Luxová and Gašparíková, 1999). KCN (0.5 mM) was used as an inhibitor of the cytochrome pathway and SHAM (5-15 mM) as an inhibitor of the cyanide-resistant alternative pathway of respiration. For anatomy, diameters of xylem vessel element cross sections were measured and cross-section area was calculated in hand sections taken from the base of the primary and 1st node roots.

RESULTS AND DISCUSSION

Growth
The exposure of plants to 6°C for 6 days significantly reduced shoot and root growth compared with control plants growing at 24°C (Table 1). The mean shoot dry matter was reduced. Almost no increase in mean root dry matter and no increase in the length of primary and adventitious seminal roots in Penjalinan indicate that under this severe chilling stress the growth of roots was stopped in this genotype. Total length of the first-order laterals was also dramatically reduced. Plants of Z7 showed greater ability to withstand chilling stress than those of Penjalinan. Inhibition but not cessation of root growth was observed. Furthermore, under chilling, an enhanced formation of seminal adventitious roots can partially compensate for lower rate of primary seminal root extension. Similar results have been previously observed in maize at mild chilling stress 10 - 15°C (Feil *et al.*, 1991).

TABLE 1. SHOOT AND ROOT DRY MATTER (MG PER PLANT) AND TOTAL LENGTH (CM PER PLANT) OF MAIN ROOTS AND LATERAL ROOTS OF MAIZE GENOTYPES PENJALINAN AND Z7 BEFORE CHILLING STRESS (AFTER PRE-GROWTH AT 24°C TILL THE THIRD-LEAF STAGE), AFTER GROWTH AT 24°C OR 6°C FOR 6 DAYS, AND ANOTHER 5 DAYS OF RECOVERY AT 24°C.

	before chilling 24 °C	control 24 °C	chilling 6 °C	recovery 24 °C
		Penjalinan		
Shoot dry matter	71.1 ± 9	228.0 ± 7	93.0 ± 9	192.0 ± 8
Roots dry matter	48.1 ± 8	84.7 ± 8	42.0 ± 9	74.2 ± 10
Root length				
Main axes	84.6 ± 7	190.0 ± 13	83.0 ± 6	113.0 ± 9
Lateral roots	71.2 ± 5	164.0 ± 7	108.1 ± 9	101.0 ± 10
		Z7		
Shoot dry matter	76.6 ± 5	308.6 ± 15	134.4 ± 9	280.9 ± 13
Roots dry matter	69.1 ± 6	122.6 ± 10	84.9 ± 7	117.3 ± 11
Root length				
Main axes	56.0 ± 5	233.0 ± 12	68.1 ± 5	93.0 ± 7
Lateral roots	107.3 ± 8	303.0 ± 15	191.0 ± 12	227.0 ± 12

mean ± standard error

The changes in root traits studied indicate that even this severe chilling stress retarded but did not hamper seminal root growth. Accordingly, larger diameter due to larger area of both cortical and stelar tissues, and the greater metaxylem conducting area are intrinsic characteristics of the tolerant Z 7 primary root. This may be considered an adaptation because only the primary root is functional in transport processes during early developmental stage of maize seedlings, when spring chilling usually occurs (Èiamporová and Dekánková, 1998). In both genotypes the chilling temperature induced a decrease of cross section area of the late metaxylem vessel elements in the roots of the 1st node developing during the stress period. However, the degree of the reduction was greater in the sensitive Penjalinan than in the tolerant Z7 genotype. Root system development and anatomy at low temperature in Z7 indicate an increasing importance of seminal roots for chilling tolerance. Such constitutive adaptation might partially compensate for a decreased hydraulic conductivity at low temperatures (Ameglio *et al.*, 1990; Kiel and Stamp, 1992).

After the stress period an immediate resumption of biomass allocation to the root indicated that chilling effects did not greatly impair the capacity of the root system to recover. However, the extension of lateral roots was slow in both genotypes, although to a greater extent in Penjalinan (Table 1), possibly due to low temperature effects on root apical meristems and lateral root primordia (Barlow and Adam, 1989 b). The higher number of mesocotyl and nodal roots, the higher density and length of laterals observed in Z7 may considerably increase root surface area an thus improve the efficiency of acquisition of water and nutrients. Accordingly, the chilling tolerance of the Z7 genotype may be associated with better capability of developing root tissues with greater conductive capacity (Ciamporová and Dekánková, 1998) already at seedling stage and thus guarantee adequate acquisition of water and nutrients, and ensure the realisation of the inherent yield potential (Stamp *et al.*, 1997).

Root respiration and electron partitioning

Several studies suggest that when plants grow at lower temperatures, the respiration rate increases and also participation of the alternative, non-phosphorylating pathway increases (Stewart *et al.* 1990; Vanlerberghe and McIntosh, 1992; Moynihan *et al.*, 1995). In our previous paper (Luxová and Gašparíková, 1999) it was shown that transfer of maize seedlings from 24 to 6°C initially brought about an increase in total root respiration in the chilling-tolerant genotype Z7. Concomitantly, the alternative pathway capacity and cytochrome pathway activity increased within 2 days. On the other hand, in chilling-sensitive Penjalinan only moderate increase of cytochrome pathway was observed.

Longer exposition of seedlings to chilling (6 d) resulted in inhibition of respiration rate in both genotypes (Table 2). The inhibition was caused exclusively by inhibition of cytochrome pathway perhaps due to a decrease in the demand for respiratory energy required for root growth and ion uptake, which are drastically inhibited by low temperature (Engels and Marschner, 1992). The capacity of non-phosphorylating cyanid-resistant alternative pathway (AP) showed substantial increase in both genotypes being higher in the chilling-tolerant Z7 plants. This indicates a co-ordinate regulation of both pathways to meet the metabolic demands of the cells. Since the energy-requiring processes are reduced at low temperature while content of sugars could be relatively high (Barlow and Rathfelder, 1985; Sowinski, 1995; Sowinski *et al.*, 1998), the flow of electrons through the AP could enhance oxygen utilization. Hence, the AP could reduce the potential for the generation of reactive oxygen species in mitochondria when the availability of respiratory electrons to the dehydrogenase complexes exceeds the capacity of the cytochrome oxidase (Purvis and Shewfelt, 1993). Almost no differences in antioxidant enzyme activities (superoxide dismutase, catalase and guaiacol peroxidase) observed in maize roots during the chilling (data not shown) could support this hypothesis.

TABLE 2. ROOT RESPIRATION RATES (V_t), ACTIVITY OF CYTOCHROME PATHWAY (CP) AND CAPACITY OF ALTERNATIVE PATHWAY (AP) OF RESPIRATION EXPRESSED AS NMOL O_2 G $DW^{-1}S^{-1}$ IN PENJALINAN AND Z7 NON-CHILLED PLANTS (24°C), CHILLED (6°C FOR 6 DAYS) AND AFTER 5 DAYS OF RECOVERY AT 24°C.

	Penjalinan			Z7		
	Control	6 °C	Recovery	Control	6 °C	Recovery
V_t	87.5 ± 2.3	80.0 ± 1.8	90.0 ± 1.5	104.0 ± 1.3	88.0 ± 0.9	96.1 ± 1.4
CP activity	53.7 ± 1.5	41.0 ± 0.8	56.0 ± 1.2	72.0 ± 1.5	44.0 ± 0.6	53.0 ± 1.3
AP activity	23.0 ± 1.5	30.0 ± 1.1	27.5 ± 1.1	19.5 ± 1.3	41.5 ± 1.2	34.7 ± 0.8

ACKNOWLEDGEMENTS

This work was partially financed by Slovak Grant Agency for Science VEGA (Grant No. 5051), and by the COST 824 Action, grant No 3031.

REFERENCES

Ameglio, T., J. Morizet, P. Cruiziat and M. Martignac, 1990. The effects of root temperature on water flux, potential and root resistance in sunflower. Agronomie, 10: 331-340.

Barlow, P.W. and J.S. Adam, 1989. Anatomical disturbances in primary roots of *Zea mays* following periods of cool temperature. Environ. Environmental and Experimental Botany, 29: 323-337.

Barlow, P.W. and E.L. Rathfelder, 1985. Cell division and regeneration in primary root meristems of *Zea mays* recovering from cold treatment. Environmental and Experimental Botany, 25: 303-314.

Èiamporová, M. and K. Dekánková, 1998. Root system morphology and anatomy of cold-sensitive Penjalinan and cold-tolerant Z7 genotypes of maize. Biologia, Bratislava, 53:133-139.

Engels, C. and H. Marschner, 1992. Root to shoot translocation of macronutrients in relation to shoot demand in maize (*Zea mays* L.) grown at different root zone temperature. Z. Pflanzenernähr, Bodenkd, 155: 121-128.

Feil, B., R. Thiraporn, G. Geisler and P. Stamp, 1991. The impact of temperature on seedling root traits of European and tropical maize (*Zea mays* L.) cultivars. Journal of Agronomy and Crop Science, 166: 81-89.

Kiel, C. and P. Stamp, 1992. Internal root anatomy of maize seedlings (*Zea mays* L.) as influenced by temperature and genotype. Annals of Botany, 70: 125-128.

Moynihan, M.R., A. Ordentlich and I. Raskin, 1995. Chilling-induced heat evolution in plants. Plant Physiology, 108: 995-999.

Purvis, A.C. and R.L. Shewfelt, 1993. Does the alternative pathway ameliorate chilling injury in sensitive plant tissues? Physiol. Plant., 88: 712-718.

Sowinski, P., 1995. Transport of assimilates from leaves to roots in chilling-treated maize seedlings. Acta Physiologia Plantarum, 17: 341-348.

Sowinski, P., W. Richner, A. Soldati and P. Stamp, 1998. Assimilate transport in maize (*Zea mays* L.) seedlings at vertical low temperature gradients in the root zone. Journal of Experimental Botany, 49: 747-752.

Stamp, P., 1984. Chilling tolerance of young plants demonstrated on the example of maize (*Zea mays* L.). Forschritte im Acker- und Pflanzenbau 7. Paul Parey, Scientific Publishers, Berlin.

Stamp, P., B. Feil, M. Schortemeyer and W. Richner, 1997. Responses of roots to low temperatures and nitrogen forms. In: H.M. Anderson *et al.* (eds) Plant Roots from Cells to Systems, pp. 143-154.

Stewart, C.R., B.A. Martin, L. Reding and S. Cerwick, 1990. Respiration and alternative oxidase in corn seedling tissues during germination at different temperatures. Plant Physiology, 92: 755-760.

Vanlerberghe, G.C. and L. McIntosh, 1992. Lower growth temperature increases alternative pathway capacity and alternative oxidase protein in tobacco. Plant Physiology, 100: 115-119.

Chilling tolerance of maize - From the growth chamber to the field

J. LEIPNER

Institute of Plant Science, Swiss Federal Institute of Technology, Zurich, Switzerland
Present address: Department of Biological Sciences, University of Essex, Colchester, UK

SUMMARY

Expanding maize (*Zea mays* L.) cultivation to regions with temperate climates still requires breeding for chilling-tolerant maize genotypes and, as a result, a better under-standing of physiological responses of maize to low temperature. From a practical point of view, experiments under controlled environmental conditions are more reproducible and more convenient for the researcher than field experiments. However, results obtained under controlled conditions should be compared with field data to justify their relevance. Maize plants respond to changes in environmental conditions by alterations of their antioxidative systems, which seem to play a major role in tolerating low temperature stress. Data from experiments studying plants grown in growth chambers were compared with data from a field trial. Concerning the content of pigments and antioxidants, the comparison showed that seedlings grown at about 15°C under moderate light intensity (350 - 450 μmol m^{-2} s^{-1}) are similar to seedlings grown under field conditions in Switzerland according to regional agronomic practices.

Keywords: antioxidants, chilling stress, maize, suboptimal temperature

INTRODUCTION

During early growth of maize in the field, seedlings especially of chilling-sensitive genotypes often suffer from low temperatures resulting in reduced growth (Verheul *et al.*, 1996). The formation of reactive oxygen species (ROS) seems to be the cause of damage to the photosynthetic apparatus during exposure to chilling in the light (Wise, 1995). Maize plants respond to changes in environmental conditions by alterations of their antioxidative systems, which seem to play a major role in tolerating low temperature stress. The expanding cultivation of maize to regions with lower temperatures still requires breeding for chilling-tolerant maize genotypes and, therefore, a better understanding of physiological responses of maize to low temperature stress. To study the response of maize to low temperature stress, experiments under controlled environment are commonly conducted. Growth chamber experiments are easier to perform and more reproducible than field experiments. However, under controlled environment, growth conditions must be chosen carefully to justify the field relevance of this kind of experiment. In the present study, we compared antioxidant and pigment data obtained from various experiments done under controlled environment with data from a field experiment.

MATERIALS AND METHODS

For growth chamber experiments, *Zea mays* L. seedlings of the inbred lines Z7 and Penjalinan were grown under a photoperiod of 12 h at 350 or 450 μmol quanta m^{-2} s^{-1}, 60/70% (day/night) relative humidity, and 30/27°C, 25/22°C, 20/18°C or 15/13°C (day/night). Measurements were performed on the middle part of the third fully expanded leaf. For pigment and antioxidant assays, leaf segments were frozen in liquid nitrogen and stored at -80°C until assay. For the field experiment, *Zea mays* L. seedlings of the inbred lines Z7 and Penjalinan were grown in Eschikon, near Zurich, Switzerland (8°41' E, 47°27' N, 550 m above sea level) (Leipner *et al.*, 1999). Seeds were sown on 24 April, 2 May, and 15 May 1996. Measurements of pigments and antioxidants were made on the third leaf that reached full expansion (31 May, 5 June, and 12 June 1996). Pigments and a-tocopherol were analysed by HPLC (Leipner *et al.*, 1997, 1999, 2000). Ascorbate was assayed photometrically by the reduction of 2,6-dichlorindophenol (Leipner *et al.*, 1997) or by HPLC (Leipner *et al.*, 1999). The glutathione content was determined using the enzymatic recycling procedure in which glutathione was oxidised by 5,5'-dithio-bis(2-nitrobenzoic acid) and reduced by NADPH in the presence of glutathione reductase as described in Leipner *et al.* (1997).

RESULTS

The foliar ascorbate, glutathione and a-tocopherol contents were affected by the growth temperature as well as by the light intensity (Fig. 1 A-C). In general, low temperature or high light intensity resulted in an increase of the antioxidative compounds. The foliar ascorbate content of field-grown maize was only slightly higher than that of leaves developed at 15°C and 450 μmol m^{-2} s^{-1}. Interestingly, the genotype Penjalinan exhibited less temperature-dependence of its ascorbate content than Z7. The amount of glutathione of field grown Z7 was about the same as in maize leaves grown in growth chambers at 15°C. The growth light intensity affected the content of optimal growth temperature. Leaves that developed under field conditions were similar in their a-tocopherol amount to leaves developed at 15 or 20°C. The chlorophyll a/b ratio was only little affected by the growth conditions (Fig. 1 D). In contrast, the de-epoxidation state of the xanthophyll cycle pool (AZ:VAZ) was markedly affected by either growth temperature and growth light intensity (Fig. 1 E). High light intensity or low growth temperature resulted in de-epoxidation of the xanthophyll cycle pool, indicated by a high value for AZ: VAZ. Furthermore, the data showed higher AZ:VAZ in Penjalinan than Z7. In field grown maize leaves, the value of AZ:VAZ was very close to the AZ:VAZ value obtained from leaves grown at 15°C under controlled growth conditions.

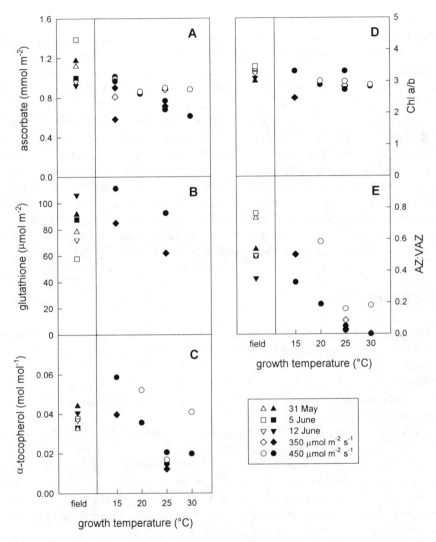

FIGURE 1. EFFECT OF GROWTH CONDITIONS ON THE CONTENTS OF ASCORBATE (A), GLUTATHIONE (B) AND A-TOCOPHEROL (C), THE CHLOROPHYLL A/B RATIO (D) AND THE DE-EPOXIDATION STATE OF THE XANTHOPHYLL CYCLE POOL (E) IN THE THIRD LEAF OF MAIZE GENOTYPES Z7 (FILLED SYMBOLS) AND PENJALINAN (OPEN SYMBOLS). PLANTS WERE GROWN EITHER IN THE FIELD AND HARVESTED AT MAY 31, JUNE 5 AND JUNE 12 OR IN GROWTH CHAMBERS AT DIFFERENT TEMPERATURES UNDER 350 μMOL M⁻² S⁻¹ OR 450 μMOL M⁻² S⁻¹. VALUES ARE MEANS OF FOUR TO FIVE REPLICATES.

DISCUSSION

In maize, growth at suboptimal temperature results in an accumulation of glutathione (Kocsy *et al.*, 1996), a-tocopherol (Leipner *et al.*, 1997) and ascorbate (Kingstom-Smith *et al.*, 1999). Furthermore, chilling tolerant maize genotypes are often characterised by a higher amount of certain antioxidants than chilling sensitive genotypes (Kocsy *et al.*, 1996; Hodges *et al.*, 1996). These findings give evidence that antioxidants play a crucial role in the response of maize to low temperature stress. Therefore, the content of antioxidants, in addition with the pigment composition, give hints of the environmental conditions during the development of plants or leaves. In the present study, the amount of the three major foliar antioxidants, namely ascorbate, glutathione and a-tocopherol, of field-grown maize leaves was alike that of leaves developed under controlled conditions at 15°C and 450 μmol m^{-2} s^{-1}. Moreover, growth under field conditions resulted in very similar values of chlorophyll a/b ratio and de-epoxidation state of the xanthophyll cycle pool (AZ: VAZ) as did growth at 15°C and 450 μmol m^{-2} s^{-1}. However, one has to keep in mind that both temperature and light intensity can alter the antioxidant and pigment composition of a leaf, and, therefore, a transpolarisation of data obtained from growth chamber experiments to results of field trials is rather critical. Nevertheless, maize seedlings grown at about 15°C under moderate light intensity seem to be a suitable plant material to study the basics of chilling stress of maize in temperate climates.

REFERENCES

Hodges, D.M., C.J. Andrews, D.A. Johnson and R.I. Hamilton, 1996. Antioxidant compound responses to chilling stress in differentially sensitive inbred maize lines. Physiologia Plantarum, 98: 685-692.

Kingston-Smith, A.H., J. Harbinson and C.H. Foyer, 1999. Acclimation of photosynthesis, H$_2$O$_2$ content and antioxidants in maize (*Zea mays*) grown at sub-optimal temperatures. Plant, Cell and Environment, 22: 1071-1084.

Kocsy, G., M. Brunner, A. Rüegsegger, P. Stamp and C. Brunhold, 1996. Glutathione synthesis in maize genotypes with different sensitivities to chilling. Planta, 198: 365-370.

Leipner, J., Y. Fracheboud and P. Stamp, 1997. Acclimation by suboptimal growth temperature diminishes photooxidative damage in maize leaves. Plant, Cell and Environment, 20: 366-372.

Leipner, J., Y. Fracheboud and P. Stamp, 1999. Effect of growing season on the photosynthetic apparatus and leaf antioxidative defenses in two maize genotypes of different chilling tolerance. Environmental and Experimental Botany, 42: 129-139.

Leipner, J., A. Basilides, P. Stamp and Y. Fracheboud, 2000. Hardly increased oxidative stress after exposure to low temperature in chilling-acclimated and non-acclimated maize leaves. Plant Biology, 2: 243-251.

Verheul, M.J., C. Picatto and P. Stamp, 1996. Growth and development of maize (*Zea mays* L.) seedlings under chilling conditions in the field. European Journal of Agronomy, 5: 31–41.

Wise, R.R., 1995. Chilling-enhanced photooxidation: the production, action and study of reactive oxygen species produced during chilling in the light. Photosynthesis Research, 45: 79–97.

Recent advances in cold tolerance research in maize

E. PÁLDI, G. SZALAI, E. HORVÁTH AND T. JANDA

Agricultural Research Institute of the Hungarian Academy of Sciences, H-2462 Martonvásár, POB 19, Hungary

SUMMARY

The paper provides a brief summary of the results achieved within the framework of the COST 814 Action on maize cold tolerance. Special mention should be made of the joint effect of low temperature and light on photosynthetic processes, the role of light in the appearance of post-chilling symptoms, the importance of the alternative pathway of polyamine biosynthesis in the cold tolerance of maize inbred lines, the correlation between glycine betaine and cold tolerance, and the enhancement of cold tolerance by certain protective compounds (salicylic acid and related compounds).

Keywords: chilling, chlorophyll fluorescence, salicylic acid, Zea mays L.

INTRODUCTION

As in many other countries, one of the main fodder crops in Hungary is maize, which is of subtropical origin. The importance of this crop is demonstrated by the fact that in recent decades its sowing area has spread ever further to the north of Europe. Hungary is situated near the northern limit for the production of grain maize, and due to the continental nature of the climate, and in addition to summer droughts, the abiotic stress factor which threatens the growth and development of the crop to the greatest extent, especially in the early stages of development, is low temperature. This means that hybrids with good seedling cold tolerance are required if maize production is to be reliable. The effect of low temperature on the maize metabolism is thus of great theoretical and practical importance and has been studied from various aspects in the Martonvásár institute over the last 40 years, in close cooperation with maize breeding and production research.

MATERIALS AND METHODS

Inbred maize lines (N 6, Co 158, F 564, F7 cmsC, Mo 17, W 153 R, Co 109, A 632) subjected by Martonvásár maize breeders and agronomists to agronomic (Marton, 1997a, b, c) and phytopathological (Marton, 1987; 1990) investigations were used in the experiments, together with a line collection available to participants in the COST 814 Action (Z 7, KW1074, CM 109, Penjalinan) and two hybrids (Norma and Furio). The chlorophyll fluorescence induction of the maize leaves was measured with a PAM instrument (Walz, Effeltrich, Germany) working on the pulse amplitude modulation principle (Schreiber *et al.*, 1986), while low temperature fluorescence spectra were recorded using a Perkin Elmer 44B spectrofluorometer (Böddi *et al.*, 1992). The quantitative and qualitative determination of polyamines and amino acids was carried out with the HPLC method (Bartók *et al.*, 1994), and that of glycine betaine by means of pyrolytic gas chromatography (Hitz and Hanson, 1980). A new, reliable HPLC method was elaborated for the determination of agmatine (Bencsik *et al.*, 1998). The experimental plants were grown and treated in homogeneous and gradient plant growth chambers (Conviron, Canada).

RESULTS

The results achieved in connection with the cold tolerance of maize can be summarised as follows on the basis of earlier papers published in this field.

Characterisation of the seedling cold tolerance of maize inbred lines with the aid of chlorophyll-a fluorescence induction parameters

Suboptimum temperatures (below 13 °C) applied during the germination and early development stages of maize had a negative influence on the photosynthetic apparatus of the plants. The F_o, F_v/F_m and F_R indexes changed with the reduction in temperature, indicating that several processes were responsible for the decline in the photochemical efficiency of photosynthesis. There was damage to the synthesis of pigments and to their incorporation into the photosynthetic membrane, and this was accompanied by an inhibition of Q_A reduction and of electron flow into the plastoquinone pool. Using the values obtained for the above-mentioned indexes at low temperature, the 18 lines and 21 crosses examined could be classified on the basis of cold sensitivity. The results were in good agreement with those of various agronomic tests carried out by breeders. It can be concluded from these results (Csapó *et al.*, 1991; Janda *et al.*, 1994; Janda *et al.*, 1995) that the kinetic method based on chlorophyll-a fluorescence induction can be applied in practice for the reliable evaluation of the cold tolerance of inbred maize lines and crosses.

Effect of low temperature on the structure and chlorophyll biosynthesis of the etioplasts

In order to carry out a detailed analysis of the Shibata shift (Shibata, 1957) low temperature (77K) spectra were measured after 5, 10, 20, 30, 40 or 50 min illumination and the curves were resolved into Gauss components: the emission spectrum into 674 and 690 nm parts and the excitation spectrum into 672 and 684 nm parts. It is clear from the curves that the greatest difference in the Shibata shift occurred after approx. 40 min illumination. The analysis of the low temperature fluorescence spectra of the leaves detected a difference between cold-sensitive (Co 109) and cold-tolerant (A 632) maize lines in the suboptimum temperature treatment which could not be demonstrated at 25°C. After illumination a delay could be registered in the Shibata shift in the cold-sensitive line. This indicated changes in the geometric parameters of energy transfer in the cold-sensitive line, associated with a change in the membrane structure during cold treatment. Electron microscope studies proved that changes in the disintegration of the prolamellar bodies, preventing the translocation of the NADPH protochlorophyllide oxidoreductase enzyme, were dependent on the degree of cold sensitivity and on the temperature applied (Böddi *et al.*, 1997).

Improvement in the seedling cold tolerance of maize using salicylic acid and its derivatives

Maize hybrids raised at normal temperature (22°C) did not suffer any damage during suboptimum temperature treatment (5 days at 2°C) in the presence of 0.5 mM salicylic acid (SA). The protective effect of salicylic acid was proved by measuring chlorophyll-a fluorescence parameters and ion leakage. The treatment caused mortality in plants not treated with salicylic acid. Due to the effect of SA two enzymes involved in the antioxidant system, guaiacol peroxidase and glutathione reductase exhibited a significant increase in activity. Compounds related to salicylic acid (acetylsalicylic acid, benzoic acid) showed a similar protective effect. In the case of peroxidase a new isoenzyme band appeared after treatment with SA. The examinations proved that SA, as part of the signal transduction chain, increases the cold tolerance of maize through the direct induction of the guaiacol peroxidase and glutathione reductase enzymes (Janda *et al.*, 1999).

Effect of low temperature on the synthesis of certain N-containing compounds in inbred maize lines with different degrees of cold tolerance

Changes in the quantities of putrescine, agmatine, proline and glycine betaine were examined in lines with different degrees of cold tolerance after various lengths of cold treatment (1, 3, 5 or 8 days at 5°C). The quantitative changes of various magnitudes found to occur in these compounds as the result of low-temperature treatment were in negative correlation with the cold tolerance of the genotypes. The alternative metabolic pathway of polyamine biosynthesis starting from arginine, and the central compound of this synthesis – agmatine, which functions primarily in higher plants, played a positive role in the development of defence mechanisms against low temperature. The experiments confirmed that glycine betaine, the quantity of which continuously declined in cold-sensitive maize lines as the result of cold treatment but rose in tolerant genotypes, may act as an osmotic agent not only in drought and salt tolerance processes, but also in tolerance to cold (Páldi, 1995; Szalai *et al.*, 1997; Páldi *et al.*, 1998).

Effect of photoinhibition occurring at low temperature

Earlier results (Janda *et al.*, 1994) indicated that the greater the light intensity and the lower the temperature, the greater the changes occurring in certain fluorescence induction parameters, including F_v/F_m. In the present experiments it was confirmed that the F_v/F_m parameter did not change in the dark at 5°C even after 48 hours, while in the light (200 ìmol m^{-2} s^{-1}) a decline was observed within 7 hours. It was clear from the results that the longer the plants were at low temperature in the dark, the greater was the reduction in the efficiency of photosystem II (PSII) when they were exposed to light. If cold treatment was carried out in the light, PSII was inhibited. There was also a reduction in the stomatal conductance and the transpiration. Net photosynthesis decreased to an even greater extent in the light (by approx. 75%, compared to only 40% in the dark). This effect could be attributed to the lower efficiency of the electron transport chain and the reduced activity of the enzymes involved in carbon dioxide fixation, as confirmed by the high level of intercellular carbon dioxide (Janda *et al.*, 1998).

ACKNOWLEDGEMENTS

This research was supported by grants from the National Scientific Research Fund (T 21115, T 32653 and F 26236), which are gratefully acknowledged.

REFERENCES

Bartók, T., G. Szalai, Zs. Lõrincz, G. Börcsök and F. Sági, 1994. High-speed RP-HPLC/FL analysis of amino acids after automated two-step derivatization with o-phthaldialdehyde/3-mercaptopropionic acid and 9-fluorenylmethyl chloroformate. Journal of Liquid Chromatography, 17: 4391-4403.

Bencsik, K., T. Kremmer, M. Boldizsár, J. Tamás, J. Mák, J. and E. Páldi, 1998. New high performance liquid chromatographic determination of agmatine. Journal of Chromatography A, 824: 175-180.

Böddi, B., M. Ryberg and C. Sundqvist, 1992. Identification of four universal protochlorophyllide forms in dark-grown leaves by analysis of the 77 K fluorescence emission spectra. Journal of Photochemistry and Photobiology, 12: 389-401.

Böddi, B., Á. Keresztes, B. Csapó, J. Kovács, E. Páldi and F. Láng, 1997. Differences in the etioplast ultrastructure and chlorophyll biosyntjhesis time course of cold tolerant and cold sensitive maize lines under cold treatment. Maydica, 42: 305-311.

Csapó, B., J. Kovács, E. Páldi and Z. Szigeti, 1991. Fluorescence induction characteristic of maize inbred lines after long-term chilling treatment during the early phase of development. Photosynthetica, 25: 575-582.

Hitz, W. D. and A. Hanson, 1980. Determination of glycine betaine by pyrolysis-gas-chromatography in cereals and grasses. Phytochemistry, 19: 2371-2374.

Janda, T., G. Szalai, J. Kissimon, E. Páldi, C. Marton and Z. Szigeti, 1994. Role of irradiance in the chilling injury of young maize plants studied by chlorophyll fluorescence induction measurements. Photosynthetica, 35: 205-212.

Janda, T., G. Szalai, Z. Szigeti and E. Páldi, 1995. Properties of F_o (q_o) occurring in chilled maize plants. In: Mathis, P., (ed.), Photosynthesis: from Light to Biosphere. Kluwer Academic Publ., Dordrecht-Boston-London. pp. 869-872.

Janda, T., G. Szalai and E. Páldi, 1996. Chlorophyll fluorescence and anthocyanin content in chilled maize plants after return to a non-chilling temperature under various irradiances. Biologia Plantarum, 38: 625-627.

Janda, T., G. Szalai, J.-M. Ducruet and E. Páldi, 1998. Changes in photosynthesis in inbred maize lines with different degrees of chilling tolerance grown at optimum and suboptimum temperatures. Photosynthetica, 35: 205-212.

Janda, T., G. Szalai, I. Tari and E. Páldi, 1999. Hydroponic treatment with salicylic acid decreases the effects of chilling injury in maize (Zea mays L.) plants. Planta, 208: 175-180.

Marton, L.C., 1997a. Development of young maize plants under a suboptimal range of temperatures. Acta Agronomica Hungarica, 45: 329-35.

Marton, L.C., 1997b. Inheritance of cold test index in sterilised and normal soil. In: Bedő, Z., Sutka, J., Tischner, T., Veisz, O. (eds.), Proceedings of International Symposium on Cereal Adaptation to Low Temperature Stress. Martonvásár, Hungary, pp. 281-284.

Marton. L.C., 1997c. Evaluation of the cold tolerance of young maize plants in the temperature gradient chamber. In: Bedő, Z., Sutka, J., Tischner, T., Veisz, O. (eds.), Proceedings of International Symposium on Cereal Adaptation to Low Temperature Stress. Martonvásár, Hungary, pp. 269-276.

Marton L.C., 1987. Cold tolerance of maize seeds infected with Fusaria species. In: Húska, J., Janda, J., Neštick?, M. (eds.), Proceedings of the 14th Congress of EUCARPIA. Nitra, Czechoslovakia, pp. 277-286.

Marton L.C., L. Kizmus T. Szundy, 1990. Germination of maize seeds infected with Fusaria in a temperature gradient chamber. In: Hinterholz, J. (ed.), Proceedings of the XVth Congress of EUCARPIA. Baden, Austria, pp. 453-458.

Páldi, E., 1995. Effect of low temperature on the synthesis of N-containing compunds in maize lines. In: Samuelson, R., Solsheim, B., Pithan, K., Watten-Melvaer,E. (eds.), Nitrogen Supply and Nitrogen Fixation of Crops for Cool and Wet Climates. EC, Brussels-Luxembourg, pp. 241-253.

Páldi, E., G. Szalai, T. Janda and L.C. Marton, 1998. Effect of low temperature on the synthesis of N-containing compounds in inbred lines with varying degrees of cold tolerance. Növénytermelés, 47: 483-490 (in Hungarian).

Schreiber, U., U. Schliwa and W. Bilger, 1986. Continuous recording on photochemical and non-photochemical chlorophyll fluorescence quenching with a new type of modulation fluorometer. Photosynthesis Research, 10: 51-62.

Shibata, K., 1957. Spectroscopic studies on chlorophyll formation in intact leaves. Journal of Biochemistry, 44: 147-173.

Szalai, G., T. Janda, E. Páldi, Z. Szigeti, 1996. Role of light in the development of post-chilling symptoms in maize. Journal of Plant Physiology, 148: 378-383.

Szalai, G., T. Janda, T. Bartók and E. Páldi, 1997. Role of light in changes in free amino acid and polyamine contents at chilling temperature in maize (*Zea mays* L.). Physiologia Plantarum, 101: 434-438.

Thermoluminescence investigation of low temperature stress in maize

T. JANDA[1], J.M. DUCRUET[2], G. SZALAI[1], E. HORVÁTH[1] AND E. PÁLDI[1]

[1]Agricultural Research Institute of the Hungarian Academy of Sciences, H-2462 Martonvásár, POB 19, Hungary
[2]SBE, Bât 532, INRA/CEA, Saclay, 91191, Gif-sur-Yvette cedex, France

SUMMARY

The thermoluminescence (TL) emission of photosynthesising materials originates from the recombination of charge pairs created by a previous excitation. Using a recently described TL set-up it is possible to investigate several TL bands occurring at positive temperatures in intact leaves. The far-red illumination of leaves at low but non-freezing temperatures induces a TL band peaking at around 40-45°C, together with a B band peaking between 20 and 35°C. In this study the effect of low-temperature stress (chilling) on the B and AG bands is shown. Low-temperature stress causes a decrease in the above-mentioned TL bands. This decrease is less pronounced in cold-tolerant genotypes and in those grown at acclimating temperatures. Furthermore, an additional band appears above 80°C after severe cold stress. This band indicates the presence of lipid peroxides. These results show that TL of unfrozen leaves can provide a new insight into the mechanism of low temperature stress.

Keywords: afterglow, chilling, peroxide, Zea mays L.

INTRODUCTION

The thermoluminescence (TL) light emission of photosynthesising materials originates from the charge recombination between the positively charged donors and negatively charged acceptors of Photosystem 2. For reviews of thermoluminescence see Vass and Govindjee (1996).

Illumination of a long-term dark-adapted leaf or intact chloroplasts with far-red light induces an AG (afterglow) TL band (Miranda and Ducruet, 1995a). This band reflects a more complex phenomenon than the B and Q TL bands, which represent the back-reaction of a PS-II charge separation. It is suggested that not only PS II, but also part of the cyclic electron pathway and transthylakoid pH gradient are involved in the occurrence of the AG emission which corresponds to a back electron transfer towards PS-II centres initially in the $S_2/S_3 Q_B$ state (Sundblad et al., 1988). Low temperature is one of the most important limiting factors in the wider spread of several crop plants (Stamp, 1984; Marton and Szundy, 1997). The far-red induced afterglow emission is very sensitive to drought and temperature stresses (Janda et al., 1999).

The aim of the present study is to investigate the effect of chilling stress on the AG TL band in young maize plants.

MATERIALS AND METHODS

Maize plants (*Zea mays* L., hybrid Norma; inbred lines Mo17 and CM 7) were grown for 2-3 weeks at 22/20°C or at 15/13°C in a growth chamber with a 16/8-h light/dark periodicity at 250 mmol m^{-2} s^{-1} PPFD and 75% RH. The cold treatment was carried out at 0°C.

TL measurements were performed using a laboratory-made apparatus and software described earlier (Miranda and Ducruet, 1995a). TL was induced by 30 s far-red light at 1°C after more than 2 h dark adaptation. The measurements were repeated several times and the representative curves are presented in the figures.

Conductivity measurements were carried out as described by Szalai et al. (1996).

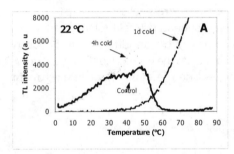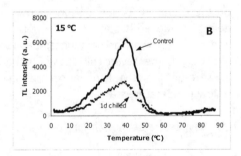

FIGURE 1. EFFECT OF LOW TEMPERATURE (0°C) ON THE TL CURVE INDUCED BY 30 S FAR-RED LIGHT IN YOUNG MAIZE PLANTS GROWN AT 22/20°C (A) OR AT ACCLIMATING TEMPERATURES OF 15/13°C (B).

Electrolyte leakage values are given as a percentage of the fully damaged samples, which were determined after incubation of the leaf disks for 1 day at –80°C. The results are the means of 10 measurements and were statistically evaluated using the t-test method.

RESULTS AND DISCUSSION

The far-red illumination of leaves at low but non-freezing temperatures induces a TL band peaking at around 40-45°C (afterglow or AG-band), together with a B-band peaking below 30°C (Miranda and Ducruet, 1995a). Short-term low temperature treatment (4 h at 0°C) causes a slight increase and a downshift towards lower temperatures in the AG-band in maize plants grown at 22/20°C (Figure 1A).

The B band induced by a single turnover flash does not exhibit this increase, although a slight downshift of T_{max} can be observed (curves not shown). Severe chilling stress causes a dramatic decrease in the AG band. After 1 day of cold treatment carried out at 0°C in the light both the B and AG bands disappeared, and a band peaking above 80°C appeared in young maize (Norma hybrid) plants grown at 22/20°C. This band was especially strong in leaf segments which lost their water content as a consequence of the cold stress and were practically dead. The TL bands arising above 60°C were reported to be independent of previous illumination and to correlate with the quantity of lipid peroxides in the plant sample (Hideg and Vass, 1993; Vavilin and Ducruet, 1998). Moisture in the sample may suppress certain HTL bands (Ducruet and Vavilin, 1999). Besides the fact that these leaf segments contained the most peroxides, this may also explain why this band was so high in leaves which dried out due to the severe low temperature stress. The loss of the AG band due to low-temperature stress was affected by several factors. For example, in plants which were grown at relatively low (15/13°C), acclimating temperature (Janda et al., 1998), the AG band was downshifted towards low temperatures, and the decrease occurring after a 1 day chilling stress was less pronounced than in those which were grown at 22/20°C (Figure 1B). Previously it was shown that the T_{max} value of the AG TL band was usually found at lower temperature in hardened, cold-tolerant genotypes than in sensitive ones (Ducruet et al., 1997).

A low growth temperature caused a slight downshift in the T_{max} of the B band induced by 1 flash. Downshifts of the B TL band have already been reported in higher plants and in green algae. In the green alga *Chlamydomonas reinhardtii* the downshift in the B band from 30 to 15-17°C after photoinhibitory treatment was assumed to be the consequence of a conformational change in the D1 protein of Photosystem 2 (Ohad et al., 1988). In another green alga *Chlamydobotrys stellata* and in pea leaves the photoinhibition-induced downshift was assigned to a different extent of reduction in the Q and B bands (Janda et al., 1992). Not only photoinhibition, but also acidification in the lumen of the thylakoid membrane may lead to a downshift of the B TL band (Miranda and Ducruet, 1995b).

To investigate how changes in the AG band reflect the chilling tolerance of plants, two inbred lines, CM 7 (cold-tolerant) and Mo 17 (cold-sensitive) were compared. Electrolyte leakage measurements clearly reflected the difference between the two lines: membrane destruction was much more pronounced in the sensitive Mo 17 line than in the tolerant CM 7 after cold treatment (Table 1).

Measurement of the far-red induced TL curve shows a similar result: although there is a significant decline in both the B and AG bands in the cold-tolerant CM 7 line after 1-day cold treatment at 0°C, this chilling stress totally suppressed these bands in Mo 17, and a considerable HTL band could be detected (curves not shown). However, it should also be mentioned that significant differences could be observed within the individual plants: for example the part of the leaves closer to the base was less sensitive than the distal parts (curves not shown), which must be taken into account when the aim is to compare different kinds of plants.

TABLE 1. ELECTROLYTE LEAKAGE VALUES GIVEN AS A PERCENTAGE OF TOTALLY DAMAGED SAMPLES (1 DAY AT −80°C) IN CONTROL (GROWN AT 22/20°C) AND LOW TEMPERATURE STRESSED (2 DAYS AT 0°C) COLD TOLERANT CM 7 AND COLD SENSITIVE MO 17 MAIZE INBRED LINES. SAMPLES WERE TAKEN FROM THE MIDDLE PART OF THE YOUNGEST FULLY DEVELOPED LEAVES. **, ***: SIGNIFICANT AT THE 0.01 AND 0.001 LEVELS, RESPECTIVELY, COMPARED TO CONTROL, UNCHILLED PLANTS (N = 10).

Genotype	Control	Cold treated
CM 7	22.3 ±4.6	31.6 ± 7.7[**]
Mo 17	23.1 ±5.9	65.8 ±16.1[***]

It can be concluded from these results that the far-red induced TL curve exhibits complex behaviour during chilling stress. Mild stress may cause a transient increase in the AG band together with a downshift in its T_{max} value. Severe stress progressively decreases both the B and AG bands, possibly leading to their complete loss (in contrast to short-term freezing in the dark, after which a substantial part of the B band still remains) and to the appearance of the HTL bands indicating the presence of lipid peroxides. Changes in the AG curve depend on the chilling tolerance of the plant.

ACKNOWLEDGEMENTS

This work was supported by grants from the Hungarian National Scientific Research Foundation (OTKA F26236, T21115, T032653) and the J. Bolyai Research Sponsorship.

REFERENCES

Ducruet, J.M., T. Janda and E. Páldi, 1997. Whole leaf thermoluminescence as a prospective tool for monitoring intra-specific cold tolerance in crop species. Acta Agronomica Hungarica, 45: 463-466.

Ducruet, J.M. and D. Vavilin, 1999. Chlorophyll high-temperature thermoluminescence emission as an indicator of oxidative stress: perturbating effects of oxygen and leaf water content. Free Radical Research, 31: 187-192.

Hideg, É. and I. Vass, 1993. The 75 °C thermoluminescence band of green tissues: chemiluminescence from membrane-chlorophyll interaction. Photochemistry and Photobiology, 58: 280-283.

Janda, T., W. Wiessner, E. Páldi, D. Mende and S. Demeter, 1992. Thermoluminescence investigation of photoinhibition in the green alga, *Chlamydobotrys stellata* and in *Pisum sativum* L. leaves. Zeitschrift für Naturforschung, 47c: 585-590.

Janda, T., G. Szalai, J.M. Ducruet and E. Páldi, 1998. Changes in photosynthesis in inbred maize lines with different degrees of chilling tolerance grown at optimum and suboptimum temperatures. Photosynthetica, 35: 205-212.

Janda, T., G. Szalai, C. Giauffret, E. Páldi and J.M. Ducruet, 1999. The thermoluminescence 'afterglow' band as a sensitive indicator of abiotic stresses in plants. Zeitschrift für Naturforschung, 54c: 629-633.

Marton, C.L. and T. Szundy, 1997. Development of young maize plants under a suboptimal range of temperatures. Acta Agronomica Hungarica, 45: 329-335.

Miranda T. and J.M. Ducruet, 1995a. Characterization of the chlorophyll thermoluminescence afterglow in dark-adapted or far-red illuminated plant leaves. Plant Physiology and Biochemistry, 33: 689-699.

Miranda T. and J.M. Ducruet, 1995b. Effects of dark- and light-induced proton gradients in thylakoids on the Q and B thermoluminescence bands. Photosynthesis Research, 43: 251-262.

Ohad, I., H. Koike, S. Shochat and Y. Inoue, 1988. Changes in the properties of reaction center II during the initial stages of photoinhibition as revealed by thermoluminescence measurements. Biochimica et Biophysica Acta, 933: 288-298.

Stamp, P., 1984. Chilling tolerance of young plants demonstrated on the example of maize (Zea mays L.). Parey, Berlin.

Sundblad, L.G., W.P. Schröder and H.E. Akerlund, 1988. S-state distribution and redox state of Q_A in barley in relation to luminescence decay kinetics. Biochimica et Biophysica Acta, 973: 47-52.

Szalai, G., T. Janda, E. Páldi and Z. Szigeti, 1996. Role of light in the development of post-chilling symptoms in maize. Journal of Plant Physiology, 148: 378-383.

Vass I. and Govindjee, 1996. Thermoluminescence from the photosynthetic apparatus. Photosynthesis Research, 48: 117-126.

Vavilin, D.V. and J.M. Ducruet, 1998. The origin of 115-130°C thermoluminescence bands in chlorophyll-containing material. Photochemistry and Photobiology, 68: 191-198.

Chilling effects on root hydraulic properties of two maize varieties differing in chilling sensitivity

R. AROCA[1], F. TOGNONI[2], J.J. IRIGOYEN[1], M. SÁNCHEZ-DÍAZ[1]
AND A. PARDOSSI[3]

[1]Departamento de Fisiología Vegetal, Universidad de Navarra, c/Irunlarrea s/n, 31008, Pamplona,
   Spain
[2]Dipartimento di Biología delle Piante Agrarie, Università degli Studi di Pisa, Viale delle Piagge
   23, 56100 Pisa, Italy
[3]Dipartimento di Produzione Vegetale, Università degli Studi di Milano, Via Celoria 2, 20133
   Milano, Italy

SUMMARY

Involvement of root hydraulic conductance (L) in chilling tolerance was studied in two varieties of maize differing in chilling sensitivity: Z7, a chilling-tolerant, and Penjalinan, chilling-sensitive. Experiments with intact plants grown in potometers showed that root water uptake (J_v) in chilled Penjalinan declined quicker than leaf transpiration (E), resulting in a rapid shoot dehydration. By contrast, the chilling-tolerant variety Z7 was able to balance E and J_v and did not suffer important water deficit. Although L was markedly depressed in both genotypes, it was higher in Penjalinan than in Z7 throughout the chilling treatment. On the other hand, in the experiments with detached roots, it was observed that, compared to Penjalinan, the roots of Z7 were less damaged by chilling and showed acclimation of J_v and L (as determined at both low and high volume flow) in response to low temperature. The duration of chilling treatment did not affect the relative inhibition of J_v by $HgCl_2$ in any of the two varieties, thus suggesting that the proportion of water moved through water channels in maize roots did not change during chilling. Also, the results of experiments with Light Green (apoplastic tracer) treated roots suggest that chilling root acclimation observed in Z7 may be related to changes in the pathway of water within the root tissues.

Keywords: apoplastic dye, chilling, hydraulic conductance, maize, mercuric chloride

INTRODUCTION

In maize, chilling tolerance has been reported to be associated with rapid stomatal closure and maintenance of a favourable plant water status (Pérez de Juan *et al.*, 1997).

However, little information is available on the influence of chilling on maize root hydraulic properties. Therefore, work was undertaken to verify the hypothesis that the tolerance of Z7 maize variety to chilling-induced water stress is associated with higher root hydraulic conductance (L) compared to Penjalinan, a chilling-sensitive variety.

MATERIALS AND METHODS

Plants of both maize varieties: Z7, chilling-tolerant and Penjalinan, chilling-sensitive, were grown at 25 ± 1°C, 60-65% RH, 12 h photoperiod and 150 mmol m^{-2} s^{-1} PPFD. When 11 d old, seedlings were transferred to a chamber at 5 ± 0.5°C, under the same light conditions. Plant water status during chilling was monitored by measuring the leaf relative water content (RWC). Root hydraulic conductance was determined by three methods: in intact plants by the potometer system (BassiriRad *et al.*, 1991), and in excised roots by collecting exudation at atmospheric pressure (Carvajal *et al.*, 1996) or pressurized with a pressure chamber (Zhang *et al.*, 1995). On the other hand, the relative contribution of water channels to root hydraulic conductance was assayed by the inhibition of free exuded sap by $HgCl_2$ (Carvajal *et al.*, 1996). Moreover, the relative contribution of apoplastic pathway was assayed by Light Green dye (Else *et al.*, 1995) (i.e. the ratio between the absorbance at 630 nm of xylem sap and that of the external solution).

RESULTS AND DISCUSSION

In Penjalinan, water uptake (J_v) decreased more quickly than transpiration (E) resulting in a rapid dehydration, as indicated by the decrease in RWC and wilting (Table 1). By contrast, the chilling-tolerant variety Z7 was able to balance E and Jv and did not suffer important water deficit maintaining leaf turgor and RWC (Table 1). On the other hand, root hydraulic conductance of intact plants (L) was higher in Penjalinan than in Z7 throughout the chilling treatment (Table 1). Since root water absorption and L depend on the water flux within the whole plant, such behaviour seems to be a consequence of higher leaf transpiration in Penjalinan than in Z7. In order to evaluate the direct effects of chilling on root water transport properties, some experiments were conduced with excised roots.

Root damage caused by chilling in Penjalinan can be inferred from the decrease found in L (Fig. 1). By contrast, Z7 increased L at both atmospheric and hydrostatic pressures during chilling treatment. Such behaviour was probably caused by a process of root acclimation to low temperatures as previously found in cold-tolerant species (Fennel and Markhart, 1998). Moreover, this root acclimation observed in Z7 could be due to higher membrane permeability caused by an increase in unsaturated fatty acids and/or amount of water channels (Fennel and Markhart, 1998).

TABLE 1. INFLUENCE OF CHILLING (5ºC) ON RWC, LEAF TRANSPIRATION RATE (E, G H_2O M^{-2} H^{-1}), ROOT WATER UPTAKE (J_v, G H_2O G ROOT DM^{-1} H^{-1}) AND ROOT HYDRAULIC CONDUCTANCE (L. G H_2O G ROOT DM^{-1} MPA^{-1} H^{-1}) IN HYDROPONICALLY-GROWN PLANTS OF THE TWO MAIZE VARIETIES. MEAN HOURLY VALUES DETERMINED WITH POTOMETER IN INTACT PLANTS DURING THE FIRST (CH-1D), SECOND (CH-2D) AND THIRD (CH-3D) DAYS AT 5°C ARE COMPARED TO THE VALUES OF NON-CHILLED PLANTS (CONTROL) MAINTAINED AT 25°C. VALUES ARE MEAN ± SE (N=3-6).

Variety	Treatment	E	J_v	L	RWC
Penjalinan	Control	93.15 ± 8.67	3.81 ± 0.30	25.40 ± 2.00	96.61 ± 1.62
	Ch-1d	45.05 ± 7.09	2.52 ± 0.21	11.99 ± 0.98	71.22 ± 13.01
	Ch-2d	39.88 ± 7.30	1.46 ± 0.11	8.58 ± 0.62	85.72 ± 1.22
	Ch-3d	25.93 ± 3.40	1.24 ± 0.12	4.98 ± 0.48	80.50 ± 0.80
Z7	Control	77.98 ± 5.42	4.64 ± 0.19	20.17 ± 0.83	95.65 ± 1.35
	Ch-1d	26.43 ± 2.89	0.70 ± 0.05	2.51 ± 0.17	93.34 ± 4.34
	Ch-2d	23.20 ± 1.48	0.63 ± 0.03	3.52 ± 0.14	94.19 ± 0.41
	Ch-3d	18.26 ± 1.00	0.52 ± 0.02	1.68 ± 0.77	92.55 ± 2.86

To evaluate the involvement of water channels during chilling, free exuded sap flow (J_v) was inhibited by $HgCl_2$ (Carvajal *et al.*, 1996). The inhibition of J_v by $HgCl_2$ (60-70%), did not differed significantly in plants of both varieties exposed to different periods of chilling. This suggests that the proportion of water that moved through water channels in maize roots did not change during chilling. The contribution of apoplastic path to water

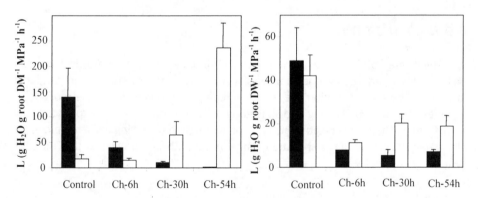

FIGURE 1. INFLUENCE OF CHILLING (5°C) ON HYDRAULIC CONDUCTANCE (L) IN EXCISED ROOTS OF HYDROPONICALLY-GROWN PLANTS OF THE TWO MAIZE VARIETIES. L WAS DETERMINED BY COLLECTING ROOT EXUDATION AT ATMOSPHERIC PRESSURE (LEFT) OR BY PRESSURIZED INDUCED ROOT EXUDATION (RIGHT). THE VALUES DETERMINED ON PLANTS CHILLED FOR 6 H (CH-6H), 30 H (CH-30H) AND 54 H (CH-54H) ARE COMPARED TO THOSE OF NON-CHILLED PLANTS (CONTROL). THE BARS REPRESENT THE MEAN VALUES (±SE) OF 3-6 REPLICATES.

flux in roots was also evaluated by determining the presence of the dye Light Green in the xylem sap collected from pressurized roots. As shown in Figure 2, the relative concentration of Light Green in the xylem sap was not affected by chilling in Penjalinan, but significantly increased in Z7, compared to non-chilled plants. Results suggest that increased L in Z7 during chilling was associated with increased in the proportion of water moving through the apoplastic path.

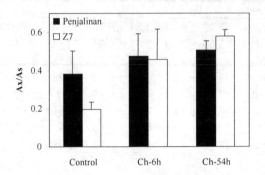

FIGURE 2. INFLUENCE OF CHILLING (5°C) ON THE PRESENCE OF APOPLASTIC TRACER LIGHT GREEN IN THE XYLEM SAP COLLECTED FROM PRESSURIZED ROOTS OF THE TWO MAIZE VARIETIES. TRACER CONCENTRATION WAS EXPRESSED AS THE RATIO BETWEEN THE SAP ABSORBANCE AT 630 NM OF XYLEM SAP (A_x) AND THAT OF THE EXTERNAL SOLUTION (A_s). THE VALUES DETERMINED AT 5°C ON PLANTS CHILLED FOR 6 H (CH-6H) AND 54 H (CH-54H) ARE COMPARED TO THOSE OF NON-CHILLED PLANTS (CONTROL) DETERMINED AT 25°C. THE BARS REPRESENT THE MEAN VALUES (±SE) OF 3-6 REPLICATES.

CONCLUSION

The greater tolerance of Z7 variety to chilling-induced water stress mostly depended on the ability to reduce leaf conductance and to maintain balance between transpirational lost and root water absorption. Nevertheless, compared to Penjalinan, the roots of Z7 were less damaged by chilling and showed acclimation of J_v and L in response to low temperature. The factors responsible for root acclimation to chilling in Z7 remain to be elucidated, but results suggest that a change in the pathway of water within the root system may be involved.

REFERENCES

BassiriRad, H., J.W. Radin and K. Matsuda, 1991. Temperature-dependent water and ion transport properties of barley and sorghum roots. Plant Physiology, 97: 426-432.

Carvajal, M., D.T. Cooke and D.T. Clarkson, 1996. Responses of wheat plants to nutrient deprivation may involve the regulation of water-channel function. Planta, 199: 372-381.

Else, M.A., K.C. Hall, G.M. Arnold, W.J. Davies and M.B. Jackson, 1995. Export of abscisic acid,

1-aminocyclopropane-1-carboxylic acid, phosphate, and nitrate from roots to shoots of flooded tomato plants. Accounting for effects of xylem sap flow rate on concentration and delivery. Plant Physiology, 107: 377-384.

Fennell A. and A.H. Markhart III, 1998. Rapid acclimation of root hydraulic conductivity to low temperature. Journal of Experimental Botany, 49: 879-884.

Pérez de Juan J., J.J. Irigoyen and M. Sánchez-Díaz, 1997. Chilling of drought-hardened and non-hardened plants of different chilling-sensitive maize lines. Changes in water relations and ABA contents. Plant Science, 122: 71-79.

Zhang J., X. Zhang and J. Liang, 1995. Exudation rate and hydraulic conductivity of maize roots are enhanced by soil drying and abscisic acid treatment. New Phytologist, 131: 329-336.

Chilling tolerance of maize in relation to abscisic acid

K. DÖRFFLING[1], B. MAAS[1], B. CAPELL[1] AND F. JANOWIAK[2]

[1]Institute of General Botany and Botanical Garden, University of Hamburg, Ohnhorststr. 18, D-20609 Hamburg, Germany
[2]Institute of Plant Physiology, Polish Academy of Sciences, Podluzna 3, PL-30-239 Cracow, Poland

SUMMARY

Within the frame of the COST 814 action we have studied several physiological aspects of chilling stress in maize. A main project was a study on changes in abscisic acid (ABA) during a chilling-stress period and its relation to genotype-specific chilling tolerance (Capell and Dörffling, 1993; Janowiak and Dörffling, 1996). A broad spectrum of inbred lines and hybrids with pronounced differences in chilling tolerance was used. Seedlings in the three-leaf stage were either chilled in growth chambers or exposed to chilling weather in the field. Chilling injury was determined by several physiological methods including electrolyte leakage test, chlorophyll *a* fluorescence and whole plant survival. Chilling at low relative humidity caused more injury than chilling at 100% humidity. During chilling stress the ABA level increased. The increase was more pronounced under low than under high humidity and was higher and faster in tolerant than in susceptible lines. Acclimation by low, non-chilling temperature enhanced the rise of ABA during subsequent chilling and increased chilling tolerance. Application of norflurazone, a carotenoid biosynthesis inhibitor, decreased the level of ABA and reduced chilling tolerance, whereas application of norflurazone + ABA overcame this effect. These results support the hypothesis that the ability to cope with chilling stress is related to the early and pronounced formation of ABA as a protective agent against chilling injury.

Keywords: abscisic acid, chilling tolerance, maize, norflurazone

INTRODUCTION

A main objective of our studies within the frame of COST 814 was to elucidate the possible protective role of endogenous abscisic acid (ABA) against chilling injury. For this purpose maize seedlings belonging to a broad spectrum of inbred lines and hybrids with pronounced differences in chilling tolerance were exposed to chilling temperature. Changes in ABA content as well as several physiological parameters which characterise extent of chilling injury were measured. Based on the results (Fig. 1) a hypothesis was developed that the ability to cope with chilling stress relies on the early and pronounced formation of ABA as a protective agent against chilling injury (Capell and Dörffling, 1993, Janowiak and Dörffling, 1996). This hypothesis has been critically reinvestigated recently by Ristic *et al.* (1998) who stated from their results that "higher chilling tolerance is not always related to the ability for greater and faster ABA accumulation". Therefore, we have tried to provide further evidence for our hypothesis by manipulating the endogenous ABA level. We expected that a reduction of the endogenous ABA level by application of norflurazone, an inhibitor of ABA biosynthesis, should result in a decrease in chilling tolerance.

MATERIALS AND METHODS

Maize seedlings were exposed in the three-leaf stage to chilling stress at 5°C for several days. Norflurazone (0.1 mmol/l) and ABA (0.1 mmol/l) were applied via the root. ABA content was determined by ELISA, chilling tolerance by chlorophyll *a* fluorescence (Fv/Fm), by electrolyte leakage test and by plant survival.

RESULTS AND DISCUSSION

Changes in ABA content in third leaves of two inbred lines which were chilled at two degrees of humidity are presented in Fig. 1. It demonstrates that chilling causes an increase in ABA content which is higher and faster in the chilling-tolerant genotype F7 than in the chilling-sensitive Co125 and is more pronounced under low than under high humidity. These data, obtained with two genotypes, have been confirmed with studies on 12 other genotypes and form the basis of the above-mentioned hypothesis. To obtain further proof for it, plants grown in nutrient solution or in soil were watered with aqueous solutions of norflurazone (NF) alone or in combination with ABA. Subsequently the plants were chilled and ABA content and chilling injury determined. In Fig. 2 results are presented on changes in ABA content. Whereas in control plants the ABA level in third leaves increased up to day 6, there was nearly no chilling-induced increase in NF-treated plants. When plants were treated with a combination of NF+ABA or ABA alone via their roots, their leaf ABA content increased considerably. The responses of the treated plants to chilling stress were in accordance with the changes in ABA. In Fig. 3 survival rates are presented which show that NF-treated plants have the lowest percent survival, whereas plants treated with NF+ABA or ABA were much more chilling-tolerant. Control plants had an intermediate tolerance. Measurements of chilling injury by electrolyte leakage test and chlorophyll *a* fluorescence resulted in a similar ranking (Fig. 4). Thus our hypothesis that chilling tolerance in maize relies on the endogenous level of ABA is supported by these data.

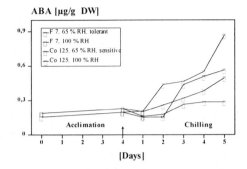

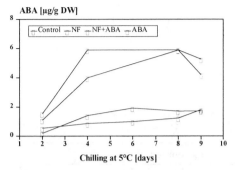

FIGURE 1. CHANGES IN ABA CONTENT IN THIRD LEAVES OF TWO MAIZE GENOTYPES DURING CHILLING AT 5°C AT 65% AND 100% HUMIDITY. THE PLANTS WERE ACCLIMATED AT 14/12°C DAY/ NIGHT. FROM JANOWIAK AND DÖRFFLING 1996, MODIFIED.

FIGURE 2. EFFECT OF ROOT-APPLIED NORFLURAZONE (NF) 0.1 MMOL/L ON THE LEVEL OF ABA IN CHILLED SEEDLINGS OF MAIZE INBRED LINE F7.

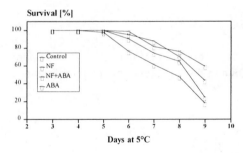

FIGURE 3. SURVIVAL OF MAIZE SEEDLINGS (CV. GARANT) AFTER CHILLING STRESS. SEEDLINGS WERE TREATED BEFORE CHILLING VIA THE ROOTS WITH NORFLURAZONE (NF), ABSCISIC ACID (ABA) OR WITH NF AND ABA (NF+ABA). CONTROL PLANTS WERE PRE-TREATED WITH WATER. SURVIVAL WAS DETERMINED AFTER SEVEN DAYS OF RECOVERY.

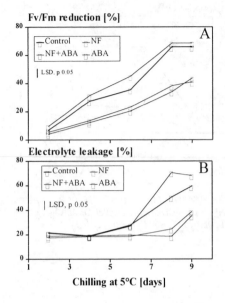

FIGURE 4. EFFECT OF ROOT-APPLIED NORFLURAZONE (NF) 0.1 MMOL/L ALONE OR IN COMBINATION WITH ABA 0.1 MMOL/L ON THE DEVELOPMENT OF CHILLING INJURY IN LEAVES OF MAIZE INBRED LINE F7. CHILLING INJURY WAS DETERMINED BY CHLOROPHYLL A FLUORESCENCE (A, PERCENT REDUCTION OF FV/FM) AND BY ELECTROLYTE LEAKAGE TEST (B).

ACKNOWLEDGEMENTS

This research was supported by Deutsche Forschungsgemeinschaft (DFG, Bonn) Project No. DO 104/24-1, 436 POL 17/6/98 and by the State Committee for Scientific Research (KBN, Warsaw) Project No. 5 P06A 029 14.

REFERENCES

Capell, B. and K. Dörffling, 1993. Genotype-specific differences in chilling tolerance of maize in relation to chilling-induced changes in water status and abscisic acid accumulation. Physiologia Plantarum, 88: 638-646.

Janowiak, F. and K. Dörffling, 1996. Chilling of maize seedlings: changes in water status and abscisic acid content in ten genotypes differing in chilling tolerance. Journal of Plant Physiology, 147: 582-588.

Ristic, Z., G. Yang, A. Sterzinger and L. Zhang, 1998. Higher chilling tolerance is not always related to the ability for greater and faster abscisic acid accumulation. Journal of Plant Physiology, 153: 154-162.

Studies on in vitro-selected winter wheat mutants with increased frost tolerance

K. DÖRFFLING[1], H. DÖRFFLING[1], E. LUCK[1], R. MÜLLER[1]
AND F. JANOWIAK[2]

[1]Institute of General Botany and Botanical Garden, University of Hamburg, Ohnhorststr. 18, D-20609 Hamburg, Germany
[2]Institute of Plant Physiology, Polish Academy of Sciences, Podluzna 3, 30-239 Cracow, Poland

SUMMARY

Recently we have selected homozygous lines with increased frost tolerance from a winter wheat genotype (Jo 3063) by an in vitro-technique. Hydroxyproline was used as a selection tool. The resulting higher proline levels of the selected, cold-acclimated lines and their progenies were significantly correlated with the increased frost tolerance, which was determined under growth-chamber as well as under field conditions by means of the electrolyte leakage test, by use of chlorophyll fluorescence parameters and by estimating whole plant survival. Both traits proved to be heritable. Besides increased proline levels, the selected lines had higher glucose and fructose contents in the cold-acclimated state. The drought tolerance of potted plants of the selected lines was tested with the same methods after withholding watering and was found to be higher than that of the wild type. Proline levels of the mutants were also higher than those of the wild type under drought conditions.

Keywords: drought tolerance, frost tolerance, genetic stability, in vitro-selection, mutants, winter wheat

INTRODUCTION

In the frame of the COST Action 814 we have selected by in vitro-technique homozygous lines from a winter wheat genotype (Jo 3063) which accumulate higher proline amounts than the wild type during cold hardening and possess, in correlation with this, increased frost tolerance (Dörffling et al., 1997). From segregation studies in the F_2 progeny it was concluded that the mutation was due to a single incompletely-dominant gene.

Here we report studies on the genetic stability of these traits in the F_4, F_5 and F_7 progenies. Moreover, we demonstrate that cold-acclimated plants of the mutant lines possess besides enhanced proline content increased levels of glucose and fructose. This observation and the additional finding that the mutants are not only more frost tolerant than the wild type but also more drought tolerant, can be explained as a pleiotropic effect of the mutated gene.

MATERIALS AND METHODS

Seedlings of the respective progenies (F_4, F_5 and F_7) of the mutant lines were cultivated together with the wild type either in growth chambers or in the field during winter. They were cold acclimated at $2°C$ in the growth chamber and by natural winter conditions in the field. At short intervals leaf samples were collected for determination of their proline content using the ninhydrin reaction. Glucose and fructose levels were determined enzymatically. Frost tolerance of leaves was determined by the electrolyte leakage test and by means of chlorophyll fluorescence parameters and frost tolerance of whole plants by determination of percent survival after exposure to frost. Drought tolerance of the mutants and their wild type was determined using plants grown under warm, not cold, acclimating conditions. They were exposed to drought stress by withholding watering. Several parameters including chlorophyll fluorescence, proline content and percent survival after the drought stress treatment were used to characterise drought tolerance.

RESULTS AND DISCUSSION

Fig. 1 demonstrates that the trait "increased proline content" exists still in the F_5 of the mutant lines Hyp 90, Hyp 110, Hyp 272 and Hyp 329. In comparison to the wild type their proline contents are up to 100 percent higher. Studies on F_6 and F_7 progenies revealed similar results (data not shown). In Table 1 LT_{50} values are presented from leaves of field grown F_4 plants in the winter season 1996 which show that the mutants possess greatly improved frost tolerance. Further data in Table 1 indicate that the higher frost tolerance of the mutants seems to be correlated with higher effective quantum yield of PSII, measured in the field by means of a PAM 2000 fluorometer at the end of November when the plants were fully cold hardened. Fig. 2 presents data on whole plant survival of wild type and mutant plants (F_5) grown in the field in wooden boxes, exposed to an artificial frost and afterwards returned to field conditions. The data confirm the higher frost tolerance of the mutants in comparison to the wild type. Besides increased proline content, the mutants proved to accumulate higher glucose and fructose contents during cold hardening in the field (Fig. 3). When the mutants were exposed to drought by withholding watering, they proved to be more drought tolerant than the wild type (Fig. 4). Moreover, the mutants formed higher amounts of proline during the drought stress than the wild type (Fig. 5). In accordance with this are survival data of the comparative varieties Roughrider and Capelle: high frost tolerance (Table 1) is correlated with high drought tolerance (Fig. 4).

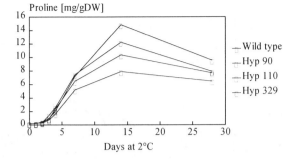

FIGURE 1. PROLINE ACCUMULATION DURING COLD HARDENING AT 2°C IN FOUR HYP MUTANTS (F_5) IN COMPARISON TO THE WILD TYPE CV. JO 3063.

FIGURE 2. EFFECT OF FROST TREATMENT (- 25°C UP TO 22 H) ON SURVIVAL OF FOUR HYP MUTANTS (F_5) IN COMPARISON TO THE WILD TYPE (JO 3063). PLANTS WERE CULTIVATED BEFORE AND AFTER THE (ARTIFICIAL) FROST TREATMENT UNDER FIELD CONDITIONS.

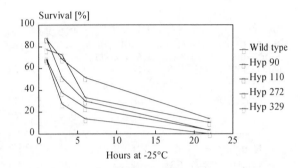

FIGURE 3. GLUCOSE AND FRUCTOSE CONTENTS IN WHEAT PLANTS GROWN IN THE FIELD IN THE WINTER SEASONS 1998/99 AND 1999/2000. SUGAR CONTENTS WERE DETERMINED FROM OCTOBER TO MARCH AT 21 TIMES AND THE MEANS ARE PRESENTED.

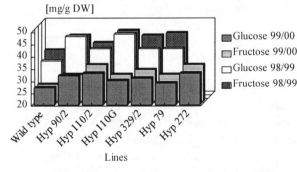

FIGURE 4. PERCENT SURVIVAL OF WHEAT PLANTS WHICH WERE DROUGHT STRESSED FOR 7, 10 AND 14 DAYS IN TWO DIFFERENT SOILS. AFTER THE STRESS PHASE THEY WERE WATERED AND 21 DAYS LATER PERCENT SURVIVAL WAS DETERMINED. ROUGHRIDER AND CAPELLE ARE COMPARATIVE VARIETIES WITH HIGH AND LOW FROST TOLERANCE, RESPECTIVELY.

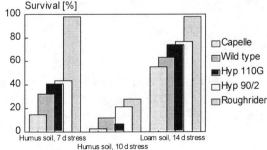

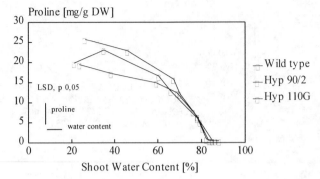

FIGURE 5. PROLINE CONTENT PLOTTED AGAINST SHOOT WATER CONTENT IN DROUGHT STRESSED PLANTS OF TWO HYP MUTANTS (F_5) IN COMPARISON TO THE WILD TYPE JO 3063.

TABLE 1. LT_{50} VALUES AND EFFECTIVE QUANTUM YIELD OF PSII OF FIELD GROWN WINTER WHEAT PLANTS (F_4 AND F_7) OF THE HYP MUTANTS AND THEIR WILD TYPE TOGETHER WITH A COMPARATIVE VARIETY (ROUGHRIDER, HIGH FROST TOLERANCE). LT_{50} VALUES WERE OBTAINED BY MEANS OF THE ELECTROLYTE LEAKAGE TEST, EFFECTIVE QUANTUM YIELD OF PSII WITH A PAM FLUOROMETER.

Genotype	LT_{50} (°C) F_4, Feb. 1996	Yield of PSII F_7, Nov. 1998
Roughrider	- 16.9	0.36 +/- 0.04
Wild type Jo 3063	- 12.2	0.22 +/- 0.07
Mutant Hyp 90	- 15.7	0.31 +/- 0.04
Mutant Hyp 110	- 16.2	0.24 +/- 0.06
Mutant Hyp 114	- 14.4	——
Mutant Hyp 272	- 14.3	——
Mutant Hyp 329	——	0.25 +/- 0.06

The studies confirm that the trait "increased frost tolerance" obtained by in vitro-selection of proline-overproducing lines from the winter wheat variety Jo 3063 is stable over several generations. The increased frost tolerance is related not only to increased proline accumulation, but also to increased sugar accumulation. Moreover, increased frost tolerance is correlated with increased drought tolerance.

REFERENCES

Dörffling K., H. Dörffling, G. Lesselich, E. Luck, C. Zimmermann, G. Melz and H. U. Jürgens, 1997. Heritable improvement of frost tolerance in winter wheat by in vitro-selection of hydroxyproline-resistant proline overproducing mutants. Euphytica, 93: 1-10.

Induction of freezing tolerance in cold-or drought-hardened plants of barley cv. Lunet

Z. KADLECOVÁ, M. FALTUS AND I. PRÁŠIL

Research Institute of Crop Production, Drnovská 507, CZ-16106 Prague 6, Czech Republic.

SUMMARY

Freezing tolerance is induced by a cold-hardening process, which is accompanied with many physiological changes such as dry weight accumulation. The role of ABA in cold hardening is not quite clear. Drought treatment accompanied with ABA accumulation increased the freezing tolerance of plants only in some cases. We compared the changes in dry weight, ABA content and osmotic potential with changes of freezing tolerance in second fully-expanded leaves of cold-or drought-hardened plants of barley cv. Lunet. After 15 days of cultivation under controlled conditions at 17 °C the plants were exposed to the cold of 3 °C or drought-treated by application of PEG8000 (20%) into the growth medium of the plants at 17 °C. Cold hardening induced freezing tolerance accompanied with dry weight accumulation and osmotic potential decrease, but without changes in ABA content. The ABA content transiently increased at the onset of drought treatment. Drought treatment induced only negligible increase of freezing tolerance and of dry weight accumulation in the leaves, but the osmotic potential was decreased. Low temperature treatment resulting in increase of dry weight content is a prerequisite for the development of full freezing tolerance of plants. The role of ABA in induction of freezing tolerance could be mediated via different mechanisms in cold-or drought-hardened plants.

Keywords: abscisic acid (ABA), barley, drought, cold hardening, freezing tolerance, PEG

INTRODUCTION

Freezing tolerance of cereals is induced by a cold-hardening process; the involvement of some phytohormones, especially abscisic acid (ABA), is being considered. The role of ABA in this process was deduced from various findings including increase in endogenous level during low-temperature treatment (Murelli et al., 1995; Bravo et al., 1998), increase of plant freezing tolerance induced by ABA application under non-acclimatising conditions (Veisz et al., 1996), and reduced tolerance to freezing in ABA-mutant plants (Lång et al., 1994). The data indicating a role of ABA in cold-hardening process are not uniform (Dallaire et al., 1994). Drought clearly causes an increase in

ABA (Wright, 1977. Quarrie, 1993) and therefore it may be a suitable model for investigating the influence of increased ABA content on freezing tolerance. Prolonged drought as well as cold hardening (Lalk and Dörffling, 1985), lead to accumulation of osmotically-active compounds (osmotic adjustment) and to accumulation of dry weight. However, the increased level of freezing tolerance of plants affected by drought was lower than that of plants hardened by low temperature (Dallaire et al., 1994). The aim of the present study was to investigate relationships between ABA content, dry weight, osmotic potential and freezing tolerance in fully expanded leaves of barley in cold-hardened or drought-affected plants.

MATERIALS AND METHODS

Winter barley (*Hordeum vulgare* L. cv. Lunet) was cultivated hydroponically under controlled conditions (16 h photoperiod, light intensity of 400 ìmol. m^{-2} .s^{-1}, relative humidity 65 ± 5% and 90 ± 5% (D/N), temperature 17 ± 1 °C) 15 days, until the second leaf was fully expanded. Then the plants remained under the same conditions (control) or were exposed to cold hardening (3 °C) or were exposed to dehydration by PEG 8000 applicated into the growth solution. The ABA content was determined by radioimmunoassay using monoclonal ABA- antibody MAC252 (obtained from Dr. S.A. Quarrie -John Innes Centre, Norwich, UK). Osmotic potential was determined psychrometrically from leaf sap using a Wescor H-33 micrometer. The level of freezing tolerance in the second leaf was measured by a laboratory freezing test (Prášil and Zámeèník, 1998) and their lethal temperature (LT50) was calculated according to Janáèek and Prášil (1991).

RESULTS AND DISCUSSION

The freezing tolerance increase of the barley second leaf induced by cold hardening (Fig. 1C) was accompanied with accumulation of dry weight (Fig. 1B) and with osmotic potential decrease (Fig. 1D). The same results were described by Lalk and Dörffling (1985) in wheat plants. The ABA content did not change during cold hardening (Fig. 1A). These results are in agreement with Dallaire et al. (1994), where they tested wheat plants. Only a moderate increase of leaf freezing tolerance was observed after 14 d of PEG treatment (long-term drought) (Fig. 1C), when RWC of the second leaves decreased by only 6- 10 %. Long- term drought as well as cold hardening caused accumulation of osmotically-active compounds in leaves (Fig. 1D) (osmotic adjustment), but drought leads to a smaller accumulation of dry weight in leaves in comparison with cold hardening (Fig. 1B). Leaf ABA content increased on the second day of PEG treatment especially, but after 14 d of PEG treatment it was not significantly higher than the ABA content in leaves of control plants (Fig. 1A). We found out, like to Dallaire et al. (1994), that the increased

106

level of freezing tolerance of plants affected by drought was lower than that of plants hardened by low temperature.

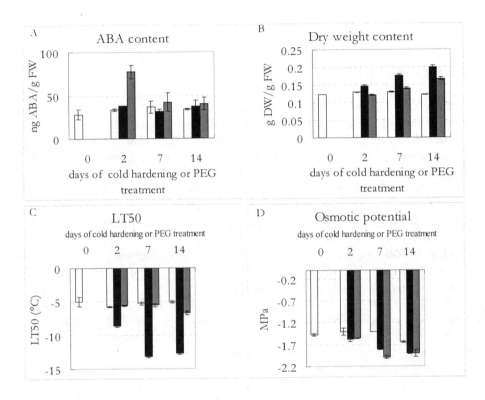

FIGURE 1. CHANGES IN ABA CONTENT (A), FREEZING TOLERANCE (LT50) (B), DRY WEIGHT CONTENT (C) AND OSMOTIC POTENTIAL (D) IN SECOND FULLY EXPANDED LEAVES OF BARLEY PLANTS
☐ -CONTROL PLANTS
■ -COLD HARDENED PLANTS
▨ -PEG TREATED PLANTS.
THE VERTICAL BARS GIVE THE MEAN SE.

CONCLUSION

The small ability of PEG treatment to increase freezing tolerance could be caused by the smaller accumulation of dry weight compared to the extent of dry weight accumulation induced by cold hardening. We suggest that ABA involvement in plant freezing tolerance is not mediated by an increase of its endogenous content.

ACKNOWLEDGEMENTS

These results were obtained with subvention from The Ministry of Education, Youth and Sports of The Czech Republic (project OC 814.20).

REFERENCES

Bravo, L.A., G.E. Zuñiga, M. Alberdi and L.J. Corcuera, 1998. The role of ABA in freezing tolerance and cold acclimation in barley. Physiologia Plantarum, 103: 17-23.

Dallaire, S., M. Houde, Y. Gagné, H.S. Saini, S. Boileau, N. Chevrier and F. Sarhan, 1994. ABA and low temperature induce freezing tolerance via distinct regulatory pathways in wheat. Plant Cell Physiology, 35(1): 1-9.

Janáèek J. and I. Prášil, 1991. Quantification of plant frost injury by non-linear fitting of an S-shaped function. Cryo- Letters, 12: 47-52.

Lalk, I. and K. Dörffling, 1985. Hardening, abscisic acid, proline and freezing resistance in two winter wheat varieties. Physiologia Plantarum, 63: 287-292.

Lång, V., E. Mäntylä, B. Welin, B. Sundberg and T. Palva, 1994. Alteration in water status, endogenous abscisic acid, and expression of rab18 gene during the development of freezing tolerance in *Arabidopsis thaliana*. Plant Physiology, 104: 1341-1349.

Murelli, C., F. Rizza, F.M. Albini, A. Dulio, V. Terzi and L. Cattivelli, 1995. Metabolic changes associated with cold-acclimation in contrasting cultivars of barley. Physiologia Plantarum, 94: 87-93.

Prášil, I. and J. Zámeèník, 1998. The use of a conductivity measurement method for assessing freezing injury. I. Influence of leakage time, segment number, size and shape in a sample on evaluation of the degree of injury. Environmental and Experimental Botany, 40: 1-10.

Quarrie, S.A., 1993. Understanding plant responses to stress and breeding for improved stress resistance- the generation gap. In: Close, T.J. and E.A. Bray (eds.): Plant Responses to Cellular Dehydration During Environmental Stress. Current Topics in Plant Physiology: An American Society of Plant Physiologists Series 10, 224-245.

Wright, S.T.C., 1977.The relationship between leaf water potential (øleaf) and the levels of abscisic acid and ethylene in excised wheat leaves. Planta,134: 183-189.

Effect of chemical manipulation of glutathione synthesis on chilling tolerance of maize

G. KOCSY[1], P. VON BALLMOOS[2], G. SZALAI[1], G. GALIBA[1]
AND C. BRUNOLD[2]

[1]Agricultural Research Institute of the Hungarian Academy of Sciences, Matonvásár, Hungary
[2]Institute of Plant Physiology, University of Berne, Berne, Switzerland

SUMMARY

Chilling induces oxidative stress because of the accumulation of reactive oxygen species (ROS) which damage proteins, nucleic acids and membrane lipids. Glutathione (GSH) removes one of these ROS, hydrogen peroxide, as a component of the ascorbate-glutathione pathway. The involvement of GSH in the response to chilling stress has been investigated in a chilling-tolerant maize (*Zea mays* L.) genotype, Z 7 using buthionine sulfoximine (BSO), which is a specific inhibitor of g-glutamylcysteine (gEC) synthetase, the first enzyme of GSH synthesis. While the fresh and dry weight of the shoots and roots of chilled seedlings gradually decreased with increasing BSO concentrations, the injury of the seedlings increased from 10 to almost 40 % as detected at the end of the recovery. The accumulation of cysteine and decrease in gEC and GSH contents after chilling ·depended on the BSO concentrations. Relative protection of the shoots was gradually decreased by gradual reduction of GSH level. Addition of exogenous gEC could compensate the inhibitory effect of BSO on recovery of the seedlings and GSH accumulation, and the level of compensation depended on the concentration of gEC. Application of exogenous gEC reduced the injury from 48 to 25 %. The good correlation between chemically manipulated GSH content and chilling tolerance represents evidence for a quantitative contribution of GSH to chilling tolerance of maize.

Keywords: abscisic acid, buthionine sulfoximine, chilling, g-glutamylcysteine, glutathione reductase, Zea mays L.

INTRODUCTION

GSH is a component of the ascorbate-glutathione pathway which is involved in degradation of the excess of H_2O_2 generated during oxidative stress (Noctor and Foyer, 1998). During detoxification of H_2O_2 in the ascorbate-GSH pathway, GSH is oxidised to GSSG and its regeneration to GSH is catalysed by GSH reductase (GR) (Noctor *et al.*, 1998). Results corroborating a correlation between GSH levels, GR activity and chilling tolerance were obtained with a chilling-tolerant species of *Lycopersicon* (Walker and McKersie, 1993) and with maize genotypes with different chilling tolerance (Kocsy *et al.,* 1996). More information about the role of GSH and GR during chilling resulted from genetic studies with wheat which indicated a contribution of GSH to an improved low-temperature tolerance (Kocsy *et al.,* 1999). Plants overexpressing enzymes of GSH synthesis provide additional evidence for the involvement of GSH in reduction of damages caused by low-temperature-induced oxidative stress, as shown in paraquat-induced oxidative stress in transgenic popular overexpressing gEC synthetase, the rate-limiting enzyme of GSH synthesis (Noctor *et al.,* 1998). Overexpression of GR in chloroplasts increased low-temperature tolerance in poplar (Foyer *et al.,* 1997).

With the aim to clarify the relative contribution of GSH in protecting plants from chilling stress, we applied BSO, a specific inhibitor of gEC synthesis to a chilling-tolerant maize variety grown on nutrient solution. This system has the additional benefit that the GSH level decreased by BSO can be increased by simultaneous addition of gEC (Farago and Brunold, 1994). The effect of the manipulation of GSH level on GR activity was also investigated.

MATERIALS AND METHODS

The highly chilling tolerant maize (Zea mays L.) inbred line Z 7 (Kocsy *et al.,* 1996) was used in our experiments. The maize kernels were germinated between two layers of damp paper in a photoperiod of 12 hours at 25 °C for three days. The plants were cultivated in hydroponics on modified Henschel nutrient solution (Kocsy *et al.,* 1996) in a photoperiod of 12 h at 300 μmol m^{-2} s^{-1}, 25°C and 60 % RH for 4 d. The experimental procedure routinely consisted of a precultivation of 4 d at 25°C, subsequent chilling at 5°C for 7 d and a recovery phase at 25°C for additional 7 days. Addition of BSO or BSO in combination with gEC was done at the beginning of precultivation. The culture medium was renewed at the beginning of the recovery phase. The relative injury of the plants was routinely estimated according to the followings scale: 0: no necrosis of the shoot; 1: less than 25 %; 2: 25 – 50 %; 3: 50 – 75 %; 4: 75 – 90 %; 5: 90 – 100 % necrosis of the shoot at the end of the recovery phase. The mean values of these estimations were calculated as percentage of completely necrotic shoots.

To determine the GR activity the plant material was homogenised in 0.1 M Na-K-phosphate buffer, pH 7.5, (1:5, w/v), containing 0.2 mM diethylenetriaminepentaacetic acid and 4 % (w/v) polyvinylpolypyrrolidone in an ice-cooled glass homogeniser and centrifuged at 30,000 g for 10 min at 4°C. The supernatant was used for measuring GR activity according to Smith *et al.* (1988). For the investigation of cysteine, gEC and GSH the plant material was extracted 1:10 (w/v) in 0.1 M HCl containing 1 mM Na$_2$EDTA in an ice-cooled glass homogeniser. The extracts were centrifuged for 30 min at 30,000 g and 4 °C. The thiol content was determined in the supernatants as described previously by reverse-phase HPLC and fluorescence detection (Kocsy *et al.,* 1996).

110

RESULTS

During the 7 d chilling period there was no visible difference between the BSO-treated and control plants. At the end of the recovery phase, however, the fresh and dry weight of shoots and roots of BSO-treated seedlings were lower compared to controls (data not shown). The chilling-induced injury of the seedlings also increased with BSO concentration, 1 mM BSO resulting in 4-fold increase of injury compared to the control (Table 1). GSH content, as expected, gradually decreased with increasing BSO levels (Table 1). Cysteine content increased and gEC content decreased because of the inhibiton of gEC synthetase (data not shown). BSO treatment also affected GR activity at 5°C (Table 1)). At the end of the chilling period, the GR level in shoots was decreased with increasing BSO concentrations.

TABLE 1. EFFECT OF DIFFERENT BSO CONCENTRATIONS ON INJURY, GSH CONTENT AND GR ACTIVITY OF MAIZE SEEDLINGS CULTIVATED AT 25 °C FOR 4 D, THAN AT 5 °C FOR 7 D AND AT 25 ° C FOR ADDITIONAL 7 D. SAMPLING FOR THE BIOCHEMICAL MEASUREMENTS WAS DONE AT THE END OF THE ONE WEEK CHILLING PERIOD AND FOR THE ESTIMATION OF THE INJURY AT THE END OF THE SUBSEQUENT RECOVERY. MEAN VALUES FROM THREE INDEPENDENT EXPERIMENTS ARE PRESENTED. VALUES CARRYING DIFFERENT LETTERS ARE SIGNIFICANTLY DIFFERENT AT THE $P \leq 0.05$.

BSO (mM)	0.00	0.25	0.50	0.75	1.00
Injury (%)	10.1 ± 2.3^a	14.5 ± 3.2^{ab}	17.3 ± 3.7^b	26.2 ± 6.8^c	39.2 ± 8.4^d
GSH (nmol [g FW]$^{-1}$)	234.6 ± 25.2^a	86.4 ± 21.7^b	49.1 ± 7.2^c	34.5 ± 5.7^d	15.2 ± 1.6^e
GR (μkat [g protein]$^{-1}$)	1.03 ± 0.18^a	0.64 ± 0.12^{ab}	0.52 ± 0.06^b	0.37 ± 0.02^c	0.27 ± 0.03^c

When 1 mM BSO and concentrations of gEC up to 1 mM were added simultaneously fresh weight and dry weight of both roots and shoots increased (data not shown). The relative injury gradually decreased compared to controls which were only treated with 1 mM BSO (Table 2). Addition of gEC together with 1 mM BSO increased the level of glutathione significantly already at the lowest gEC concentration of 0.25 mM (Table 2). The gEC content was also higher, whereas the amount of cysteine decreased (data not shown). The highest GSH levels obtained by this treatment was only half of that of seedlings cultivated without BSO (Tables 1, 2). gEC also increased GR activity at 5°C in shoots (Table 2). GR activity of plants treated with 0.75 or 1.00 mM gEC was higher than that obtained during chilling without BSO (Tables 1, 2).

TABLE 2. EFFECT OF DIFFERENT GEC CONCENTRATIONS IN THE PRESENCE OF 1 MM BSO ON INJURY, GSH CONTENT AND GR ACTIVITY OF MAIZE SEEDLINGS CULTIVATED AT 25 °C FOR 4 D, THAN AT 5 °C FOR 7 D AND AT 25 ° C FOR ADDITIONAL 7 D. SAMPLING AND SYMBOLS AS IN TABLE 1.

γEC (mM)	0.00	0.25	0.50	0.75	1.00
Injury (%)	48.3±7.4[a]	41.2±5.2[a]	30.2±4.1[b]	25.2±2.9[b]	32.1±3.6[b]
GSH (nmol [g FW]$^{-1}$)	12.5±1.9[a]	25.2±3.6[b]	76.4±9,7[c]	81.2±11.9[c]	115.2±15.4[d]
GR (μkat [g protein]$^{-1}$)	0.29±0.08[a]	1.05±0.21[b]	1.25±0.08[b]	3.53±0.47[c]	4.92±0.57[d]

DISCUSSION AND CONCLUSIONS

In the present work we show unequivocally for the first time the relative contribution of GSH and GR to chilling tolerance of maize. In the system used, the GSH level could be gradually decreased to extremely low levels using various concentrations of BSO or increased to almost normal levels by simultaneous addition of BSO and gEC (Farago and Brunold, 1994). Consistent with previously formulated assumptions chilling tolerance of a chilling tolerant maize genotype was decreased by simultaneous reduction of the GSH content and GR activity after BSO treatment. Exogenous gEC added in the presence of BSO increased the GSH content and also the GR activity. If the plants were subjected to a chilling phase, however, decreased GSH levels correlated with decreased fresh and dry weights and increased relative injury clearly demonstrating the putative protective function of GSH (Foyer et al., 1997; Noctor et al., 1998; Kocsy et al., 1996).

Together with previously published results, the present findings can be used for establishing a comprehensive picture of GSH functions during chilling stress. Beside the function in the ascorbate-GSH pathway (Noctor et al., 1998) in which H_2O_2 is detoxified, GSH can be involved as a reductant in assimilatory sulfate reduction (Suter et al., 2000). In this pathway cysteine is formed (Brunold and Rennenberg, 1997) which is subsequently used for GSH synthesis. An additional function might be the reduction of lipid peroxidation products (Mullineaux et al., 1998).

From the present study it becomes also evident, that GSH is involved in increasing the level of GR. This induction contributes to the beneficial effect of GSH, because GR will reduce GSSG produced during detoxification of H_2O_2, during reduction of lipid peroxidation and during the increased synthesis of cysteine in a situation of chilling stress (Kocsy et al., 1996). Beside the detoxification of H_2O_2, GSH and GR contribute to an increased chilling tolerance by their involvement in stress signalling (Foyer et al., 1997).

ACKNOWLEDGEMENTS

This work was supported by the Swiss National Science Foundation (C.B.), the Hungarian National Science Foundation (OTKA F025190, F026236 and M28074), the Hungarian Scientific Technical Committee (OMFB 013904/V-038/98) and János Bolyai Research Grant.

REFERENCES

Brunold, C. and H. Rennenberg, 1997. Regulation of sulfur metabolism in plants: first molecular approaches. Progress in Botany, 58: 164-186.

Farago, S. and C. Brunold, 1994. Regulation of thiol contents in maize roots by intermediates and effectors of glutathione synthesis. Journal of Plant Physiology, 144: 433-437.

Foyer, C.H., H. Lopez-Delgado, J.F. Dat and I.M. Scott, 1997. Hydrogen peroxide- and glutathione-associated mechanisms of acclimatory stress tolerance and signalling. Physiologia Plantarum, 100: 241-254.

Kocsy, G., M. Brunner, A. Rüegsegger, P. Stamp and C. Brunold, 1996. Glutathione synthesis in maize genotypes with different sensitivity to chilling. Planta, 198: 365-370.

Kocsy, G., G. Szalai, A. Vágújfalvi, L. Stéhli, G. Orosz and G.Galiba, 2000. Genetic study of glutathione accumulation during cold hardening in wheat. Planta, 210: 295-301.

Mullineaux, P.M., S. Karpinski, A. Jimenez, S.P. Cleary, C. Robinson and G.P. Creissen, 1998. Identification of cDNAs encoding plastid-targeted glutathione peroxidase. The Plant Journal, 13: 375-379.

Noctor, G., A.-C.M. Arisi, L. Jouanin, K.J. Kunert, H. Rennenberg and C.H. Foyer, 1998. Glutathione: biosynthesis, metabolism and relationship to stress tolerance explored in transformed plants. Journal of Experimental Botany, 49: 623-647.

Smith, I.K., T.L. Vierheller and C.A. Thurne, 1988. Assay of glutathione reductase in crude tissue homogenates using 5,5'dithiobis(2-nitrobenzoicacid). Analytical Biochemistry, 175: 408-413.

Suter, M., P. von Ballmoos, S. Kopriva, R. Op den Camp, J. Schaller, C. Kuhlemeier, P. Schürmann, and C. Brunold, 2000. Adenosine 5-phosphosulfate sulfotransferase and adenosine 5-phosphosulfate reductase are identical enzymes. Journal of Biological Chemistry, 275: 930-936.

Walker, M.A. and B.D. McKersie, 1993. Role of the ascorbate-glutathione antioxidant system in chilling resistance of tomato. Journal of Plant Physiology, 141: 234-239.

Photoprotection in maize at suboptimal temperature

Y. FRACHEBOUD[1], M.A. IANNELLI[2], F. PIETRINI[2] AND A. MASSACCI[2]

[1]Swiss Federal Institute of Technology, Zurich, Switzerland
[2]CNR Institute of Plant Biochemistry and Ecophysiology, Monterotondo (Roma), Italy

SUMMARY

The responses of photoprotective mechanisms upon chilling were investigated in maize lines bred for contrasting cold tolerance of photosynthesis both in controlled environment and in the field. Low photosynthetic capacity was associated with an increase of excess energy dissipation related to the xanthophyll cycle and increased activities of superoxide dismutase and ascorbate peroxidase, which are involved in the detoxification of reactive oxygen species. These data suggest that an increase of these photoprotective mechanisms was not the cause of improved cold tolerance, but rather a consequence of chilling susceptibility.

Keywords: antioxidative defences, chilling, maize, photoprotection

INTRODUCTION

As with other plants from tropical origin, maize is very susceptible to low temperature. In temperate areas, young maize seedlings often exhibit poor growth associated with low photosynthetic performance. Comparisons between genotypes from different origins suggest that there is a high genetic variability in cold tolerance of photosynthesis within the *Zea* species both in controlled environment (Pietrini *et al.*, 1999) and in the field (Leipner *et al.*, 1999). The cause of this variability might be related to the capacity of the plants to develop photoprotective mechanisms, which might enable the leaf to avoid damage from excess light energy. Upon exposure to low temperature, maize chloroplasts accumulate large amounts of the pigment zeaxanthin (Haldimann *et al.*, 1995), which is involved in the dissipation of excess energy as heat. Maize leaves are also known to increase their antioxidative defences in response to chilling temperature. These include superoxide dismutase and ascorbate peroxidase (Massacci *et al.*, 1995), glutathione reductase (Fryer *et al.*, 1998; Leipner *et al.*, 1999), glutathione (Kocsy *et al.*, 1996) and a-tocopherol (Leipner *et al.*, 1997; Fryer *et al.*, 1998). However, the importance of these mechanisms to explain the genotypic variability of cold-tolerance is not yet fully elucidated, and results are often contradictory.

Doulis *et al.* (1997) showed a marked differential distribution of antioxidant enzymes between the mesophyll and bundle sheath cells of maize leaves which might imply that the intercellular transport of antioxidant metabolites at low temperature could be one factor contributing to the unusual chilling sensitivity of maize. In addition, the SOD and APX isoforms, localised in the various cellular sites where active oxygen species are produced, respond differently to a given environmental condition. In the present study we investigated the relationships between chilling tolerance and some photoprotective mechanisms in maize lines breeded for contrasting cold tolerance of photosynthesis.

MATERIALS AND METHODS

F4 inbred maize lines with different cold tolerance of photosynthesis were produced using chlorophyll florescence as a selection tool as described elsewhere (Fracheboud *et al.*, 1998; Fracheboud *et al.*, 1999). The selection was applied to three breeding populations: Swiss Dent, Swiss Flint and Exotic Mexican highland. One tolerant and one sensitive line from each group were used for the experiments. Plants grown in growth chamber were first grown at 25 / 22°C (day/night) for 7 days, and then at 14 / 13°C (day / night) for 15 days. The photoperiod was 12 hours at 650 mmol photons m^{-2} s^{-1}. All measurements were performed on the third fully expanded leaf. All selected lines were also planted in the field at Eschikon, Switzerland (8°41' E, 47°27' N, 550 m above see level). The seeds were sown on 29 April 1999 in 5-m rows of 50 plants. There were three replication rows for each genotype. The last fully developed leaf was measured or harvested on 9 June 1999. All data presented represent the average ± SEM of 3-5 replicates.

Simultaneous measurements of photosynthesis and chlorophyll fluorescence were performed in a leaf disc chamber (LS2, Hansatech). Fluorescence was recorded with a PAM-2000 (Walz) fluorometer.

The pigment analysis was performed according to Leipner *et al.* (1999). SOD and APX activities were measured according to Fridovich (1986) and Asada (1992), respectively.

RESULTS AND DISCUSSION

The light response of photosynthetic oxygen evolution of leaves developed at 25°C or 14 °C is shown in Fig. 1. Whilst all lines behaved similar at 25°C, the sensitive lines showed lower photosynthetic rates than the tolerant lines when grown and measured at 14°C. The poor photosynthetic performance of the sensitive lines at low temperature was associated with enhanced photoinhibition as indicated by the maximum quantum efficiency of PSII primary photochemistry and with low chlorophyll contents (Table 1). Similar differences for Fv/Fm and chlorophyll contents were found between tolerant and sensitive lines grown in the field (Table 1). Altogether these data suggest that the cold-tolerant and sensitive phenotypes are expressed at low temperature both in controlled environment and in the field. The possible physiological basis for this genotypic difference was assessed by investigating two photoprotective mechanisms: excess energy dissipation in the pigment bed related to the xanthophyll cycle and antioxidative defences.

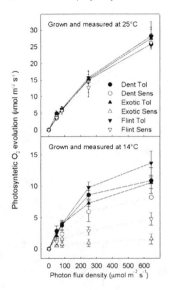

FIGURE 1. THE EFFECT OF LIGHT INTENSITY ON THE PHOTOSYNTHETIC OXYGEN EVOLUTION OF MAIZE LINES WITH CONTRASTING COLD TOLERANCE.

TABLE 1. THE MAXIMUM QUANTUM EFFICIENCY OF PSII PRIMARY PHOTOCHEMISTRY (F_v/F_m) AND THE CHLOROPHYLL CONTENT OF MAIZE LINES WITH CONTRASTING COLD TOLERANCE.

| Parameter | Line | Growth condition | | |
		14°C	25°C	Field
Fv /Fm	Exotic Tol	0.671 ± 0.014	0.791 ± 0.004	0.620 ± 0.019
	Exotic Sens	0.236 ± 0.060	0.765 ± 0.000	0.539 ± 0.016
	Flint Tol	0.663 ± 0.022	0.742 ± 0.004	0.632 ± 0.005
	Flint Sens	0.445 ± 0.015	0.721 ± 0.005	0.574 ± 0.018
	Dent Tol	0.613 ± 0.008	0.764 ± 0.002	0.600 ± 0.009
	Dent Sens	0.546 ± 0.023	0.770 ± 0.010	0.598 ± 0.009
Chlorophyll $a+b$ (μmol m^{-2})	Exotic Tol	331 ± 8	491 ± 16	352 ± 10
	Exotic Sens	80 ± 22	435 ± 15	272 ± 22
	Flint Tol	296 ± 39	558 ± 39	288 ± 24
	Flint Sens	163 ± 25	473 ± 19	311 ± 15
	Dent Tol	309 ± 12	571 ± 38	435 ± 8
	Dent Sens	234 ± 25	390 ± 10	264 ± 34

Leaves grown at 14°C contained higher amounts of xanthophyll cycle pigments than leaves grown at 25°C, but this increase was particularly important in sensitive lines (Table 2). Further more, sensitive lines accumulated more zeaxanthin than tolerant lines when the leaves were grown at 14 °C (Table 2) whilst zeaxanthin was mostly absent in leaves developed at 25°C. Higher amounts of total xanthophyll cycle pigments and zeaxanthin were also observed in leaves of the sensitive lines grown in the field. In growth chamber, the accumulation of zeaxanthin in sensitive lines was associated with a strong decrease of the quantum efficiency of open PSII reaction centers (Fig. 2). These data suggest that energy dissipation as heat is enhanced in sensitive lines in response to their low photosynthetic activity. The hypothesis that tolerance is achieved by increasing excess energy dissipation is very unlikely in the view of these data obtained from lines selected for contrasting quantum yields.

TABLE 2. THE TOTAL XANTHOPHYLL CYCLE PIGMENTS CONTENT (V+A+Z) AND THEIR PROPORTION OF ZEAXANTHIN (Z/V+A+Z) OF MAIZE LINES WITH CONTRASTING COLD TOLERANCE.

		Growth condition		
Parameter	Line	14°C	25°C	Field
	Exotic Tol	0.12 ± 0.01	0.05 ± 0.00	0.16 ± 0.00
	Exotic Sens	0.44 ± 0.07	0.08 ± 0.00	0.23 ± 0.01
V+A+Z	Flint Tol	0.15 ± 0.01	0.07 ± 0.00	0.17 ± 0.01
(mol mol^{-1} Chl)	Flint Sens	0.34 ± 0.06	0.08 ± 0.01	0.22 ± 0.01
	Dent Tol	0.14 ± 0.02	0.06 ± 0.00	0.23 ± 0.01
	Dent Sens	0.29 ± 0.04	0.10 ± 0.00	0.35 ± 0.01
	Exotic Tol	0.15 ± 0.06	0.00 ± 0.00	0.38 ± 0.09
Z / V+A+Z	Exotic Sens	0.63 ± 0.01	0.00 ± 0.00	0.51 ± 0.04
(mol mol^{-1})	Flint Tol	0.23 ± 0.04	0.10 ± 0.08	0.34 ± 0.04
	Flint Sens	0.66 ± 0.03	0.07 ± 0.05	0.51 ± 0.07
	Dent Tol	0.05 ± 0.04	0.00 ± 0.00	0.36 ± 0.02
	Dent Sens	0.38 ± 0.09	0.00 ± 0.00	0.53 ± 0.07

The role of antioxidative defences was investigated by analysing the leaf contents of antioxidants and the activities of enzymes involved in the scavenging of reactive oxygen species. Although the contents of ascorbate, glutathione and a-tocopherol were higher in leaves grown at low temperature than leaves grown at 25°C, there were no consistent differences between tolerant and sensitive lines in plants grown in growth chambers or in the field (data not shown). In contrast consistent patterns were observed for the activities of the enzymes superoxide dismutase (SOD) and ascorbate peroxidase (APX). SOD activity was greater in sensitive lines than in tolerant lines in field grown leaves. This was not always the case in leaves grown at low temperature in controlled environment (Table 3). This discrepancy is maybe due to the fact that leaves in the field were eventually exposed to much higher light intensity than leaves in growth chambers. This may also explain why field-grown leaves often contained much higher SOD activity than leaves grown under controlled conditions. The difference between tolerant and sensitive lines was more consistent when the activity of APX is considered, the sensitive lines showing

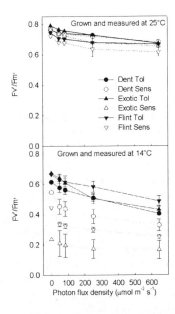

FIGURE 2. THE QUANTUM EFFICIENCY OF OPEN PSII REACTION CENTERS OF MAIZE LINES WITH CONTRASTING COLD TOLERANCE.

generally higher activity than tolerant lines at low temperature and in the field. Here again it seem that an important increase of certain antioxidative defences occurs in the sensitive line in response to low temperature because of their low photosynthetic performance. However, an increase in cold tolerance through an increase of antioxidative defences can not be excluded since they are not evenly distributed between bundle sheet and mesophyll cells (Pastori *et al.*, 2000). It is therefore possible that tolerance rely on a different compartmentation of theses antioxidants, not readily visible at the whole leaf level (Doulis *et al.*, 1997).

TABLE 3. THE ACTIVITIES OF SUPEROXIDE DISMUTASE (SOD) AND ASCORBATE PEROXIDASE (APX) OF MAIZE LINES WITH CONTRASTING COLD TOLERANCE.

| Enzyme | Line | Growth condition | | |
		14°C	25°C	Field
SOD (U mg^{-1} protein)	Exotic Tol	177 ± 15	158 ± 6	90 ± 4
	Exotic Sens	54 ± 2	93 ± 17	258 ± 11
	Flint Tol	24 ± 1	33 ± 7	89 ± 7
	Flint Sens	99 ± 14	23 ± 2	317 ± 6
	Dent Tol	96 ± 10	108 ± 11	146 ± 12
	Dent Sens	84 ± 4	94 ± 12	282 ± 14
APX (µmol ASA min^{-1} mg^{-1} prot)	Exotic Tol	0.86 ± 0.02	0.93 ± 0.02	0.19 ± 0.01
	Exotic Sens	7.30 ± 0.55	0.18 ± 0.00	4.10 ± 0.16
	Flint Tol	0.70 ± 0.02	0.63 ± 0.03	0.95 ± 0.03
	Flint Sens	4.52 ± 0.12	1.14 ± 0.02	0.89 ± 0.02
	Dent Tol	2.76 ± 0.18	0.60 ± 0.03	1.41 ± 0.09
	Dent Sens	3.87 ± 0.33	1.06 ± 0.26	2.12 ± 0.20

REFERENCES

Asada, K., 1992. Ascorbate peroxidase - A hydrogen peroxide scavenging enzyme in plants. Physiologia Plantarum, 85: 235-41.

Doulis, A.G., N. Debian and A.H. Kingston-Smith, C.H. Foyer, 1997. Differential localisation of antioxidants in maize leaves. Plant Physiology, 114: 1031-37.

Fracheboud, Y., P. Haldimann, J. Leipner and P. Stamp, 1999. Chlorophyll fluorescence as a selection tool for cold tolerance of photosynthesis in maize (*Zea mays* L.). Journal of Experimental Botany, 50: 1533-40.

Fracheboud, Y., J. Leipner and P. Stamp, 1998. Selection for cold tolerance in maize using chlorophyll fluorescence. In: Sowinski, P., Zagdanska, B., Aniol, A., Pithan, K., (eds.) Crop Development for the Cool and Wet Regions of Europe. Brussels: Office for the Official Publications of the European Communities, 116-21.

Fridovich, I., 1986. Biological effects of the superoxide radical. Archives of Biochemistry and Biophysics, 247: 1-11.

Fryer, M.J., J.R. Andrews, K. Oxborough, D.A. Blowers and N.R. Baker, 1998. Relationship between CO2 assimilation, photosynthetic electron transport, and active O2 metabolism in leaves of maize in the field during periods of low temperature. Plant Physiology, 116: 571-80.

Haldimann, P., Y. Fracheboud and P. Stamp, 1995. Carotenoid composition in *Zea Mays* developed at sub-optimal temperature and different light intensities. Physiologia Plantarum, 95: 409-14.

Kocsy, G., M. Brunner, A. Rüegsegger , P. Stamp and C. Brunold, 1996. Glutathione synthesis in maize genotypes with different sensitivities to chilling. Planta, 198: 365-70.

Leipner, J., Y. Fracheboud and P. Stamp, 1997. Acclimation by suboptimal growth temperature diminishes photooxidative damage in maize leaves. Plant, Cell and Environment, 20: 366-72.

Leipner, J., Y. Fracheboud and P. Stamp, 1999. Effect of growing season on the photosynthetic apparatus and leaf antioxidative defences in two maize genotypes of different chilling tolerance. Environmental and Experimental Botany, 42: 129-39.

Massacci, A., M.A. Iannelli , F. Pietrini and F. Loreto, 1995. The effect of growth at low temperature on photosynthetic characteristics and mechanisms of photoprotection of maize leaves. Journal of Experimental Botany, 46: 119-27.

Pastori, G., C.H. Foyer and P. Mullineaux, 2000. Low temperature-induced changes in the distribution of H_2O_2 and antioxidants between the bundle sheath and mesophyll cells of maize leaves. Journal of Experimental Botany, 51: 107-13.

Pietrini, F., M.A. Iannelli, A. Battistelli, S. Moscatello, F. Loreto and A. Massacci, 1999. Effects on photosynthesis, carbohydrate accumulation and regrowth induced by temperature increase in maize genotypes with different sensitivity to low temperature. Australian Journal of Plant Physiology, 26: 367-73.

Photoassimilate transport in maize seedlings at moderately low temperatures (10 - 14°C). The path from chloroplast to vein

P. SOWIÑSKI[1], A. DALBIAK[1] AND A. SOWIÑSKA[2]

[1] Plant Breeding and Acclimatization Institute, Radzików, Poland
[2] The Children Memorial Health Institute, Warszawa, Poland

SUMMARY

Low temperatures cause many responses in chilling-sensitive plants such as maize. Some of them, e.g. accumulation of carbohydrates, shoot/root ratio changes as well as a photosynthesis inhibition are often interpreted as an effect of disturbances in photoassimilate transport. Different aspects of assimilate transport have been studied in maize seedlings treated with moderately low temperatures (10 – 14° C) since the start of COST 814 Action. Studies concer-ned short- and long-distance transport kinetics, a carbohydrate accumulation in leaves, sucrose phosphate synthase activity and the role of roots as the assimilate acceptor. It has been found that short-distance transport in leaf and phloem loading are key processes which limit the export of sugars from the leaves at low temperature, although phloem unloading may determine to some extent, photoassimilate distribution pattern in chilled plants. Results reported in this work demonstrated a symplastic continuity between companion cell/sieve tube complexes and both bundle sheath cells and parenchyma cells in a chilling-sensitive, dent-type CM 109 inbred line. In contrast, chilling-tolerant, the flint-type KW 1074 inbred line showed symplastic isolation of the cc/se complex. It is suggested that symplastic transport retardation in CM 109 line is the reason for observed changes in assimilate export from leaves. It is also concluded that some anatomical traits, possibly related to subspecies origin, might be responsible for observed genotypical diversity in maize chilling-sensitivity.

Keywords: assimilate movement, chilling, maize seedling, phloem loading, plasmodesmata

INTRODUCTION

Studies on assimilate transport in maize seedlings treated with moderately low temperatures (10-14°C) realised in the frame of COST 814 Action have shown distinct genotypical differences in respect to that process (Sowiński, 1995). Among several genotypes, those reported as chilling-sensitive ones responded to low temperatures by 4 to 6 fold extension of the "entrance time" (time between radiolabel incorporation into the leaf feeding area and radioactivity appearing in the transport path). This period in chilling-tolerant lines was only twice longer than that in control plants. It was found in other experiments, that such "entrance time" depended strongly on a leaf temperature, particularly in the line chilling-sensitive CM 109 inbred (Sowiński et al., 1998a). The genotypical diversity in the "entrance time" was accompanied by differences in the amount of radiolabel imported by roots (Sowiński, 1995). Studies with vertical low-temperature gradients in the root zone showed however, that supply of assimilates to roots as well as transport speed strongly depended on activity of roots (Sowiński et al., 1998a). Detailed studies have shown both a strong retardation of short-distance transport and an inhibition of phloem loading (Sowiński et al., 1999a). It was accompanied by a stronger accumulation of starch in leaves of chilling-sensitive line, as compare to chilling-tolerant one. Simultaneously, no genotypical differences were found in activity of sucrose phosphate synthase (Sowiński et al., 1999a) in a cold. SPS was postulated to be the key enzyme involved in controlling the size of the transport pool (Kalt-Torres et al., 1987).

This work was performed to verify the hypothesis, that differences in assimilate export from leaves found between chilling-sensitive and chilling-tolerant genotypes were related to the intra-specific diversity in a vascular bundle structure. Special attention was paid to differences in plasmodesmatal connections, since a symplastic transport was shown to be inhibited strongly by low temperatures (Gamalei et al., 1994).

MATERIALS AND METHODS

Chilling-tolerant KW 1074 (flint) and chilling-sensitive CM 109 (dent) inbred line seedlings were used in 3 independent experiments. Several cuttings from a central part of the fully developed 2nd leaf were prepared according to Spurr (1969). Thin sections stained in uranyl acetate and lead citrate were investigated and photographed under transmission electron microscope. Altogether, 33 bundles per inbred line were investigated. Bundle sheath and vascular bundle area was calculated by self-made, specialised software from scanned photoprints. A Kolmogorov-Smirnov's non-parametrical ë-test (p = 0.05) was used to compare plasmodesmatal connectivities in both inbreds.

RESULTS

A structure of bundle sheaths and vascular bundles in leaves of both tested genotypes was typical for maize (Evert et al., 1978; Evert, 1986). A single vascular bundle (small or interme-diate) showed a companion cell, thin- and thick-walled sieve elements, a vessel and a few parenchyma cells. The bundles were surrounded with 4 – 6 bundle sheath cells. External walls of these cells exhibited continuous suberin lamella crossing by numerous plasmodesmata.

Generally, plasmodesmatal connections between mesophyll and bundle sheath cells were more frequent in the chilling-sensitive CM 109 line, than in the chilling-tolerant KW 1074 one (Table 1). Moreover, in opposition to KW 1074 inbred, there was no apparent symplastic isolation of a companion cell/thin-walled sieve element complex from neither bundle sheath nor paren-chyma cells in CM 109 genotype (Table 1). No differences were found in a size of bundle sheaths and vasular bundles observed in both genotypes. The total area of bundle sheath cells was 1140 ± 391 mm^2 and 1201 ± 402 mm^2, in KW 1074 and CM 109, respectively. Area of vascular bundle was 187 ± 71 mm^2 in KW 1074 and 154 ± 57 mm^2.

TABLE 1. PLASMODESMATAL CONNECTIONS (AS AVERAGE PER CELL INTERFACE) BETWEEN DIFFERENT CELL TYPES IN LEAVES OF KW 1074 (CHILLING-TOLERANT, FLINT) AND CM 109 (CHILLING-SENSITIVE, DENT) INBREDS. MC - MESOPHYLL CELL, BSC – BUNDLE SHEATH CELL, VPC - VASCULAR PARENCHYMA CELL, CC - COMPANION CELL, SE – SIEVE ELEMENT. * INDICATES SIGNIFICANT DIFFERENCES BETWEEN INBRED LINES.

Cell connections	KW 1074	CM 109
MC – BSC*	20.1	29.8
BSC – BSC	5.2	6.9
BSC – VPC	5.6	6.9
VPC – VPC	0.1	0.5
BSC – CC*	0.06	0.6
VPC – CC*	0	0.4
CC – SE (thin-walled)*	0.06	0.6
VPC – SE (thick-walled)	0.6	0.4

DISCUSSION

A companion cell/thin-walled sieve element complex in leaves of many C4 grasses, among them NADP-ME plants, is not symplastically isolated from bundle sheath cells. Maize has been believed as the only exception in respect to that (Botha, 1992). On the basis of symplastic isolation of cc/se complex from surrounding cells, maize has been assumed as an apoplastic phloem loader (Evert et al., 1978; Fritz et al., 1983; Evert, 1986). Obtained results showed however, that an intra-species diversity in symplastic isolation of a cc/se complex may exist in maize. In other words, it seems, that there is no physical barrier for a symplastic assimilate movement from bundle sheath cells to a cc/se complex in some maize materials.

Differences in a phloem structure observed in tested inbreds might be related to the genotype origin. KW 1074 and CM 109 lines are both typical representatives of flint and dent maize sub-species, respectively. Flint materials were first found in high altitude regions. They are believed to be chilling-tolerant ones in opposition to dent sub-species originated in a warmer climate of America. It should be stressed out, that both sub-species also differ in other anatomical characteristics, especially in root traits (Stamp, 1984). Some of these traits, e.g. a root architecture, seems to be of adaptive importance in a cold environment (Sowiński *et al.*, 1998a, b).

CONCLUSIONS

1. A symplastic phloem loading mechanism may co-exist beside an apoplastic one in maize.
2. A proportion of apoplastic to symplastic way may be genotype-dependent.
3. Decrease of assimilate export from leaf at low temperature may be the result of symplastic transport retardation.
4. Some anatomical traits, possibly related to the sub-species origin, may determine chilling sensitivity of maize.

ACKNOWLEDGEMENTS

This work has been carried out with the financial support from State Committee for Scientific Research (Poland) (Grant no 582/E – 173/SPUB/COST/p-06/DZ39/99).

REFERENCES

Botha, C.E.J., 1992. Plasmodesmatal distribution, structure and frequency in relation to assimilation in C3 and C4 grasses in southern Africa. Planta, 187: 348-358.

Evert, R.F., 1986. Phloem loading in maize. In: "Regulation of carbon and nitrogen reduction and utilization in maize". Eds. J.C. Shanon, D.P. Knievel, C.D. Boyer, ch. 6.

Evert, R.F., W. Eschrich and W. Heyser, 1978. Leaf structure in relation to solute transport and phloem loading in Zea mays L. Planta, 138: 279-294.

Fritz, E., R.F. Evert and W. Heyser, 1983. Microautoradiographic studies of phloem loading and transport in the leaf of *Zea mays*. Planta, 159: 193-206.

Gamalei, Y.V., A.J.E. Van Bel, M.V. Pakhomova and A.V. Sjutkina, 1994. Effects of temperature on the conformation of the endoplasmic reticulum and on starch accumulation in leaves with the symplasmic minor-vein configuration. Planta, 194: 443-453.

Hodges, D.M., C.J. Andrews, D.A. Johnson and R.I. Hamilton, 1997. Antioxidant enzyme and compound responses to chilling stress and their combining abilities in differentially sensitive maize hybrids. Crop Science, 37: 857-863.

Kalt-Torres, W., P.S. Kerr, H. Usuda and S.C. Huber, 1987. Diurnal changes in maize leaf photosynthesis. Plant, Cell Environment, 20: 366-372.

Sowiński, P., 1995. Transport of assimilates from leaves to roots in chilling-treated maize seedlings. Kinetics and assimilate distribution. Acta Physiologia Plantarum, 17: 341-8.

Sowiński, P., 1998. The effect of irradiance, p-chloromercuribenzensulphonicacid and fusicoccin on the long distance transport in *Zea mays* L. seedlings. Acta Physiologia Plantarum 20: 79-84.

Sowiński, P., W. Richner, A. Soldati and P. Stamp, 1998a. Assimilate transport in maize (*Zea mays* L.) seedlings at vertical low temperature gradients in the root zone. Journal of Experimental Botany, 49: 747-752.

Sowiński, P., A. Dalbiak, A. Sowińska, Z. Królikowski, J. Adamczyk and J. Szczepańska, 1998b. Root architecture and field characteristics in maize seedlings of flint and dent type adapted to Polish climate. Plant Breeding Seed Science, 42: 101-108.

Sowiński, P., A. Dalbiak, P. Ochodzki and J. Tadeusiak, 1999a. Relations between sugar accumulation and SPS activity in leaves and photoassimilate transport in chilling-treated maize seedlings. Acta Physiologia Plantarum, 21: 375-381.

Sowiński, P., A. Dalbiak, P. Ochodzki, J. Adamczyk and Z. Królikowski, 1999. Carbohydrate accumulation in seedling leaves at moderate low temperature and early field characteristics in flint and dent maize genotypes adapted to Polish climate. Plant Breeding Seed Science, 43: 35-44.

Spurr, A.R., 1969. A low-viscosity epoxy resin embedding medium for electron microscopy. J. Ultrastruct. Res. 26: 31-43.

Stamp, P., 1984. Chilling tolerance of young plants demonstrated on the example of maize (*Zea mays* L.). In: Advances in Agronomy and Crop Science 7. Ed. Geisler, Berlin.

Parey, P., M.J. Verheul,C. Picatto and P. Stamp, 1996. Growth and development of maize (*Zea mays* L.) seedlings under chilling conditions in the field. European Journal of Agronomy, 5: 31-43.

Photosynthetic CO_2 exchange and carbon metabolism in leaves of cold-hardened and non-hardened winter rye

O. KEERBERG[1], P. GARDESTRÖM[2], H. IVANOVA[1],H. KEERBERG[1], P. TALTS[1]
AND T. PÄRNIK[1]

[1] Institute of Experimental Biology, Estonian Agricultural University, 76902 Tastu, Estonia
[2] Department of Plant Physiology, University of Umeå, S-901 87 Umeå, Sweden

SUMMARY

Leaves of cold-hardened (CH, grown at 5°C) and non-hardened (NH, grown at 25°C) winter rye (*Secale cereale* L.) were exposed to $^{14}CO_2$ under saturating light at 25°C or 5°C and the kinetics of ^{14}C incorporation into the products of steady-state photosynthesis was determined. From kinetic data the rates of carbon fluxes and the pool sizes of the metabolites in the biochemical system of CO_2 assimilation were calculated. At 25°C the total rate of CO_2 fixation was approximately equal in NH and CH rye. Lowering temperature to 5°C didn't change the photosynthesis rate in CH leaves while in NH leaves a 20% decrease was detected. Efficiency of regeneration of ribulose 1,5-bisphosphate in the reductive pentose phosphate cycle and the rate constant of glycine decarboxylation in the glycolate cycle increased during cold hardening. Acclimation to the low growth temperatures resulted in a severe suppression of starch synthesis measured at both 25°C and 5°C. It was accompanied by the higher rate of carbon incorporation into malate and other C_3- and C_4-acids in CH rye. The rates of sucrose synthesis were equal in NH and CH rye and didn't depend on temperature of measurement. This fact suggests that higher content of sucrose found in the photosynthesizing cells of cold-hardened leaves is not the result of its more rapid synthesis but rather of the lower rate of its consumption

Keywords: cold hardening, leaf temperature, photosynthetic carbon metabolism, Secale cereale L., winter rye

INTRODUCTION

Acclimation of plants during growth at low temperatures leads to substantial changes in photosynthetic carbon metabolism. It has been shown that cold hardening results in an increase of the photosynthetic capacity measured as the rate of O_2 evolution at saturating levels of CO_2 and irradiance (Öquist *et al.*, 1993). This was accompanied by an increase of the activity of the key enzymes of sucrose synthesis and of the reductive pentose phosphate cycle (Hurry *et al.*, 1995). An increase of the content of soluble sugars with specific accumulation of fructans in response to cold acclimation has been demonstrated (Chatterton *et al.*,1988). These data indicate that the reaction system of the photosynthetic carbon metabolism must have been rearranged during cold acclimation. However no quantitative information about the changes of the rates of partial reactions of the biochemical system of CO_2 assimilation is available so far. The goal of this study was to establish (1) how the rates of carbon fluxes and pool sizes of the intermediates of this system are modified during cold acclimation and (2) how the photosynthetic carbon metabolism in leaves of cold-hardened (CH) and non-hardened (NH) plants respond to the changes of the temperature of ambient air. With this aim we analysed the kinetics of ^{14}C incorporation into the products of steady-state photosynthesis in leaves of CH and NH winter exposed to $^{14}CO_2$ at 5°C and 25°C.

MATERIALS AND METHODS

Winter rye (*Secale cereale* L., cv. Musketeer) was grown in vermiculite under fluorescent lamps at 25°C (NH plants) or at 5°C (CH plants). Fully expanded third or fourth leaves of NH and CH plants of the same stage of development were exposed to $^{14}CO_2$ (300 μmol mol^{-1}) for different time intervals ranging from 5 s to 10 min. Exposures were performed at 25°C or 5°C under saturating light. After the exposure leaves were killed in liquid nitrogen. Labelled photosynthates were extracted with cold perchloric acid and separated by paper chromatography combined with additional separation of phosphorylated compounds in Partisil column (5x150 mm) and amino acids with analyzer AAA 339. Radioactivity of individual compounds was determined and plotted against the duration of exposure to $^{14}CO_2$. The curves obtained were analysed according to a special interpretation procedure enabling to calculate the rates of carbon fluxes and pool sizes of intermediates of carbon metabolism in intact leaves *in vivo* (Keerberg and Pärnik, 1998).

RESULTS

Table 1 summarises the calculated rates of carbon fluxes in the biochemical system of CO_2 assimilation in leaves of NH and CH rye at different temperatures of measurement medium. At 25°C the rate of true photosynthesis in the atmosphere with normal concentration of CO_2 was approximately equal in NH and CH rye. Lowering temperature to 5°C did not change the rate of photosynthesis in CH rye while in NH rye a decrease of about 30% was detected.

The rate of carbon flux through the glycolate cycle was 80% in CH rye at 25°C and at 5°C about 4 times higher than in NH rye (Table 1). The flux of carbon through the glycolate cycle is determined by the rate of oxygenation of ribulose bisphosphate (RuBP). The relative rate of oxygenation is dependent on the ratio of concentrations CO_2/O_2 in the carboxylation centres: the lower the internal concentration of CO_2 the higher the rate of oxygenation. In CH leaves the resistance for CO_2 diffusion was always higher than in NH leaves resulting in a decrease of the internal concentration of CO_2 (at 25 °C 9.1 and 6.0 μM in NH and CH leaves, respectively).

TABLE 1. RATES OF CARBON FLUXES AND POOL SIZES OF METABOLITES IN THE BIOCHEMICAL SYSTEM OF CO_2 ASSIMILATION IN LEAVES OF NON-HARDENED AND COLD-HARDENED WINTER RYE AT DIFFERENT AMBIENT AIR TEMPERATURES.

	NH rye		CH rye	
	25°C	5°C	25°C	5°C
Carbon fluxes (μg-atom C m^{-2} s^{-1}):				
true photosynthesis	7.10±0.22	4.99±0.30	6.29±0.14	6.60±0.57
carbon flux through the glycolate cycle	2.85±0.19	1.04±0.07	4.73±0.38	4.14±0.69
synthesis of				
sucrose	4.69±0.10	3.98±0.01	4.13±0.09	5.00±0.16
starch	0.40±0.02	0.18±0.01	0.09±0.01	0.06±0.01
C_3- and C_4-acids total	0.71±0.06	0.29±0.02	0.76±0.07	0.48±0.01
Refixation of respiratory CO_2 inside the leaf (%)	35.7	29.3	67.5	76.7
Pool sizes:				
total pool of sugar phosphates (μg-atom C m^{-2})	431± 7	648±10	514±24	1382±203
pools (μmol m^{-2}) of				
PGA	20± 3	28± 1	24± 4	73± 1
RuBP	12± 2	11± 1	26± 1	59± 1
HMP	38± 1	53± 1	25± 2	101± 2
glycine	>146	72± 5	84± 2	258±88
serine	78±17	67± 9	120±28	>98
contents (μmol m^{-2}) of				
glycine	602±48	123±10	262±25	194±10
serine	322±10	333±17	1284±99	1347±62
Ratio of				
RuBP/HMP pools	0.32	0.21	1.04	0.68
serine/glycine contents	0.53	2.71	4.90	6.94
Rate constants of glycine decarboxylation (10^3s^{-1})	17.2	7.3	32.8	>10.7

PGA: 3-phosphoglyceric acid; RuBP: ribulose-1,5-bisphosphate; HMP: hexose monophosphates

The higher stomatal resistance in CH leaves may be concluded also from the extent of refixation of respiratory CO_2 inside the leaf: 30- 40% and 70-80% in NH and CH leaves, respectively (Table 1). Higher stomatal resistance and lower internal CO_2 concentration may be regarded as the only reasons for the higher rate of carbon flux through the glycolate cycle in CH leaves. No changes were found in the CO_2/O_2 specificity of Rubisco measured at 25°C (71 and 74 in NH and CH rye, respectively).

Acclimation to the low growth temperatures resulted in a severe suppression of starch synthesis measured at both 25°C and 5°C. It was accompanied by the higher rate of carbon incorporation into malate and other C_3- and C_4-acids (Table 1). The relative rates of sucrose synthesis (per cent the rate of true photosynthesis) were equal in NH and CH rye at both temperatures of measurement. This fact suggests that higher content of sucrose found in the photosynthesizing cells of cold-hardened leaves is not the result of its more rapid synthesis but rather of the lower rate of its consumption in growth processes.

At 25°C the total pool of sugar phosphates was approximately equal in CH and NH leaves (Table 1). Temperature shift from 25°C to 5°C resulted in an increase of the total pool of sugar phosphates in both NH and CH rye, to a higher extent in CH rye. This may reflect the decrease of rate constants of the reactions converting sugar phosphates to the end products of photosynthesis. The more pronounced increase of sugar phosphates in CH leaves may be the result of the higher rate of CO_2 fixation in these leaves. The pools of phosphoglyceric acid (PGA) followed the same pattern of temperature dependence as the total pools of sugar phosphates. At both temperatures the pools of RuBP were in CH leaves significantly larger than in NH leaves. The same was valid for the ratio of the pool of RuBP to the pools of hexose monophosphates (Table 1). These results may be interpreted as an increase of the enzymatic potential of the regenerative phase of the reductive pentose phosphate cycle. At normal concentration of CO_2 this higher potential could not be realised in higher rate of photosynthesis due to stomatal limitation of CO_2 fixation. In CH leaves the larger pool of RuBP compensates the lower level of internal CO_2 to give the rate of photosynthesis equal to that in NH leaves (see Table 1, 25°C). However in the conditions where stomata do not limit photosynthesis, for instance at high CO_2 concentrations, one can expect the elevated rates of photosynthesis in CH leaves compared to NH ones. Indeed, in the study of Öquist *et al.,* (1993) carried out with winter rye of the same cultivar has been demonstrated that CO_2- and light-saturated rate of photosynthetic O_2 evolution was in CH leaves about 40% higher than in NH leaves. In CH leaves the active pools of serine measured at both 25 and 5°C were larger than in NH leaves (Table 1). The same was valid for the total content of serine measured with amino acid analyzer and for the ratio of the contents of serine /glycine. The apparent rate constants of glycine decarboxylation (calculated as the ratio of glycine conversion to its pool size) were also higher in CH plants (Table 1). These facts suggest that cold acclimation of winter rye leads to an increase of the activity (or content) of glycine decarboxylase system. This adaptive feature may have a preventive significance avoiding glycine decarboxylase become a limiting enzyme at elevated rates of carbon flux through the glycolate cycle in CH plants.

DISCUSSION AND CONCLUSIONS

Acclimation results in an increase of the enzymatic capacity of the regenerative phase of the reductive pentose phosphate cycle and in the corresponding increase of the rate of photosynthesis in the conditions where stomata do not limit CO_2 fixation. Higher stomatal resistance of CO_2 diffusion in CH plants leads to the elevated rates of carbon flux through the glycolate cycle. This is accompanied by a specific increase of the activity of glycine decarboxylase system. In cold-hardened plants the synthesis of starch is almost entirely suppressed. Triose phosphates which could not be used for starch synthesis in CH plants are exported out of chloroplasts to cytosol where they are preferentially directed to the synthesis of the intermediates of respiratory pathways.

ACKNOWLEDGEMENTS

This study was supported by a grant from the Estonian Science Foundation (project no.2197).

REFERENCES

Chatterton, N., W. Thornley., P. Harrison and J. Bennett, 1988. Dynamics of fructan and sucrose biosynthesis in crested wheatgrass. Plant Cell Physiology, 29: 1103-1108.

Hurry, V. M., O. Keerberg, T. Pärnik, P. Gardeström and G. Öquist, 1995. Cold-hardening results in increased activity of enzymes involved in carbon metabolism in leaves of winter rye (Secale cereale L.). Planta, 195: 554-562.

Keerberg, O. and T. Pärnik, 1998. Modelling and quantification of carbon fluxes in photosynthesizing cells of intact plant leaves in vivo. Bio ThermoKinetics in the Post Genomic Era, Chalmers Reproservice, Göteborg, pp. 303-306.

Öquist, G., V.M. Hurry and N.P.A. Huner, 1993. Low temperature effects on photosynthesis and correlation with freezing tolerance in spring and winter cultivars of wheat and rye. Plant Physiology, 101: 245-250.

Effect of cool soil conditions on photosynthetic efficiency in maize seedlings

F. JANOWIAK[1] AND K. DÖRFFLING[2]

[1] Institute of Plant Physiology, Polish Academy of Sciences, Podluzna 3, PL-30-239 Cracow, Poland
[2] Institute of General Botany and Botanical Garden, University of Hamburg, Ohnhorststr. 18, D-20609 Hamburg, Germany

S U M M A R Y

Photosynthesis rate of maize plants decreases under low temperature conditions. The aim of the present studies was to determine the effect of cool soil conditions on photosynthetic efficiency of maize seedlings. The investigations were performed with chilling-tolerant (F7) and sensitive (Co151) maize inbreds. Plants were grown in a growth chamber in pots filled with soil. At the third leaf stage roots of seedlings were exposed to chilling ($8°C$). During a five day-long root chilling and a two day-long recovery period, the effective quantum yield of PSII electron transport (Yield), the photochemical quenching (qP) of chlorophyll a fluorescence and the stomatal resistance on the first, second and the third leaves were measured. In both inbreds Yield decreased significantly during the 3rd, 4th and 5th day of root chilling. These drops were greater in Co151 (sensitive) than in F7 (tolerant). QP decreased in the 4th and 5th day of root cooling, but again it was lower in Co151 than in F7. Leaf stomatal resistance (SR) increased enormously in both inbreds already after 2 and 4 hours of root chilling. In the course of further chilling SR decreased nearly to the level before chilling. However, during long-time root chilling the stomata closed again, especially in Co151. Photochemical activity of PSII and photochemical quenching (Yield, qP) do not change up to 2 days of root chilling. Obviously, under cool soil conditions the photosynthetic efficiency in maize seedlings is limited by stomata closing. The long-term root cooling limits the photosynthetic efficiency by both stomata closing and decrease of photochemical activity of PSII. Similarly, during the recovery period after long-term root cooling, both factors limit photosynthetic efficiency, especially in the sensitive maize genotypes.

Keywords: chilling tolerance, chlorophylla florescence, cool soil, photosynthetic apparatus, stomata, Zea mays L.

INTRODUCTION

Photosynthetic efficiency (PE) of maize plants decreases under low-temperature conditions (Long et al., 1983; Stirling et al., 1991). This reduction is accompanied by various changes in the photosynthetic apparatus i. e. by depression in the photochemical activities of PSII and dysfunction of photosynthetic membranes (Hayden and Baker, 1990; Baker, 1991). Chilling-induced stomata closing can be another limiting factor for PE under low-temperature stress (Willmer and Fricker, 1996).

The aim of the present studies was to clarify causes of the decrease of PE under cool soil conditions in maize seedlings by determining the effect of this kind of stress on the status of photosynthetic apparatus and on the stomata closing rate.

MATERIALS AND METHODS

Plant material

The investigations were performed with chilling tolerant (F7) and sensitive (Co151) maize inbreds.

Growth and chilling conditions

Plants were grown in a growth chamber in pots filled with soil. At the third leaf stage roots of seedlings were exposed to chilling (8°C), while the shoots remained at warm temperature (22°C).

Chlorophyll fluorescence and stomatal resistance measurements

During a five-day-long root chilling and a two-day-long recovery period, the effective quantum yield of PSII electron transport (Yield), the photochemical quenching (qP) of chlorophyll a fluorescence and the stomatal resistance (SR) on the first, second and the third leaves were measured. Chlorophyll fluorescence was measured by means of fluorometer PAM 2000 and stomatal resistance by means of porometer Delta T A4. Yield was calculated according to the equation: $(Fm'-Ft)/Fm'$ where: Fm' – fluorescence when the primary acceptors of PSII reaction centres are fully reduced in light-adapted leaves, Ft – fluorescence under steady-state illumination and qP to the equation: $(Fm'-Ft)/(Fm'-Fo')$ (Walz, 1993). Experiments were performed in completely randomised design and for each treatment ten measurements were done.

RESULTS

In both inbreds Yield decreased significantly during the 3rd, 4th and 5th day of root chilling (Fig.1). These drops were greater in Co151 (sensitive) than in F7 (tolerant). After two days of recovery Yield was still significantly lower in both inbreds than in those before chilling. QP decreased in the 4th and 5th day of root cooling, but again it was lower in Co151 than in F7 (Fig. 2). After the 1st day of recovery qP was significantly higher in

F7 in comparison with Co151. After 2 days of recovery qP reached the initial values in both inbreds. Leaf stomatal resistance (SR) increased enormously in both inbreds already after 2 and 4 hours of root chilling (Fig. 3). In the course of further chilling SR decreased nearly to the level before chilling. However, during long-time root chilling the stomata closed again, especially in Co151. During two days of recovery SR reached the initial value in F7, but in Co151 it was still significantly higher than before chilling.

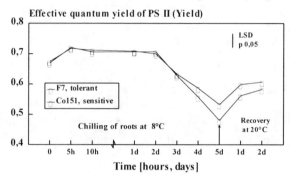

FIGURE 1. EFFECTIVE QUANTUM YIELD OF PSII ELECTRON TRANSPORT (YIELD) DURING CHILLING OF THE ROOT AND DURING RECOVERY OF TWO MAIZE INBREDS DIFFERING IN CHILLING TOLERANCE. THE MEASUREMENTS WERE MADE FOR THE 1ST, 2ND, AND 3RD LEAF WITH TEN REPLICATES. THE PRESENTED DATA ARE MEAN VALUES FOR ALL THREE LEAVES.

FIGURE 2. PHOTOCHEMICAL QUENCHING (QP) OF CHLOROPHYLL A FLUORESCENCE DURING CHILLING OF THE ROOT AND DURING RECOVERY OF TWO MAIZE INBREDS DIFFERING IN CHILLING TOLERANCE. THE MEASUREMENTS WERE MADE FOR THE 1ST, 2ND, AND 3RD LEAF WITH TEN REPLICATES. THE PRESENTED DATA ARE MEAN VALUES FOR ALL THREE LEAVES.

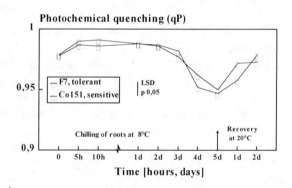

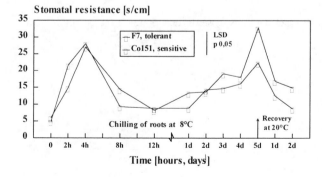

FIGURE 3. STOMATAL RESISTANCE DURING CHILLING OF THE ROOT AND DURING RECOVERY OF TWO MAIZE INBREDS DIFFERING IN CHILLING TOLERANCE. THE MEASUREMENTS WERE MADE FOR THE 1ST, 2ND, AND 3RD LEAF WITH TEN REPLICATES. THE PRESENTED DATA ARE MEAN VALUES FOR ALL THREE LEAVES.

CONCLUSIONS

Photochemical activity of PSII and photochemical quenching (Yield, qP) do not change up to 2 days of root chilling. Obviously, under cool soil conditions the photosynthetic efficiency in maize seedling is limited by stomata closing. The long-term root cooling limits the photosynthetic efficiency by both stomata closing and decrease of photochemical activity of PSII. Similarly, during the recovery period after long-term root cooling, both factors limit photosynthetic efficiency, especially in the sensitive maize genotypes.

ACKNOWLEDGEMENTS

This research was supported by Deutsche Forschungsgemeinschaft (DFG, Bonn) Project No. DO 104/24-1, 436 POL 17/6/98 and by the State Committee for Scientific Research (KBN, Warsaw) Project No. 5 P06A 029 14.

REFERENCES

Baker, N.R., 1991. A possible role for photosystem II in environmental perturbations of photosynthesis. Physiologia Plantarum, 81: 563-570.

Hayden, D.B. and N.R. Baker, 1990. Damage to photosynthetic membrane in chilling sensitive plants: maize, a case study. Critical Reviews in Biotechnology, 9: 321-341.

Long, S.P., T.M. East and N.R. Baker, 1983. Chilling damage to photosynthesis in young *Zea mays* I. Effect of light and temperature variation on photosynthetic CO_2 assimilation. Journal of Experimental Botany, 34:177-188.

Stirling, C. M., G.Y. Nie, C. Aguilera, A. Nugawela, S.P. Long and N.R. Baker, 1991. Photosynthetic productivity of an immature maize crop: changes in quantum yield of CO_2 assimilation, conversion efficiency and thylakoid proteins. Plant, Cell and Environment, 14: 947-954.

Walz, H., 1993. Portable Fluorometer PAM-2000 and data acquisition software DA-2000. Handbook, 2nd edition, Effeltrich, Germany.

Willmer, C. and M. Fricker, 1996. Stomatal responses to environments factors. In: Stomata. Chapman & Hall, London, 126-191.

Salicylic acid may decrease chilling-induced ACC accumulation in maize

G. SZALAI[1], I. TARI[2], T. JANDA[1], E. HORVÁTH[1] AND E. PÁLDI[1]

[1] Agricultural Research Institute of the Hungarian Academy of Sciences, H-2462 Martonvásár, POB 19, Hungary
[2] Department of Plant Physiology, József Attila University, H-6701 Szeged, POB 654, Hungary

SUMMARY

The effect of 0.5 mM salicylic acid pre-treatment on chilling-induced changes in ACC and its malonyl conjugate MACC was investigated in young maize (*Zea mays* L.) plants grown in hydroponic solution at 22/20°C. The ACC content in the leaves exhibited a progressive increase in control, untreated maize plants under chilling conditions (5°C). This increase was less pronounced in plants pre-treated with salicylic acid. In plants grown at hardening temperatures (13/11°C) this cold stress did not cause a significant increase in the ACC content of untreated or SA-treated leaves after 4 days. These data support the concept that the endogenous ACC level may indicate the chilling stress status of plant tissues. Both hardening and the 0.5 mM salicylic acid treatment caused an increase in the ACC content of the roots. The ACC content in the control plants showed a rapid increase for 2 days during chilling, after which it started to decrease, though it remained at a substantially higher level than before the cold treatment. In plants treated with SA or grown at hardening temperature the ACC content did not change significantly even after 4 days of low-temperature stress. The MACC content showed an increase in the leaves due to the low temperature treatment. In unchilled plants the MACC content in the leaves was significantly higher in the acclimated plants than in the controls. However, changes in the MACC content were not correlated with the chilling tolerance in maize.

Keywords: 1-aminocyclopropane-1-carboxylic acid, cold stress, malonyl 1-aminocyclopropane-1-carboxylicacid, salicylic acid, Zea mays L.

INTRODUCTION

Maize plants, which are sensitive to chilling, may suffer severe damage at low temperature (Marton and Szundy, 1997; Marton, 1997a; Marton, 1997b; Stamp, 1984).

Low-temperature stress may cause the accumulation of ACC in maize seedlings (Janowiak and Dörffling, 1995) due to the stimulation of ACC synthase. Higher ACC contents in the chilling-sensitive genotypes were accompanied by greater injuries.

Several studies have been made on the role of salicylic acid (SA) in defence mechanisms against pathogen attack (Raskin, 1992). It was recently shown that salicylic acid and certain related compounds may also decrease the symptoms of low-temperature damage in young maize plants (Janda et al., 1999; Janda et al., 2000). The aim of the present work was to investigate the effects of salicylic acid pre-treatment, which increased the chilling tolerance of the plants, on changes in ACC and MACC contents in maize during low-temperature stress.

MATERIALS AND METHODS

Maize seeds (Zea mays L., hybrid Norma) were allowed to germinate for 4 days at 26 °C, and were then grown for 10 days in Hoagland solution at 22/20 °C (non-acclimated plants) with a 16/8-h light/dark periodicity with a RH of 75 % and 200 mmol m^{-2} s^{-1} PPFD. Cold acclimation was carried out at 13/11 °C for 4 days before chilling. One day before the cold treatment (5 °C) some of the plants were treated with 0.5 mM salicylic acid. The ACC and MACC contents were determined as described by Tari and Nagy (1994). The results are the means of 3-5 measurements and were statistically evaluated using the t-test methods and ANOVA to assess significant differences (p £ 0.05) between the means.

RESULTS AND DISCUSSION

The ACC content in the leaves exhibited a progressive increase in control, untreated maize plants under chilling conditions (Fig. 1). This increase was less pronounced in plants pretreated with salicylic acid. On average (plants chilled for 1-4 days) the ACC content in SA-treated plants was 53 % of the controls, although there was no statistically significant difference between the ACC contents of the non-chilled plants. In plants which were grown at hardening temperatures (acclimated plants grown at 13/11 °C), this cold stress (5 °C) did not cause a significant increase in the ACC content of untreated and SA-treated leaves after 4 days. These data support the concept that the endogenous ACC level may indicate the status of chilling stress in plant tissues.

Both hardening and the 0.5 mM salicylic acid treatment caused an increase in the ACC content of the roots (Fig. 2). The ACC content in the control plants showed a rapid increase for 2 days during chilling, after which it started to decrease, but it remained at a substantially higher level than before the cold treatment. In plants treated with SA or grown at hardening temperature the ACC content did not change significantly even after 4 days of low temperature stress. In this case SA prevented the bulk accumulation of ACC in the roots at the outset of chilling in non-acclimated plants. At the whole-plant level the successful adaptation of the roots determines the regrowth capacity, ion and water uptake and/or transport of the seedlings during dehardening. The elongation of the roots is very sensitive to ethylene, so a decrease in ACC content is very important if the growth rate of the roots is to be sufficient for the successful acquisition of soil resources after chilling.

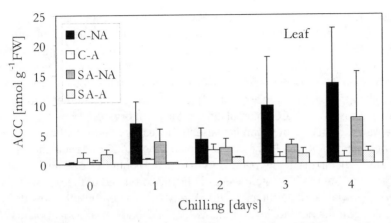

FIGURE 1. CHANGES IN THE ACC CONTENT IN THE YOUNGEST FULLY DEVELOPED LEAVES OF YOUNG MAIZE PLANTS DURING 5 °C CHILLING STRESS. (C – CONTROL; SA – PRETREATED WITH 0.5 MM SALICYLIC ACID 1 D BEFORE THE COLD STRESS; NA – NON-ACCLIMATED; A – ACCLIMATED).

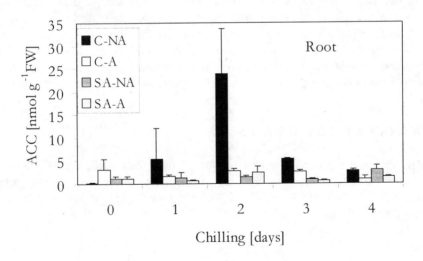

FIGURE 2. CHANGES IN THE ACC CONTENT IN THE ROOTS OF YOUNG MAIZE PLANTS DURING 5 °C CHILLING STRESS. FOR SYMBOLS SEE LEGEND OF FIGURE 1.

An increase in the ACC content due to low-temperature stress was also observed by other authors in several inbred maize lines and hybrids (Janowiak and Dörffling, 1995; 1996). This increase showed a high positive linear correlation with the chilling sensitivity of the genotype (Janowiak and Dörffling, 1996). This correlation is supported by the observation that maize plants grown at hardening temperatures, which were therefore better able to tolerate low temperatures (Janowiak and Dörffling, 1995; Janda et al., 1998), showed a lower increase in the ACC content during low-temperature stress. Similarly, the ACC accumulation was less pronounced in unhardened plants pretreated with salicylic acid. The decreasing effect of salicylic acid on ACC accumulation in the roots was especially remarkable during the first three days of chilling. The inhibition of ethylene biosynthesis by SA pretreatment may be involved in the adaptation of unhardened roots to chilling temperatures. In acclimated plants, however, SA treatment did not cause a further decrease in the ACC accumulation in the plant organs.

The MACC content showed an increase in the leaves due to the low-temperature treatment (data not shown). In the unchilled plants the MACC content in the leaves was significantly higher in the acclimated plants than in the controls. However, in contrast to ACC, changes in the MACC content were not highly correlated to the chilling tolerance of maize (Janowiak and Dörffling, 1996). The MACC content in the roots decreased during chilling in the non-acclimated plants (data not shown). In wheat plants MACC accumulates in the roots during the low-temperature hardening (Macháèková et al., 1992). In maize this accumulation could not be observed, the MACC concentration was never significantly higher in the cold acclimated plants than in the controls.

In conclusion, it was shown in the present work that not only low-temperature acclimation, but also a 1-day pretreatment with 0.5 mM salicylic acid, which was earlier shown to decrease the symptoms of chilling injury, may decrease the accumulation of ACC under chilling conditions in young maize plants. These results support the hypothesis that ACC accumulation is a reliable marker of low-temperature damage. The malonyl conjugate of ACC also changed during low-temperature stress; however, these changes in the MACC content were not correlated with the chilling tolerance in maize.

ACKNOWLEDGEMENTS

The authors are gratefully indebted to Anna Novák, Zsuzsa Kóti and Edit Kövesdi for their technical assistance. This work was supported by grants from the Hungarian National Scientific Research Foundation (OTKA F26236, T21115, T032653, M28074) and the J. Bolyai Research Sponsorship.

REFERENCES

Janda, T., G. Szalai, J.M. Ducruet and E. Páldi, 1998. Changes in photosynthesis in inbred maize lines with different degrees of chilling tolerance grown at optimum and suboptimum temperatures. Photosynthetica, 35: 205-212.

Janda, T., G. Szalai, I. Tari and E. Páldi, 1999. Hydroponic treatment with salicylic acid decreases the effects of chilling injury in maize (*Zea mays* L.) plants. Planta, 208: 175-180.

Janda, T., G. Szalai, Zs. Antunovics, E. Horváth and E. Páldi, 2000. Effect of benzoic acid and aspirin on chilling tolerance and photosynthesis in young maize plants. Maydica, 45: (in press).

Janowiak, F. and K. Dörffling, 1995. Chilling-induced changes in the contents of 1-aminocyclopropane-1-carboxylic acid (ACC) and its N-malonyl conjugate (MACC) in seedlings of two maize inbreds differing in chilling tolerance. Journal of Plant Physiology, 147: 257-262.

Janowiak, F. and K. Dörffling, 1996. Chilling tolerance of 10 maize genotypes as related to chilling-induced changes in ACC and MACC contents. Journal of Agronomy and Crop Sciences, 177: 175-184.

Macháèková, I., A. Hanišová and J. Krekule, 1992. Changes in the level of MACC during cold hardening and dehardening in winter wheat. Physiologia Plantarum, 84: 399-402.

Raskin, I., 1992. Role of salicylic acid in plants. Annual Review of Plant Physiology and Plant Molecular Biology, 43: 439-463.

Marton, L.C., 1997a. Evaluation of the cold tolerance of young maize plants in the temperature gradient chamber. In: Bedō, Z., Sutka, J., Tischner, T. and Veisz, O. (eds) Proceedings of the International Symposium on Cereal Adaptation to Low Temperature Stress in Controlled Environments. pp. 269-276. ARI-HAS, Martonvásár, Hungary.

Marton, L.C., 1997b. Inheritance of cold test index of maize in sterilised and normal soil. In: Bedō, Z., Sutka, J., Tischner, T. and Veisz, O. (eds) Proceedings of the International Symposium on Cereal Adaptation to Low Temperature Stress in Controlled Environments. pp. 281-284. ARI-HAS, Martonvásár, Hungary.

Marton, C.L. and T. Szundy, 1997. Development of young maize plants under a suboptimal range of temperatures. Acta Agronomica Hungarica, 45: 329-335.

Stamp, P., 1984. Chilling tolerance of young plants demonstrated on the example of maize (*Zea mays* L.). Parey, Berlin.

Tari, I. and M. Nagy, 1994. Enhancement of extractable ethylene at light/dark transition in primary leaves of paclobutrazol-treated Phaseolus vulgaris seedlings. Physiologia Plantarum, 90: 353-357.

Factors influencing the effect of in vitro salicylic acid on catalase activity in maize genotypes with different cold tolerance

E. HORVÁTH, T. JANDA, G. SZALAI AND E. PÁLDI

Agricultural Research Institute of the Hungarian Academy of Sciences, H-2462 Martonvásár, POB 19, Hungary

SUMMARY

Salicylic acid is known to inhibit catalase activity in several plant species. However, contradictory results have been published on its inhibitory effect in maize (*Zea mays* L.). In order to elucidate this question 6 different genotypes of maize at different developmental stages were used for catalase activity studies. The plants were grown at 22/20 °C. All genotypes proved to have salicylic acid-inhibitable catalase activity, but significant differences were observed in the level of inhibition. Enzyme kinetic measurements were carried out and the nature of the inhibition was shown to be of mixed type. The developmental stage of the leaves was also found to have an influence on the inhibitability of catalase by salicylic acid, a lower inhibitory effect being observed in older leaves.

Keywords: catalase, enzyme inhibition, phenolic compounds, Zea mays L.

INTRODUCTION

Examinations in recent years have shown salicylic acid to play an important role in many physiological processes, such as thermogenesis and the induction of pathogen resistance. Furthermore its role in abiotic stress resistance is also emerging. Exogenous salicylic acid increased the heat tolerance of mustard (Dat *et al.*, 1998) and the cold tolerance of maize plants (Janda *et al.*, 1999). Salicylic acid may also have a role in the defence against ozone stress, as demonstrated in *Arabidopsis thaliana* (Sharma *et al.*, 1996). A direct physiological effect of salicylic acid is through the alteration of antioxidant enzyme activities. Certain enzymes (guaiacol peroxidase and glutathione reductase) were activated by the salicylic acid treatment, while others were found to be inhibited (catalase). Catalase seems to be a key enzyme in salicylic acid-induced stress tolerance. The heat tolerance in mustard and the cold tolerance in maize mentioned above were accompanied by decreased catalase activities. It was reported earlier that salicylic acid may bind to the catalase enzyme directly and inhibit its activity in several plant species

(Sanchez-Casasand Klessig, 1994; Conrath *et al.*, 1995), although this binding is probably not specific to catalase (Rüffer *et al.*, 1995). However, other authors reported no decrease in the catalase activity after salicylic acid treatment in maize seedlings at certain developmental stages (Guan and Scandalios, 1995).

The aim of the present work is to investigate the effect of *in vitro* salicylic acid and related compounds on the activity of catalase from maize plants at different developmental stages and with different degrees of chilling tolerance.

MATERIALS AND METHODS

Plant material and growth conditions: Maize plants were grown at 22/20°C with a 16/8-hour light-dark periodicity in a plant growth chamber at 200 mmol m^{-2} s^{-1} PPFD. Cold-tolerant (CM7, Z7, KW 1074) and cold-sensitive (Mo17, Penjalinan) maize lines and the hybrid Norma were examined.

Enzyme extraction: The youngest fully developed leaves (if not otherwise indicated) were used for protein extraction. 1 g of the leaf was ground in a mortar and pestle with 1 g quartz sand and 3 ml TRIS buffer pH 6.8. It was filtered through four layers of cheesecloth and centrifuged for 30 min at 12000g. The protein concentration of the supernatant was determined according to the Bradford method, with bovine serum albumin as standard.

Enzyme activity assay: catalase activity measurements were carried out in citrate buffer solution (pH = 6.8) as described by Sanchez-Casas and Klessig (1994). The evolution of oxygen was followed using a Clark-type oxygen electrode (Hansatech Ltd, England). The inhibitory effect of the following compounds was examined: salicylic acid, benzoic acid, acetylsalicylic acid, p-hydroxybenzoic acid and o-coumaric acid at a concentration of 1 mM (from Sigma-Aldrich).

RESULTS AND DISCUSSION

Despite the fact that salicylic acid was previously shown to inhibit catalase activity in various plant species, it is still unclear how it affects catalase activity in maize. Our results show that salicylic acid has an inhibitory effect on maize catalase. The addition of 1 mM salicylic acid to the protein extract from the leaves of maize hybrid Norma grown at 22/20 °C caused an approx. 25 % decrease in the catalase activity. To further investigate this question, the effect of four compounds related to salicylic acid (benzoic acid, acetylsalicylic acid, p-hydroxybenzoic acid, o-coumaric acid) was also examined. In a previous study some of these compounds (benzoic acid and aspirin) were shown to be able to increase the chilling tolerance of young maize plants, similarly to salicylic acid (Janda *et al.*, 2000). Each of these compounds decreased significantly the activity of catalase *in vitro* (Fig. 1). The most pronounced decrease was observed in the case of salicylic acid and o-coumaric acid, while the lowest rate of inhibition was measured with p-hydroxybenzoicacid.

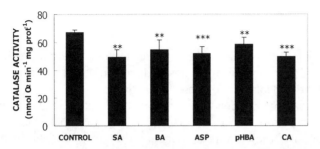

FIGURE 1. CATALASE ACTIVITY IN THE ABSENCE (CONTROL) AND IN THE PRESENCE OF 1 MM INHIBITOR (SA: SALICYLIC ACID, BA: BENZOIC ACID, ASP: ACETYLSALICYLIC ACID, PHBA: P-HYDROXYBENZOIC ACID AND CA: COUMARIC ACID) AT 50 MM H_2O_2. THE INHIBITORS WERE ADDED TO THE PROTEIN EXTRACT OF THE YOUNGEST FULLY DEVELOPED LEAVES OF MAIZE (NORMA HYBRID) PLANTS. **, ***: SIGNIFICANT AT THE 0.01 AND 0.001 LEVELS, RESPECTIVELY, COMPARED TO CONTROL PLANTS.

To describe the nature of the inhibition, catalase activity was measured at different H_2O_2 concentrations using four different salicylic acid concentrations. These enzyme kinetic measurements showed that the inhibition of catalase by salicylic acid is of mixed type (Fig. 2). K_i for salicylic acid was found to be 0.387 mM.

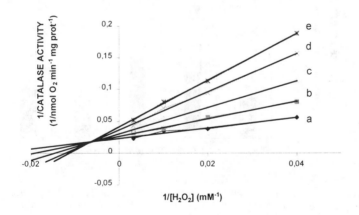

FIGURE 2. LINEWEAVER-BURK PLOT OF THE SUBSTRATE CONCENTRATION DEPENDENCE OF THE ACTIVITY OF CATALASE ENZYME FROM THE YOUNGEST FULLY DEVELOPED LEAVES OF MAIZE (NORMA HYBRID) PLANTS IN THE PRESENCE OF A: 0 MM, B: 0.1 MM, C: 0.25 MM, D: 0.5 MM AND E: 1 MM SALICYLIC ACID. H_2O_2 CONCENTRATIONS WERE 25, 50, 100 AND 300 MM.

It was reported that 1-day 0.5 mM salicylic acid pre-treatment (added to the hydroponic solution) not only increased the chilling tolerance of young maize plants, but also caused a significant decrease in the catalase activity. In this study the correlation between the chilling tolerance of maize and the *in vitro* catalase inhibitability by salicylic acid was also investigated. 1 mM salicylic acid was added to the protein extract from 3 chilling-tolerant (CM 7, Z 7, KW 1074) and 2 chilling-sensitive (Mo 17, Penjalinan) inbred lines. It can be seen in Figure 3 that although the relative decrease in the activity varied strongly according to the genotypes, there was no direct correlation between the catalase inhibitability and the cold tolerance of these lines.

It was also found that not only the genotype, but also the mature status of the plant affected the catalase inhibitability: catalase activity was usually higher in young plants, but salicylic acid caused a more pronounced decrease in these than in older plants. A similar correlation was found when leaves of different age from the same plant were compared (data not shown).

It can be concluded from these results that salicylic acid (and certain related compounds) may cause a direct inhibition in the activity of catalase enzyme from maize leaves. However, the level of this inhibition is affected by several factors, including the genotype and the age of the leaf. A direct correlation between the cold tolerance of young maize plants and the catalase inhibitability by salicylic acid could not be found.

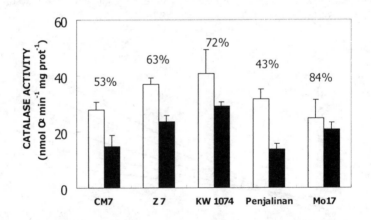

FIGURE 3. CATALASE ACTIVITY OF 3 CHILLING TOLERANT (CM7, Z7, KW1074) AND 2 CHILLING SENSITIVE (MO 17, PENJALINAN) INBRED MAIZE LINES OBSERVED IN THE ABSENCE (CONTROL) AND IN THE PRESENCE OF 1 MM SALICYLIC ACID AT A CONCENTRATION OF 50 MM H_2O_2.

ACKNOWLEDGEMENTS

The authors are gratefully indebted to Zsuzsa Kóti and Edit Kövesdi for their technical assistance. This work was supported by grants from the Hungarian National Scientific

Research Foundation (OTKA F26236, T21115, T032653, M28074) and the J. Bolyai Research Sponsorship.

REFERENCES

Bradford, M.M., 1976. A rapid and sensitive method for the quantification of microgram quantities of protein utilizing the principle of protein-dye binding. Analytical Biochemistry, 72: 248-254.

Conrath, U., Z. Chen, J.R. Ricigliano and D.F. Klessig, 1995. Two inducers of plant defense responses, 2,6-dichloroisonicotinic acid and salicylic acid, inhibit catalase activity in tobacco. Proceedings of National Academy of Sciences USA, 92: 7143-7147.

Dat, J.F., H. Lopez-Delgado, C.H. Foyer and I.M. Scott, 1998. Parallel changes in H_2O_2 and catalase during thermotolerance induced by salicylic acid or heat acclimation in mustard seedlings. Plant Physiology, 116: 1351-1357.

Guan, L. and J.G. Scandalios, 1995. Developmental related responses of maize catalase genes to salicylic acid. Proceedings of National Academy of Sciences USA, 92: 5930-5934.

Janda, T., G. Szalai, I. Tari and E. Páldi, 1999. Hydroponic treatment with salicylic acid decreases the effect of chilling injury in maize (*Zea mays* L.) plants. Planta, 208: 175-180.

T. Janda, G. Szalai, Zs. Antunovics, E. Horváth and E. Páldi, 2000. Effect of benzoic acid and aspirin on chilling tolerance and photosynthesis in young maize plants. Maydica, 45: (in press).

Rüffer, M., B. Steipe and M.H. Zenk, 1995. Evidence against specific binding of salicylic acid to plant catalase. FEBS Letters, 377: 175-180.

Sanchez-Casas, P. and D. F. Klessig, 1994. A salicylic acid-binding activity and a salicylic acid-inhibitable catalase activity are present in a variety of plant species. Plant Physiology, 106: 1675-1679.

Sharma, Y.K., J. León, I. Raskin and K.R. Davis, 1996. Ozone-induced responses in *Arabidopsis thaliana*: The role of salicylic acid in the accumulation of defense-related transcripts and induced resistance. Proceedings of National Academy of Sciences USA, 93: 5099-5104.

Impact of suboptimal shoot and/or root temperatures on growth and carbohydrates in *Lycopersicon esculentum* and *L. hirsutum*

M. DURENKAMP, J. H. VENEMA AND P. R. VAN HASSELT

Department of Plant Biology, University of Groningen, PO Box 14, 9750 AA Haren, The Netherlands

SUMMARY

In order to examine the role of the root on growth and carbon metabolism in tomato (*Lycopersicon esculentum* Mill. cv. Moneymaker) at suboptimal temperatures, seedlings were grown hydroponically at optimal and/or suboptimal shoot/root temperatures (i.e. 25/25, 25/15, 15/25 and 15/15°C) for 3 weeks. Exposure of only the shoot or the root of *L. esculentum* to suboptimal temperatures (15/25 or 25/15°C) resulted in relative growth rates that were intermediate to the rates at 25/25 and 15/15°C. Higher shoot temperatures (25/15 and 25/25°C compared to 15/15 and 15/25°C) positively affected relative growth rates *of L. hirsutum*. Shoot/root ratio of *L. esculentum* remained constant in all treatments. Shoot/root ratio of *L. hirsutum* depended on shoot temperatures. Carbohydrate levels in *L. esculentum* were only significantly higher in the 15/15°C plants and there was no difference between the levels in shoot and root. Carbohydrate levels of *L. hirsutum* were not affected by suboptimal temperatures. It is concluded that tomato plants maintain a 'functional equilibrium': growth inhibition of one compartment, caused by suboptimal temperature, is compensated by the other compartment, which is not inhibited. As a result, heating of roots can partially overcome growth inhibition of shoots at suboptimal temperatures. This was not observed in *L. hirsutum*, where growth was only affected by shoot temperatures. Accumulation of carbohydrates in 15/15°C plants of *L. esculentum* was not induced by limitation of phloem transport but could be ascribed to sink limitation.

Keywords: carbohydrates, growth, Lycopersicon (tomato) species, suboptimal shoot/root temperature

INTRODUCTION

Growth and carbohydrate levels of the domestic tomato (*Lycopersicon esculentum*) and a high-altitude accession of the wild species *L. hirsutum* were compared at 4 shoot/root temperature regimes. Previous studies showed that the domestic tomato accumulated more starch at suboptimal temperatures, correlated with a greater reduction in growth (Venema *et al.*, 1999). It was concluded that photosynthesis was not the limiting factor for growth under applied suboptimal conditions. Aim of this study was (i) to get insight in the role of the root in growth inhibition at suboptimal temperatures and (ii) to examine if the accumulation of carbohydrates in *L. esculentum* was either induced by inhibition of C-export from source leaves or by limitation of the sink activity.

MATERIALS AND METHODS

After appearance of the first true leaf, seedlings of *Lycopersicon esculentum* Mill cv. Moneymaker and *L. hirsutum* Humb. & Bonpl. LA 1777 (originating from Peru, 3200m above sea level) were grown hydroponically (nutrient solution according to Doddema *et al.*, 1986). Shoot and root compartments were independently treated at optimal and/or suboptimal temperatures (i.e. 25/25, 25/15, 15/25, and 15/15°C) for 3 weeks. Plants were harvested at days 0, 7, 14 and 21. Fresh and dry weights of shoot and root were measured. Mean relative growth rates (RGR) of shoot and root were calculated during a 21-day time interval from the ln transformed mean plant dry weight (Hunt, 1982). Shoot/root ratios were calculated. Amounts of water-soluble sugar and starch of shoot and root were measured colorimetrically using anthrone as a reagent (Fales, 1951).

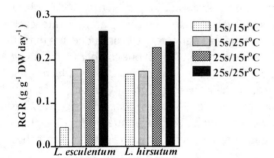

FIGURE 1. MEAN RELATIVE GROWTH RATE OF *L. ESCULENTUM* AND *L. HIRSUTUM*, GROWN AT 4 SHOOT/ROOT TEMPERATURE REGIMES (I.E. 25/25, 25/15, 15/25 AND 15/15°C) FOR 21 DAYS. DATA WERE CALCULATED FROM THE LN TRANSFORMED MEAN PLANT DRY WEIGHT OF 6 PLANTS.

FIGURE 2. SHOOT/ROOT RATIOS OF *L. ESCULENTUM* AND *L. HIRSUTUM*, GROWN AT 4 SHOOT/ROOT TEMPERATURE REGIMES (I.E. 25/25, 25/15, 15/25 AND 15/15°C) FOR 21 DAYS. DATA REPRESENT THE MEAN OF SIX PLANTS (± SD).

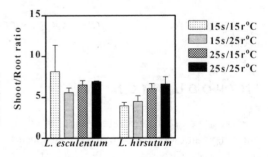

RESULTS

Exposure of only the shoot or the root of *L. esculentum* to suboptimal temperatures (15/25 and 25/15°C) resulted in relative growth rates that were intermediate to the rates at 15/15 and 25/25°C (Fig. 1). Higher shoot temperatures (25/15 and 25/25°C compared to 15/15 and 15/25°C) positively affected relative growth rates *of L. hirsutum* (Fig. 1). Shoot/root ratio of *L. esculentum* remained constant in all treatments. Shoot/root ratio of *L. hirsutum* depended on shoot temperature (Fig. 2). Carbohydrate levels of *L. esculentum* were only significantly higher in the 15/15°C plants and there was no difference between the levels in shoot and root (Fig. 3A, 3C). Carbohydrate levels of *L. hirsutum* were not affected by suboptimal temperatures (Fig. 3B, 3D). Levels of soluble sugar were in both species about 3 times lower than starch levels.

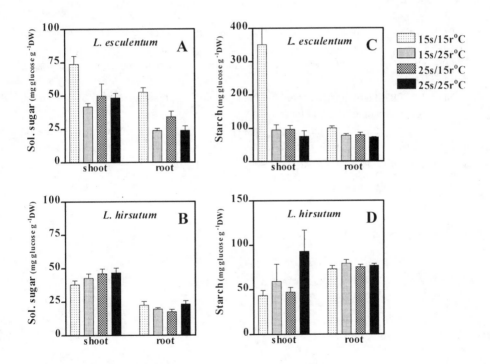

FIGURE 3. SOLUBLE SUGAR (A, B) AND STARCH (C, D) CONTENTS OF SHOOT AND ROOT OF *L. ESCULENTUM* AND *L. HIRSUTUM*, GROWN AT 4 SHOOT/ROOT TEMPERATURE REGIMES (I.E. 25/25, 25/15, 15/25 AND 15/15°C) FOR 21 DAYS. DATA REPRESENT THE MEAN OF 6 PLANTS (± SD).

CONCLUSIONS

It is concluded that *L. esculentum* maintains a 'functional equilibrium': growth inhibition of one compartment, caused by suboptimal temperature, is compensated by the other compartment, which is not inhibited. This is observed in intermediate growth rates, constant shoot/root ratios and absence of carbohydrate accumulation in 15/25 and 25/15°C plants. As a result, heating of roots could partially overcome growth inhibition of shoots at suboptimal temperatures. This was not observed in *L. hirsutum*, where growth was only affected by shoot temperature. Accumulation of carbohydrates in 15/15°C plants of *L. esculentum* was not induced by limitation of phloem transport but could be ascribed to sink limitation.

REFERENCES

Doddema, H., I. Stulen and J.J. Hofstra, 1986. The distribution of nitrate reductase in tomato (*Lycopersicon esculentum*) leaves as affected by age. Physiogia Plantarum, 68: 615-619.

Fales, F.W., 1951. The assimilation and degradation of carbohydrates by yeast cells. Journal of Biological Chemistry, 193: 113-124.

Hunt, R., 1982. Plant growth curves. In: The Functional Approach to Plant Growth Analysis, pp. 5-13. E. Arnold Publishers, London.

Venema, J.H., F. Posthumus and P.R. van Hasselt, 1999. Impact of suboptimal temperature on growth, photosynthesis, leaf pigments and carbohydrates of domestic and high-altitude wild *Lycopersicon* species. Journal of Plant Physiology, 155: 711-718.

Comparison of suboptimal temperature tolerance between domestic and high-altitude wild *Lycopersicon* species: the role of the chloroplast

J. H. VENEMA AND P. R. VAN HASSELT

Department of Plant Biology, University of Groningen, P.O. Box 14, 9750 AA Haren, The Netherlands

SUMMARY

Growth and photosynthetic properties of the domestic tomato (*Lycopersicon esculentum* Mill.) and more cold-tolerant high-altitude wild *Lycopersicon* species were compared at optimal (25/20°C) and suboptimal temperatures (16/14°C). Aim of the research was to get insight in the processes limiting growth at suboptimal temperatures. The results showed that relative to performance at optimal temperatures (1) growth rate of the domestic tomato was more inhibited at suboptimal temperatures than its wild relatives, (2) the initiation rate of new leaves was similar in all *Lycopersicon* species at suboptimal temperatures, (3) leaf expansion was more inhibited in the domestic tomato, (4) wild species showed better photosynthetic acclimation to suboptimal temperatures due to a higher Calvin cycle activity, (5) starch accumulated in source leaves at suboptimal temperatures particularly in the domestic tomato, (6) transfer of chloroplasts from a more chilling-tolerant *L. hirsutum* accession to a domestic tomato genotype via asymmetric somatic hybridisation (cybridisation), did not result in improved growth and photosynthetic performance at suboptimal temperatures. It is concluded that (i) photosynthesis is not limiting growth at suboptimal temperatures and a non-photoinhibiting light intensity and (ii), cybridisation is not a useful tool for improving suboptimal-temperature tolerance of the domestic tomato.

Keywords: Alloplasmic tomato, carbohydrates, chloroplast, cybrid(isation), growth, Lycopersicon (tomato) species, photosynthesis, suboptimal-temperature tolerance

INTRODUCTION

Species of the genus *Lycopersicon* are native to a wide range of altitudes, from sea level in Equador to over 3,000 m in Peru and Chile. At altitudes of 2,000 m and higher, night temperatures regularly fall below 10°C in this tropical region. Accessions of wild *Lycopersicon* species originating from high altitudes were expected to possess a relatively high level of genetically determined cold tolerance. As in many crop species, the domestication of the tomato resulted in a marked reduction of genetic variability, so that breeders have to rely on these related high-altitude wild accessions for germplasm sources to improve low-temperature tolerance.

A comparative physiological study with a domestic tomato (*Lycopersicon esculentum* Mill.) genotype and accessions of several wild *Lycopersicon* species from low and high altitude showed better regrowth capacity and faster recovery of photosynthesis in the wild species after a long-term temperature shift to 10°C under low, non-photoinhibitory light (Venema *et al.*, 1999b). In the present study, the response of two *L. esculentum* genotypes and high-altitude accessions of both *L. peruvianum* and *L. hirsutum* were compared in order to obtain more insight in the physiological background of suboptimal-temperature acclimation. Additionally, the effect of chloroplast transfer from a more chilling-tolerant *L. hirsutum* accession to a domestic tomato genotype was examined on growth- and photosynthetic-related traits at a near-optimal and suboptimal temperature regime.

MATERIALS AND METHODS

Plants of *L. esculentum* Mill. cv. Abunda and cv. Large Red Cherry (LRC), and of high-altitude accessions of two related wild species, *L. peruvianum* (L.) Mill. LA 385 and *L. hirsutum* Humb. & Bonpl. LA 1777 were grown from seed in 1 l potting soil at 25/20°C, 14/10 h day/night regime at a minimum photosynthetic photon flux density (PPFD) of 225 μmol m^{-2} s^{-1}. At a plastochron index of 5, plants were randomly distributed between two growth cabinets with an optimal (25/20°C) and suboptimal (16/14°C) day/night temperature regime. In both cabinets, the PPFD was 225 μmol m^{-2} s^{-1} during a 12-h photoperiod.

The used cytoplasmic hybrid (cybrid), line AH47, was obtained from a study of Derks *et al.* (1992). This cybrid contains the nuclear genome of the chilling-sensitive cytoplasmic albino mutant of *L. esculentum* cv. LRC and the plastid genome (plastome) of the more chilling-tolerant *L. hirsutum* LA 1777. Plants of AH47, and its euplasmic parents *L. esculentum* cv. LRC and *L. hirsutum* LA 1777, were grown between November 1997 and March 1998 in two adjacent glasshouses with an optimal (25/20°C) and suboptimal (16/14°C) day/night temperature regime. In both glasshouses, a minimum PPFD of 225 μmol m^{-2} s^{-1} during a 12-h photoperiod was provided by supplementary lighting.

CO_2 exchange was analysed in a temperature-controlled metal leaf chamber by infrared gas analysis at a saturating PPFD of 1,200 μmol m^{-2} s^{-1} as described by Venema *et al.* (1999a).

Starch was hydrolysed from the pellet that remained after extraction of dried leaf material with 80% ethanol, by boiling in 3% (v/v) HCl for 3 h. Glucose content was then determined colorimetrically, using anthrone as a reagent.

Oxygen evolution was measured in a temperature-controlled leaf chamber with a

Clark-type electrode (Model LD2, Hansatech, King's Lynn, Norfolk, UK) at 2% O_2 and 4.5% CO_2 in a nitrogen atmosphere. Maximum photosynthetic capacity (P_{max}) was determined at a PPFD of 1,200 μmol m^{-2} s^{-1}.

R E S U L T S

The difference in relative shoot growth rate (RGR_{shoot}), determined at 16/14°C and 25/20°C, demonstrated that growth of both *L. esculentum* genotypes was more susceptible to suboptimal temperature than in the wild species (Fig. 1A). Additional analysis of growth-related traits indicated that the initiation rate of new leaves was similarly affected by suboptimal growth temperatures, however, leaf expansion was affected differentially in all species (Venema *et al.*, 1999a). The low RGR_{shoot} of *L. esculentum* cv. Abunda at 16/14°C was associated with a strong inhibition in leaf expansion. Light-saturated net photosynthtic rate (A_{sat}) was about 25% lower in suboptimal-grown leaves of both *L. esculentum* genotypes whereas in the two wild species, A_{sat} was similar in leaves of plants grown at optimal and suboptimal temperature (Fig. 1B). Also at a PPFD similar to the growth irradiance, net photosynthetic rate was only significantly lower in suboptimal-grown leaves of both *L. esculentum* genotypes (Venema *et al.*, 1999a). In addition, maximum Rubisco activity on a fresh weight basis was also reduced only in suboptimal-grown leaves of both *L. esculentum* genotypes (data not shown). Growth at suboptimal temperatures resulted in accumulation of starch in all species (Fig. 1C). In Abunda, the genotype witch the lowest RGR_{shoot} at 16/14°C, starch accumulation was strongest.

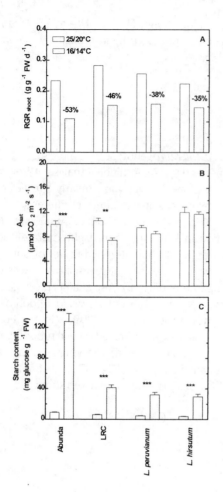

FIGURE 1. MEAN RELATIVE SHOOT GROWTH RATE (RGR$_{SHOOT}$; A), LIGHT-SATURATED NET PHOTOSYNTHETIC RATE (A$_{SAT}$; B) AND STARCH CONTENT (C) IN *L. ESCULENTUM* CV. ABUNDA AND CV. LRC, *L. PERUVIANUM* LA 385 AND *L. HIRSUTUM* LA 1777 GROWN AT 25/20°C AND 16/14°C. SIGNIFICANT DIFFERENCES BETWEEN TEMPERATURE TREATMENTS ARE INDICATED BY: *. $P<0.05$; **. $P<0.01$; ***. $P<.0.001$.

Irrespective of the temperature regime, shoot biomass production was similar in LRC and the cybrid (Fig. 2). Shoot biomass production of the plastome donor *L. hirsutum* was less inhibited by suboptimal growth temperature than in LRC and the cybrid. Light-response curves of CO_2 exchange and chlorophyll *a* fluorescence parameters, leaf pigment, carbohydrate and soluble protein contents of the cybrid resembled those of the nuclear parent *L. esculentum* at both growth temperatures (Venema *et al.*, 2000). Leaves of LRC, cybrid AH47 and *L. hirsutum* plants grown at 25/20°C demonstrated comparable temperature dependence of P$_{max}$ (Fig. 3A). In contrast to LRC and the cybrid, P$_{max}$ was significantly increased at all temperatures in leaves of *L. hirsutum* acclimated to 16/14°C (Fig. 3B). An adverse consequence of inter-specific chloroplast transfer was an increased susceptibility to chill-induced photoinhibition of the cybrid (Venema *et al.*, 2000).

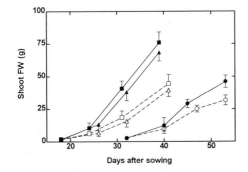

FIGURE 2. TIME-DEPENDENT INCREASE OF SHOOT FRESH WEIGHT OF *L. ESCULENTUM* CV. LRC (■,□), CYBRID AH47 (▲, △) AND *L. HIRSUTUM* LA 1777 (●,○) AT 25/20°C (CLOSED SYMBOLS) AND 16/14°C (OPEN SYMBOLS).

FIGURE 3. TEMPERATURE DEPENDENCE OF THE MAXIMUM PHOTOSYNTHETIC CAPACITY (P_{MAX}) IN *L. ESCULENTUM* CV. LRC (■), CYBRID AH47 (△) AND *L. HIRSUTUM* LA 1777 (○) GROWN AT 25/20°C (A) AND 16/14°C (B).

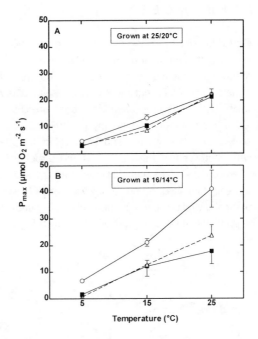

DISCUSSION AND CONCLUSIONS

With respect to the measured relative shoot growth rates at both temperature regimes, high-altitude accessions of wild *Lycopersicon* species showed higher tolerance to suboptimal temperatures than *L. esculentum* genotypes. The pronounced accumulation of starch indicated that photosynthesis was not the rate-limiting factor for growth of domestic tomato genotypes at suboptimal temperatures and moderate irradiance.

Although combining a *L. esculentum* genome with a *L. hirsutum* plastome resulted in viable and compatible cybrids, this study indicated that cybridisation is not a useful tool to improve growth and photosynthetic performance of the domestic tomato at suboptimal temperatures.

ACKNOWLEDGEMENTS

This research was financially supported by the Life Sciences Foundation (SLW), which is subsidised by the Netherlands Organisation of Scientific Research (NWO).

REFERENCES

Derks, F.H.M., J.C. Hakkert, W.H.J. Verbeek and C.M. Colijn-Hooymans, 1992. Genome composition of asymmetric hybrids in relation to the phylogenetic distance between the parents. Nucleus-chloroplast interaction. Theoretical and Applied Genetics, 84: 930-940.

Venema, J.H., M. Eekhof and P.R. van Hasselt, 2000. Analysis of low-temperature tolerance of a tomato (*Lycopersicon esculentum*) cybrid with chloroplasts from a more chilling-tolerant *L. hirsutum* accession. Annals of Botany, 85: 799-807.

Venema, J.H., F. Posthumus and P.R. van Hasselt, 1999a. Impact of suboptimal temperature on growth, photosynthesis, leaf pigments and carbohydrates of domestic and high-altitude wild *Lycopersicon* species. Journal of Plant Physiology, 155: 711-718.

Venema, J.H., F. Posthumus, M. de Vries, and P.R. van Hasselt, 1999b. Differential response of domestic and wild Lycopersicon species to chilling under low light: growth, carbohydrate content, photosynthesis and the xanthophyll cycle. Physiologia Plantarum, 105: 81-88.

WORKING GROUP 2

Overwintering and spring growth of white clover

Invited papers

Physiological and molecular bases of alfalfa adaptation to harsh winter conditions

Y. CASTONGUAY, P. NADEAU, S. LABERGE AND R. MICHAUD

Soils and Crops Research and Development Centre, Agriculture and Agri-Food Canada, Ste-Foy (Qué), Canada

SUMMARY

Alfalfa (*Medicago sativa L.*) cultivars of high agronomic value are not fully adapted to harsh winter conditions and severe damage to overwintering stands are recurrently observed. Our objective is to accurately identify genotypes with superior hardiness potential. Winter survival of alfalfa is a complex trait involving a number of interacting factors such as freezing stress, ice encasement, diseases and cutting management. However a close relationship between winter survival of alfalfa and genetic potential for tolerance to subfreezing temperatures has been established. We have documented a number of molecular changes that occur during the acquisition of freezing tolerance in alfalfa including modifications in carbohydrate composition and changes in gene expression. A close link has been established between the accumulation of the galactose-containing oligosaccharides stachyose and raffinose and cold tolerance of alfalfa. Genes differentially expressed between cultivars of contrasting winterhardiness have been identified and characterized. The heritability of these traits and their relationship with freezing tolerance have been assessed. The exhaustive characterization of cold-regulated genes in alfalfa using high throughput sequencing of cDNAs is in progress and will be used in future functional genomic studies. Current efforts are being devoted to the development of an integrated perspective on the effects of various environmental parameters and management practices affecting field survival on molecular and genetic changes related to freezing tolerance in alfalfa. This information will be key for the development of selection approaches based on the knowledge of the genetic bases required for optimal adaptation to a set of environmental and agronomic conditions.

Keywords: alfalfa, breeding, cold tolerance, gene expression, persistence, soluble sugars

INTRODUCTION

Forage crops account for 60-90% of ruminants' diet (Barnes and Baylor, 1994) and cover a large proportion of agricultural land throughout the world (Mooney, 1993). Alfalfa and other forage legumes are considered as high-quality forages because of their superior feeding value, their symbiotic fixation of atmospheric nitrogen and their positive contribution to soil structure (Frame *et al.*, 1998). These attributes of forage legumes translate into greater farm profitability through increased animal productivity and better sustainablity of agricultural production. It is predicted that forage legumes will be increasingly cultivated in temperate regions of the world as a result of changes in environmental policies on N-fertilizer use and stocking rates (Frame *et al.*, 1998) as well as in response to the need for greater farm of competitiveness in global markets.

Alfalfa (*Medicago sativa L.*) is a major forage crop in eastern Canada with approximately 0.8 Mha in production in 1996 covering nearly 40% of the total hay production area (Statistics Canada, 1998). This proportion is, however, far from the 70-85% of total hay area that alfalfa covers in the milk producing states of the American MidWest (USDA, 1994). A lower reliance on alfalfa for hay production in eastern Canada is mainly the result of its lack of persistence under harsh winter conditions. Recurrent drops in forage yields in the 1953-1996 period (Fig. 1) are likely attributable to the combined effects of winterkill of legumes and growth reduction of grasses during summer drought. These significant yield reductions have enormous economic impact on the costs of production for milk and beef producers and ultimately on their competitiveness in open markets.

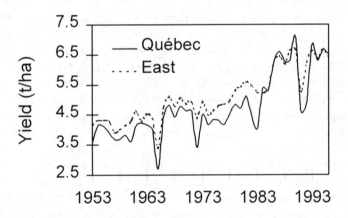

FIGURE 1. EVOLUTION OF FORAGE YIELD (T HA⁻¹) IN EASTERN CANADA AND IN QUÉBEC FROM 1953 TO 1996. SOURCE: STATISTICS CANADA.

Although sources of winterhardiness do exist within the genus *Medicago*, they often bring undesirable agronomic background such as low yields and early-fall dormancy (Stout and Hall, 1989). There are however indications that winter hardiness could be improved without the concurrent increase in fall dormancy (McCaslin *et al.*, 1990). As a consequence, the improvement of alfalfa winter hardiness has historically been based on the recurrent selection within populations with good agronomic performance of genotypes that survived harsh winter conditions. This selection approach has allowed the development of better-adapted cultivars but remains a tedious and unpredictable process that relies on the random occurrence of test winters for adequate screening and the costly maintenance of multi-year tests at several locations. In the last ten years, our multidisciplinary research group (breeder, biochemist, physiologist and molecular biologist) has been studying the physiological, molecular and genetic bases of alfalfa adaptation to subfreezing temperatures in an effort to develop more rapid and efficient selection approaches for the improvement of alfalfa winter hardiness.

Freezing tolerance and winter survival of alfalfa

Winter hardiness of alfalfa is, to a large extent, determined by its capacity to withstand subfreezing temperatures (McKenzie *et al.*, 1988). Winterkill of alfalfa depends on a number of genetic (choice of cultivars), management (cutting schedule, fertilization, drainage) and environmental (cold, snow, ice) factors that either expose the plants to lethal temperatures or affect their capacity to tolerate subfreezing temperatures (Fig. 2). Alfalfa becomes progressively tolerant to subfreezing temperatures with the decline in temperature and the reduction of photoperiod in the fall and reaches it maximum tolerance later in winter when soil temperature has dropped below freezing (McKenzie *et al.*, 1988). Our studies under environmentally-controlled conditions revealed that freezing tolerance of alfalfa increases markedly after 2 weeks at 2°C (Castonguay *et al.*, 1993). A subsequent 2-week exposure to non-lethal subzero temperatures (-2°C) induced greater tolerance to subfreezing temperatures and brings about the greatest differences between cultivars of contrasting hardiness. However, a lengthening of the acclimation period at 2°C from 2 to 4 weeks caused a reduction in freezing tolerance. Numerous studies have confirmed the existence of a large genetic variability for freezing tolerance within alfalfa (Schwab *et al.*, 1996). Although alfalfa cultivars of contrasting winter hardiness show significant potential to increase their freezing tolerance upon exposure to low temperature, they differ in the maximum level of freezing tolerance that they can achieve. These cultivars must therefore share some common bases of adaptation allowing for their cold acclimation; the limited response of non hardy cultivars probably results from a lack or the inability to express important adaptive traits. In spite of a large body of molecular and genetic studies on cold adaptation of alfalfa, the determinants of freezing tolerance still remain elusive.

It has often been pointed out that freezing and desiccation tolerance must rely on the plant capacity to tolerate protoplasmic desiccation (Guy, 1990). Thus , freezing and desiccation tolerance might share certain protective mechanisms. The observation by Paquin (1984) of a strong correlation between freezing tolerance and soil temperature suggests that the extent of freeze-induced dessication is probably an important factor contributing to the full expression of freezing tolerance in alfalfa. In our studies, we observed numerous analogies between cold-induced changes in alfalfa and molecular changes occurring during the acquisition of desiccation tolerance. These similitudes are pointed out throughout this paper.

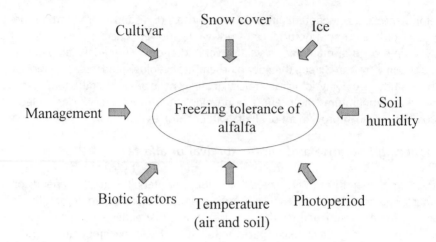

Cold-induced changes in gene expression

Cold acclimation of plants is the result of major biochemical changes associated with extensive changes in gene expression (Guy, 1990). Our analysis of the changes in populations of translatable mRNAs in cold-acclimated crowns of alfalfa indicated extensive changes in gene expression at low temperatures (Castonguay *et al.*, 1993; 1997a). We found that translation profiles from cultivars of contrasting winter hardiness were strikingly similar with a limited number of cold-regulated (COR) translation products that were more highly or specifically expressed in cold-tolerant cultivars. A zone of low-molecular-weight basic polypeptides was markedly enhanced at subzero temperatures (Castonguay *et al.*, 1993). Similar accumulations of low molecular weight basic polypeptides were documented during the acquisition of desiccation and drought tolerance (Bray, 1990) and were shown to encode for heat-stable and highly hydrophilic proteins that were classified as members of the Late-Embryogenesis-Abundant (LEA) and Dehydrins family of proteins (Han *et al.*, 1997). Water stress induced the expression of many alfalfa COR genes although the extent of the induction and repression differed sensibly from the changes observed during cold acclimation (Castonguay *et al.*, 1997a).

Acclimation at non-lethal subzero temperatures enhanced the translation of COR polypeptides and induced the accumulation of new translation products. More significantly, a relationship was observed between the number of translation products that accumulate in a group of low-molecular-weight basic polypeptides and hardiness potential in alfalfa (Castonguay *et al.*, 1997a). These unique changes in populations of translatable mRNAs in frozen plants could bear important adaptive value and help determine maximum hardiness level of alfalfa under snow cover when soil has frozen.

Down-regulated COR translation products cumulatively showed a stronger decline in the fall in two cold-hardy cultivars than in a non-hardy cultivar of alfalfa while up-regulated COR translation products were cumulatively more abundant in hardy cultivars than in the non-hardy cultivar during that same period (Castonguay *et al.*, 1997a). Delays in cold-induced modification of gene expression between non-hardy and hardy cultivars of alfalfa could be the result of differences in the capacity of the plant to perceive and transduce the environmental signals and ultimately to regulate gene transcription. Reversible protein phosphorylation has been shown to play an important role in response to biotic and abiotic signals in animal and plant systems. Evidences concur for the involvement of a protein phosphorylation-mediated pathway in cold acclimation response in alfalfa. Monroy *et al.* (1993a) reported that Ca^{2+}-dependent phosphorylation of pre-existing proteins is involved in the early events leading to cold-induced changes in gene expression in alfalfa. Accumulation of phosphoproteins in cold-acclimated nuclei of alfalfa was greater in the freezing-tolerant cultivar Apica than in the sensitive cultivar Trek (Kawczynski and Dhindsa, 1996). Jonak *et al.* (1996) observed a post-translational activation of a mitogen-activated (MAP) kinase in cold-treated alfalfa. Interestingly, the MAP kinase pathway appeared to be specifically induced by cold and drought but not by high-temperature and osmotic stresses. The involvement of a transcription factor (protein) that binds to cis-acting regulatory sequences of COR genes and regulate their expression has recently been demonstrated in Arabidopsis (Jaglo-Ottosen *et al.*, 1998). Overexpression of CBF1 in transgenic Arabidopsis induced the expression of some COR genes and increase the freezing tolerance of unacclimated transformants. Overexpression of Alfin1, a putative transcription factor associated with NaCl tolerance, in transgenic alfalfa led to the accumulation of transcripts of the NaCl-inducible MsPRP2 gene and improved the NaCl tolerance of these plants (Winicov and Bastola, 1999). Similar mechanisms of regulation of transcription are likely to occur during cold acclimation of alfalfa. Whether variations in freezing tolerance between cultivars are related to genetic variance in the activation or accumulation of specific transcription factors deserves a closer scrutiny.

Function of cold-inducible genes in alfalfa

Many COR complementary deoxyribonucleic acid fragments (cDNAs) have been isolated from cold-acclimated alfalfa (reviewed by Castonguay *et al.*, 1997b). Northern blot analysis of transcripts of alfalfa COR genes showed a great diversity in the regulation of these genes with differences in expression between tissues (leaves vs crowns vs roots) and cultivars. Many COR genes are expressed at the same level between alfalfa cultivars of contrasting hardiness while other COR genes showed a higher level of expression in hardy cultivars. This observation suggests a potential link between the latter genes and freezing tolerance of alfalfa. Mohapatra *et al.* (1989) reported a positive correlation between the expression of three alfalfa COR genes and freezing tolerance of four alfalfa cultivars. Search in gene data banks revealed that many of these genes encode for small hydrophilic proteins with isoelectric points ranging from neutral to basic that are homologous to stress- or developmentally-regulated proteins. One gene family (cas17 and cas18; Wolfraim *et al.*, 1993a; 1993b) encodes for putative proteins with dehydrin-like motifs. Dehydrins are proteins commonly induced by environmental stresses with a dehydration component. The accumulation of cold-regulated proteins of the wcs120 groups showing homology with the dehydrins was shown to be positively correlated with the capacity of wheat and other cereal genotypes to develop freezing tolerance (Sarhan *et al.*, 1997). Interactions with membranes, protein stabilization and synergistic interactions with compatible solutes have been proposed as potential protective roles of dehydrins in freeze-desiccated cells (Close, 1997). The observation by Salzman *et al.* (1996) that substantial accumulation of a 27 kD dehydrin-like protein in desiccated grape buds occurs only after cold acclimation, indicates that in spite of their similarities, there are important differences in gene induction by cellular desiccation and freezing stress.

Antibody raised against polypeptides encoded by msaCIA (Laberge *et al.*, 1993) and msaCIB (Monroy *et al.*, 1993b) confirmed the cold-induced accumulation of these proteins in alfalfa (Ferrullo *et al.*, 1997). Comparison between cultivars showed that differences in the levels of the polypeptides encoded by msaCIA and msaCIB are consistent with the level of their corresponding transcripts. While the lowest MSACIA and MSACIB protein contents were observed in non hardy cultivars, the highest contents were found in cultivars of intermediate hardiness. This observation underscores the complexity of the winterhardiness trait and our fragmentary knowledge of the physiological and molecular changes required for cold adaptation. At least one COR cDNA from alfalfa encoding for a glycine-rich protein (msaCIA) was shown to be cold-inducible in red clover (*Trifolium pratense* L.) indicating some common genetic bases of adaptation to cold in forage legumes (Nelke *et al.*, 1999). In the same study, two other COR genes from alfalfa (msaCIB and msaCIC) were not induced or detected in cold-acclimated red clover. Differences in acclimation temperatures (5°C vs 2°C for alfalfa) and length of acclimation period (5 weeks vs 2 weeks for alfalfa) may explain these differences in gene expression. Preliminary results with plants acclimated to winter conditions in an unheated greenhouse system has confirmed the cold-inducibility of msaCIC in crowns of red clover (Castonguay, Nadeau and Laberge unpublished).

Cold-induced accumulation of cryoprotective sugars

Significant increase in crown levels of soluble sugars with concomittant decrease in starch have long been documented during cold hardening of alfalfa (McKenzie *et al.*, 1988). High-starch genotypes of alfalfa had higher levels of soluble sugars during winter than low starch genotypes (Boyce and Volenec, 1992). Differences in freezing tolerance between cold-tolerant and cold-sensitive cultivars were shown to be more closely related to the accumulation of the galactose-containing oligosaccharides raffinose and stachyose than to the levels of the known cryoprotectant sucrose (Castonguay *et al.*, 1995). Acclimation at subfreezing temperatures (-2°C) increased freezing tolerance and caused a significant rise in the levels of both raffinose and stachyose. These raffinose family oligosaccharides (RFO), conspicuously absent from crowns of unacclimated alfalfa, accumulate later in fall when the soil has frozen. Similar accumulations of sucrose, raffinose and stachyose have been described during the acquisition of desiccation tolerance in seeds and pollen grains and are thought to play key roles in tolerance to protoplasmic dehydration (Black *et al.*, 1999). We documented a close relationship between the activity of galactinol synthase (GS), a key regulatory enzyme, and the levels of raffinose and stachyose in crowns of alfalfa (Castonguay and Nadeau, 1998). The increase in GS activity occurred earlier and reached higher levels in the two hardy cultivars than in a non hardy cultivar. Similar activities of galactosidase, the main enzyme responsible for the degradation of galactose-containing oligosaccharides, in the three cultivars suggest that their differential accumulation is controlled by their synthesis rather than by their degradation. Using a nondestructive screening approach based on RFO accumulation in leaves, a wide variability has been demonstrated for the cold-inducibility of that trait within alfalfa (Castonguay *et al.* 1998). Specific crosses between genotypes selected for their high or low levels of leaf RFO have been used to study the inheritance of that trait (Fig. 3). The progeny derived from crosses between genotypes with low levels of leaf RFO was found at a higher frequency in classes of low raffinose while the reverse was observed with the progeny derived from crosses between genotypes with high levels of RFO. Crosses between genotypes with low and high RFO levels gave intermediate values.

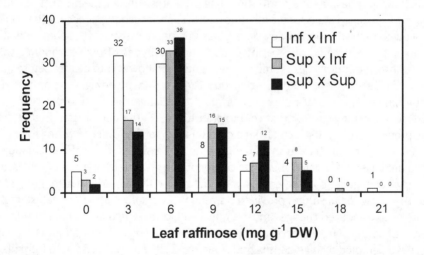

FIGURE 3. FREQUENCY DISTRIBUTION IN VARIOUS CLASSES OF LEAF RAFFINOSE ACCUMULATION FOR PROGENIES DERIVED FROM SPECIFIC CROSSES BETWEEN THREE GENOTYPES CHARACTERIZED FOR THE INFERIOR (INF X INF) OR THREE GENOTYPES CHARACTERIZED FOR THEIR SUPERIOR (SUP X SUP) COLD-INDUCED ACCUMULATION OF LEAF RAFFINOSE AND CROSSES BETWEEN GENOTYPES FROM BOTH GROUPS (SUP X INF). PLANTS WERE COLD ACCLIMATED UNDER ENVIRONMENTALLY-CONTROLLED CONDITIONS AND EXPOSED TO A CONSTANT 2°C TEMPERATURE, 8H PHOTOPERIOD AND 150 :MOL M⁻² S⁻¹ PPFD FOR A PERIOD OF 2 WEEKS. SOLUBLE SUGARS WERE QUANTITATED BY HIGH PERFORMANCE LIQUID CHROMATOGRAPHY AND DETECTED BY REFRACTOMETRY (CASTONGUAY, NADEAU AND MICHAUD, UNPUBLISHED).

Improvement of freezing tolerance in alfalfa by a selection approach based on successive freezing stress led to a significant increase in stachyose and raffinose, at the crown level (Classens, 1998). Interestingly, the selections did not modify the expression of two COR genes (msaCIA and msaCIC) further supporting a close relationship between cryoprotective sugars and low temperature adaptation. However differences in freezing tolerance between the selections and maximum hardiness occurred before the surge in stachyose and raffinose and in the absence of significant differences in their levels. Black *et al.* (1999) recently reported barely detectable levels of raffinose in wheat embryos exposed to conditions leading to desiccation tolerance. Although raffinose did not appear to be essential for the development of tolerance, desiccation did however enhance its accumulation. These authors raised the interesting possibility that raffinose-family oligosaccharides might be involved in mechanism related to seed longevity under extended period of desiccation rather than to the acquisition of desiccation tolerance. Current evidence indicates that these sugars are intimately related to the acquisition of desiccation and freezing tolerance but their adaptive value and mechanisms of action are still unclear.

Functional analysis of cold regulated genes

The identification of gene products or allelic variants closely related to winter hardiness in alfalfa would be a great asset for breeding programs. These gene products could be used as molecular markers for the identification of superior genotypes or could be applied to follow the introgression of desirable genes in a backcross strategy. Genes with large phenotypic effects could also be integrated into genotypes of high agronomic value using transgenic approaches. Some requirements need however to be met before these genes can be routinely used as selection markers in a breeding program: 1- The establishment of a causal rather than a mere correlative relationship between gene expression and the acquisition of cold tolerance and; 2- The demonstration that these gene products are limiting factors in the determination of the level of freezing tolerance.

Current data on changes in whole genome expression during cold acclimation of alfalfa are based on *in vivo* labeling of polypeptides, *in vitro* translation of mRNA and cloning of COR genes by differential hybridization of cDNA libraries (Castonguay *et al.*, 1997b). These initial studies provided a strong basis of information on the extent and nature of cold-induced changes and are now being complemented by high throughput analysis of partial DNA sequences along with the simultaneous hybridization of thousands of genes assembled on high density grids (microarrays) with mRNA isolated from plants that vary in their freezing tolerance. Such an exhaustive genomic analysis has been recently initiated in our laboratories and will provide a unique basis of information for the elucidation of the genetic bases of adaptation of alfalfa and other forage legumes. The development of genetic markers for cold resistance in alfalfa and the understanding of their adaptative value will also benefit from another project that we currently pursue using DNA-based molecular markers to construct linkage maps and to identify Quantitative Trait Loci (QTL) associated with cold tolerance in alfalfa. Marker-assisted selection for freezing tolerance offers many advantages including trait specificity and shorter selection cycles.

Not only will it be important to identify the genetic bases of cold adaptation in alfalfa but it will be necessary to understand how environmental factors interact with the genome and affect the expression of these genes. New genomic technologies such as microarrays will allow a more integrated perspective of the effects of biotic and abiotic factors on freezing tolerance of alfalfa and their impact on the expression of genes closely related to freezing tolerance. Our goal is to develop selection approaches based on a more precise knowledge of the genetic bases required to insure optimal adaptation of cultivars to a given set of environmental or management conditions. With that information, breeders will be able to develop cultivars better adapted to distinct environments and thus enhance persistence and productivity of forage legumes produced under cold and wet climates.

CONCLUSION

Lack of persistence of alfalfa affects the reliability of its production in cold climates. Our knowledge on the molecular bases of freezing tolerance in alfalfa has progressed considerably in the last decade. Molecular studies have indicated that the acquisition of cold tolerance of alfalfa is associated with extensive changes in gene expression and numerous biochemical changes. We gathered evidence that the differences in levels of freezing tolerance between cultivars of contrasting hardiness does not involve the whole complement of COR genes and are probably controlled by a more limited number of genes. Experiments performed in our laboratories and by other groups have led to the isolation and characterization of cold-regulated genes whose expression in some cases correlates with winterhardiness. We observed that variation in freezing tolerance among alfalfa cultivars is more closely related to the capacity of the plants to accumulate the galactose-containing oligosaccharides, stachyose and raffinose than to accumulate the known cryoprotectant sucrose. Projects currently underway at the Sainte-Foy Research Centre study the impact of environmental factors such as excess soil humidity, ice, cutting management on molecular changes associated with the acquisition of freezing tolerance in alfalfa. New technologies for genomic studies will allow an exhaustive analysis of the changes in gene expression and will provide information on the genetic bases of adaptation to complex genome-environment interactions.

REFERENCES

Barnes, R. F. and J. Baylor, 1994. Forages in a Changing World. In: Forages Vol 1: An Introduction to Grassland Agriculture. Iowa State University Press, Ames, U.S.A., 3-13.

Black, M., F. Corbineau, H. Gee and D. Côme, 1999. Water content, raffinose, and dehydrins in the induction of desiccation tolerance in immature wheat embryos. Plant Physiology, 120: 463-471.

Boyce, P. J. and J. J. Volenec, 1992. Taproot carbohydrate concentrations and stress tolerance of contrasting alfalfa genotypes. Crop Science, 32: 757-761.

Bray, E. A.,1990. Drought-stress-induced polypeptide accumulation in tomato leaves. Plant Cell and Environment, 13: 531-538.

Castonguay, Y., P. Nadeau and S. Laberge,1993. Freezing tolerance and alteration of translatable mRNAs in alfalfa (*Medicago sativa L.*) hardened at subzero temperatures. Plant Cell Physiology, 34: 31-38.

Castonguay, Y., P. Nadeau, P. Lechasseur and L. Chouinard,1995. Differential accumulation of carbohydrates in alfalfa cultivars of contrasting winter hardiness. Crop Science, 35: 509-516.

Castonguay, Y., P. Nadeau, S. Laberge and L. P. Vézina,1997a. Changes in gene expression in six alfalfa cultivars acclimated under winter hardening conditions. Crop Science, 37: 332-342.

Castonguay, Y., S Laberge, P. Nadeau and L. P. Vézina,1997b. Temperature and drought stress. 175-202. In, McKersie, B.D. and D. W. Brown (eds.). Biotechnology and the Improvement of Forage Legumes. CAB International, Wallingford, UK., 175-202.

Castonguay, Y. and P. Nadeau,1998. Enzymatic control of soluble carbohydrate accumulation in cold-acclimated crowns of alfalfa. Crop Science, 38: 1183-1189.

Castonguay, Y., P. Nadeau and R. Michaud,1998. Differential accumulation of oligosaccharides and freezing tolerance of alfalfa. In: Li, P.H. and Chen, T.H.H. (eds). Plant Cold Hardiness. Plenum Press, New York, U.S.A,, 293-299.

Classens, A. ,1998. Caractérisation de populations de luzerne sélectionnées pour la tolérance au gel. Master thesis, Laval University, Québec, Canada. 87 pp.

Close, T. J. ,1997. Dehydrins: A commonality in the response of plants to dehydration and low temperature. Physiologia Plantarum, 100: 291-296.

Ferrullo, J. M., L. P. Vézina, J. Rail, S. Laberge, P. Nadeau and Y. Castonguay,1997. Differential accumulation of two glycine-rich proteins during cold acclimation of alfalfa. Plant Molecular Biology, 33: 625-633.

Frame, J., J. F. L. Charlton and A. S. Laidlaw, 1998. Temperate Forage Legumes. CAB International, Wallingford, UK, 1-13.

Guy, C. L., 1990. Cold acclimation and freezing stress tolerance: Role of protein metabolism. Annual Review of Plant Physiology and Plant Molecular Biology, 41: 187-223.

Han, B., W. Hughes, G. A. Galau, J. D. Bewley and A. R. Kermode, 1997. Changes in late-embryogenesis-abundant(LEA) messenger RNAs and dehydrins during maturation and premature drying of *Ricinus communis L.* seeds. Planta, 201: 27-35.

Jaglo-Ottosen, K. R., S. J. Gilmour, D. G. Zarka, O. Schabenberger, M. Thomashow,1998. Arabidopsis CBF1 overexpression induces COR genes and enhances freezing tolerance. Science, 280: 104-106.

Jonak, C., Kiegerl, S., Ligterink, W., Barker, P.J., Huskisson, N.S. and Hirt, H. ,1996, Stress signaling in plants : A mitogen-activated protein kinase pathway is activated by cold and drought. Proceedings of the National Academy of Sciences, USA, 93 : 11274-11279.

Kawczynski, W. and Dhindsa, R.S. ,1996, Alfalfa nuclei contain cold-responsive phosphoproteins and accumulate heat-stable proteins during cold treatment of seedlings. Plant Cell Physiology, 37: 1204-1210.

Laberge, S., Y. Castonguay and L. P. Vézina,1993. New cold- and drought-regulated gene from Medicago sativa. Plant Physiology, 101: 1411-1412.

McCaslin, M., D. Brown, H. Deery and D. Miller,1990. Fall dormancy and winter survival and alfalfa variation within and between populations. In, G. R. Bauchan et al. (ed) Reports of the 32nd North American Alfalfa Improvement Conf., Pasco, WA. 19-23 Aug. 1990. North American Alfalfa Improvement Conf., Beltsville MD, 9.

McKenzie, J.S., R. Paquin and S. H. Duke,1988. Cold and heat tolerance. In: A.A. Hanson (ed.). Alfalfa and Alfalfa Improvement. ASA-CSSA-SSSA, Agronomy monograph, No 29, 259-302.

Mohapatra, S.S., L. Wolfraim, R. J. Poole and R. S. Dhindsa,1989. Molecular cloning and relationship to freezing tolerance of cold-acclimation-specific genes of alfalfa. Plant Physiology, 89: 375-380.

Monroy, A. F., Y. Castonguay, S. Laberge, F. Sarhan, L. P. Vézina and R. S. Dhindsa,1993a. A new cold-induced alfalfa gene is associated with enhanced hardening at subzero temperature. Plant Physiology, 102: 873-879.

Monroy A. F., F. Sarhan and R. S. Dhindsa,1993b. Cold-induced changes in freezing tolerance, protein phosphorylation, and gene expression. Evidence for a role of calcium. Plant Physiology, 103: 1227-1235.

Mooney, H. A.,1993. Human impact on terrestrial ecosystems-What we know and what we are doing about it. In: Proceedings XVII International Grassland Congress, 11-14.

Nelke, M., J. Nowak, J. M. Wright, N. L. McLean, S. Laberge, Y. Castonguay and L. P. Vézina,1999. Enhanced expression of a cold-induced gene coding for a glycine-rich protein in regenerative somaclonal variants of red clover (Trifolium pratense L.). Euphytica, 105: 211-217.

Paquin. R. ,1984. Influence of the environment on cold hardening and winter survival of forage plants and cereals species with consideration of proline as a metabolic marker of hardening. In, N.S. Margaris et al. (ed) Being Alive on Land. Kluwer Academic Publishers, Boston, 137-154.

Salzman, R. A., R. A. Bressan, P. M. Hasegawa, E. N. Ashworth and B. P. Bordelon,1996. Programmed accumulation of LEA-like proteins during desiccation and cold acclimation of overwintering grape buds. Plant Cell and Environment, 19: 713-720.

Sarhan, F., F. Ouellet and A. Vazquez-Tello,1997. The wheat wcs120 gene family. A useful model to understand the molecular genetics of freezing tolerance in cereals. Physiologia Plantarum, 101: 439-445.

Schwab, P. M., D. K. Barnes, C. C. Sheaffer and P. H. Li,1996. Factors affecting a laboratory evaluation of alfalfa cold tolerance. Crop Science, 36: 318-324.

Statistics Canada ,1997. Agricultural profile of Canada. Catalogue No. 93-356-XPB

Stout, D. G. and J. W. Hall, 1989. Fall growth and winter survival of alfalfa in interior British Columbia. Canadian Journal of Plant Science, 69: 491-499.

USDA., 1994. Agricultural Statistics. United States Department of Agriculture. United States government printing office, Washington, D.C.

Winicov, I. and D. R. Bastola,1999. Transgenic overexpression of the transcription factor Alfin1 enhances expression of the endogeneous MsPRP2 gene in alfalfa and improves salinity tolerance of the plants. Plant Physiology, 120: 473-480.

Wolfraim, L. A. and R. S. Dhindsa,1993a. Cloning and sequencing of the cDNA for cas17, a cold acclimation-specific gene of alfalfa. Plant Physiology, 103: 667-668.

Wolfraim, L. A., R. Langis, H. Tyson and R. S. Dhindsa, 1993b. cDNA sequence, expression, and transcript stability of a cold acclimation-specific gene, cas18, of alfalfa (*Medicago falcata*) cells. Plant Physiology, 101: 1275-1282.

Breeding for cold tolerance in white clover

J. R. CARADUS

AgResearch, Private Bag 11008, Palmerston North, New Zealand

S U M M A R Y

White clover, a temperate forage legume, is found growing over both a wide range of latitude and altitude. The genome of white clover provides adaptation to subzero temperatures and allows selection for improved winter hardiness and frost tolerance. Stress tolerance is most often identified in germplasm collected from environments experiencing that stress. Occasionally, such germplasm is good enough to become a cultivar but more frequently genes for stress tolerance are in germplasm that is poor in other agronomic respects. Crossing the germplasm with agronomically more suitable germplasm or existing cultivars and selecting for stress tolerance is a common option. This strategy for improving frost tolerance in white clover is described using an artificial frost-tolerance screening technique that has been validated through field trials.

Heritability for frost tolerance is moderately high in white clover. Direct selection for frost tolerance resulted in small leaf types with low growth rates. Breeding strategies ensured that selection occurred for both frost tolerance and medium to large leaf size that has resulted in germplasm with good growth rates and adequate frost tolerance. Evaluation in field trials has identified well adapted and agronomically suitable germplasm for northern European environments.

Keywords: breeding, cold tolerance, frosting, screening, white clover, winter hardiness

I N T R O D U C T I O N

White clover, a temperate forage legume, is found growing over both a wide range of latitude (70° N to the subtropics) and altitude (sea level to 6000 m in the Himalayas). While optimal temperatures for growth of white clover are between 22 and 25° C (Mitchell and Lucanus, 1962) and some growth can occur over a much wider range (5 to 40° C), it is apparent that the genome of white clover provides adaptation to subzero temperatures.

Cold tolerance, or cold hardiness, is an inclusive term which covers a wide array of responses caused by low temperature. Cold tolerance can be defined in two principal ways: (i) the ability to grow at low, but not freezing, temperatures, or (ii) the ability to survive subzero temperatures.

Plant breeders in warm and cool temperate climates have endeavoured to select for improved winter growth, resulting in cultivars such as Grasslands Pitau. However, in cold temperate and continental climates adaptation has been for winter hardiness and frost tolerance so that white clover cultivars can survive ground frosts and ice sheeting. Attempting to combine both the ability to grow at low but not freezing temperatures and yet withstand frosting has been pursued through selection of germplasm from Switzerland and has resulted in cultivars such as AberHerald (Rhodes and Webb, 1993; Robin *et al*, 1999).

Many believe, with good evidence, that there is no substitute for direct field screening for cold tolerance. It is well known that plants grown in controlled environments can differ significantly from plants grown in the field. However, from a breeder's viewpoint winter environments are variable and unreliable in providing conditions severe enough to differentiate between cold tolerant and sensitive plants. Additionally, selection of sole survivors from winter kill does not necessarily result in increased cold tolerance, winter hardiness, or frost resistance (Marshall *et al.*, 1981). Increased precision in plant selection has been achieved through the use of differential check cultivars to determine the magnitude of frosting needed, and through using freezing tests that are uniform and can screen large numbers of genotypes with good replication.

For any plant breeding programme to be successful, four ingredients are required: 1) genetic variability, 2) an effective stress screen, 3) intermating of surviving or least-damaged plants, and 4) recurrent selection to increase the frequency of genes that provide greater stress tolerance. Stress tolerance is most often identified in germplasm collected from environments experiencing that stress. Occasionally, such germplasm is good enough to become a cultivar but more frequently genes for stress tolerance are in germplasm that is poor in other agronomic respects. Crossing this germplasm with agronomically more suitable germplasm or existing cultivars and selecting for stress tolerance is a common option.

This paper describes a breeding programme aimed at producing white clover cultivars with the ability to survive subzero temperatures. The impact of this selection strategy on other agronomic characteristics was identified in field trials.

MATERIALS AND METHODS

Conduct of artificial frosting test

Plants were subjected to a single controlled frost of -12° C as described by Greer and Warrington (1982). The temperature declined over a 6 h period from the day temperature of 12° C to the minimum temperature, was held at the minimum for 6 h, and then increased to 12° C over 4 h. All freezing tests were carried out in the controlled environment facilities of HortResearch, Palmerston North, New Zealand. After frosting, plants were placed outside and 2 days later the percentage of leaves damaged per row was recorded. Plants with low percentage of leaves damaged were classified as more frost tolerant than those with a higher percentage of leaves damaged by frosting.

Plant propagation
Pre-germinated seed of white clover lines was sown into trays (430 x 300 mm) of potting mix in March (early autumn) and grown in a glasshouse for 6 weeks before placing outside at the end of April 1988. Plants were trimmed in late autumn and continued to harden through winter until early August (late winter) when frost treatment occurred.

Plant material
A wide range of white clover cultivars from Europe and USA were compared alongside ecotypes collected from Canada and northern USA.

Selection programmes
Two selection programmes are reported, each resulting in pre-release cultivars from recurrent selection for tolerance to artificial frosting.

Programme A began with making selections from the cultivars Undrom, Fries Groninger, Nelson Lakes (a frost tolerant ecotype from New Zealand), and Huia with a deliberate attempt to avoid selection of genotypes with small leaf size. However, as a result of the germplasm originally used it was difficult to select genotypes with leaf sizes equivalent to or larger than that of Huia. Two pre-release cultivars Frost T_4 and Frost T_5 came from this programme.

Programme B built on the advances made in programme A but incorporated new germplasm that included ecotypes from Canada and Wisconsin with the aim of only selecting genotypes with a leaf size equivalent to or larger than Huia. Pre-release cultivar Frost T_1 was from 14 genotypes selected from material with frost tolerance >55% <85% leaf damage; Frost T_2 was from 30 genotypes selected for frost tolerance with leaf damage <55%; and Frost T_3 was a restricted selection within Frost T_2 of only 19 parental genotypes following a progeny test of the 30 half sib families. In the selection trial that produced pre-release cultivars Frost T_1 and Frost T_2, Huia had 82% of leaves damaged by frosting.

Artificial frost tolerance
Pre-release cultivars Frost T_1, T_2, and T_3 were tested for frost tolerance, using the artificial frosting test, against the cultivars Huia, Kopu, Undrom, Podkowa, Milkanova and Retor. Measurements were made of percentage of lines damaged by frosting at -12° C (frost tolerance score), leaf size (width of middle leaflet on second open distal leaf on a main stolon), and percentage of plants (in a sample of 24 plants) that were cyanogenic (measured using the picric acid test).

Field trialling
The 5 pre-release cultivars were compared with cultivars Menna, Alice, Alberta,

Merwi, Avoca, and Gwenda at two sites in Europe. The site in the Netherlands, at Wolfheze, regularly experiences cold winters with occasional ice-sheeting and heavy frosts. The site in southern France, at Mas Grenier, has warmer winters but can experience frosting.

At each site plants of each cultivar were planted into 1 x 2.5 m grass swards (perennial ryegrass in Netherlands, and tall fescue in southern France) and grown under a mowing regime. Trials were established in spring 1995. White clover leaf size and growth as visually scored using a 1-9 scale (where 1 denoted very small leaf or minimal clover, and 9 very large leaves or clover dominance, respectively). Leaf size was scored in either autumn 1995, in the Netherlands or autumn 1996, in France. In the Netherlands, clover growth was scored in March, April, May, June, August, and September 1996, April and June 1997, and in France in April, May, June, September, and October 1996, March, April, and June 1997. Visual scores of frost damage (1 = heavy frost damage, to 9 = no frost damage) were made in March 1997, in the Netherlands after 6 weeks of frosting, and in France in January 1997 after an usually severe frosting event.

Analysis of data

All data were analysed by analysis of variance. Where appropriate data were log-transformed or arcsin-square-root transformed prior to analysis of variance. Untransformed means are presented.

RESULTS

Meteorological data

Monthly rainfall and average monthly temperatures from meteorological stations close to Wolfheze and at Mas Grenier are given in Figure 1. At Wolfheze, average monthly temperatures dropped below zero in December 1995 and January 1997. During January and February 1997 significant frosting occurred causing damage to white clover shoot growth. At Mas Grenier, average monthly temperatures were always above zero, although a single frosting event occurred in January 1997 that caused damage to white clover.

Artificial frosting

The frost tolerance of all 3 pre-release cultivars tested was significantly ($P<0.05$) better than that of Huia while having a leaf size equivalent to, or significantly ($P<0.05$) larger than that of Huia (Table 1). The frost tolerance of Frost T_2 and Frost T_3 was not significantly different from that of the European cultivars Podkowa, Milkanova and Retor. Only Undrom showed significantly ($P<0.05$) greater frost tolerance. The large-leaved New Zealand cultivar Kopu was very frost sensitive. All four European cultivars had no

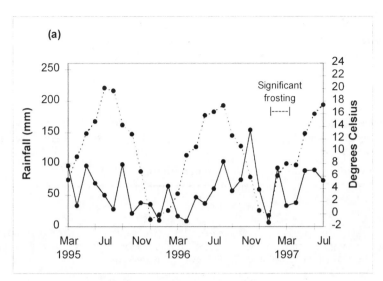

(a)

FIGURE 1. TOTAL MONTHLY RAINFALL (——) AND AVERAGE MONTHLY TEMPERATURE (---) AT (A) A SITE NEAR WOLFHEZE, THE NETHERLANDS, AND (B) MAS GRENIER, SOUTHERN FRANCE. TIMING OF LOW TEMPERATURES THAT RESULTED IN SIGNIFICANT FROSTING DAMAGE ARE INDICATED.

plants testing positive for cyanogenesis. Huia had the highest percentage of cyanogenic plants. The frost tolerant pre-release cultivars differed significantly (P<0.05) from each other with Frost T_2 the highest and Frost T_3 the lowest.

TABLE 1. FROST TOLERANCE SCORE (PERCENTAGE OF LEAVES DAMAGED BY -12°C ARTIFICIAL FROST), LEAF SIZE (WIDTH OF MIDDLE LEAFLET ON SECOND OPEN DISTAL LEAF) AND PERCENTAGE OF PLANTS CYANOGENIC OF FROST TOLERANT SELECTIONS AND CONTROL CULTIVARS OF WHITE CLOVER.

Cultivars	Frost tolerance score (%)	Leaf size (mm)	Cyanogenesis (% of plants)
Frost T_1	55	11.3	13
Frost T_2	42	9.5	29
Frost T_3	35	11.5	4
Huia	65	9.8	86
Kopu	75	14.1	53
Undrom	24	7.5	0
Podkowa	38	8.3	0
Milkanova	42	10.9	0
Retor	47	8.8	0
P	***	***	***
$LSD_{0.05}$	8	0.9	5

Field trials

In the Netherlands field trial, cultivars differed significantly (P<0.01) for frost tolerance (Table 2). Frost T_3 had the highest frost tolerance score, significantly (P<0.05) higher than that for Frost Selections T_4, T_5, Menna, Merwi, Avoca and Gwenda. In France, the cultivars showed no significant difference in tolerance to frosting.

The mean growth score over the length of the trials was highest for Frost T_3 and Frost T_2 in Netherlands and France, respectively (Table 2); significantly higher than Menna and Gwenda (in Netherlands), and Frost T_3, T_4, and T_5, Alberta, Merwi, Avoca and Gwenda (in France).

Frost T_1 had the highest leaf-size score in both trials (Table 2). In France, only Alice had a leaf-size score not significantly (P<0.05) lower than that of Frost T_1.

TABLE 2. VISUAL SCORES FOR LEAF SIZE, GROWTH AND FROST TOLERANCE (1 = HEAVY FROST DAMAGE TO 9 = NO FROST DAMAGE) OF FROST TOLERANT SELECTIONS AND CONTROL CULTIVARS OF WHITE CLOVER AT WOLFHEZE, THE NETHERLANDS AND MAS GRENIER, SOUTHERN FRANCE.

Cultivar	Leaf size		Growth		Frost tolerance	
	Netherlands	France	Netherlands	France	Netherlands	France
Frost T_4	5.8	4.8	3.9	5.3	2.5	6.7
Frost T_5	5.2	4.6	4.5	5.0	2.3	7.0
Frost T_1	7.1	6.4	4.9	7.2	3.9	6.2
Frost T_2	6.3	5.5	5.4	7.5	3.6	6.9
Frost T_3	6.2	5.1	5.5	6.4	5.6	7.0
Menna	5.8	5.2	3.6	6.6	2.1	7.4
Alice	6.7	5.6	5.4	6.8	4.6	6.7
Alberta	5.5	4.5	4.7	5.2	3.6	6.5
Merwi	5.7	5.2	4.1	5.8	2.8	7.4
Avoca	5.9	4.2	4.1	5.4	3.2	7.0
Gwenda	4.0	3.4	2.7	5.4	1.1	7.2
P	***	**	**	**	**	ns
$LSD_{0.05}$	1.4	0.8	1.8	1.0	2.3	–

DISCUSSION

Artificial frosting can be used to successfully identify genotypes of white clover that when intercrossed lead to pre-release cultivars that show good frost tolerance in both artificial frosting studies and field trials. Previous studies have shown that selection for frost tolerance alone in white clover can result in progeny that are prostrate, small-leaved and unproductive (Caradus and Eerens, 1992). Pre-release cultivars Frost T_4 and T_5 were produced from genotypes selected from relatively small-leaved cultivars or ecotypes, Undrom, Nelson Lakes and Fries Grominger (leaflet widths of 7.6 mm, 5.7 mm and 9.3 mm compared with Huia of 8.2 mm – Caradus et al., 1990). Components of these two pre-release cultivars showed good survival under ice sheeting in Canada compared to zero survival of Huia genotypes (Caradus and Christie, 1998).

The second round of breeding for frost tolerance where a more concerted effort was made to include larger-leaved, frost-tolerant genotypes resulted in pre-release cultivars Frost T_1, T_2 and T_3 that performed well in northern Europe through a severe winter of heavy frosting (Table 2). The difference in selection criteria for these three pre-release cultivars related to balancing selection for large leaf size and frost tolerance. Frost T_1 had the least constraining criteria for frost tolerance to allow for some larger-leaved genotypes to be included, whereas Frost T_3 had the most constraining criteria plus another cycle of selection based on progeny test of half-sib families. Both the artificial frosting trial (Table 1) and the field trials (Table 2) indicate that Frost T_3 was more frost tolerant than Frost T_1. At the southern France site the Frost T_1 was able to express its larger leaf size and growth potential (Table 2). Frost T_2 also had excellent growth at the southern France site.

The relationship between frost tolerance and cyanogenesis levels is well documented (Caradus et al., 1989; Caradus and Eerens, 1992). A clinal relationship where the frequency of acyanogenic plants increases as mid-winter temperature decreases has been established for white clover (Daday, 1954). The most frost-tolerant cultivars and selections in the current study were also acyanogenic or had a low percentage of plants that were cyanogenic (Table 1). However, the European cultivars, Alice, Alberta, and Avoca showed good frost tolerance in the field trials but have moderate to high cyanogenic levels based on results from other studies (75%, 48%, and 68% respectively – Caradus and Woodfield, 1997). Apparently, these cultivars selected for high yield and persistence have characteristics which restrict frost damage to leaves that in cyanogenic plants releases cyanide inhibiting photosynthesis and respiration (Foulds and Young, 1977).

From the five pre-release cultivars produced from this artificial frosting breeding programme two (Frost Selection T_2 and T_3) have been identified in field trials that both exhibit good winter hardiness and high forage yields and warrant consideration for release as commercial cultivars.

ACKNOWLEDGEMENTS

The artificial frosting trials were financially supported by a contract (C10640) from the New Zealand Foundation for Research, Science and Technology. Thanks to Dennis Greer, Tony Dunn, John Ford, and Kylie Miller for assistance with the artificial frosting selection trials, and to Lian van Kruijssen (Barenbrug Research, Wolfheze) and Nicolas van Hanja (Barenbrug Tourneur Recherches, Mas Grenier) and their staff for management of the field trials.

REFERENCES

Caradus, J. R. and B. R. Christie, 1998. Winterhardiness and artificial frost tolerance of white clover ecotypes and selected breeding lines. Canadian Journal of Plant Science, 78: 251-255.

Caradus, J. R. and J. P. J. Eerens, 1992. Genetic adaptation to frost tolerance in white clover. Proceedings of Agronomy Society of New Zealand, 22: 103-109.

Caradus, J. R., A. C. Mackay, J. van den Bosch, D. H. Greer and G. S. Wewala, 1989. Intraspecific variation for frost hardiness in white clover. Journal of Agricultural Science, Cambridge, 112: 151-157.

Caradus, J. R., A. C. Mackay, J. van den Bosch, S. Wewala and D. H. Greer, 1990. Heritability of frost tolerance in white clover (*Trifolium repens*). Journal of Agricultural Science, Cambridge, 114: 151-155.

Caradus, J. R. and D. R. Woodfield, 1997. World checklist of white clover varieties II. New Zealand Journal of Agricultural Research, 40: 115-206.

Daday, H., 1954. Gene frequencies in wild populations of *Trifolium repens* L. I. Distribution to Latitude. Heredity, 8: 61-78.

Foulds, W. and L. Young, 1977. Effect of frosting, moisture stress and potassium cyanide on the metabolism of cyanogenic and acyanogenic phenotypes of *Lotus corniculatus* L., and *Trifolium repens* L. Heredity, 38: 19-24.

Greer, D. H. and I. J. Warrington, 1982. Effect of photoperiod, night temperature, and frost incidence on development of frost hardiness in *Pinus radiata*. Australian Journal of Plant Physiology, 9: 333-342.

Marshall, H. G., C. R. Olien and E. H. Everson, 1981. Techniques for selection of cold hardiness in cereals. In: Analysis and Improvement of Plant Cold Hardiness. Olien, C.R. and M. N. Smith (eds). CRC Press Inc., Boca Raton, Florida, USA, 139-160.

Mitchell, K. J. and R. Lucanus, 1962. Growth of pasture species under controlled environment III. Growth at various levels of constant temperature with 8 and 16 hours of uniform light per day. New Zealand Journal of Agricultural Research, 5: 135-144.

Rhodes, I. and K. J. Webb, 1993. Improvement of white clover. Outlook on Agriculture, 22: 189-194.

Robin, C., G. Corbel, M. P. Guinchard, C. Bazard and A. Guckert, 1999. Overwintering and spring growth of white clover: importance of the cultivar. Fourrages, 157:21-32.

A model approach to climatic, geographic and edaphic determinants of overwintering of white clover

M. WACHENDORF

Department of Statistics, University College Dublin, Ireland

S U M M A R Y

The purpose of the EU COST 814 joint research program at twelve sites in Europe was to test the advantages of increased winter hardiness and increased growth rates at low temperatures for the sustainability of white clover under a range of different climatic conditions. This was facilitated by a common experimental protocol under which detailed information about the morphogenesis of white clover during winter and spring was collected. This should help to identify the basis of the variation in white clover content in mixtures with grasses. At all sites yields of total swards and of components were measured on each cut of several growing seasons. Morphological and chemical measurements were performed on several occasions during winter. Meteorological variables were recorded daily. For purposes of a comprehensive analysis the annual cycle was split into several functional periods. Modelling was carried out within each period using as response some variables, measured at the end of the period and relating them to both meteorological variables reflecting growing conditions during the period, and biological variables measured on the vegetation at the start of the period. The most informative explanatory biological variables themselves became the object of modelling in the preceding functional period. Thus, statistical analysis for the spring period highlighted clover leaf area and grass tiller number at the end of winter as good predictors for the clover content of swards in the first cut. Both of these plant variables were modelled in the preceding dormancy period. All models represent links in a series of models covering the whole annual cycle of clover development.

Keywords: AberHerald, Huia, multisite modelling, overwintering, perennial ryegrass, spring growth, Trifolium repens, white clover

I N T R O D U C T I O N

White clover is the most important legume in pastures in the regions of cool and temperate climate. For a maximum benefit from the advantages of this legume (biological nitrogen fixation, forage quality), a sufficiently large proportion of clover in the sward is required. To maintain such a proportion is a major problem in the management of clover/grass mixtures. Even optimized management strategies can not fully eliminate annual fluctuations in clover yield. The limited winter hardiness and low growth rates of the clover at cool temperatures (Harris *et al.*, 1983) may be responsible for its poor ability to compete with grasses in the spring. This could also be important for variation in white clover yield between years as there is considerable experience that consequences of a poor sward clover content in spring persist throughout the following summer as reduced proportions and yields (Eagles and Othman, 1988; Collins *et al.*, 1991). It is noteworthy that most studies were conducted in rather homogenous geographical regions. Therefore results usually do not cover a very wide range of growth conditions. The purpose of the COST 814 joint research program at twelve sites in Europe was to test the advantages of increased winter hardiness and increased growth rates at low temperatures for the sustainability of white clover under very different climatic conditions. This was facilitated by a common experimental protocol under which detailed information about the morphogenesis and carbohydrate reserves of white clover during winter and spring was collected. This should help to identify the basis of the variation in white clover content in mixtures with grasses.

MATERIALS AND METHODS

Within the frame of the COST 814 working group "Overwintering and Spring Growth of White Clover" field experiments were conducted at twelve sites in Europe according to a common protocol: Aberystwyth (UK), Athenry (IRL), Kiel (GER), Nancy (F), Melle (BEL), Mikkelli (FIN), Pordenone (ITA), Reykjavik (ISL), Uppsala (S), Wageningen (NL), Weihenstephan (GER) and Zürich (CH). Swards were established using either *Trifolium repens* cv. AberHerald (IGER, Aberystwyth, Wales UK) which is cold hardy and shows increased leaf growth rates at cool temperatures or cv. Huia (Grasslands Division, DSIR, NZ) together with *Lolium perenne*, generally cv. Preference. Swards were cut 2 to 7 times during the growing season depending on the growth conditions of the sites. Fertilizer nitrogen supply was mostly low to encourage clover growth. Dry matter yields of the total sward and of the components were recorded at each defoliation. During winter several destructive samplings of whole plants were made to determine the dynamics of dry mass and morphological and chemical characters of different plant parts. At all sites precipitation, air and soil temperatures and total irradiance were recorded daily.

Modelling strategy

These data provide a rare opportunity to develop perspectives on species performance over a very wide range of conditions but their analysis provides a challenge in extracting information on relationships from a broad and complex body of data. The modelling strategy had a number of guiding principles, which are discussed in detail elsewhere (Connolly and Wachendorf, 2000). The partition of the annual cycle into a number of functional periods, the use of reverse-direction modelling and the use of internal covariates as explanatory variables in addition to external (across-site) variables. Confining attention to a number of functionally meaningful periods (Growing Season - from the first to the last growing season cut; Start of Growth - From the last morphological measurement to the first growing season cut; Dormancy - from the first to the last morphological measurement; End of growth - from the last growing season cut to the first morphological measurement; see Fig. 1) simplifies the modelling and the understanding. A reverse-time modelling strategy was adopted as the most economical way to establish a linked series of models covering the whole year. For morphological data the list of available variables includes, for clover, clover stolon dry matter, stolon length, terminal bud number, leaf area, total nonstructural carbohydrates of stolons and several variables derived from these and, for the companion grass, tiller number. For data from sward cuts the internal explanatory variable used was clover content. For external variables, possible candidates include average and accumulated temperature, precipitation and radiation. Note that since the periods varied greatly in length from site to site, average and accumulated versions of the same variable may not be very closely related across sites. The reverse-time strategy was to use the internal variables chosen as explanatory variables in a particular period as the response variables in the previous period. For example, for the Growing Season the internal variable included in the model was clover content in the first cut. This was modelled in the Start of Growth period using leaf area and tiller density as explanatory variables. These in turn became the objects of modelling in the Dormancy period and so on. Since the starting response variable is an aggregate over the Growing Season and not a response at the end of that period these four models do not complete

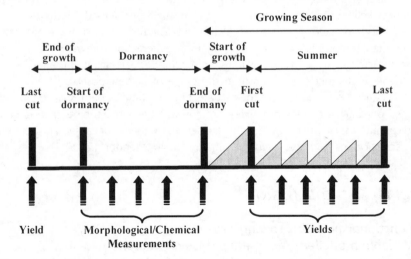

FIGURE 1. ORDER OF EXPERIMENTAL ACTIVITIES IN THE COURSE OF ONE YEAR AND DEFINITIONS OF FUNCTIONAL PERIODS.

an annual cycle. A fifth model completes the cycle by relating the clover content in the final cut of the Growing Season to internal variables at the start of that period and external variables through it.

Three variables were transformed before inclusion in the models: clover content, leaf area and tiller numbers. Clover content (CL) (g 100 g^{-1} DM) was measured as a percentage of dry matter but whether as a response or explanatory variable the logit of clover content, defined as log(CL/(100-CL)), was used. This is to avoid interactions induced by scale rather than biology and also to avoid heteroscedasticity in response. The log of leaf area was a much better explanatory variable than leaf area, suggesting that a fixed proportional increase in leaf area produced a constant effect on the response. When tiller number was the response variable it was analysed on the log scale to eliminate difficulties with heteroscedasticity. The inverse of tiller density was a better explanatory variable than tiller density, perhaps reflecting the common experience in competition models that response is inversely related to the density of competitors (Connolly, 1986). However, in one case the log of tiller number was used as explanatory variable as it gave better fit than either tiller number or the inverse of tiller number.

Statistical analysis

Models in terms of initial biotic variables and climatic and topographical variables were developed using the usual model selection methods for decisions as to the inclusion of meteorological and initial state variables in the model. The multi-site and multi-year structure of the study suggests that the error structure may be complex. Mixed model analysis was performed using the MIXED procedure of SAS with the REML (Restricted Maximum Likelihood) option (SAS Institute, 1996). An F-ratio of $P < 0.05$ was regarded as significant both for fixed and random effects. In all cases the main features of the models are presented graphically. Predictions for significant interactions between a factor and a continuous variable were plotted as lines, with a line for each level of the factor while the variable was varied continuously in the range of highest observed frequency of values. Predictions for significant interactions of continuous variables were plotted as two lines, one each for a high or low level of one variable, while the other variable was varied continuously in the range of highest observed frequency of values. Further details on the statistical methods are given by Connolly and Wachendorf (2000).

RESULTS AND DISCUSSION

Functional period: Growing season
Variable modelled: Mean annual clover content

The impact of significant effects in the model for the mean annual clover content (Table 1), is illustrated by three different plots in Fig. 2. The significant interaction between clover content in the first cut and clover variety indicates positive but differing effects on annual clover content for both varieties. With increasing spring clover content the difference between AberHerald and Huia increased to a maximum of 9 g 100 g⁻¹ DM. Further increases in spring clover content above 70 g 100 g⁻¹ DM again resulted in a reduced difference. Among the available explanatory climatic variables the cumulative degree days (days with a mean temperature >5°C) and the mean daily precipitation turned out to be significant in the model. The interaction of clover variety with precipitation showed a stronger increase in annual clover content with low (1 mm day⁻¹) compared to high (6 mm day⁻¹) mean daily rainfall over the growing season. With clover contents above 40 g 100 g⁻¹ DM in spring less moist conditions produced higher mean annual clover contents. On the contrary swards with poor clover contents in spring produced higher annual contents under more moist conditions. An increasing temperature sum from 600 to 2600 °C resulted in an increase in annual clover content of approximately 20 g 100 g⁻¹ DM of DM. The model is based on a total of 207 datapoints including all twelve sites and covers a range of observed clover contents from 0.05 to 99.6 g 100 g⁻¹ DM.

TABLE 1. DETAILS OF THE MODEL FOR MEAN ANNUAL CLOVER CONTENT (G 100 G⁻¹ DM). THE RESPONSE VARIABLE WAS TRANSFORMED TO THE LOGIT SCALE.

Effect	Estimate	Std Error	DF	t	Pr > |t|
INTERCEPT	-0.922	0.4167	33.7	—†	—
Clover variety (C)	0.311	0.0749	121	—	—
Logit clover content in the first cut (SCP) (g 100 g⁻¹ DM)	0.641	0.0537	194	—	—
Mean daily precipitation (PP) (mm)	-0.058	0.0974	29.2	—	—
Temperature sum >5°C (TS) (°C)	0.00044	0.000174	28.6	2.52	0.0175
SCP*C	0.064	0.0320	180	2.01	0.0456
SCP*PP	-0.070	0.0102	196	-6.86	0.0001

† t-values and probabilities of intercept was omitted as well as main effects were when the effect was included in a significant interaction.

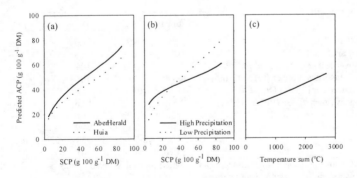

FIGURE 2. DISPLAY OF KEY TERMS IN THE MODEL DETAILED IN TABLE 1. SHOWN ARE PREDICTIONS FOR MEAN ANNUAL CLOVER CONTENT (ACP) (G 100 G⁻¹ DM) FOR (A) THE INTERACTION OF SPRING CLOVER CONTENT (SCP) (G 100 G⁻¹ DM) WITH CLOVER VARIETY (B) THE INTERACTION OF SPRING CLOVER CONTENT WITH MEAN DAILY PRECIPITATION (MM) AND (C) FOR THE TEMPERATURE SUM (°C).

Functional period: Start of growth
Variable modelled: Clover content in the first cut

The previous model showed the importance of high clover contents in spring. This is now modelled using meteorological data from the end of dormancy to the first spring cut and using sward variables measured at the end of dormancy. The selected model which links the end of dormancy with the first cut in spring indicates that the clover leaf area and tiller number of the companion grass were good biotic predictors for the spring clover content (Table 2). The clover variety interacted with the daily average precipitation for the period (Fig. 3). Increasing precipitation in early spring resulted in an increase in spring clover content with bigger increases for AberHerald. While the difference between the two clover varieties was minor at low levels of rainfall it increased to more than 20 g 100 g^{-1} DM under moist conditions. Contrary to precipitation both radiation and temperature entered the model accumulated over the period. High clover leaf area at the end of dormancy favoured spring clover contents. This effect was pronounced at high levels of radiation (35000 J m^{-2}) where the clover content increased fivefold with an increase in leaf area from close to 0 to 24000 cm^2 m^{-2} but only doubled at low levels of radiation (20000 J m^{-2}). The inverse grass tiller number interacted with the temperature sum. Under mild conditions (230 degree days) the effect of grass tiller number was very small, whereas under colder conditions (150 degree days) clover proportion of swards was strongly depressed by an increased tiller density. The model was based on 115 values from eight different sites. While both low (<20 g 100 g^{-1} DM) and very high levels (>90 g 100 g^{-1} DM) of actual spring clover content were well predicted by the model, there was considerable variation at intermediate levels.

TABLE 2. DETAILS OF THE MODEL FOR THE CLOVER CONTENT IN THE FIRST CUT (G 100 G^{-1} DM). THE RESPONSE VARIABLE WAS TRANSFORMED TO THE LOGIT SCALE.

Effect	Estimate	Std Error	DF	t	Pr > |t|
INTERCEPT	-4.506	3.9252	51.6	—[†]	—
Clover variety (C)	-0.717	0.3019	93.8	—	—
Log clover leaf area (LA) (cm^2 m^{-2})	-0.700	0.4114	104	—	—
Inverse grass tiller number (GTNO) (m^{-2})	5400.598	1599.9884	101	—	—
Temperature sum >5°C (TS) (°C)	0.0369	0.01215	14.7	—	—
Mean daily precipitation (PP) (mm)	0.539	0.4023	12.6	—	—
Radiation sum (RRS) (J m^{-2})	-0.00039	0.000152	75.6	—	—
PP*C	0.405	0.1550	94.7	2.62	0.0104
LA*RRS	0.000049	0.0000177	103	2.76	0.0069
GTNO*TS	-23.702	8.3451	101	-2.84	0.0055

[†] t-values and probabilities of intercept was omitted as well as main effects were when the effect was included in a significant interaction.

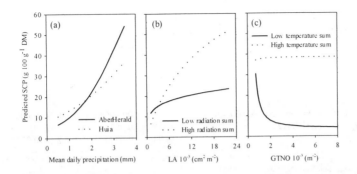

FIGURE 3. DISPLAY OF KEY TERMS IN THE MODEL DETAILED IN TABLE 2. PREDICTIONS OF THE SPRING CLOVER CONTENT (SCP) (G 100 G⁻¹ DM) ARE SHOWN FOR THE INTERACTIONS OF (A) MEAN DAILY PRECIPITATION (MM) WITH CLOVER VARIETY, (B) CLOVER LEAF AREA AT THE END OF DORMANCY (LA) (CM² M⁻²) WITH MEAN DAILY RADIATION (J M⁻²) AND (C) GRASS TILLER NUMBER AT THE END OF DORMANCY (GTNO) (M⁻²) WITH TEMPERATURE SUM (°C) (C).

Functional period: Dormancy

In the statistical analysis of the previous period clover leaf area and grass tiller number at the end of dormancy turned out to be good predictors for the clover content in the spring growth. These plant variables are now subject to modelling. The task will be to identify important climatic variables which explain the change of the plant status (in particular these two variables) over the dormancy period. Levels of clover leaf area and grass tiller number at the start of dormancy were the only significant biotic covariates.

Variable modelled: Clover leaf area at the end of dormancy

In the selected model radiation and temperature over the dormancy period were the only significant environmental covariates (Table 3). Both were included as mean values, as accumulated degree or irradiance days did not turn out to be significant (Fig. 4). The log-transformed clover leaf area as well as the mean radiation entered as main effects in the model. An increase in either variable induced an increase in clover leaf area at the end of dormancy, which is fairly reasonable, as the leaves are the primary receptors of incoming radiation and benefit initially from it. The effect of mean daily temperature was different for the two clover varieties. With cold dormancy conditions leaf area of AberHerald was nearly twice as high as for Huia. With increasing temperatures during dormancy the difference between the two clover varieties diminished and disappeared at a temperature level of approximately 7 °C. While Huia showed a small increase in leaf area with increasing temperature, AberHerald's total leaf area decreased. These facts point at complex plant-internal responses due to mild dormancy conditions where an increased biogen activity of the plant leads to higher demands on the energy status due to increased respiration losses. In such situations it can be advantageous for the plant to reduce the size of single parts, particularly those with a big surface, such as leaves. The model is based on 124 values from 9 different sites.

TABLE 3. DETAILS OF THE MODEL FOR CLOVER LEAF AREA AT THE END OF DORMANCY (CM² M⁻²). THE RESPONSE VARIABLE WAS TRANSFORMED TO THE LOG SCALE.

Effect	Estimate	Std Error	DF	t	Pr > |t|
INTERCEPT	1.602	1.4820	18.6	—[†]	—
Clover variety (C)	0.618	0.1735	108	—	—
Mean daily temperature (T) (°C)	0.023	0.0932	15	—	—
Log clover leaf area in autumn (LA) (cm² m⁻²)	0.449	0.0899	116	4.99	0.0001
Mean daily radiation (RR) (J cm⁻²)	0.005	0.0021	14.2	2.51	0.0247
T*C	-0.080	0.0373	107	-2.16	0.0334

[†] t-values and probabilities of intercept was omitted as well as main effects were when the effect was included in a significant interaction.

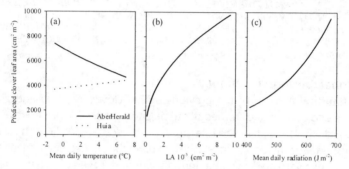

FIGURE 4. DISPLAY OF KEY TERMS IN THE MODEL DETAILED IN TABLE 3. PREDICTIONS OF CLOVER LEAF AREA AT THE END OF DORMANCY (CM² M⁻²) ARE SHOWN FOR (A) THE INTERACTION OF MEAN DAILY TEMPERATURE (°C) WITH CLOVER VARIETY (B) CLOVER LEAF AREA AT THE START OF DORMANCY (LA 10⁻³) (CM² M⁻²) AND (C) THE MEAN DAILY RADIATION (J M⁻²) (C).

Variable modelled: Grass tiller number at the end of dormancy

In the selected model grass tiller numbers at the start of dormancy entered significantly as a quadratic term (Table 4). Increasing tiller numbers up to 2000 m⁻² at the start of dormancy resulted in a pronounced increase of tillers at the end of the period. Further increases before dormancy had no effect (Fig. 5). Both environmental variables (mean daily temperature and radiation) worked in significant interactions with the clover variety. Tiller numbers increased with increasing temperature for both clover varieties. At low levels of temperature grass in mixture with Huia showed higher tiller numbers than with AberHerald. Under mild dormancy conditions the difference between clover varieties levelled off. Increasing precipitation during dormancy reduced grass tiller numbers. This might have been due to adverse effects of high soil moistures and/or a result of a lack of oxygen, as some of the precipitation fell in form of snow, which covered the swards and separated them from the atmosphere. Under dry dormancy conditions AberHerald allowed higher grass tiller number than Huia did, whereas under mois conditions it was vice versa. An increase in grass tiller numbers up to 2000 m⁻² at the start of dormancy resulted in an increase in tiller numbers up to 3000 m⁻² at the end of dormancy. Further increases at the start of the period had no effects. The selected model is based on 120 values from 9 different sites.

TABLE 4. DETAILS OF THE MODEL FOR GRASS TILLER NUMBERS AT THE END OF DORMANCY (M⁻²). THE RESPONSE VARIABLE WAS TRANSFORMED TO THE LOG SCALE.

Effect	Estimate	Std Error	DF	t	Pr > |t|
INTERCEPT	0.170	2.4568	86.4	—[†]	—
Clover variety (C)	0.038	0.1798	73.7	—	—
Log grass tiller number at the start of dormancy (GTNO) (m⁻²)	2.129	0.6799	79.3	—	—
Mean daily temperature (T) (°C)	0.053	0.1250	13.6	—	—
Mean daily precipitation (PP) (mm)	-0.256	0.2731	13.2	—	—
GTNO* GTNO	-0.131	0.0469	76.9	-2.79	0.0067
T*C	0.106	0.0487	60.4	2.18	0.0331
PP*C	-0.233	0.1037	45.3	-2.24	0.0298

[†] t-values and probabilities of intercept was omitted as well as main effects were when the effect was included in a significant interaction.

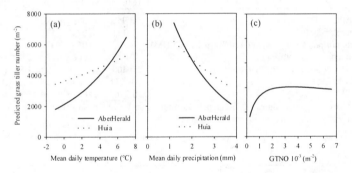

FIGURE 5. DISPLAY OF KEY TERMS IN THE MODEL DETAILED IN TABLE 4. SHOWN ARE PREDICTIONS FOR THE GRASS TILLER NUMBER AT THE END OF DORMANCY (M⁻²) BY INTERACTIONS OF THE CLOVER VARIETY WITH (A) MEAN DAILY TEMPERATURE (°C) AND (B) WITH MEAN DAILY PRECIPITATION (MM) AND (C) ALSO AS AFFECTED BY GRASS TILLER NUMBERS AT THE START OF DORMANCY (GTNO) (M⁻²).

Functional period: End of growth

It was shown that both clover leaf area and grass tiller number at the end of the dormancy were related to the status at the start of of that period but were also affected by certain environmental variables. The next step in the modelling work will be to check if the two plant variables at the start of dormancy show any relationship to clover performance in the growing season which was finished by the last cut approximately 30 to 40 days before the onset of the dormancy period.

Variable modelled: Clover leaf area at the start of dormancy

Analysis showed that clover contribution in the last cut in autumn was an important factor affecting the clover leaf area at the start of dormancy (Table 5). Autumn clover content was significant both as a quadratic term and in interaction with the clover variety. Increasing clover contents in the last cut of swards with AberHerald resultes in a slight increase in clover leaf area at the start of dormancy, whereas leaf area of Huia showed no clear response (Fig. 6). Both significant environmental variables enter as main effects in the model. Clover leaf area is favoured by mild conditions with plentiful rainfall (Fig. 6) in the period immediately after the last cut in autumn, where the plant recovers from the damage of defoliation and prepares its metabolism for the coming winter. Thus, clover leaf area at the start of dormancy seems to be lowest for swards with low clover contents particularly if cold and dry conditions occur immediately after the last cut. The model fit is fairly good at low and moderate levels of actual clover contents but there is more variation at high levels mainly due to some data from the Swedish and Italian site. The model is based on 137 data from all twelve sites.

TABLE 5. DETAILS OF THE MODEL FOR THE CLOVER LEAF AREA AT THE START OF DORMANCY (CM² M⁻²). THE RESPONSE VARIABLE WAS TRANSFORMED TO THE LOG SCALE.

Effect	Estimate	Std Error	DF	t	Pr > |t|
INTERCEPT	5.959	0.5960	18.1	—[†]	—
Clover variety (C)	0.131	0.0742	115	—	—
Logit autumn clover content (AUCP) (g 100 g⁻¹ DM)	-0.067	0.0558	126	—	—
Mean daily temperature (T) (°C)	0.180	0.0605	17.8	2.98	0.0081
Mean daily precipitation (PP) (mm)	0.409	0.1149	16.6	3.56	0.0025
AUCP*AUCP	-0.034	0.0086	118	-3.96	0.0001
AUCP*C	0.2467	0.0426	114	5.79	0.0001

[†] t-values and probabilities of intercept was omitted as well as main effects were when the effect was included in a significant interaction.

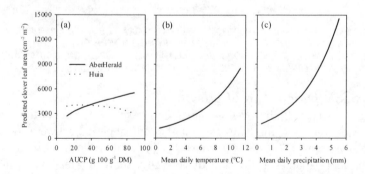

FIGURE 6. DISPLAY OF KEY TERMS IN THE MODEL DETAILED IN TABLE 4. SHOWN ARE PREDICTIONS OF CLOVER LEAF AREA AT THE START OF DORMANCY (CM⁻² M⁻²) FOR (A) THE INTERACTION OF CLOVER CONTENT AT THE LAST CUT OF THE GROWING SEASON (AUCP) (G 100 G⁻¹ DM) WITH CLOVER VARIETY, (B) THE EFFECT OF MEAN DAILY TEMPERATURE (°C) AND (C) THE EFFECT OF MEAN DAILY PRECIPITATION (MM).

Grass tiller number at the start of dormancy

Autumn clover content (again logit-transformed) significantly affected grass tiller numbers at the onset of the dormancy period (Table 6). Invers to the AUCP*C interaction in the leaf area model for the same functional period grass tiller numbers were strongly reduced with increasing clover contents in swards with AberHerald, whereas grass grown with Huia did not seem to be affected at all (Fig. 7). Mean daily temperature modified the effect of autumn clover content on grass tiller numbers. With increasing autumn clover contents reduction in tiller number was more pronounced under cold autumn conditions (4°C). With high temperatures between the last cut and the start of dormancy (10°C) grass tiller numbers were in the range of 3000 m^{-2} even with clover contents above 80 g 100 g^{-1} DM. The biggest part of the 118 observed data were below 8000 tillers per m^2. Only some Swedish data were at higher levels including one extremely high datapoint close to 15000 which was not satisfactorily fit by the model. The model comprises growth conditions of 10 different sites.

TABLE 6. DETAILS OF THE MODEL FOR THE GRASS TILLER NUMBERS AT THE START OF DORMANCY (M^{-2}). THE RESPONSE VARIABLE WAS TRANSFORMED TO THE LOG SCALE.

Effect	Estimate	Std Error	DF	t	Pr > |t|
INTERCEPT	7.372	0.5389	15.7	—[†]	—
Clover variety (C)	-0.115	0.0810	103	—	—
Logit autumn clover content (AUCP) (g 100 g^{-1} DM)	-0.418	0.1891	112	—	—
Mean daily temperature (T) (°C)	0.070	0.0660	15.8	—	—
AUCP*C	-0.194	0.0719	101	-2.7	0.0082
AUCP*T	0.056	0.0222	112	2.5	0.0139

[†] t-values and probabilities of intercept was omitted as well as main effects were when the effect was included in a significant interaction.

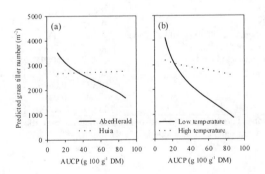

FIGURE 7. DISPLAY OF KEY TERMS IN THE MODEL DETAILED IN TABLE 6. SHOWN ARE PREDICTIONS FOR THE GRASS TILLER NUMBERS AT THE START OF DORMANCY (M^{-2}) FOR THE INTERACTION OF THE CLOVER CONTENT AT THE LAST CUT OF THE GROWING SEASON (AUCP) (G 100 G^{-1} DM) WITH (A) THE CLOVER VARIETY AND (B) WITH THE MEAN DAILY TEMPERATURE (°C).

Subject modelled: Autumn clover content

As presented in the previous chapters the aim of modelling the clover performance from one growing season through the dormancy period back to the previous has been achieved. Nevertheless one more model is presented. It links the clover content in the autumn to that of the spring, which is necessary for a complete series where one model is fed with the output of the one of the previous period. By means of such a chain of models the performance of clover around the whole annual cycle could be predicted. Table 7 gives the details of the selected model for the autumn clover content. The relation between spring and autumn clover content was different for the two clover varieties (Fig. 8). Generally autumn clover content increased with increasing spring clover content. The difference between clovers was small at low level but increased with increasing level of spring clover content, AberHerald being superior over the whole range of values. Increased temperature during the last growth negatively affected the clover content of swards (16 vs 11 °C in the figure). The figure also shows that at low levels of temperature AberHerald was able to realise significantly higher clover contents in the autumn which is in turn a prerequisite for successful overwintering. With mild autumn conditions (>15 °C) the difference between clovers was negligible. Given high levels of clover content in the spring cut, autumn growths could realize a much bigger clover contribution when there was a high amount of radiation income during the growth (1800 J m^{-2}). At low level of radiation (1100 J m^{-2}) increases in spring clover content did not result in big increases in autumn. The model is based on 186 observed datapoints from all twelve sites.

TABLE 7. DETAILS OF THE MODEL FOR THE AUTUMN CLOVER CONTENT (% OF DM). THE RESPONSE VARIABLE WAS TRANSFORMED TO THE LOGIT SCALE.

Effect	Estimate	Std Error	DF	t	Pr > |t|
INTERCEPT	2.415	2.2811	32.6	—[†]	—
Clover variety (C)	3.105	0.9540	163	—	—
Logit spring clover content (SCP) (g 100 g^{-1} DM)	0.260	0.4363	119	—	—
Mean daily temperature (T) (°C)	-0.307	0.2084	32	—	—
Mean daily radiation (RR) (J cm^{-2})	0.0011	0.00092	25.7	—	—
SCP*C	0.216	0.0735	156	2.94	0.0038
T*C	-0.177	0.0689	162	-2.56	0.0112
SCP*T	-0.096	0.0410	113	-2.35	0.0204
SCP*RR	0.0010	0.00020	158	5.05	0.0001

[†] t-values and probabilities of intercept was omitted as well as main effects were when the effect was included in a significant interaction.

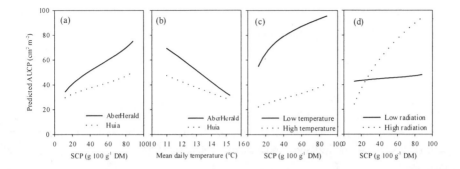

FIGURE 8. DISPLAY OF KEY TERMS IN THE MODEL DETAILED IN TABLE 7. SHOWN ARE PREDICTIONS FOR THE CLOVER CONTENT AT THE LAST CUT OF THE GROWING SEASON (AUCP) (G 100 G⁻¹ DM) FOR THE INTERACTIONS OF CLOVER VARIETY WITH (A) THE CLOVER CONTENT IN THE SPRING CUT (SCP) (G 100 G⁻¹ DM) AND (B) WITH THE MEAN DAILY TEMPERATURE (°C), AS WELL AS FOR THE INTERACTIONS OF SPRING CLOVER CONTENT (SCP) (G 100 G⁻¹ DM) WITH (C) THE MEAN DAILY TEMPERATURE (°C) AND (D) WITH THE MEAN DAILY RADIATION (J M⁻²) AGGREGATED FOR THE PERIOD OF THE LAST GROWTH).

CONCLUSIONS

This paper provides models which describe changes in the status of white clover growing in clover/grass-mixtures over a very wide range of growth conditions (latitude of sites between 46° and 64°N). The results feature the importance of high clover contents in spring for high clover contributions in the yield of clover/grass-mixtures over the whole growing season. Clover leaf area and grass tiller numbers over the dormancy period were found to be the major factors determining clover contents in spring. The relationships developed in these models are not claimed to be causal; they serve rather as tentative explanations and form the basis for hypotheses about some of the main forces driving the dynamics of clover-ryegrass systems. Nor are they claimed to be complete; there are many other factors involved, and many other regulators of growth which have not been tested here or which have not appeared to be important in this analysis but may await a more refined approach. However, in reducing the vast amount of data to some plausible structures we believe that they will focus attention more closely on certain areas for further investigation.

ACKNOWLEDGEMENTS

The author is grateful for support by the Commission of the European Community. Thanks are due to the Department of Statistics, National University of Ireland, Dublin for hosting the author during the execution of this work. Many thanks to all the involved investigators, namely R. P. Collins, J. Connolly, A. Elgersma, M. Fothergill, B. E. Frankow-

Lindberg, A. Ghesquiere, A. Guckert, M. P. Guinchard, A. Helgadottir, A. Lüscher, T. Nolan, P. Nykänen-Kurki, J. Nösberger, G. Parente, S. Puzio, I. Rhodes, C. Robin, A. Ryan, B. Stäheli, S. Stoffel and F. Taube.

REFERENCES

Collins, R. P., M. J. Glendining and I. Rhodes, 1991. The relationships between stolon characteristics, winter survival and annual yields in white clover (Trifolium repens L.). Grass and Forage Science, 46: 51-61.

Connolly, J., 1986. On difficulties with replacement-series methodology in mixture experiments. Journal of Applied Ecology, 23: 125-137.

Connolly, J. and M. Wachendorf, 2000. Combining data on clover overwintering across 12 sites. A time-based modelling strategy. This volume.

Eagles, C. F., O. B. Othman, 1988. Variation in growth of overwintered stolons of contrasting white clover populations in response to temperature, photoperiod and spring environment. Annals of Applied Biology, 112: 563-574.

Harris, W., I. Rhodes and S. S. Mee, 1983. Observations on environmental and genotypic influence on the overwintering of white clover. Journal of Applied Ecology, 20: 609-624.

SAS Institute, 1996. SAS/STAT User's Guide, Release 6.12 Edition. Cary, NC: SAS Institute.

WORKING GROUP 2

Overwintering and spring growth of white clover
Offered papers

Spread and growth of white clover under grazing

M. FOTHERGILL, C.T MORGAN, S. JONES, T.P.T. MICHAELSON-YEATES AND D.A. DAVIES

IGER, Plas Gogerddan, Aberystwyth, SY23 3EB, UK

SUMMARY

Continuous grazing of grass/white clover swards according to recommended sward height guidelines for sheep (4cm sward surface height) can cause the white clover content to cycle in an unacceptable way. An experiment was started in 1997 to study the effect of a late silage cut on the white clover component of the sward. Unique leaf-mark plants (genets) were introduced into known positions in the sward and monitored under two grazing regimes: 1) Continuous grazing 2) Grazing followed by a single late-season silage cut, a brief rest period and back to autumn sheep grazing (Graze-rest-graze). The Graze-rest-graze treatment had a highly significant effect on the white clover component producing larger genets with higher plant numbers, greater number of apices and larger amounts of stolon with a superior weight per unit length. It also increased the number of directions of growth and increased plant spread. The overall effect was to improve the ability of the genets to survive and colonise the surrounding sward. The data also suggested that treatment effects could still be identified 15 months later.

Keywords: grazing, morphology, white clover

INTRODUCTION

In temperate climates grass/white clover associations form the basis of low-input sustainable grassland production. Thus clover is an important component of productive swards. One of the obstacles limiting greater reliance on white clover in grazed systems is the perception that clover in unreliable. The sward height guidelines recommended for grazing, particularly those for continuous sheep grazing, are based on information concerning the physiology of the grass plant and the needs of the grazing animal with little regard for the effect of such a regime on the white clover component of the sward. Grazing to 4cm with sheep has been shown to be a good compromise between loss of herbage through plant senescence, reasonable herbage production, acceptable stocking rate and adequate individual animal performance (Maxwell, 1986). Yet constant observance of this regime can cause grass/clover swards to experience declines in clover content. It is clear that inclusion of clover into the sward necessitates a modification to the grazing regime.

Acceptable grass/clover balance within mixed swards is dependent on the compatibility of the sward components, the ability of the components to withstand a range of abiotic and biotic stresses and the development of a flexible management system that will optimize the legume component of the sward. Understanding the basis of stress tolerance, the mechanisms involved and their interaction with management practices are therefore crucial for the formulation of suitable guidelines. These management regimes should seek to allow sustainable sheep grazing by encouraging the expression of characters that are known to improve tolerance to stress.

Evidence suggests that late-summer silage cuts or rotational grazing should effect an increase in the clover component of swards and allow further continuous stocking to take place (Curll and Wilkins, 1985). The experiment described here investigates the effect of a single late-season silage cut on the clover component of a grass/clover sward.

MATERIALS AND METHODS

An experiment was initiated in 1997 at Bronydd Mawr Research Station, South Powys, Wales (51° 58' N, 03° 38' W) to compare the spread and growth of white clover under two grazing regimes: 1) Continuous grazing to 4cm with sheep (known to cause severe fragmentation and decline in plant size) 2) Graze-rest-graze (thought to be beneficial to clover within swards). The experimental site was on an acid brown earth soil of the Milford series overlying Devonian Red Sandstone at 370-390m above sea level.

A population of 192 identical, individual white clover plants displaying a unique leaf-mark (developed at IGER) was created from parent stock by taking stolon cuttings. Careful pruning produced plants that, although of stoloniferous origin, were similar in form to the rosette structure seen in developing white clover plants These plants were introduced into known locations in a grass/clover sward in 1997 to measure the effect of grazing management on plant spread and morphology. From the beginning of 1998 the swards were grown under the two grazing regimes (each replicated 4 times). During 1999 both treatments were maintained at a sward height of 4cm by continuous grazing by sheep. The spread and population structure of each genet was monitored during 1998 and 1999. Sampling commenced in spring 1998 employing two very different sampling protocols. A large quadrat (85x55 cm) was centred over each plant (a 15cm metal pin marked the original centre of the plant) with each internal cell of the quadrat measuring 2.5x2.5cm. All plants were assessed by recording the presence or absence of clover leaves exhibiting the 'filled V' mark in each of the internal cells of the quadrat. This enabled assessments of plant spread to be made. Immediately following the measurement of plant spread the morphology and population structure of the white clover plants was assessed by randomly selecting three original plant locations from each block of 24 plants (3x8 = 24 in total). Turves were removed from each selected plant location in such a way that all plant material, derived from the original introduced unit (genet), was taken. The soil was washed from each turf and leaf-mark white clover plants gently teased out of the resulting vegetation mat. Great care had to be taken to ensure that all plant units were located and removed with no further damage to the plant structure. Each genet was then described, in detail, by measuring a range of simple morphological characters (Brock *et al.*, 1988). Data from each sampling were expressed as plot means and analysed by ANOVA.

RESULTS

The data from destructive sampling, showing the detailed morphology of the white clover genets for autumn 1997 - autumn 1999, are presented in Table 1. The results indicate that fragmentation of the original plant took place during the winter of 1997-98 producing 3.12 plants within each genet. The overall morphology of the genets was unchanged apart from a significant reduction (32.5%) in stolon thickness and a reduction in plant complexity (order) over the same period. The grazing regimes were initiated in 1998 and the autumn 1998 data indicated that there were highly significant differences between the treatments for a range of characters. The Graze-rest-graze treatment produced larger genets with higher plant numbers, greater number of apices and larger amounts of stolon with a superior weight per unit length. When the individual areas of the plants within genets were added together the total area of the Graze-rest-graze genets covered approximately five times the area of the continuously grazed genets. The data from autumn 1999 indicated that the treatment effect could still be detected for stolon length but differences in other morphological characters had started to disappear.

TABLE 1. MORPHOLOGICAL CHARACTERISTICS OF WHITE CLOVER GENETS (AUTUMN 1997-AUTUMN 1999).

Sampling date	Treatment	Plant no.	Order	Bud no.	Leaf no.	Stolon length (cm)	Stolon Thickness (g/cm)	Plant Area (cm2)
Autumn 1997	G	1.00	2.75	21.26		42.12	0.0087	95.8
Spring 1998	G	2.8	2.29	25.4	27.5	58.1	0.0062	110.4
	G-R-G	3.4	1.96	16.1	17.8	44.2	0.0056	81.7
Significance		NS	NS	x	x	NS	NS	NS
Autumn 1998	G	3.0	2.15	13.3	17.8	26.2	0.0049	47.1
	G-R-G	5.9	1.98	24.9	27.4	94.2	0.0058	256.3
Significance		x	NS	xxx	NS	xx	x	xx
Autumn 1999	G	6.1	2.16	33.0	50	64.0	0.0057	131.0
	G-R-G	13.2	2.08	74.0	113	175.0	0.0060	194.0
Significance		NS	NS	NS	NS	x	NS	NS

G - continuous grazing, G-R-G - Graze-rest-graze
NS - Not significant, x = P<0.05, xx = P<0.01, xxxP<0.001

Table 2 presents data derived from the quadrat measurements taken in autumn 1998. The data are means of the remaining genets in each plot and allows estimates of characters that could not be assessed from destructive sampling techniques. Significant treatment effects were present for all the characters with the Graze-rest-graze treatment possessing a larger number of axes of growth (directions), greater area of influence of the genet (area of ground cover by the genet) and greater maximum spread from the centre of the genet (length of the longest axis of growth)

TABLE 2. GROWTH PATTERNS OF WHITE CLOVER GENETS FROM GRID QUADRATS (AUTUMN 1998).

Treatment	No. of axes of growth	Area of influence (cm2)	Maximum spread (cm)
G	2.2	72	12.1
G-R-G	3.4	146	17.1
Significance	x	x	xx

G - continuous grazing, G-R-G - Graze-rest-graze
NS - Not significant, x = P<0.05, xx = P<0.01,

DISCUSSION

Grazing to 4cm with sheep is a widely accepted management practice and has well-documented benefits (Maxwell, 1986). Yet constant adherence to this regime causes problems with clover declines occurring every 3 –4 years (Fothergill *et al.*, 1996). It is clear that the clover plant must be encouraged to increase in size occasionally, to enable further grazing at 4cm to take place. Essentially, management can be used to manipulate the environment of the sward to create 'optimal condition periods' for different species. Recruitment of plant units into the population will occur by the production of vegetative offshoots leading to large numbers of new ramets. This could be considered as exploiting a 'storage effect', where individuals recruited during optimal periods are stored to be utilised during suboptimal conditions. In the case of white clover the storage effect works, through the Graze-Rest-Graze treatment, in two ways; firstly, it increases plant number and secondly it increases genet size. This is a consequence of the manipulation of key morphological characteristics. The subsequent utilisation of the grass/clover swards at a grazing height of 4cm will increase the grazing pressure on the clover component. However, these large clover plants will be able to compensate for loss of individual plant stolon length by increasing plant number through fragmentation. The information from the autumn 1999 sampling suggests that the treatment effect were beginning to dissipate. Although the mean values still seem to indicate a residual effect the variability of the plants did not allow significance to be attached to the difference.

REFERENCES

Brock, J. L., M. J. M. Hay, V. J. Thomas and J. R. Sedecole,1988. Morphology of white clover (*Trifolium repens L.*) plants in pastures under intensive sheep grazing. Journal of Agricultural Science, Cambridge, 111: 273-283.

Curll, M. L. and R. J. Wilkins, 1985. The effect of cutting for conservation on a grazed perennial ryegrass - white clover pasture. Grass and Forage Science, 40: 19-30.

Fothergill, M., D. A. Davies, C. T. Morgan and J. R. Jones, 1996. White clover crashes. In: Younie, D. (ed.) Legumes in Sustainable Farming Systems. Occasional Symposium No. 30. British Grassland Society; 172-176.

Maxwell, T. J.,1986. System studies in upland sheep production: some implications for management and research. The Hill Farming Research Organisation, Biennial Report, 1984-85: 155-163.

Clover persistence, stolon and tiller density in grazed pastures

A. ELGERSMA AND H. SCHLEPERS

Wageningen University, Crop and Weed Ecology, Haarweg 333, 6709 RZ Wageningen, The Netherlands

SUMMARY

The performance of grass-clover mixtures using grass cultivars with contrasting growth habits and a small-leaved white clover cultivar was evaluated under cattle grazing during seven years at three locations in the Netherlands. The prostrate diploid perennial ryegrass cultivar formed a dense sward with less weeds than the tetraploid or the erect diploid ryegrass cultivars, but the effect on the amount of clover in the mixture was variable. The ryegrass tiller density was lowest in the tetraploid. Seasonal patterns and long-term fluctuations in grass and clover abundance over years are discussed in relation to mixture and soil type.

Keywords: animal production, cattle grazing, clover persistence, grass-clover mixtures, grass tiller density, stolon abundance

INTRODUCTION

It is very difficult to maintain desired levels of white clover (*Trifolium repens* L.) within the sward over an extended period. Sudden severe reductions in clover content ('clover crashes') which seem to occur in a 3-4 year cycle have been reported (Fothergill *et al.*, 1996).

Clover content and persistence are affected by many factors; Schwinning and Parsons (1996) distinguished between intrinsic oscillations with a phase of 3-4 years, and external sources of legume variation. In our experiment the effect of companion grass on botanical composition was studied on two soil types. Grass cultivars with contrasting growth habits were included. Earlier observations (Elgersma and Schlepers, 1996) had shown that from 1992 to 1994 mixtures with prostrate perennial ryegrass (*Lolium perenne* L.) cv. Wendy contained less clover than mixtures with erect 'Barlet' or tetraploid 'Condesa'. The results of 1995 and 1996 were reported in Elgersma and Schlepers (1999). A total overview of results from 1992 to 1998 is presented here.

MATERIALS AND METHODS

Grazing trials were established on river clay at Wageningen (HW) and on sandy soil at Achterberg (ACH), the Netherlands. ACH was sown in April and HW in August 1991. The experimental design was a randomized block with three replications onHW and two on ACH. Plot size was approximately 3300 m². Perennial ryegrass cultivars with a contrasting growth habit: Condesa (tetraploid), Barlet (diploid, erect) and Wendy (diploid, prostrate), were sown in mixture with the small-leaved white clover cultivar Gwenda. The soil was fertilized with P and K, but no N was applied. The pastures were continuously stocked during the growing season with steers in 1991 - 1993, and with pregnant heifers during 1994 - 1996.

Average sward height was maintained at 7-8 cm by adjusting the number of animals weekly. Rejected areas were topped at 8 cm height every month during the grazing season. Dry matter (DM) yield of clover leaves and stolons, stolon length and tiller numbers of various grass species were assessed in 20 circular 0.25 dm² cores per plot taken in April prior to the turnout of the animals and again in November. Because the amount of stolons fluctuates less than the amount of clover leaves, stolon abundance (m stolon m^{-2}) was used to estimate clover performance.

RESULTS AND DISCUSSION

There were clear effects of grass cultivar on clover abundance, which was consistently lowest in mixtures with Wendy (Fig. 1). Perennial ryegrass cv. Wendy had the highest tiller density and Condesa the lowest. Despite the lower ryegrass tiller density of Condesa compared with Barlet, mixtures with Condesa did not contain more clover. Thus factors other than ryegrass tiller density also affect clover growth in mixed swards. Mixtures with Barlet and Condesa had about the same number of tillers of the weed grass *Poa annua*, but mixtures with Wendy had significantly less weeds.

The clover stolon abundance strongly varied between sites and years years (Fig. 1), albeit not always in 3-4 year cycles as reported by Fothergill *et al.* (1996) and Schwinning and Parsons (1996). At all sites it reached a maximum, followed for unknown reasons by a sharp decline and a partial recovery, but this happened at different moments. In ACH the peak stolon abundance occurred in October 1992, 18 months after sowing, followed by a severe crash the next winter. Only from April 1994 onwards, there was a recovery of the stolon abundance. In HW the peak occurred from October 1992 (one year after sowing) until April 1993; the lowest stolon abundance was measured in April 1994 with a recovery thereafter; a lower peak was observed from October 1994 until April 1995, followed by a decline. Because the locations were within 7 km distance, the weather conditions were similar and differences will mainly have been caused by soil type and soil ecosystem associated with it. Besides an effect on the timing of fluctuations, soil type also had a large effect on the levels of species abundance and animal output (Elgersma and Schlepers, 1996).

Under the continuous-stocking management imposed and despite 'clover crashes' the small-leaved white clover cv. Gwenda has persisted in all paddocks for more than seven years after sowing.

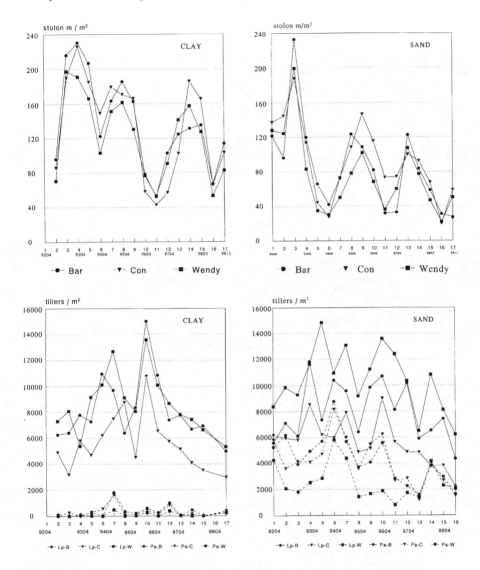

FIGURE 1. STOLON ABUNDANCE OF WHITE CLOVER (M.M⁻²) AND TILLER DENSITY OF PERENNIAL RYEGRASS (LP) (___) AND *POA ANNUA* (PA) (---) (NUMBER M⁻²) IN CONTINUOUSLY STOCKED PASTURES. IN THE UPPER FIGURES THE 'BULLET' SYMBOL (B) INDICATES WHITE CLOVER STOLON IN MIXTURES WITH GRASS CV. BARLET; IN THE LOWER FIGURES GRASS TILLERS IN MIXTURES WITH BARLET, ETC.

REFERENCES

Elgersma, A. and H. Schlepers, 1996. Cattle production on white clover - perennial ryegrass mixtures. pp. 142-144. In: Groen, A.F. and J. Van Bruchem (eds), 1996. Utilization of local feed resources in dairy cattle. EAAP Publication no. 84, Wageningen Pers, Wageningen. 153 pp.

Elgersma A. and H. Schlepers, 1999. Cattle production and botanical composition in continuously stocked grass-clover swards. Proceedings XVII International Grasslnd Congress, June 1997, Canada. Vol. 2, session 29, 87-88.4.

Fothergill, M., D. A. Davies, C. T. Morgan and J. R. Jones, 1996. White clover crashes. In: Younie, D. (ed.) Legumes in Sustainable Farming Systems, Occasional Symposium of the British Grassland Society, No.30, 172-176.

Schwinning S. and A. J. Parsons, 1996. In: Younie, D. (ed.) Legumes in Sustainable Farming Systems, Occasional Symposium of the British Grassland Society, No.30, 153-163.

Determining the C assimilation during winter by steady-state labelling with $^{13}CO_2$ in the field

S. V. PASUMARTY, A. LÜSCHER, M. FREHNER AND J. NÖSBERGER

Institute of Plant Sciences, Swiss Federal Institute of Technology (ETH), Universitätstrasse 2, 8092 Zürich, Switzerland

SUMMARY

Long-term measurement of often low rates of photosynthesis during winter without changing the environmental conditions (mainly temperature and shading by other leaves of the canopy) is a difficult task. The stable isotope ^{13}C provides a sensitive method to determine the gain and loss of C in the plant. Input of new C into the plant can be determined when the new C is isotopically distinct from the old C that is already in the plant. In the present experiment, white clover (*Trifolium repens* L.) plants were established in the fumigated plots of the Swiss FACE (Free Air Carbon dioxide Enrichment) array during summer and autumn (ä^{13}C = -18‰ of atmospheric CO_2). In late autumn the plants were switched to non-fumigated ambient atmosphere (ä^{13}C = -8‰ of CO_2) where they grew during winter and spring. Thus, during the winter/spring period the newly assimilated C was isotopically different (ä^{13}C = -27‰) from the old C (ä^{13}C = -36‰) and could be quantitatively determined. The results demonstrate that by mid March only about 50% of the total nonstructural carbohydrate (TNC) in the white clover stolons derived from old C that was assimilated before the 7th of November, while the other 50% derived from newly assimilated C during winter and early spring. In contrast, continuously defoliated plants showed a clearly reduced proportion of new C. Hence, this method allows to obtain integral long-term estimates of C assimilation in the field without affecting the environmental conditions. The results underline the significance of C assimilation during winter and early spring.

Keywords: C assimilation, ^{13}C stable isotope, nonstructural carbohydrate, overwintering, steady- state labelling, white clover

INTRODUCTION

One of the problems associated with the maintenance of an adequate proportion of white clover in grass/clover swards is the susceptibility of clover to winter damage (Woledge *et al.*, 1990). Maintaining a network of live stolon over winter is important as the amount of stolon present in early spring significantly relates to the subsequent annual yield (Collins *et al.*, 1991). Thus, the lack of cold hardiness and consequently the loss of stolon in winter may severely reduce clover yield in the following year. In early spring, white clover is at a competitive disadvantage with the earlier growing companion grasses. Until recently, it was assumed that the two desirable characteristics of (i) cold hardiness and (ii) active low-temperature growth are negatively correlated. However, the white clover cultivar AberHerald exhibited good winter hardiness coupled with fast regrowth in spring. The results from the COST 814 white clover experiment carried out in 11 European countries (Wachendorf, 2000) suggest that an important advantage of the cultivar AberHerald over Huia is due to a higher leaf area per bud during winter and in early spring (Stäheli, 1998; Stäheli *et al.*, 1997). It was suggested that the photosynthetic C assimilation, even if low, during winter and in early spring contributes significantly to the survival of white clover stolons and to the rate of regrowth of white clover in spring (Lüscher *et al.*, 1999). However, only short-term measurements of leaf photosynthesis of white clover under winter conditions are available (Woledge and Dennis, 1982; Woledge *et al.*, 1989). They show that the photosynthetic C assimilation of white clover leaves during winter is low, mainly due to the short photoperiod, low radiation and due to shading by grass leaves. Long-term measurement of such low rates of photosynthesis during winter without changing the environmental conditions (mainly temperature and shading by other leaves of the canopy) is a difficult task. Thus, reliable data on the C gains and C losses of white clover plants during winter are not available.

The aim of this contribution is to establish an experimental method, based on steady-state labelling with the stable ^{13}C isotope, that enables to determine C gain and C loss of field grown plants. With this set up the significance of the leaves for the C budget of white clover plants during winter was examined.

MATERIALS AND METHODS

The stable isotope ^{13}C provides a sensitive method to determine the C flux in the plant. Input of new C into the plant can be determined when the new C is isotopically distinct from that of the C already present in the plant. The ä^{13}C value in C3 plants has an overall mean of -27‰ (Boutton, 1991) when grown under ambient atmospheric CO_2 (ä^{13}C of -8‰). In the Swiss FACE experiment (Free Air CO_2 Enrichment; Hebeisen *et al.*, 1997; Lüscher *et al.*, 1998), the fossil derived CO_2 that was used to augment the concentration of atmospheric CO_2 is depleted in ^{13}C (ä^{13}C between -35‰ and -50‰). After mixing of the fossil derived CO_2 with the ambient atmosphere the ä^{13}C in the atmosphere in the experimental area of the Swiss FACE was -18‰. Thus, the plant material grown in the fumigated plots had a ä^{13}C of -36‰ (Nitschelm *et al.*, 1997; van Kessel *et al.*, 2000a).

For our experiment, white clover plants (cv. Huia and AberHerald) were established in the fumigated FACE plots during summer and autumn. In late autumn (7th of November) the plants were switched to ambient atmosphere where they grew during winter and spring. Thus, during the winter/spring period the newly assimilated C was isotopically different from the old C and could be quantitatively determined. One half of the plants was continuously defoliated throughout the whole winter; the other half of the plants were left undefoliated. The aim of this treatment was to vary the leaf area of the plants to be able to determine the significance of the leaves for the C assimilation during winter. At different sampling times between November and the following April, plants were harvested destructively. In the stolon material the concentration of total nonstructural carbohydrate (TNC) was measured as described by Fischer *et al.* (1997). The ä¹³C of the TNC was determined as described by Nitschelm *et al.* (1997) and the proportion of new C in the sample was calculated according to Balesdent *et al.* (1988).

RESULTS AND DISCUSSION

The ¹³C labelling was constant and sufficient to accurately determine new C assimilates. At the end of the establishment period in the fumigated FACE plots the plant material of *Trifolium repens* had a ä¹³C value of -36‰. This value was as observed in other experiments with *Trifolium repens* and *Lolium perenne* grown in the Swiss FACE experiment (Nitschelm *et al.*, 1997; van Kessel *et al.*, 2000a). For the reliability of the labelling technique two points are of primary importance. First the isotopic signal of the new assimilates has to be sufficiently different from the value of the old plant C. Second, the isotopic signal of the new C assimilated by the plant has to be relatively stable over the experimental period. Due to the isotopic discrimination during the photosynthesis process of the C3 plants the isotopic signal of the assimilated C cannot be accurately predicted based on the ä¹³C of the atmospheric CO_2 alone. Thus, the isotopic signal of the newly assimilated C has to be directly determined to be able to calculate the proportion of new C in the plant. The isotopic signal of the new assimilates was repeatedly measured in the leaf sucrose of our experimental plants. Sucrose in the leaves represents the pool of the recently assimilated C. The ä¹³C of this pool was quite constant at -27‰ throughout the experimental period. This value was within the expected range (Boutton 1991; Nitschelm *et al.*, 1997) for plants grown in ambient atmosphere. The ä¹³C value of this newly assimilated C was sufficiently different from that of the old C in the plant to enable an accurate determination of the proportion of the new C in the plants. In other experiments the ä¹³C differences between old and new C used to trace the C input into the soil were smaller or comparable to the values in our experiment (Balesdent *et al.*, 1988; Nitschelm *et al.*, 1997; van Kessel *et al.*, 2000a; 2000b)

Leaves contribute significantly to the C budget of white clover during winter

The results clearly demonstrate the importance of the remaining leaf area for the C budget of white clover during winter. The continuously defoliated (after 19ᵗʰ of December) plants had significantly lower concentrations of TNC in their stolons. The effect of the continuous defoliation was, however, not that strong as in a previous experiment where continuous defoliation was started in the beginning of November (Stäheli, 1998; Lüscher et al., 1999). There are two main reasons that can explain this difference. First, the continuous defoliation started in the present experiment later in autumn and thus the accumulation of TNC, which is strong during autumn (Stäheli, 1998), was not hindered by the continuous defoliation. Second, the plants that were not continuously defoliated in present experiment had a smaller residual leaf area as compared to the experiment of Stäheli (1998).

The results of the labelling experiment demonstrate that by mid March only about 50% of the total nonstructural carbohydrate of the white clover stolons derived from old C assimilated before the 7th of November, while the other 50% derived from newly assimilated C during winter and early spring. This is the first time that the significance of C assimilated during winter was quantitatively determined under field conditions. The continuously defoliated plants, in contrast, showed a clearly reduced proportion of new C. That is, from the beginning of the continuous defoliation (19th December) until mid March nearly no new C was assimilated by those plants. These results strongly support the idea that the C assimilated by the leaves are the key factor for an increased growth rate and a decreased death rate as observed in undefoliated white clover plants (Stäheli, 1998; Lüscher et al., 1999).

In conclusion, this method allows to obtain integral long-term estimates of C assimilation under field conditions without affecting the environmental conditions. The results underline the significance of C assimilation during winter and early spring for the C budget of white clover.

ACKNOWLEDGEMENTS

The study was supported by a grant from the Swiss Federal Office for Science and Education (COST).

REFERENCES

Balesdent, J., G. H. Wagner and A. Mariotti, 1988. Soil organic matter turnover in long-term field experiments as revealed by C-13 natural abundance. Soil Science Society of America Journal, 52: 118-124.

Boutton, T. W., 1991. Stable carbon isotope ratios of natural materials, II. Atmospheric, terrestrial, marine, and freshwater environments. In: Coleman, D.C.; Fry, B. (eds) Carbon Isotope Techniques. Academic Press, San Diego, CA, USA: 173-185.

Collins, R. P., M. J. Glendining and I. Rhodes, 1991. The relationships between stolon characteristics, winter survival and annual yield in white clover. Grass and Forage Science, 46: 51-61.

Fischer, B. U., M. Frehner, T. Hebeisen, S. Zanetti, F. Stadelmann, A. Lüscher, U. A. Hartwig, G. R.

Hendrey, H. Blum and J. Nösberger, 1997. Source-sink relations in *Lolium perenne* L. as reflected by carbohydrate concentrations in leaves and pseudo-stems during regrowth in a free air carbon dioxide enrichment (FACE) experiment. Plant Cell and Environment, 20: 945-952.

Hebeisen, T., A. Lüscher, S. Zanetti, B. U. Fischer, U. A. Hartwig, M. Frehner, G. R. Hendrey, H. Blum and J. Nösberger, 1997. Growth response of *Trifolium repens* L. and *Lolium perenne* L. as monocultures and bi-species mixture to free air CO_2 enrichment and management. Global Change Biology, 3: 149-160.

Lüscher, A., G. R. Hendrey and J. Nösberger, 1998. Long-term responsiveness to free air CO_2 enrichment of functional types, species and genotypes of plants from fertile permanent grassland. Oecologia, 113: 37-45.

Lüscher, A., B. Stäheli and J. Nösberger, 1999. Überwinterung und Wiederaustrieb von Weissklee im Frühling: Grosse Bedeutung der Blattfläche. Mitteilungen der Arbeitsgemeinschaft Grünland und Futterbau, 1: 120-123.

Nitschelm, J. J., A. Lüscher, U. A. Hartwig and C. van Kessel, 1997. Using stable isotopes to determine soil carbon input differences under ambient and elevated atmospheric CO_2 conditions. Global Change Biology, 3: 411-416.

Stäheli, B., 1998. Overwintering and spring growth of white clover - development and importance of leaves. Dissertation ETH No. 12514.

Stäheli, B., A. Lüscher and J. Nösberger, 1996. Growth of white clover plants in relation to temperature in winter and spring. Grassland and Land Use Systems. Proceedings of the 16th General Meeting of the European Grassland Federation Grado (Gorizia), Italy: pp309-312.

Wachendorf, M., 2000. A model approach to climatic, geographic and edaphic determinants of overwintering of white clover. This volume.

Woledge, J., V. Tewson and I. A. Davidson, 1990. Growth of grass/clover mixtures during winter. Grass and Forage Science, 45: 191-201.

Woledge, J. and W. D. Dennis, 1982. The effect of temperature on photosynthesis of ryegrass and white clover leaves. Annals of Botany, 50: 25-35.

Woledge, J., I. A. Davidson and V. Tewson, 1989. Photosynthesis during winter in ryegrass/white clover mixtures in the field. New Phytologist, 113: 275-281.

Van Kessel, C., W. R. Horwath, U. A. Hartwig, D. Harris and A. Lüscher, 2000a. Net soil carbon input under ambient and elevated CO_2 concentrations: Isotopic evidence after four years. Global Change Biology, 6: 435-444.

Van Kessel, C., J. Nitschelm, W. Horwath, D. Harris, F. Walley, A. Lüscher and U. A. Hartwig, 2000b. Carbon-13 input and turn-over in a pasture soil exposed to long term elevated atmospheric CO_2. Global Change Biology, 6: 123-135.

Significance of legumes and symbiotic N_2 fixation along an altitudinal gradient

K.A. JACOT, A. LÜSCHER, J. NÖSBERGER AND U.A. HARTWIG

Institute of Plant Sciences, Swiss Federal Institute of Technology (ETH), Universitätstrasse 2, 8092 Zürich, Switzerland

SUMMARY

The significance of symbiotic N_2 fixation for the N budget of the legume plant itself and for the whole species-rich grassland ecosystem were studied along an altitudinal gradient from 900 to 2770 m a.s.l. in the Swiss Alps. The following legume species were found and investigated: *Lotus corniculatus, L. alpinus, Vicia sativa, Trifolium pratense, T. repens, T. nivale, T. thalii, T. badium, T. alpinum*. Up to 2700 m a.s.l. legumes grew in the grassland communities; only the extreme conditions at and above the highest site (2770 m a.s.l.) did prevent the legumes to grow. Symbiotic N_2 fixation was measured by a ^{15}N isotope dilution method, developed for low N input, species-rich systems, and was compared with the ^{15}N natural abundance method. Over the whole altitudinal gradient, all legume species covered most of their N demand by symbiotically fixed N (59% to 93%). Even at the legumes' upper altitudinal limit, all legume species showed high proportion of N derived from symbiosis. Nevertheless, the total N input into the ecosystem through symbiotic N_2 fixation decreased significantly with increasing altitude due to (i) a strong decrease in plant growth and to (ii) a decrease in the proportion of legumes in the plant community from 15% to 5%. We conclude that symbiotic N_2 fixation is important for the N budget of legume plants up to their altitudinal limit, but its significance for the whole ecosystem decreases with increasing altitude.

Keywords: alpine ecosystem, Lotus, N budget, ^{15}N isotope dilution, Swiss Alps, Trifolium

INTRODUCTION

Symbiotic N_2 fixation of leguminous plants is important for the world-wide N budget, for forage production and for sustainable agriculture. The contribution of symbiotically fixed N_2 to the N yield of productive grassland can reach as much as 30 g m^{-2} y^{-1} (Boller and Nösberger, 1987; Zanetti *et al.*, 1996). The amount of N that is apparently transferred from legumes to non-legumes can reach 8 g m^{-2} y^{-1} in lowland grassland ecosystems (Boller and Nösberger, 1988; Zanetti *et al.*, 1997) and the positive effects of legumes to their companion grass was impressively demonstrated by Hebeisen *et al.* (1997). Plants that symbiotically fix N_2 occur also in several nutritionally and climatically stressed arctic, subarctic and alpine environments. The degree to which their symbiotic N_2 fixation contributes to the N yield of alpine grassland is, however, not known.

In regions of cool and temperate climate the legumes have, due to their higher temperature requirements compared to the companion grasses, a competitive disadvantage in grass / clover mixtures or in natural, permanent grassland. Consequently the proportion of legumes in grassland is often low. Thus, in the COST 814 common white clover experiment the performance of white clover in sown grass / white clover mixtures was studied at twelve sites over a latitudinal gradient ranging from Italy to Scandinavia (Wachendorf, 2000). However, the performance of native legumes and of their symbiotic N_2 fixation in species rich alpine ecosystems was not investigated. Alpine conditions are characterised by a relatively stressful climate with low temperatures, short growing seasons, and often low soil pH. Under these conditions both, the legume's growth and the performance of symbiotic N_2 fixation may be limited. The aim of this study was to examine the performance of native legume species and of symbiotic N_2 fixation in undisturbed species-rich permanent grassland as affected by changing environmental conditions along an altitudinal gradient in the Swiss Alps.

MATERIAL AND METHODS

The study was conducted on a southern slope of the upper Rhine valley between Sumvitg and Trun, approximately 45 km south-west of Chur in the eastern Alps in Switzerland (see Jacot *et al.*, 2000). The geology of this area is uniform and dominated by gneiss of granitic composition (siliceous soil substrate). The studies were carried out at six sites (900, 1380, 1900, 2100, 2300 and 2770 m a.s.l.) in unsown species-rich permanent grassland from 1996 to 1998.

The total aboveground dry mass yield was measured by cutting at each site 12 plots of 0.25 m². These harvests followed the recommended harvest dates for adapted grassland management in this region and were as follows: mid June, mid August, end of September at 900 m a.s.l.; end of June, mid September at 1380 m a.s.l.; end of July at 1900 m a.s.l.; end of August at 2100 and 2300 m a.s.l.. Plant material was separated into non-legumes and legumes and dried at 65 °C for 48h. N concentration of plant material (50 mg) was analysed using an elemental analyser.

Symbiotic N_2 fixation was assessed for all legume species at each site using an enriched ^{15}N isotope dilution method with various reference species. This method was developed especially for species-rich undisturbed grassland and was confirmed by the ^{15}N natural abundance method; for details see Jacot *et al.* (2000). The proportion of N derived from symbiotic N_2 fixation was calculated for each individual legume species at each altitude for each regrowth period according to McAuliffe *et al.* (1958).

RESULTS AND DISCUSSION

Symbiotic N_2 fixation in all legume plants was high throughout the whole altitudinal gradient.

Along the whole altitudinal gradient each legume species obtained between 59 and 93% of N through symbiotic N_2 fixation (Jacot *et al.*, 2000). Averaged over all legume species present at each altitude the proportion of N derived from symbiotic N_2 fixation was between 72% (at 900 m a.s.l.) and 88% (at 2600 m a.s.l.). There was no indication found that the proportion of N from symbiosis was reduced with increasing altitude. The results demonstrate that, even at the upper altitudinal limit of each individual legume species, symbiotic N_2 fixation was important for their N budget. This result is in contrast to results under controlled environments where symbiotic N_2 fixation was inhibited by low temperature and low soil pH, to a greater extent than plant growth (Kessler *et al.*, 1990; Nesheim and Boller, 1991). In our study both the temperature (from 13 °C at 900 m a.s.l. to 3 °C at 2770 m a.s.l.) and soil pH (from 5.6 at 900 m a.s.l. to 3.1 at 2770 m a.s.l.) decreased gradually with increasing altitude. It was therefore unexpected that with increasing altitude the proportion of N derived from symbiotic N_2 fixation remained as high. The explanation may be that in laboratory experiments such as those by Kessler *et al.* (1990), the same (lowland) genotypes of legume and rhizobium were used in all treatments, while in the present study the indigenous genotypes at each altitude were investigated. Adaptation of plant and rhizobium populations to their biotic and abiotic environment were demonstrated (Expert *et al.*, 1997; Lüscher and Jacquard, 1991; Lüscher *et al.* 1992; Schortemeyer *et al.*, 1996; Svenning *et al.*, 1991).

N input into the ecosystem by symbiotic N_2 fixation decreased with increasing altitude Both, the annual N yield and the annual input of N from symbiotic N_2 fixation into the grassland ecosystems decreased with increasing altitude (Jacot *et al.*, unpublished). The average input of N from symbiotic N_2 fixation over the two years ranged from 0.1 g m^{-2} y^{-1} at 2100 and 2300 m a.s.l. to 1.8 g m^{-2} y^{-1} at 900 and 1380 m a.s.l. The average contribution of symbiotically fixed N to the total annual yield of N over the two years increased from 0 % at 2770 m a.s.l. to 9 % at the two higher sites where legumes grew (2100 and 2300 m a.s.l.), to 16 % at the lower sites (900 and 1380 m a.s.l.). The decrease in the proportion of symbiotically fixed N_2 in the total N yield with increasing altitude was entirely due to a decrease in the yield proportion of legumes in the sward (Jacot *et al.*, unpublished). The average yield proportion of the legumes decreased from 15 % (900 and 1380 m a.s.l.) to 5 % (2100 and 2300 m a.s.l.).

Since symbiotic N_2 fixation is well adapted to the unfavourable environmental conditions at high altitude (i.e. the proportion of N derived from symbiosis is high over the whole altitudinal gradient), inappropriate N_2 fixation cannot be the reason for the decrease in the yield proportion of the legumes with increasing altitude. The low proportion of legumes at high altitudes may be due to a high availability of mineral N in comparison to the N demand of the ecosystem. Thereby total symbiotically fixed N at the ecosystem level may be down-regulated through a low legume proportion rather than through low

N$_2$ fixation in each legume according to the concept of N demand driven symbiotic N$_2$ fixation (Hartwig, 1998). In addition to the decreasing yield proportion of legumes with increasing altitude, they are more patchily distributed above 2100 m a.s.l. At high altitudes, only a few legume species grow and they tend to occur where the conditions for growth are most favourable, e.g. on southern slopes and under well watered conditions. Thus, increasingly growth limiting environmental conditions may explain the reduction in legume proportion and variability of microclimatic conditions may explain the increasing patchy presence of legumes.

In conclusion, at high altitudes the legume rhizobium system seems to be able to adapt to unfavourable environmental conditions resulting in a high performance of the symbiotic N$_2$ fixation at the individual plant level. At the whole ecosystem level, however, the significance of input of symbiotically fixed N is decreasing with increasing altitude due to a decreasing proportion of legumes in the sward.

ACKNOWLEDGEMENTS

The study was supported by a grant from the Swiss National Science Foundation. We thank J. Connolly for helpful statistical advice.

REFERENCES

Boller, B. C. and J. Nösberger, 1987. Symbiotically fixed nitrogen from field-grown white and red clover mixed with ryegrasses at low levels of ^{15}N-fertilization. Plant and Soil, 104: 219-226.

Boller, B. C. and J. Nösberger, 1988. Influence of dissimilarities in temporal and spatial N-uptake pattern on ^{15}N-based estimates of fixation and transfer of N in ryegrass-clover mixtures. Plant and Soil, 112: 167-175.

Expert, J. M., P. Jacquard, M. Obaton and A. Lüscher, 1997. Neighbourhood effect of genotypes of *Rhizobium leguminosarum* biovar trifolii, *Trifolium repens* and *Lolium perenne*. Theoretical and Applied Genetics, 94: 486-492.

Hartwig, U. A., 1998. The regulation of symbiotic N$_2$ fixation: a conceptual model of N feedback from the ecosystem to the gene expression level. Perspectives in Plant Ecology Evolution and Systematics, 1: 92-120.

Hebeisen, T., A. Lüscher, S. Zanetti, B. U. Fischer, U. A. Hartwig, M. Frehner, G. R. Hendrey, H. Blum and J. Nösberger, 1997. Growth response of *Trifolium repens* L. and *Lolium perenne* L. as monocultures and bi-species mixture to free air CO$_2$ enrichment and management. Global Change Biology, 3: 149-160.

Jacot, K. A., A. Lüscher, J. Nösberger and U. A. Hartwig, 2000. Symbiotic N$_2$ fixation of various legume species along an altitudinal gradient in the Alps. Soil Biology and Biochemistry, in press.

Kessler, W., B. C. Boller and J. Nösberger, 1990. Distinct influence of root and shoot temperature on nitrogen fixation by white clover. Annals of Botany, 65: 341-346.

Lüscher, A., J. Connolly and P. Jacquard, 1992. Neighbour specificity between *Lolium perenne* and *Trifolium repens* from a natural pasture. Oecologia, 91: 404-409.

Lüscher, A. and P. Jacquard, 1991. Coevolution between interspecific plant competitors? Trends in Ecology and Evolution, 6: 355-358.

McAuliffe, C., D. S. Chamblee, H. Uribe-Arango and W. W. Woodhouse, 1958. Influence of inorganic nitrogen on nitrogen fixation by legumes as revealed by [15]N. Agronomy Journal, 50: 334-337.

Nesheim, L. and B. C. Boller, 1991. Nitrogen fixation by white clover when competing with grasses at moderately low temperatures. Plant and Soil, 122: 47-56.

Schortemeyer, M., U. A. Hartwig, G. R. Hendrey and M. J. Sadowsky, 1996. Microbial community changes in the rhizospheres of white clover and perennial ryegrass exposed to free air carbon dioxide enrichment (FACE). Soil Biology and Biochemistry, 28: 1717-1724.

Svenning, M. M., O. Junttila and B. Solheim, 1991. Symbiotic growth of indigenous white clover (*Trifolium repens*) with local *Rhizobium-leguminosarum* biovar *trifolii*. Physiologia Plantarum, 83: 381-389.

Wachendorf, M., 2000. A model approach to climatic, geographic and edaphic determinants of overwintering of white clover. This volume.

Zanetti S., U. A. Hartwig, A. Lüscher, T. Hebeisen, M. Frehner, B. U. Fischer, G. R. Hendrey, H. Blum and J. Nösberger, 1996. Stimulation of symbiotic N_2 fixation in *Trifolium repens* L. under elevated atmospheric pCO_2 in a grassland ecosystem. Plant Physiology, 112: 575-583.

Zanetti S., U. A. Hartwig, C. van Kessel, A. Lüscher, T. Hebeisen, M. Frehner, B. U. Fischer, G. R. Hendrey, H. Blum and J. Nösberger, 1997. Does nitrogen restrict the CO_2 response of fertile grassland lacking legumes? Oecologia, 112: 17-25.

White clover overwintering under snow conditions

P. NYKÄNEN-KURKI AND T. TONTTI

MTT, Agricultural Research Centre of Finland, FIN-50600 Mikkeli, Finland

SUMMARY

In order to evaluate the performance of white clover under snow conditions, a field trial with binary mixtures of perennial ryegrass and white clover cultivars AberHerald, Huia, Jögeva 4 and AberCrest was carried out in Mikkeli in 1993-1997. Overwintering, with morphological aspects and carbohydrate reserves in autumn and spring, was determined according to the common protocol of the COST 814 White Clover Group. On average, the permanent snow cover lasted in Mikkeli from 14 November until 27 April. White clover only started to branch in autumn 1993 and the winter damage of the first winter varied from 37 % in AberHerald to 73 % in Huia. In the subsequent years Huia was damaged the most (30-80 %) and AberHerald together with Jögeva 4 the least (0-20 %). During the first two winters stolon length was similar in AberHerald and Jögeva 4. AberHerald showed both a rapid start of growth and a high growth rate at low temperatures. The conditions of the last winter (cold periods without snow cover) favoured AberHerald in comparison to Jögeva 4. The results of morphological and biochemical parameters suggested higher consumption of carbohydrate reserves during winter in AberHerald than in Jögeva 4. AberCrest was poorer than AberHerald but AberCrest performed as well as Jögeva 4 in consideration of morphological parameters.

Keywords: AberCrest, AberHerald, overwintering, snow cover, stolon parameters, Trifolium repens

INTRODUCTION

White clover is a valuable but vulnerable species, and there is a lack of suitable cultivars to overwinter in Finland. The first results of new white clover cultivars are encouraging (Nykänen-Kurki and Kivijärvi, 1996). White clover overwintering under uninterrupted snow cover was evaluated according to the common protocol of the COST 814 White Clover Group (Wachendorf, 2000). Stolon parameters and carbohydrate reserves are presented over three winters.

MATERIALS AND METHODS

A field trial with binary mixtures of perennial ryegrass cultivars Preference and Riikka and white clover cultivars AberHerald, Huia, Jögeva 4 and AberCrest with four replicates was established in Mikkeli on 3 June 1993. The soil was loam sand, gleyic podzol, pH 6.2 (H_2O). The swards were cut three times per growing season and fertilized with 25 kg ha^{-1},N per cut. White clover overwintering was observed during 1993-1997. Stolon length and weight and total growing point number were determined in autumn and spring. Four sub-samples (cores 12 cm in diameter and 10 cm deep) per 5 m x 5 m plot were taken. Stolon starch content was analysed by the Boehringer Mannheim UV method and total nonstructural carbohydrate content by the modified Weinman method.

The mean monthly temperature was below zero from November to March during the experiment. The soil was under continuous snow cover from 14 November until 27 April on average. The snow cover was rather complete during the first winters and it started two to three weeks earlier than normal. During the last winter, snow cover started two weeks later than normal. Besides that, in March the fields were not covered by snow but the temperatures were below zero. Snowfall started again at the end of March and there was 15-25 cm snow in April. Over the years, the snow cover was 69 cm at the deepest. The growing period started on 4 May and ended on 9 October on average. May was always exceptionally cold and August warm.

RESULTS AND DISCUSSION

The swards were well established in 1993, but white clover cultivars only started to branch in autumn. Stolon length averaged 11 m m^{-2} in all plots at the beginning of the first winter, and winter damage varied from 37 % in AberHerald to 73 % in Huia. Also in the subsequent years Huia was damaged the most (30-80 %) and AberHerald together with Jögeva 4 the least (0-20 %). Winter damage of AberCrest varied from 0 to 50 %. Huia performed more poorly than other cultivars as measured by stolon parameters or stolon starch content (Tables 1-3).

AberHerald showed both a rapid start of growth and a high growth rate at low temperatures (Svenning et al., 1997). Among cultivars, Jögeva 4 was the best adapted to the region at the beginning of the trial. During the first two winters stolon length in AberHerald was similar to Jögeva 4 but in the last winter (cold periods without snow) there were significantly more stolons in AberHerald (Table 1). In autumn, both stolon weight (stolon weight per area) and specific stolon weight (stolon weight per stolon length) were always greater in AberHerald than in Jögeva 4 (Table 2). After disappearance of snow (early spring) there was no difference. One month later the specific stolon weight was again greater in AberHerald. Similarly to stolon length, AberHerald had more stolons also according to weight parameters in the spring 1997. Stolon parameters of AberCrest were often equal to Jögeva 4. The growing points averaged 2350 m^{-2} in AberHerald

TABLE 1. WHITE CLOVER STOLON LENGTH IN MIKKELI IN 1994-1997.

	5 Oct	5 May	31 May	21 Sep	7 May	29 May
	Stolon length, m m^{-2}					
	1994	1995	1995	1995	1996	1996
Huia	95 a	19 b	13 b	57 c	19 b	19 b
AberHerald	111 a	66 a	64 a	113 a	59 a	59 a
Jögeva 4	103 a	49 ab	57 a	94 ab	39 ab	39 ab
AberCrest	93 a	34 ab	44 a	79 bc	44 ab	44 ab
	1996	1997	1997			
Huia	52 c	49 b	46 b			
AberHerald	112 a	95 a	94 a			
Jögeva 4	83 bc	63 b	48 b			
AberCrest	104 ab	67 b	57 b			

Differing small letters indicate significance P<0.05.

TABLE 2. WHITE CLOVER STOLON WEIGHT IN MIKKELI IN 1994-1997.

	5 Oct	5 May	31 May	21 Sep	7 May	29 May
	Stolon weight, g m^{-2}					
	1994	1995	1995	1995	1996	1996
Huia	70 C[***]	12 B	6 B	42 C	22 b	28 a
AberHerald	127 A[***]	68 A	52 A	162 A	66 a	51 a
Jögeva 4	90 BC[***]	46 AB	35 AB	93 B	32 ab	27 a
AberCrest	92 B[***]	32 AB	32 AB	88 B	42 ab	45 a
	1996	1997	1997			
Huia	48 C[***]	38 B	35 B[***]			
AberHerald	168 A[***]	116 A	109 A[***]			
Jögeva 4	91 BC[***]	69 B	43 B[***]			
AberCrest	130 AB[***]	69 B	54 B[***]			

Differing small letters indicate significance P<0.05, capital letters P<0.01 and [***]P<0.001.

and Jögeva 4 in autumn. In early spring the number was greater in AberHerald than in Jögeva 4 (1780 vs. 980 m^{-2}). One month later there was no difference, the growing points averaging 2060 m^{-2}. AberCrest was always equal to Jögeva 4 in this respect.

In autumn the total nonstructural carbohydrate contents tended to be higher in AberHerald than in Jögeva 4 (0.371 vs.0.323 g g^{-1} stolon DM), but the difference was significant only in 1996. In early spring, the contents were the opposite. Later in spring the carbohydrate reserves were again greater in AberHerald (0.371 vs.0.323 g g^{-1} stolon DM) which accumulated starch more rapidly (Table 3). The results of biochemical parameters suggested higher consumption of carbohydrate reserves in AberHerald than in Jögeva 4 during winter.

TABLE 3. STARCH CONTENT OF WHITE CLOVER STOLONS IN MIKKELI IN 1994-1997.

	9 Oct	30 Oct	27 Apr	25 May	Jun 4
	Starch, mg g⁻¹ stolon DM				
	1994	1994	1995	1995	
Huia	53 b	33 b	1 a	12 b	
AberHerald	87 a	55 a	4 a	22 a	
Jögeva 4	82 a	59 a	4 a	8 b	
AberCrest	97 a	59 a	6 a	11 b	
	1995	1995	1996	1996	
Huia	55 c	44 c	1 b	2 a	
AberHerald	124 a	89 a	9 a	6 a	
Jögeva 4	81 bc	60 bc	5 ab	4 a	
AberCrest	92 ab	72 ab	4 ab	5 a	
	1996	1996	1997	1997	1997
Huia	124 BC	84 B	1 a	1 B	12 B***
AberHerald	168 A	122 A	6 a	5 A	41 A***
Jögeva 4	116 C	87 B	3 a	5 A	20 B***
AberCrest	140 B	113 A	1 a	3 AB	19 B***

Differing small letters indicate significance P<0.05, capital letters P<0.01 and ***P<0.001.

CONCLUSIONS

Huia showed no potential to survive under a 5-month uninterrupted snow cover. AberHerald performed at least as well as Jögeva 4. AberHerald showed a rapid start of growth at low temperatures. Cold periods without snow favoured it in comparison with Jögeva 4. AberCrest was damaged more than AberHerald but it was often equal to Jögeva 4.

REFERENCES

Nykänen-Kurki, P. and P. Kivijärvi, 1996. Growth and seed production characteristics of white clover cultivars in the Lake District of Finland. Grassland Science in Europe, 1: 127-131.

Svenning, M. M., K. Røsnes and O. Junttila, 1997. Frost tolerance and biochemical changes during hardening and dehardening in contrasting white clover populations. Physiologia Plantarum, 101: 31-37.

Wachendorf, M., 2000. A model approach to climatic, geographic and edaphic determinants of overwintering of white clover. Invited paper at the Final Conference of COST 814, 10-13 May 2000, Pordenone, Italy. This volume.

Extensive and intensive lamb grazing on white clover pasture

R. SORMUNEN-CRISTIAN[1] AND P. NYKÄNEN-KURKI[2]

MTT, Agricultural Research Centre of Finland, [1] FIN-31600 Jokioinen, [2] FIN-50600 Mikkeli

SUMMARY

A field trial of grass/white clover mixtures of meadow fescue/perennial ryegrass/timothy/white clover cultivars AberHerald and Jögeva 4 was established in June 1997 on clay soil. A grass-only mixture was included as a control plot. Except for the control, nitrogen fertilization was not applied. All swards were nearly totally killed due to ice encasement, and they were reseeded in May 1998. AberHerald was more poorly established in autumn 1998 than Jögeva 4. Winter damage averaged 44 and 64% in AberHerald and Jögeva 4, respectively. Clover content of AberHerald and Jögeva 4 averaged 4 and 11% in 1997, 8 and 28% in 1998 and 3 and 12% in 1999, respectively. Clover content did not differ between grazing intensities. In 1998, extensive grazing favoured white clover DM yield. Over all periods, intensive white clover plots were grazed by growing lambs for 1670 days and extensive ones for 1467 days. The grazing intensity of the common protocol was not met due to establishing and overwintering problems and drought in 1999.

Keywords: AberHerald, grazing, Jögeva 4, lamb, pasture, Trifolium repens

INTRODUCTION

White clover is often damaged due to the long winters in Finland and, consequently, its dry matter production decreases. Promising results of white clover performance on lamb pasture have also been reported, however (Sormunen-Cristian et al., 1996). Cultivation techniques like grazing regime, white clover cultivar and species of companion grasses besides pedoclimatic conditions have a strong influence on white clover persistence and content in a sward. The aim of this study was to investigate the effect of gentle and hard grazing regimes on white clover winter damage and summer performance without N application over a three-year period.

MATERIALS AND METHODS

Lamb pastures with white clover (*Trifolium repens* L.) and grass mixtures of meadow fescue (*Festuca pratensis* Huds.)/perennial ryegrass (*Loliumm perenne* L.)/timothy (*Phleum pratense* L.) were established in June 1997 with four replicates on clay soil in Jokioinen (60° 54´N, 23° 30´E, 107 m above sea level). White clover cultivars AberHerald and Jögeva 4 were the main plots and grazing intensities extensive (pre-grazing herbage mass 1500 → post-grazing herbage mass 800 kg DM ha⁻¹) and intensive (1100 → 400 kg DM ha⁻¹) the sub-plots. A grass-only mixture was included as a control plot. The seed mixture was grass 25 kg ha⁻¹/white clover 3 kg ha⁻¹. Clover seeds were inoculated by rhizobia before sowing. At sowing the plots (6 x 40 m) were fertilized with 36 kg ha⁻¹ P and 42 kg ha⁻¹ K. In 1997, the control plot was not fertilized with N, but on 30 June 1998, 40 kg ha⁻¹ N was applied.

The soil was covered permanently with snow from 20 December 1997 to 30 March 1998, except for warm period of 22 - 27 February without snow. All swards were nearly totally killed due to ice encasement, and they were reseeded (grass 15 kg ha⁻¹/white clover 3 kg ha⁻¹) on 27 May 1998. The following winter the temperature was fluctuating in December and in January again causing freezing and thawing. Ice encasement caused some damage, but no reseeding was done in spring 1999.

Dry matter (DM) was determined before and after grazing. Botanical composition was determined on a DM basis. Samplings for botanical composition and feeding values were based on five cuttings, each of 10 x 100 cm, taken with clippers before grazing. Morphological determinations were made in autumn just before the start of the winter, in spring at the beginning of the growing season and once a month in the summer.

In 1997, extensive pastures were grazed twice (29 August - 16 September and 22 - 29 September) and intensive pastures once (29 August- 29 September) by three growing lambs. The following years, all pastures were grazed twice by four to six lambs (3-8 August and 28 September-5 October 1998, and 8-18 June and 20-26 July 1999).

RESULTS AND DISCUSSION

Winter damage averaged 71% in all plots in spring 1998. In autumn 1998, AberHerald was more poorly established than Jögeva 4. The following winter, winter damage averaged 44 and 64% in AberHerald and Jögeva 4, respectively. Still, stolon parameters of AberHerald showed worse performance in summer 1999 than those of Jögeva 4 (Fig. 1): stolon length averaged 7 and 22 m m⁻², stolon weight 8.8 and 25.3 g m⁻² and total growing point number 325 and 863 points m⁻², respectively. Clover content averaged 4 and 11% in 1997, 8 and 28% in 1998 and 3 and 12% in 1999 in AberHerald and Jögeva 4, respectively. Clover content did not differ between grazing intensities. Grazing in September seemed to increase winter damages. Intensive treatment was destructive, but even extensive treatment seemed to be too hard in autumn.

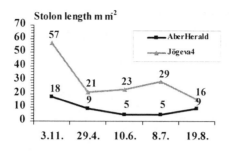

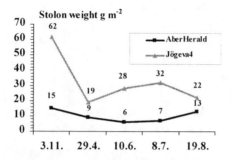

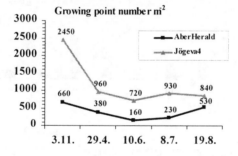

FIGURE 1. WHITE CLOVER STOLON LENGTH, WEIGHT AND GROWING POINT NUMBER IN GRASS MIXTURE UNDER LAMB GRAZING. JOKIOINEN 1998-1999.

The grazing intensity of the common protocol was not met due to establishing and overwintering problems and drought in 1999. At the beginning of grazing, herbage on offer varied according to period from 930 to 4030 kg ha⁻¹ and from 980 to 3640 kg ha⁻¹ in extensive and intensive pastures, respectively. At the end of grazing it varied from 500 to 1430 kg ha⁻¹ and from 340 to 850 kg ha⁻¹, respectively. Sward height of all plots averaged 31, 17 and 22 cm in 1997, 1998 and 1999, respectively. Swards were not fully dense due to the sowing method, and sward height was higher than the recommended 5 - 8 cm for continuous sheep grazing (Hodgson, 1990).

In 1997, neither white clover cultivar nor grazing intensity affected the white clover DM yield of the mixture (Fig. 2). In 1998 and 1999, white clover DM yield averaged 330 and 580 kg ha⁻¹ and 30 and 150 kg ha⁻¹ in AberHerald and Jögeva 4, respectively. In 1998, white clover yield was higher under extensive than under intensive grazing (710 vs. 500 kg DM ha⁻¹). In 1999, the growth was suppressed by severe drought. Over all periods, intensive white clover plots were grazed for 1670 days and extensive ones for 1467 days.

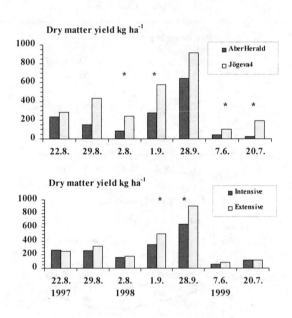

FIGURE 2. WHITE CLOVER DRY MATTER YIELD OF GRASS MIXTURE UNDER LAMB GRAZING. JOKIOINEN 1997-1999. * SIGNIFICANT DIFFERENCE (P=0.05).

In 1997, white clover-grass and control pastures contained crude protein 176 g kg⁻¹ DM and neutral detergent fibre 526 g kg⁻¹ DM. Organic matter digestibility (OMD) averaged 795 g kg⁻¹. In agreement with Munro et al. (1992), the OMD was higher in the white clover/grass swards than in the grass/only swards. Over the years 1997 and 1998, mineral contents of Ca, Mg, P and K averaged 6.9, 2.1, 4.0 and 39 g kg⁻¹ DM, respectively, and those of Fe, Cu, Zn and Mn 110.5, 9.4, 29.6 and 133.7 mg kg⁻¹ DM, respectively.

CONCLUSIONS

Jögeva 4 performed clearly better than AberHerald under harsh conditions. Extensive lamb grazing resulted in higher DM yield of white clover than intensive grazing.

REFERENCES

Hodgson, J., 1990. Grazing Management Science into Practice. Longman Handbooks in Agriculture. Longman Group UK Ltd. 203.

Munro, J. M. M., D. A. Davies, W. B. Evans and R. V. Scurlock, 1992. Animal production evaluation of herbage varieties. 1. Comparison of Aurora with Frances, Talbot and Melle perennial ryegrasses when grown alone and with clover. Grass and Forage Science, 47: 259 – 273.

Sormunen-Cristian, R., P. Nykänen-Kurki and J. Peltola, 1996. On white clover-based grazing of lamb pastures. In: Parente, G. (eds.). Grassland and Land Use Systems. Proceedings of the 16th General Meeting of the European Grassland Federation, Grado (Gorizia), Italy, September 15–19, 1996: 625-628.

Does winter affect the growth potential of white clover buds?

G. CORBEL[1], C. ROBIN[1], C. BAZARD[2] AND A. GUCKERT [1]

[1] Laboratoire Agronomie-Environnement-INRA, BP 172, 54 505 Vandoeuvre lès Nancy
[2] INRA-SAD, 88 500 Mirecourt, France

SUMMARY

In order to compare the growth potential of buds of white clover (*Trifolium repens* L.) we used a method to assess the potential for activity of shoot buds and root primordia. Two contrasting cultivars (cv. AberHerald and Grasslands Huia) were tested. The growth potential was evaluated following the excision of individual stolon nodes sampled in the field on experimental plots located in eastern part of France. Two populations of nodes were sampled: 1) the youngest node emerged from the apical bud (node 1), 2) the third node behind the apex (node 3). Nodes were incubated in controlled conditions after dissection and the outgrowth of axillary buds and roots was recorded every day for a week. The study demonstrated a seasonal influence on the potential activity of axillary buds and root primordia, particularly for buds at node 3. The data indicated a genetic variation in potential for outgrowth during winter: AberHerald had a higher percentage of potentially active buds than Huia during winter, irrespective of the node position. Moreover AberHerald buds had faster rates of outgrowth than Huia buds. We conclude that the fate of the buds is certainly a key point in relation both to cultivar differences in winter tolerance and to their growth potential when temperatures increase.

Keywords: bud bank, growth potential, nodes, overwintering, potentially active buds, white clover

INTRODUCTION

White clover (*Trifolium repens* L.) is a common forage legume of temperate pastures world-wide. However, its contribution to total yield varies within and between years (Collins *et al.* 1991). In continental climates, the persistence of clover was determined by the ability of stolons to survive the winter (Harris *et al.*, 1983; Woledge *et al.*, 1990) and to compete with the companion grass in the growing season (Collins *et al.*, 1991).

In established pastures, white clover regenerates mainly from the bud bank (Harper, 1977) of surviving stolons in spring (Turkington *et al.* ,1979). The development of axillary buds to form plagiotropic branches allows the plant to explore patchy environments and to compete with the companion grass. In order to examine variation in bud activity during winter and spring, we adapted a method published by Newton and Hay (1992) which assesses the potential for growth of shoots and roots of white clover buds sampled in field conditions. The purposes of our study were to 1) study the viability of buds during winter and spring in the field so as to evaluate the extent of winter damage to buds ; 2) determine whether there is a genetic influence on the viability of buds during winter and spring.

MATERIALS AND METHODS

The experimental site was in the INRA-SAD of Mirecourt, in the eastern part of France. Two medium-leaved white clover cultivars were compared: 1) AberHerald, selected in Aberystwyth from material collected in the Swiss Alps. This cultivar is reputedly more tolerant to winter extremes and shows good spring growth (Rhodes and Fothergill, 1992; Caradus and Woodfield, 1997) 2) Grasslands Huia is produced in New Zealand under mild oceanic conditions. On six occasions from February to May 1998, stolons of each cultivar were sampled. The potential activity of buds was evaluated following the excision of individual nodes from a stolon. We defined as a node, a phytomer with the subtending leaf and the roots removed and internode was restricted to 2mm proximal and distal to the node (Newton and Hay, 1992). We sampled two populations of nodes: 1) the nearest node emerged from the apical bud (node 1), 2) the third node emerged from the apical bud behind the apex (node 3). After dissection, nodes were placed in plastic boxes, sealed by clear plastic sheet to maintain constant high humidity around the nodes and then incubated in a growth chamber. Nodes were assessed for shoot and root appearance every day for a week. Shoot appearance was defined as occurring when the unfolding leaf had reached 0.1 on the Carlson scale (Carlson, 1966) and root appearance as when a root bud had made >1mm of growth (Newton and Hay, 1992). We considered as "active buds" all shoot and root buds showing growth as described above.

RESULTS AND DISCUSSION

Influence of node position
The proportion of potentially active buds (shoot and root) was high (above 80%) from February to May for the node nearest the apical bud (Fig. 1). However, the proportion of potentially active buds declined with the distance of nodes from apex. At the third node, the proportion of active shoot and root buds was significantly lower than for node 1 from February to March, with less than 50% of buds being active at the end of March. Low temperature of winter had no effect on the potential activity of buds at node 1 but influenced the potential activity of buds of node 3. This lower potential activity of buds at node 3 could be explained by: 1) the exposure period to low

temperatures; buds at node 3 have been exposed over a longer time 2) a decrease of bud activity attributable to ageing and/or to a gradient of resources along the stolon (Newton and Hay, 1992). The method did not discriminate amongst the population of nodes those that were dead or dormant.

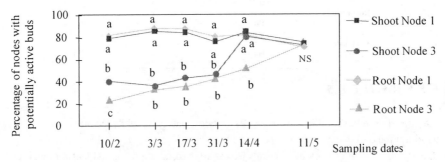

FIGURE 1. PERCENTAGE OF NODES WITH POTENTIALLY ACTIVE SHOOT AND ROOT BUDS, FROM NODES SAMPLED IN FIELD ON 6 HARVEST OCCASIONS, AFTER 7 DAYS OF INCUBATION. MEANS WITH THE SAME LETTERS ARE NOT SIGNIFICANTLY DIFFERENT AT 5% (TUCKEY TEST, P<0.05). VALUES ARE THE MEAN OF THE TWO CULTIVARS (N=64).

Genetic influence

During winter, the proportion of potentially active buds of AberHerald was higher than for Huia, with significant differences for node 3 (data not shown). Moreover, AberHerald buds had faster rates of outgrowth than Huia buds (Table 1). The mean duration required for 50% of the buds to produce shoots at nodes 3 was significantly lower for Aberherald than for Huia. In March, whereas Huia needed 7 days to reach 50 % of emergence of shoot and root from buds, AberHerald needed only 4.3 days. These data confirmed the superior cold tolerance of AberHerald which has been consistently demonstrated through morphological investigations : leaf size, leaf appearance rate, mean leaf area per shoot axis, stolon thickness (Collins *et al.*, 1991; Robin *et al.*, 1999) and physiological processes: reserve storage and utilisation (Guinchard *et al.*, 1997; Frankow-Lindberg 1997, Corbel *et al.*, 1999).

ACKNOWLEDGEMENTS

The authors are grateful to Patrice Marchal for his skilful technical assistance.

TABLE 1. MEAN DURATION (IN DAYS) REQUIRED TO 50 PERCENT OF EMERGENCE OF SHOOT AND ROOT FROM BUD ON NODE 1 AND NODE 3, ON FEBRUARY, MARCH AND MAY.

Cultivar		February	March	May
Shoot node 1				
	Huia	3.8	3.5	5.3
	AberHerald	3.8	4.0	4.0
Shoot node 3				
	Huia	6.8 **	7.0 *	4.3 *
	AberHerald	4.0	4.3	2.5
Root node 1				
	Huia	4.0	3.0	4.0
	AberHerald	2.8	3.0	4.3
Root node 3				
	Huia	7.0	7.0 *	1.8
	AberHerald	5.8	4.3	3.0

REFERENCES

Caradus, J. R. and Woodfiled, D. R., 1997. World checklist of white clover varieties II. New Zealand Journal of Agricultural Research, 40: 115-206.

Carlson, G. E., 1966. Growth of clover leaves after complete or partial leaf removal. Crop Science, 6: 419-422.

Corbel, G., Ch. Robin, B. E. Frankow-Lindberg, A. Ourry and A. Guckert, 1999. Regrowth of white clover after chilling : assimilate partitioning and vegetative storage proteins. Crop Science, 39 (6): 1756-1761.

Collins, R. P., M. J. Glendinning and I. Rhodes, 1991. The relationships between stolon characteristics, winter survival and annual yields in white clover (*Trifolium repens* L.). Grass & Forage Science 46, 51-61.

Frankow-Lindberg, B. E., 1997. Assimilate partitioning in three white clover cultivars in the autumn, and the effect of defoliation. Annals of Botany, 79: 83-87.

Guinchard, M. P., Ch. Robin, P. Grieu and A. Guckert , 1997. Cold acclimation in white clover subjected to chilling and frost : changes in water and carbohydrates status. European Journal of Agronomy, 6: 225-233.

Harper, J.L. (Ed.), 1977. Population Biology of Plants. London: Academic Press.

Harris, W., I. Rhodes and S. S. Mee, 1983. Observations on environmental and genotypic influences on the overwintering of white clover. Journal of Applied Ecology 20, 609-624.

Newton, P. C. D. and M. J. M. Hay, 1992. Technique for evaluating the potential for growth of shoot and root buds of white clover (*Trifolium repens* L.). Journal of Agricultural Science, 119: 179-183.

Rhodes, I. and M. Fothergill, 1992. Plant genetics and breeding. In White Clover Breeding. 33-34. Aberystwyth: AFRC. Institute of Grassland and Environmental Research.

Robin, Ch., G. Corbel, M.P. Guinchard, C. Bazard and A. Guckert, 1999. Comportement hivernal et repousse printanière du trèfle blanc: importance du cultivar. Fourrages 157, 21-32.

Turkington, R., M. A. Cahn, A. Vardy and J. L. Harper, 1979. The growth distribution and neighbour relationships of *Trifolium repens* in a permanent pasture. Journal of Ecology, 67: 231-243.

Woledge, J., V. Tewson and I. A. Davidson, 1990. Growth of grass/clover mixtures during winter. Grass & Forage Science, 45: 191-202.

Analysis of climatical and management impacts on the growth of white clover/grass swards with a dynamic growth model

M. WACHENDORF, A. KORNHER, S. PUZIO AND F. TAUBE

Department of Grass and Forage Science, University of Kiel, 24098 Kiel, Germany

SUMMARY

In the frame of the COST 814 action a field experiment was conducted to investigate herbage production of mixtures with white clover (*Trifolium repens,* cs. AberHerald, Huia, Milkanova, N. F. G. Gigant) and perennial ryegrass (*Lolium perenne,* cv. Preference, Vigor). To obtain the seasonal pattern of herbage production four series of plots were cut in sequence, in each case after four weeks' growth, so that one series was cut each week. Performance over the growing season was significantly reduced for swards with Huia. Growth was not influenced by the grass variety. The impact of climatic factors on the growth of swards with AberHerald, Milkanova and Preference was determined by an evaluation of the data with a dynamic model. Simulations for different defoliation regimes illustrate the impact of defoliation time and frequency on the total annual performance of clover/grass swards. Irrespective of weather conditions frequent defoliation (e.g. rotational pasture) resulted in lowest yields whereas highest yields were achieved in a regime with longer growth intervals (e.g. silage regime). Generally the use of weather-driven models supports the transfer of findings from few experimental sites to other environments or larger landscape units.

Keywords: drought stress, dry matter yield, growth model, perennial ryegrass, simulation, white clover

INTRODUCTION

Forage production on permanent grassland in Germany often suffers from a lack of water during dry spells in the growing season. Particularly on sandy soils biomass accumulation can be strongly reduced. The main purpose of this study was to describe the effects of weather conditions on the growth of clover/grass swards by means of a dynamic weather-based model. Once mathematical functions between stands and the environment (precipitation, temperature, radiation and available water capacity) have been developed through some systematic field trials, growth of swards can be simulated under any weather and site conditions. The study was conducted in the frame of the COST 814 Action "Crop Development for Cool and Wet Regions of Europe".

MATERIALS AND METHODS

In the COST 814 field experiment the growth of four white clover (*Trifolium repens* L.) varieties (AberHerald, Huia, Milkanova, N. F. G. Gigant) grown in binary mixtures with two varieties of perennial ryegrass (*Lolium perenne* L.) (Preference, Vigor), was investigated in two consecutive years (1995 and 1996). The swards received no mineral nitrogen. The soil was a sandy loamy luvisol. Soil nutrient status and pH were maintained at a sufficient level. To obtain the seasonal pattern of herbage production four series of plots were cut in sequence, in each case after four weeks' growth, so that one series was cut each week. This technique has been widely used to evaluate species and varieties (Corrall and Fenlon, 1978). From the plots with AberHerald and Milkanova cut in series samples were taken weekly during the growing season. Dry matter yield of the total swards and their components was calculated and used for parameterization of the growth model FOPROQ (Kornher and Nyman, 1992). Due to severe drought in spring and summer of 1996 only data from 1995 could be used for development of the model. Computer simulations were performed for three different weather conditions (nearly optimum, dry spring, dry autumn) and various defoliation regimes (pasture, hay pasture, silage regime).

RESULTS AND DISCUSSION

The following results refer to the year 1995 as these data were used for modelling. The clover content of swards was approx. 70 g 100 g^{-1} DM on average for the total growth period and varied from 40 to 80 g 100 g^{-1} DM for spring/autumn and summer growths respectively. Both clover and grass varieties had no significant effect on the growth of total swards. In the process of parameterization of the model the growth data were separated into three groups with clearly distinguishable phenological characteristics: early growths (grass tillers mostly fertile, clover biomass vegetative), second growths (grass tillers vegetative, clover flowering), late growths (grass tillers and clover biomass vegetative). Regarding all 186 datapoints included in the parameterization process the calculated values accounted for 88% of the variation occuring among the observed values with a standard error of 31.2 g m^{-2} (Fig. 1). Figure 2 shows simulated growth series for three different weather scenarios which are characterised by a calculated water index with values close to 1 when the amount of plant available water is sufficient and decreasing values with an increasing water deficiency. The pattern of growth corresponds very well with the water supply indicating its superior impact on herbage accumulation. Simulations for different defoliation regimes illustrate the impact of defoliation time and frequency on the total annual performance of clover/grass swards (Table 1). Irrespective of weather conditions frequent defoliation (e.g. rotational pasture) results in lowest yields whereas highest yields are achieved in a regime with longer growth intervals (e.g. silage regime).

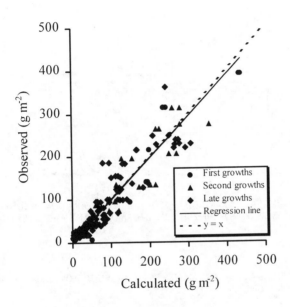

FIGURE 1. STATISTICS OF THE PARAMETERIZATION OF THE MODEL FOR THE DRY MATTER YIELD OF WHITE CLOVER/GRASS SWARDS (T HA⁻¹). OBSERVED YIELDS WERE MEASURED WEEKLY DURING 4-WEEK GROWTHS.

CONCLUSIONS

The presented results highlight the accuracy of the model and its sensitivity in growth simulations to changes in weather conditions. The model provides a useful tool to analyse complex plant-environment relationships during growth of clover/grass swards and supports scaling up findings from a few experimental sites to larger landscape units.

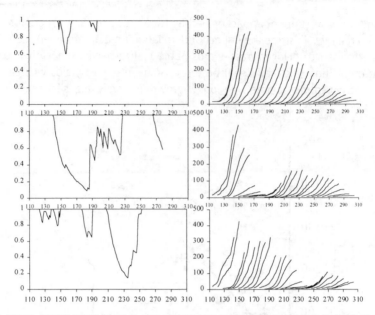

FIGURE 2. WATER SUPPLY INDEX (A TO C) AND PATTERN OF HERBAGE PRODUCTION (D TO F) (G M⁻²) FROM A WHITE CLOVER/GRASS SWARD FOR DIFFERENT WEATHER CONDITIONS AS CALCULATED BY THE MODEL.

TABLE 1. SIMULATIONS OF TOTAL ANNUAL DRY MATTER YIELDS OF WHITE CLOVER/GRASS SWARDS (T HA⁻¹) FOR DIFFERENT DEFOLIATION REGIMES.

	Pasture	Hay pasture	Silage regime
Scenario A (Optimum weather conditions)	13.1	14.0	14.8
Scenario B (Dry spring)	10.6	12.0	12.4
Scenario C (Dry autumn)	11.5	13.1	13.2

Defoliation criteria was a critical DM yield (t ha⁻¹) :

	1.	2.	3.	4.	5. Growth
Pasture:	2.4	2.2	2.0	2.0	2.0
Hay pasture:	4.4	2.2	2.0	2.0	
Silage regime:	4.4	3.3	3.0	2.0	

ACKNOWLEDGEMENTS

The authors are grateful to the Deutsche Forschungsgemeinschaft for supporting the project.

REFERENCES

Corrall, A. J. and J. S. Fenlon, 1978. A comparative method for describing the seasonal distribution of production from grasses. Journal of Agricultural Science, Cambridge, 91, 61-67.

Kornher, A. and P. Nyman, 1992. A model for prediction of growth and quality change of grass swards. 14th General Meeting of the European Grassland Federation, Lahti/Finland, 378-382.

Puzio, S., 1998. Untersuchungen zur Überwinterung und zum jahreszeitlichen Verlauf der Ertragsbildung von Weißklee in Abhängigkeit von der Witterung und der Sorteneigenschaft. Schriftenreihe des Instituts für Pflanzenbau und Pflanzenzüchtung der Christian-Albrechts-Universität Kiel. Heft 6. pp. 178 (in German).

Analysis of climatical and management impacts on herbage quality of white clover/grass swards with a dynamic growth model

M. WACHENDORF, A. KORNHER, S. PUZIO AND F. TAUBE

Department of Grass and Forage Science, University of Kiel, 24098 Kiel, Germany

SUMMARY

In the frame of the COST 814 Action "Crop Development for Cool and Wet Regions of Europe" a field experiment was conducted to describe the evolution of herbage quality of four white clover (*Trifolium repens L.*) varieties (AberHerald, Huia, Milkanova, N. F. G. Gigant), grown in binary mixtures with two perennial ryegrass (*Lolium perenne L.*) varieties (Preference, Vigor). During the growing season, the in vitro digestibility and crude protein content of swards were determined weekly in 4-week growth series. There were only small differences between the clover varieties concerning the qualitative development of clover herbage. During flowering digestibility decreased with increasing flowering bud formation. This was partly compensated for by a constant high digestibility of the grass which increased herbage quality of the total sward. The impact of climatic factors on the change of herbage quality of selected clover/grass swards was determined by an evaluation of the data with a dynamic growth model. Simulations for different defoliation regimes illustrate the impact of defoliation time and frequency on the annual mean herbage quality of clover/grass swards. Irrespective of weather conditions frequent defoliation (e.g. rotational pasture) resulted in highest values of digestibility and crude protein content whereas lowest values for both variables were achieved in a regime with longer growth intervals (e.g. silage regime). Generally the use of weather-driven models supports the transfer of findings from few experimental sites to other environments or larger landscape units.

Keywords: crude protein content, growth model, organic matter digestibility, perennial ryegrass, simulation, white clover

INTRODUCTION

With increasing milk yields per cow in Europe demands for feed with a high digestibility are increasing as well. To maintain herbage quality of grassland at a high level throughout the growing season, detailed information on the impact of sward management and weather conditions on the change of certain quality characteristics is necessary. The main purpose of this study was to describe the effects of weather conditions and defoliation regime on the herbage quality of clover/grass swards by means of a dynamic weather-based model. Once mathematical functions between stands and the environment (precipitation, temperature, radiation and available water capacity) have been developed through some systematic field trials, quality of swards can be simulated under any weather and site conditions. The study was conducted in the frame of the COST 814 action "Crop Development for Cool and Wet Regions of Europe".

MATERIALS AND METHODS

In the COST 814 field experiment the herbage quality of four white clover (*Trifolium repens L.*) varieties (AberHerald, Huia, Milkanova, N. F. G. Gigant), grown in binary mixtures with two varieties of perennial ryegrass (*Lolium perenne L.*) (Preference, Vigor), was investigated in two consecutive years (1995 and 1996). The swards received no mineral nitrogen. The soil was a sandy loamy luvisol. Soil nutrient status and pH were maintained at a sufficient level. To obtain the seasonal pattern of herbage quality four series of plots were cut in sequence, in each case after four weeks' growth, so that one series was cut each week. This technique has been widely used to evaluate species and varieties (Corrall and Fenlon, 1978).

From the plots with AberHerald and Milkanova cut in series, samples were taken weekly during the growing season. Organic matter digestibility and crude protein content of the total swards and their components were calculated and parameterization of the growth model FOPROQ (Kornher and Nyman, 1992). Due to severe drought in spring and summer of 1996 only data from 1995 could be used for development of the model.

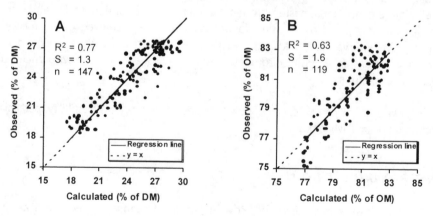

FIGURE 1. STATISTICS OF THE PARAMETERIZATION FOR THE CRUDE PROTEIN CONTENT (G 100 G⁻¹ DM) AND DIGESTIBILITY (G 100 G⁻¹ OM) OF A WHITE CLOVER/GRASS MIXTURE.

Computer simulations were performed for three different weather conditions (nearly optimum, dry spring, dry autumn) and various defoliation regimes (pasture, hay pasture, silage regime).

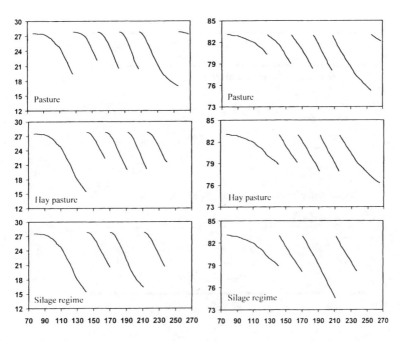

FIGURE 2. SIMULATIONS OF THE CRUDE PROTEIN CONTENT (G 100 G^{-1} DM) AND DIGESTIBILITY (G 100 G^{-1} OM) OF A WHITE CLOVER/GRASS MIXTURE WITH DIFFERENT DEFOLIATION REGIMES.

R E S U L T S

In the parameterization of the model calculated values of digestibility and crude protein content accounted for 63 and 77% rsp. of the occuring variation in the observed values (Fig. 1). Clover digestibility in summer growths declines much stronger than in spring (Fig. 2) which is mainly due to increasing formation of flowering stems and seed pots with increasing temperature and day length. Despite these obvious differences in the phenological development of clover plants during growth one single set of parameters was found to cover all occuring patterns of quality changes over the whole growing season. There is no evidence for differences in changes of crude protein content in swards between spring, summer or autumn growths. Simulations for different defoliation regimes illustrate the impact of defoliation time and frequency on the mean annual herbage quality of clover/grass swards (Table 1).

Irrespective of weather conditions frequent defoliation (e.g. rotational pasture) results in highest levels of digestibilties and crude protein contents whereas lowest levels are achieved in a regime with longer growth intervals (e.g. silage regime).

TABLE 1. SIMULATIONS OF THE MEAN WEIGHED ANNUAL CRUDE PROTEIN CONTENT (G 100 G⁻¹ DM) AND DIGESTIBILITY (G 100 G⁻¹ OM) OF A WHITE CLOVER/GRASS MIXTURE WITH DIFFERENT DEFOLIATION REGIME.

	Pasture	Hay pasture	Silage regime
Crude protein content (% of DM)			
Scenario A (Nearly optimum weather conditions)	21.8	20.7	19.6
Scenario B (Dry spring)	19.9	17.5	16.4
Scenario C (Dry autumn)	20.2	18.6	17.4
Digestibility of organic matter (% of OM)			
Scenario A (optimum climate)	79.4	79.2	78.3
Scenario B (Dry spring)	78.3	77.5	75.9
Scenario C (Dry autumn)	78.5	78.3	77.2

Defoliation criteria was a critical DM yield (t ha⁻¹) :

	1.	2.	3.	4.	5. Growth
Pasture:	2.4	2.2	2.0	2.0	2.0
Hay pasture:	4.4	2.2	2.0	2.0	
Silage regime:	4.4	3.3	3.0	2.0	

DISCUSSION AND CONCLUSIONS

Simulations were done with climatical data of a year with an early start of growth in spring and a dry autumn. Differences in patterns of quality changes between spring and summer growths were mainly genetically determined. In the simulations length of growths was determined by the exceeding of a critical DM yield. Another criteria for the release of a defoliation could be when herbage quality of the sward reaches a critical level. The presented results highlight the accuracy of the model and its sensitivity to changes among management and environmental conditions.

ACKNOWLEDGEMENTS

The author is grateful to the Deutsche Forschungsgemeinschaft for supporting the project.

REFERENCES

Corrall, A. J. and J. S. Fenlon, 1978. A comparative method for describing the seasonal distribution of production from grasses. Journal of Agricultural Science, Cambridge, 9: 61-67.

Kornher, A. and P. Nyman, 1992. A model for prediction of growth and quality change of grass swards. 14th General Meeting of the European Grassland Federation, Lahti, Finland, 378-382.

Puzio, S., 1998. Untersuchungen zur Überwinterung und zum jahreszeitlichen Verlauf der Ertragsbildung von Weißklee in Abhängigkeit von der Witterung und der Sorteneigenschaft. Schriftenreihe des Instituts für Pflanzenbau und Pflanzenzüchtung der Christian-Albrechts-Universität Kiel. Heft 6. pp. 178 (in German).

Nitrogen reserves contribution to regrowth of white clover (Trifolium repens L. cv Huia) submitted to defoliation

F. LE DILY, E. GOULAS, A. OURRY AND J. BOUCAUD

Physiologie et Biochimie Végétales, UMR INRA 950, Institut de Biochimie et de Biologie Appliquée, Université de Caen, 14 032 Caen Cedex, France

S U M M A R Y

Similar to grass and other forage legume species, regrowth of white clover after defoliation implies mobilization of soluble nitrogen from the remaining parts of the plant to sustain new organ differentiation and development. In this study, we intended to evaluate endogenous N contribution to post-clipping regrowth depending upon clover morphology or N assimilation ability, and to characterize the two main forms of proteins involved in root and stolon N storage (previously described as vegetative storage proteins - VSP). An experimental set of plants was allowed to regrow following low-temperature and short-day exposure known to lead to dwarf and prostrate phenotypes. As expected, the pre-cold-treated plants developed smaller leaves as compared to control plants, but this was largely counterbalanced with a high increase in leaf pool size (higher branching rate). Labelling nitrogen reserves with ^{15}N demonstrated that this fast development of the photosynthetical apparatus matched with a faster return to exogenous nitrogen assimilation. It also appeared from a parallel work that the previously defined VSP of 15 and 17.3 kDa may have physiological significant functions respectively in N_2 assimilation and chilling tolerance. Over their role in N storage, these specific polypeptides may act as active proteins whatever the agricultural practices.

Keywords: chilling, defoliation, nitrogen, vegetative storage proteins

I N T R O D U C T I O N

It has been shown that leaf removal of forages by grazing or mechanical harvesting leads to a severe decline in photosynthetate supply and a decrease in exogenous nitrogen assimilation. Corre et al. (1996) demonstrated the mobilization of buffer-soluble protein content of roots and stolons during the first 6 days of regrowth after defoliation. Polypeptides of 17.3 kDa (roots and stolons) and 15 kDa (roots), initially found at high concentrations, decreased to a larger extent during this period and accumulated again once N assimilation and photosynthesis were re-established. According to a commonly shared definition (Staswick, 1988), these polypeptides seems to behave as vegetative storage proteins (VSP).

In this study we attempted 1) to evaluate the morphological plasticity of a single cultivar (*Trifolium repens L.* cv Huia) using a cold pre-treatment in order to relate morphological status to N reserve-mobilization ability, 2) to evaluate the contribution of endogenous N to regrowth depending on VSP availability and 3) to investigate the physiological functions of clover VSP over their roles in N storage.

MATERIALS AND METHODS

Spontaneous inoculated white clover plants were grown hydroponically as previously described (Corre *et al.*, 1996) and submitted to $^{15}NH_4^{15}NO_3$ labeling prior to defoliation. All leaves were then removed and plants were allowed to regrow on a complete medium without ^{15}N and plants were then regularly harvested for analyses. For experiments using a cold treatment, a set of freshly defoliated plants were subjected for 31 d to 6°C. day and night and a 8 h photoperiod (vs. control conditions: 22/18°C day/night and 16h photoperiod). Exposure to ^{15}N labeling was done during this treatment. SDS-PAGE analysis and ^{15}N measurements have been previously described in Corre *et al.* (1996). Polyclonal antibodies to soybean nodule leghaemoglobin used in this study were a gift from Dr. T.J. Gordon (IGER, Aberystwyth, UK).

RESULTS

Effects of culture conditions on leaf production

At the end of the cold-treatment (6°C day and night) associated to short-day exposure (8 h photoperiod), treated-plants exhibited a leaf pool size 5 time less than control plants, and a 35% reduction in leaf area. Following the cold treatment, plants were then defoliated and allowed to regrow in control conditions. During the first 10 days, pre-cold-treated plants developed smaller leaves as compared to control plants. Nevertheless, reduction in leaf area was largely counterbalanced with a high increase in leaf pool size during the same period. It also appeared that pre-cold-treated plants had the greatest ability to produce new ramifications. These severe increases in branching rate and new leaf production sites led to a morphological status that can be considered as a dwarf type.

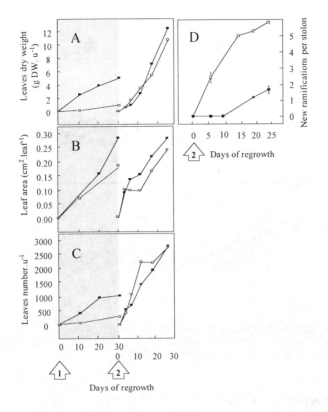

FIGURE 1. TIME COURSE OF LEAF APPEARANCE AND DEVELOPMENT DURING TWO SUCCESSIVE REGROWTH OF CLOVER FOLLOWING DEFOLIATIONS (ARROWS). GREY BACKGROUND, FIRST REGROWTH ; WHITE BACKGROUND, SECOND REGROWTH. BLACK SQUARES, PLANTS CONTINUOUSLY SUBMITTED TO CONTROL CONDITIONS ; WHITE SQUARES, PLANTS TREATED TO LOW TEMPERATURE (6°C) AND SHORT DAYS EXPOSURE (8H PHOTOPERIOD) DURING THE FIRST REGROWTH (BROKEN LINE) AND THEN ALLOWED TO GROW IN CONTROL CONDITIONS FOLLOWING THE SECOND DEFOLIATION (FULL LINE). A, MASS OF LEAVES PER CULTURE AREA UNIT; B, MEAN LEAF AREA; C, NUMBER OF NEW LEAVES DEVELOPED PER CULTURE AREA UNIT; D, NUMBER OF NEW RAMIFICATIONS PER STOLON.

Origins of nitrogen in regrowing leaves

During the first 3 days of regrowth in control conditions, nitrogen in regrowing leaves (petioles and laminae) of control plants came mainly from N reserves of organs remaining after defoliation. For pre-cold-treated plants, it was noticeable that N reserve contribution to regrowth of leaves was about 30% lower. At the end of the regrowth period, most of the leaf nitrogen was derived from exogenous nitrogen uptake, while the contribution of nitrogen reserves decreased, for both control and pre-cold-treated plants. Nevertheless, the fastest development of the photosynthetical apparatus previously noticed for pre-cold-treated plants seems to allow a faster return to exogenous nitrogen assimilation.

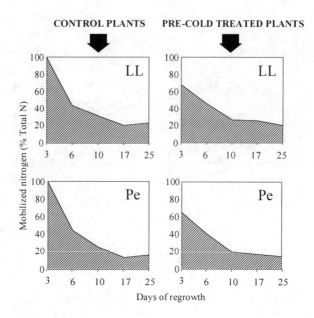

CONTROL PLANTS   PRE-COLD TREATED PLANTS

FIGURE 2. MOBILIZED NITROGEN RECOVERED IN REGROWING LEAVES (LL, LEAF LAMINAE ; PE, PETIOLES) AND DERIVED FROM EXOGENOUS N ASSIMILATION (WHITE BACKGROUND) OR ENDOGENOUS N RESERVES (HATCHED BACKGROUND) DEPENDING ON PREVIOUS CULTURE CONDITIONS.

Characterization of VSP

Vegetative storage proteins (VSP) from both types of culture were analyzed using mono-dimensional SDS electrophoresis. Analysis revealed that the protein of 15 kDa was especially located in efficient-nodules and exhibited a typical pattern of hydrolysis/accumulation following defoliation (fig. 3). This protein was neither detected in nodule-free roots or stolons. Having regard to the localization of this protein (nodule), its abundance and its molecular weight (15 kDa), we used polyclonal antibodies raised against (soybean) leghaemoglobin (Lb) to probe Western blots of protein extracts, and demonstrated that the previously defined VSP of 15 kDa was the white clover Lb.

The other VSP (17.3 kDa) was only detected in stolons and nodule-free roots. On the basis of its N-terminal sequence (data not shown), we identified a 93% homology with a well-known referenced " abscisic acid-responsive protein " encountered in pea seeds. In white clover, it appeared that chilling exposure (6°C) and 15μM ABA treatment effectively led to significant increases in 17.3 kDa contents in roots.

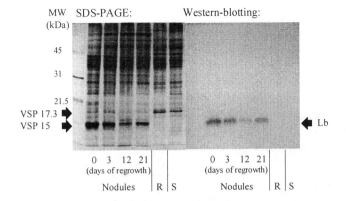

FIGURE 3. SDS-PAGE ANALYSIS OF SOLUBLE PROTEINS EXTRACTS FROM EXCISED NODULES, DENODULATED ROOTS (R) AND STOLONS (S) EXHIBITING VEGETATIVE STORAGE PROTEINS (VSP), AND CORRESPONDING WESTERN-BLOTTING USING AN ANTIBODY RAISED AGAINST SOYBEAN LEGHEMOGLOBIN (LB).

DISCUSSION AND CONCLUSIONS

Overall results agree with the mobilization of the VSP of 15 kDa pointed out by Corre *et al.* (1996) in defoliated clover, and with the rapid decrease in N_2 fixation and the depletion of proteins and leghaemoglobin contents observed previously by Gordon *et al.* (1990). Finally, it appeared that significant amounts of N in regrowing shoot of white clover is derived from mobilization of root and stolon N reserves. The role of endogenous N to sustain growth after defoliation is closely associated to the ability of plants to recover photosynthesis and to N assimilation efficiency since clover Lb contributes to nitrogen supply before (N_2 fixation) and after clipping (mobilization). In a similar manner, over its participation in N reserves, the second clover VSP (17.3 kDa) seems to behave as an ABA-responsive protein, and should therefore be implicated in frost tolerance and winter survival.

ACKNOWLEDGMENTS

The authors are grateful to Dr. A. J. Gordon from IGER Aberystwyth (UK) for providing the Lb antibodies used in this study.

REFERENCES

Corre, N., V. Bouchart, A. Ourry and J. Boucaud, 1996. Mobilization of nitrogen reserves during regrowth of defoliated Trifolium repens L. and identification of potential vegetative storage proteins. Journal of Experimental Botany, 47: 1111-1118.

Gordon, A. J., W. Kessler and F. R. Minchin, 1990. Defoliation-induced stress in nodules of white clover. Journal of Experimental Botany, 41: 1245-1253.

Staswick, P. E., 1988. Soybean vegetative storage protein structure and gene expression. Plant Physiology, 87: 250-254.

Evaluation of white clover under grazing management

A. GHESQUIERE, J. BAERT AND E. VAN BOCKSTAELE

Department Plant Genetics and Breeding (DvP) - CLO-Gent, Caritasstraat 21, B-9090 Melle, Belgium

SUMMARY

Results are presented of an experiment evaluating the performance of two white clover cultivars, AberHerald and Huia under grazing management. The cultivars differed significantly in spring yield and clover percentage.

In a second experiment we evaluated six candivars from the breeding programme and compared the original and the selected populations of AberHerald and Huia . The clover percentage of the Huia plots was higher than the clover percentage of the AberHerald and the candivar plots. There were no significant differences between the original and the selected populations of AberHerald and Huia.

Keywords : cultivar differences, grazing, morphology, white clover, yield

INTRODUCTION

White clover is mainly used for grazing. Therefore it is important to evaluate white clover under grazing conditions. In a previous multi-site experiment throughout Europe carried out within the framework of COST 814, we compared two white clover varieties, AberHerald and Huia under cutting management (Collins *et al.*, 1996). In a first experiment we evaluated the same varieties under grazing management. In a second grazing trial we tested six candivars from the breeding programme and we compared the survival populations of AberHerald and Huia from the previous COST 814 white clover experiment with the original populations.

MATERIALS AND METHODS

The experiments are based on ploughing/reseeding. The perennial ryegrass cultivar Fennema was sown at a seeding rate of 25 kg ha^{-1} on the 8th of May 1998. The clover populations of both experiments were broadcasted on the 11th of May 1998. The seeding rate was 4 kg ha^{-1} but we made a correction based on the differences in germination between the clover populations. We applied adequate P and K to maintain normal soil levels. The establishment was irregular. On the 16th of June we had to sow some extra perennial ryegrass. The plots were mown twice in the early summer of 1998. After the first cut we applied 25 N ha[-1]. From the end of July 1998 onwards the experiments were intensively grazed by sheep. In 1999 we only applied nitrogen fertiliser (50 N ha[-1]) on the plots of the second grazing trial.

In the first grazing trial we tested two white clover varieties, AberHerald and Huia, under two grazing regimes. The difference between the two grazing regimes was the heaviness of the first cut. Under the first grazing regime (R1) the first grazing period of the year started when the dry matter yield (DMY) of the plots was one t ha[-1] higher than that of the plots of the second grazing regime (R2). The DMY of the following cuts was similar for both grazing regimes. The experiment was laid down in four replicates on plots 7 m x 8 m. During the growing seasons of 1998 and 1999 total DMY and contributions of grass and clover DM to the total DM were recorded pre- and post-grazing. Each estimate is based on five cuttings each of 100 cm x 10 cm taken to ground level. Four weeks after the last grazing and at regrowth in spring three samples (cores 12 cm in diameter) were taken for morphological analyses.

In the second experiment we sowed six candivars from the breeding programme. We also evaluated the survival populations of AberHerald and Huia from the previous COST 814 white clover trial and compared them to the original populations. The ten populations laid down in three replicates on plots 5 m x 8 m. In the establishment year we evaluated the populations by visual scores. In 1999 we measured the total DMY and estimated the contributions of grass and clover DM to the total DM in spring and autumn.

RESULTS AND DISCUSSION

The winters of 1998-1999 and 1999-2000 were mild and extremely wet. We had an early frost period in November 1998 with temperatures of –8°C. During both winters the mean temperature was about 2°C above normal and we had precipitations of over 100 mm m[2-1] more than normal.

In the first trial each of the treatments had three grazing periods during the growing season of 1998. In 1999 the R1 plots were grazed three times, the R2 plots four times. There were no significant differences in clover yield or mean clover percentage in 1998. At the end of the growing season, Huia performed better in the R1 plots (Fig. 1). In 1999 Huia had a significantly higher clover yield than Aberherald. The differences in grass yield were not significant. The total DMY of the R1 Huia plots was 800 kg ha[-1] and 1500 kg ha[-1] higher than the total DMY of the R1 Aberherald plots in 1998 and 1999 respectively (Fig. 2). The differences in total DMY were not significant in the R2 plots. Taking a heavier first it seems to favour Huia.

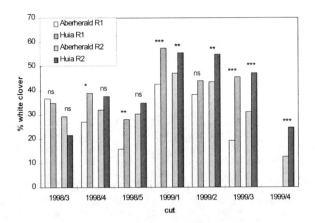

FIGURE 1. PERCENTAGE WHITE CLOVER OF ABERHERALD AND HUIA PLOTS PRE-GRAZING IN 1998 AND
1999 UNDER TWO DIFFERENT GRAZING REGIMES (R1 : FIRST CUT AT A DMY OF 1 T HA⁻¹ MORE THAN R2).

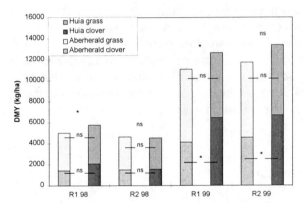

FIGURE 2. TOTAL CLOVER AND GRASS DMY OF ABERHERALD AND HUIA IN 1998 AND 1999 UNDER TWO
DIFFERENT GRAZING REGIMES (R1 : FIRST CUT AT A DMY OF 1 T HA⁻¹ MORE THAN R2).

This could be explained by the fact that Aberherald starts growing earlier in spring
(Ghesquiere, 1995; Ghesquiere and Reheul, 1996). By taking a later first cut (R1 plots)
this advantage for Aberherald is reduced. Due to the mild winter there was very little
winter damage. Under both grazing regimes Huia performed significantly better in the
spring of 1999.

Table 1 shows some results of the winter analyses of the experiment. There
were significant differences in stolon length in the R1 plots and at the beginning
of the growing season of 2000 in the R2 plots. The differences in stolon weight
were not significant. AberHerald had a higher specific stolon dry weight than
Huia.

TABLE 1. RESULTS OF THE MORPHOLOGICAL ANALYSES AT THE END AND THE BEGINNING OF THE GROWING SEASON OF A GRAZING TRIAL WITH TWO DIFFERENT TREATMENTS (R1 : FIRST CUT AT A DRY MATTER YIELD OF 1 T HA⁻¹ MORE THAN R2).

		R1				R2			
		Dec 98	Mar 99	Dec 99	Feb 00	Dec 98	Mar 99	Dec 99	Feb 00
Stolon length		*	*	**	**	ns	ns	ns	***
m m²-1	Aberherald	72.0	65.3	33.1	46.1	65.8	89.2	48.5	49.0
	Huia	102.6	98.2	80.7	89.4	90.4	96.9	61.2	97.0
Stolon weight		ns	ns	ns	**	ns	ns	ns	ns
g m²-1	Aberherald	82.6	61.9	42.7	42.0	85.8	79.5	62.5	53.1
	Huia	85.3	64.5	98.7	77.4	78.2	50.1	55.1	67.8
Specific stolon			*	*	ns	ns	***	*	**	*
dry weight	Aberherald	11.30	9.56	11.85	9.52	13.06	8.88	13.08	10.41
mg cm-1	Huia	8.45	6.41	11.71	8.82	8.62	4.92	9.24	7.13

In experiment 2 there were no significant differences in clover presence in 1998. In the spring of 1999 all plots had a high percentage of white clover (Fig. 3). The original and the selected populations of Huia had respectively 60.2 and 70.1% clover compared to respectively 28.3 and 25.4% for the AberHerald populations and an average of 39.4% for the candivars. At the end of the growing season the percentage of white clover was smaller than 10% except for the Huia plots. In the spring of 1999 the grass yield of the Huia plots was 62.5% of the mean grass yield of all the plots.

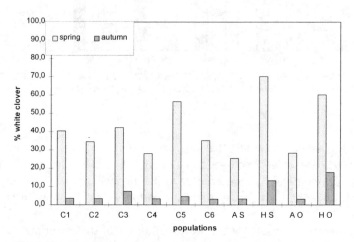

FIGURE 3. PERCENTAGE WHITE CLOVER AT THE BEGINNING AND THE END OF THE GROWING SEASON OF 1999 OF PLOTS WITH 10 DIFFERENT WHITE CLOVER POPULATIONS GRAZED BY SHEEP. C1-C6 : CANDIVARS FROM THE BREEDING PROGRAM; AS, HS, AO AND HO : SELECTED AND ORIGINAL POPULATIONS OF ABERHERALD AND HUIA.

The relative grass yield of the AberHerald plots and the average of the candivar plots was respectively 118.5% and 106.3%. At the end of the growing season, the grass yield of the Huia plots , the AberHerald plots and the candivar plots was respectively 67.0%, 122.5% and 103.5% of the mean grass yield of all the plots. In November 1999 there were a lot of weeds in the Huia plots: about 20% of the total DMY. The differences in total DMY of the different populations were small. The Huia and the AberHerald plots yielded respectively 102.3% and 96.5% of the mean of all the plots. The average relative total DMY of the six candivars was 100.4%. There were no significant differences between the original and the selected populations of AberHerald and Huia.

CONCLUSION

Based on the results of the previous COST 814 white clover experiment we expected that Aberherald would perform better than Huia (Collins *et al.*, 1996; Ghesquiere, 1995; Ghesquiere and Reheul, 1996). In these grazing experiments Huia performed significantly better than AberHerald. This could be due to the mild winters. In some cases Huia was even too competitive which reduced the grass yield and permitted weeds to invade. Further testing is needed to evaluate the persistence of the varieties under grazing management under other climatic circumstances.

REFERENCES

Collins, R. P., J. Connolly, M. Fothergill, B. E. Frankow-Lindberg, A. Guckert, M. P. Guinchard, A. Lüsher, J. Nösberger, I. Rhodes, C. Robin, B. Stäheli and S. Stoffel, 1996. Variation in the overwintering of white clover cultivars in cool and wet areas of Europe. Proceedings of the 16th EGF Meeting: Grassland and Land Use Systems, 201-204.

Ghesquiere A., 1995. Results from the COST 814 experiment in Merelbeke (1994-1995). Report on the Progress Meeting "Overwintering and spring growth of white clover", Gorizia, Italy, June 19-21 1995, p. 3.

Ghesquiere A. and D. Reheul, 1996. Results from the COST 814 experiment in Merelbeke (1995-1996). Proceedings of the Progress Meeting "Overwintering and spring growth of white clover", Hvanneyri and Reykjavik, Iceland, June 30-July 4 1996, p. 4.

Breeding white clover cultivars for northern marginal environments

Á. HELGADÓTTIR¹, P. MARUM² AND R.P. COLLINS³

¹ The Agricultural Research Institute, Keldnaholt, 112 Reykjavík, Iceland
² The Norwegian Crop Research Institute, Løken Research Station, 2940 Heggenes, Norway
³ IGER, Plas Gogerddan, Aberystwyth, Ceredigion SY23 3EB, UK

SUMMARY

The use of white clover in sustainable farming systems in northern, marginal areas has been restricted by the lack of productive, winterhardy cultivars. Recent experimental evidence reveals that Norwegian breeding material shows superior winter hardiness and yield to more southerly material under northern conditions. In a joint breeding project between Iceland and Norway attempts are being made to combine the high biomass production of commercial cultivars from Northern Europe with the winter hardiness of the superior, indigenous populations. Selected parental populations have been described in terms of biomass production, morphology and rates of stolon extension and leaf appearance. The observed variation suggests that it should be possible to improve the harvestable yield potential of white clover in northern areas without sacrificing winter hardiness. A successful outcome of the breeding programme opens up new possibilities for utilising the benefits of white clover in northern marginal environments.

Keywords: breeding, marginal conditions, white clover, winter hardiness

INTRODUCTION

In northern, marginal areas of Europe white clover commonly disappears from the grass sward as both environmental stresses and unsuitable management weaken the plants and cause poor persistence. Commercial cultivars presently available have performed badly in variety trials and cannot be recommended for cultivation. White clover plants adapted to extreme northern conditions are frost hardy and winter dormant. They are generally prostrate, with small leaves and thin, profuse stolons (e.g. Williams, 1987). They are therefore generally unproductive and hardly suitable for direct agricultural exploitation. There is, however, considerable variation between populations from northern regions and a number of characters of adaptive significance have been identified (e.g. Aasmo Finne, 2000). In addition, recent experimental evidence reveals that Norwegian breeding material shows superior winter hardiness and yield to more southerly material under northern conditions (e.g. Rapp, 1996). Survivor populations produced by the working group on 'Overwintering and spring growth of white clover', in the EU COST 814 Programme, provide us with ideal material to identify those characteristics which confer good adaptation to the various winter stresses encountered in Europe. In a recent study involving survivor populations from Sweden it was concluded that plants adapted to an environment with long and cold winters had slower stolon extension rates and lower leaf appearance rates than non-adapted plants resulting in shorter internodes and a poorer accumulation of biomass (Frankow-Lindberg, 1999). Here we present results on the characterisation of selected breeding material, including survivor populations from Iceland, and assess its potential for a newly initiated joint breeding programme between Iceland and Norway. Crosses between superior indigenous populations and more productive southerly varieties are being made with the aim of improving yielding ability of white clover in the northern marginal areas without sacrificing its persistence.

MATERIALS AND METHODS

Based on results from variety trials in Norway and Iceland and the testing of Nordic white clover populations in northern Scandinavia and Iceland we have identified a number of promising populations as potential parents in the crossing programme (Table 1). Here we present results for AberHerald, Undrom and its survivor populations from an experiment at Korpa, Iceland, and three breeding populations from The Norwegian Crop Research Institute (Planteforsk) which have been selected for further development from a large collection of indigenous white clover material. The survivor populations are based on 50 stolon tips collected from plants surviving one to three winters in experimental plots. The stolon tips were propagated and each population was polycrossed separately in isolation houses by the Legume Breeding Group at IGER in Aberystwyth. Individual plants were established in an illuminated (16 h photoperiod) and heated greenhouse at IGER, Aberystwyth at the end of September 1999. In late November they were transferred to plastic containers filled with Levington clover potting compost and left to grow for four weeks. On each plant the main stolon was then marked with a drop of red paint directly in front of the first fully expanded leaf. Three weeks later detailed morphological analyses were carried out on 28 plants from each population. The length of stolon between the marked node and the youngest identifiable node was measured, and all the leaves and branches produced after the paint mark were counted. Each leaf was scored according to the Carlson scale of leaf development (Carlson, 1966). After scoring, the metamer (modular unit comprising fully expanded leaf, internode and axillary bud (Marshall, 1996)) on every marked stolon was identified and dissected into its components. The diameter of the dissected internode was measured using calipers, the area of the dissected leaf was obtained using a leaf area meter (Delta-T, UK) and the length of its associated petiole was measured. The results were analysed by ANOVA as a randomised design without blocking and then subjected to Principal Components Analysis. Here we only present results for selected populations.

Population	Country of origin	Latitude/Altitude	Breeder
AberHerald (O)	Switzerland, developed in Wales	47°17'/890 m	IGER (52°28'/50 m)
AberHerald (S)	Survivor pop. from Iceland	64°30'/30 m	
AberCrest (O)	Switzerland, developed in Wales	47°23/960 m	IGER
AberCrest (S)	Survivor pop. from Iceland	64°30'/30 m	
Undrom (O)	Sweden	63°10'	Svalöf Weibull AB
Undrom (S)	Survivor pop. from Iceland	64°30'/30 m	
Milkanova	Denmark	55°25'	DLF Trifolium
Jõgeva 4	Estonia	55°50'	Jõgeva Plant Breeding
Sandra	Sweden	55°50'	Svalöv Weibull AB
HoKv9238	Norway	62°55'/60 m	Planteforsk
HoKv9262	Norway	62°50'/550 m	Planteforsk
HoKv9275	Norway	61°20'/20 m	Planteforsk

TABLE 2. LENGTH OF MAIN STOLON (MM) AND MEAN INTERNODE LENGTH (MM), LEAF AREA (CM²), INTERNODE DIAMETER (MM) AND TOTAL WEIGHT (MG) OF THE METAMER PRODUCED BY SELECTED POPULATIONS UNDER CONTROLLED CONDITIONS OVER A PERIOD OF 21 DAYS. *P<0.05, **P<0.01, ***P<0.001.

Population	Stolon length, mm	Internode length, mm	Leaf area, cm^2	Internode diameter, mm	Total wt., mg
AberHerald (Ah-o)	135	19.8	9.87	2.2	672
AberHerald (Ah-s)	116	16.8	8.16	2.3	653
Undrom (U-o)	115	15.1	8.93	1.8	489
Undrom (U-s)	134	18.2	9.16	2.1	553
HoKv9238 (N-38)	157	19.9	4.93	1.5	311
HoKv9262 (N-62)	124	17.9	5.15	1.6	335
HoKv9275 (N-75)	138	19.5	4.97	1.6	340
s.e.d.	9	1.2	0.74	0.1	47
Significance	***	***	***	***	***

RESULTS AND DISCUSSION

The Norwegian populations were characterised by low DM accumulation, thin stolons and small leaves compared to AberHerald (Table 1). Undrom was intermediate between the two groups except for its leaf size which was comparable to AberHerald. The survivors of AberHerald in Iceland had significantly slower stolon extension rates and mean internode lengths on the main stolon than the original population. In addition, their leaves were smaller giving higher values of specific leaf weight (results not shown). In contrast, the Undrom survivors had significantly faster stolon extension rates and mean internode lengths on the main stolon than the original population. Their stolons were thicker and heavier, giving higher values of specific stolon weight (results not shown). The Norwegian population HoKv9238 had significantly faster stolon extension rates and larger mean internode lengths than the other two Norwegian populations and it also had a greater number of leaves and mature nodes (results not shown). The first two axes in the Principal Components Analysis explained 80% of the total variation and revealed clear differences between populations (Fig. 1). The main discriminatory variables on PC I were plant dry weight (-ve), total number of leaves (+ve) and total number of nodes (+ve), and petiole length and leaf area (both –ve) on PC II.

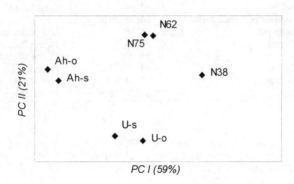

FIGURE 1. PRINCIPAL COMPONENTS ANALYSIS FOR SELECTED WHITE CLOVER BREEDING POPULATIONS USING 18 DIFFERENT MORPHOLOGICAL AND GROWTH ATTRIBUTES MEASURED UNDER OPTIMUM CONDITIONS.

The observed morphological differences between northerly and southerly populations confirm previous studies on comparable material (e.g. Williams, 1987, Frankow-Lindberg, 1999) and show that plants adapted to long winters have a lower inherent DM accumulation potential than plants from milder environments when grown in an optimum environment. The shorter internode lengths resulting from slower stolon extension rates in the AberHerald survivor population are consistent with changes observed in a population surviving in Uppsala, Sweden (Frankow-Lindberg, loc. sit). Selection for smaller leaves was, on the other hand, not observed in that population. These changes occurred after only one winter of intense selection in Iceland compared to four winters in Sweden. Surprisingly, there was a selection in the Undrom survival population for opposite traits to that in the AberHerald population. Undrom originates from comparable latitudes to those of the experimental site in Iceland. However, it comes from an area with a continental climate, similar to that in Uppsala, where winters are characterised by low temperatures and prolonged, stable snow cover. In Iceland, on the other hand, winters are fairly mild and characterised by fluctuating freeze-thaw cycles. This may cause different selection pressures in the two environments. The results obtained here are confirmed by results from a field experiment in Iceland (Dalmannsdóttir et. al, 1999). The variation observed in the breeding material suggests that it should be possible to improve harvestable yield potential of white clover in norhtern areas without sacrificing winter hardiness.

REFERENCES

Aasmo Finne, M., 2000. Genetic variation in a Norwegian germplasm collection of white clover (Trifolium repens L.). In: Proceedings of FAO/CIHEAM Lowland Grasslands Sub-Network Research Conference 1998: Lowland Grasslands of Europe – Utilization and Development, (ed. by Fisher G., Frankow-Lindberg B.), La Coruna, Spain, in press.

Carlson, G.E., 1966. Growth of clover leaves – developmental morphology and parameters at ten stages. Crop Science, 6: 293-294.

Dalmannsdóttir, S., Á. Helgadóttir, B. Gudleifsson and M. Svenning, 1999. Winter hardiness and yield of white clover in northern areas. In: Proceedings of the Progress Meeting of the working group on "Overwintering and spring growth of white clover", Kiel, Germany, 29-31 August 1999, 19-27.

Frankow-Lindberg, B.E., 1999. Effects of adaptation to winter stress on biomass production, growth and morphology of three contrasting white clover cultivars. Physiologia Plantarum, 106: 196-202.

Marshall, C., 1996. Sectorality and physiological organisation in herbaceous plants: an overview. Vegetatio, 127: 9-16.

Rapp, K., 1996. Selection response for dry matter yield in white clover (Trifolium repens L.) using different selection methods. Norwegian Journal of Agricultural Science, 10: 265-280.

Williams, W. M., 1987. Adaptive variation. In: White Clover (ed. by Baker, M.J. and Williams, W.M.). CAB International, Wallingford, 299-321.

The effect of companion grasses on the establishment of white clover in a northern environment

Á. HELGADÓTTIR, T.A. KRISTJÁNSDÓTTIR, S. DALMANNSDÓTTIR
AND J. HERMANNSSON

The Agricultural Research Institute, Keldnaholti, 112 Reykjavík, Iceland

SUMMARY

In order to identify appropriate grass companions for white clover in a northern marginal environment, interactions between contrasting grass species and a winterhardy white clover population are being investigated in a field experiment in Iceland. Timothy (*Phleum pratense L.*), cv. Adda from Iceland, meadow grass (*Poa pratensis L.*), cv. Fylking and perennial ryegrass (*Lolium perenne L.*), cv. Svea from Sweden and meadow fescue (*Festuca pratensis L.*), cv. Salten from Bodø, Norway, are grown in binary mixtures with HoKv9262 (Norstar) from northern Norway. Morphological measurements of the clover four months from sowing showed that the associated grasses influenced growing point number, length of stolon and biomass produced by the clover. The grasses were different in both tiller number and shoot dry matter. The latter character was negatively correlated with growing point number and biomass production of the clover. Ryegrass was most aggressive towards the clover followed by timothy, meadow fescue and smooth meadow grass.

Keywords: companion grasses, competition, marginal environment, white clover

INTRODUCTION

The use of white clover is expected to increase in the northern marginal areas of Europe as winter hardy varieties become available on the market. However, there is no tradition for its cultivation in these areas and management practices developed in more favourable environments cannot be adopted unchanged. White clover is always grown in a mixture, thus its compatibility with the companion grass is of great importance. Of the common agricultural grasses ryegrass is the most compatible (Chestnutt and Lowe, 1970) but is not sufficiently winterhardy in the north to give sustainable production. It is therefore important to choose the appropriate companion grass for white clover in order to utilise its full potential. In the northern maritime climate plant establishment is generally slow during the short and cool growing season in spite of early sowing in spring. The condition of the plant in autumn is decisive for its subsequent survival during the long and harsh winter. Competitive effects of the grass component will influence clover growth during establishment and the grass canopy during winter may influence clover survival. It has been shown that competitive suppression of clover is positively related to both leaf length and tiller density of the associated grass (Rhodes and Harris, 1979). In addition, a grass associate with lax or prostrate leaves produces greater suppression of clover growth than more erect types of similar leaf length. However, grasses with an upright growth habit and long, erect leaves may though be more damaging to clover under severe winter conditions (Rhodes, 1981). Here we present results from a field experiment in Iceland on the competitive effects of four contrasting grass species on the early development of white clover.

MATERIALS AND METHODS

The Norwegian white clover breeding population HoKv9262 (Norstar) was sown with four different companion grasses on 16 June 1999 at Korpa Experimental Station, Iceland (64° 30'). The grasses were timothy (*Phleum pratense L.*), cv. Adda from Iceland, meadow grass (*Poa pratensis L.*), cv. Fylking and perennial ryegrass (*Lolium perenne L.*), cv. Svea from Sweden and meadow fescue (*Festuca pratensis L.*), cv. Salten from Bodø, Norway. Seed was strip seeded with a Øjord machine at the rate of 6.7 kg ha^{-1} for the clover, 12.5 kg for Adda and Salten, 15 kg for Fylking and 17 kg for Svea ha^{-1}. Fertiliser rates were 50 kg N, 35 kg P and 65 kg K ha^{-1}. Grass companions form the main plots and within each there are three blocks of three plots each that will receive different management from spring 2000. Individual plots measure 12 m^2.

On 18-22 October 1999 three cores of 12 cm diameter were taken at random from each block of the four grass companions to a depth of approximately 10 cm. Soil was washed off, the samples were combined and grass and clover separated. Grass tillers were counted and their dry weights measured. The clover was dissected into roots, stolons, buds and leaves. Estimates were obtained for the number of taproots and growing points, length of stolon and dry matter of each component. As these measurements were taken four months after sowing the number of taproots gives an estimate of seedling density per unit area. Results were subjected to appropriate analysis of variance and regression analyses.

RESULTS AND DISCUSSION

Seedling density of white clover was very high in autumn but it was not significantly different in the four grass plots (1079 seedlings m^{-2} averaged over companions). The population size of the clover was, on the other hand, influenced by the different companion grasses, as reflected in the number of growing points (P<0.05) and amount of stolon

TABLE 1. THE EFFECTS OF DIFFERENT COMPANION GRASSES ON GROWING POINT NO. AND STOLON PRODUCTION OF THE WHITE CLOVER POPULATION HOKV9262 FOUR MONTHS FROM SOWING.

Grass companion	Growing points no. m^{-2}	Stolon production m m^{-2}
Lolium perenne, Svea	4295	16.7
Phleum pratense, Adda	5327	25.7
Festuca pratense, Salten	7746	29.7
Poa pratensis, Fylking	8719	54.3
s.e.d.	1253	7.8
Significance	P<0.05	P<0.05

TABLE 2. THE EFFECTS OF DIFFERENT COMPANION GRASSES ON DM YIELD AND ITS ALLOCATION (GM^{-2}) OF THE WHITE CLOVER POPULATION HOKV9262 FOUR MONTHS FROM SOWING.

Grass companion	Roots	Stolons	Buds	Leaves	Total DM
Lolium perenne, Svea	21	11	9	11	52
Phleum pratense, Adda	28	19	13	19	78
Festuca pratense, Salten	37	22	17	20	96
Poa pratensis, Fylking	46	41	23	30	141
s.e.d.	14	8	3	5	23
Significance	NS	P<0.05	P<0.05	P<0.05	P<0.05

TABLE 3. SHOOT DRY MATTER YIELD AND TILLER NUMBERS OF THE FOUR DIFFERENT COMPANION GRASSES FOUR MONTHS FROM SOWING.

Grass companion	Roots	Stolons	Buds	Leaves	Total DM
Lolium perenne, Svea	21	11	9	11	52
Phleum pratense, Adda	28	19	13	19	78
Festuca pratense, Salten	37	22	17	20	96
Poa pratensis, Fylking	46	41	23	30	141
s.e.d.	14	8	3	5	23
Significance	NS	P<0.05	P<0.05	P<0.05	P<0.05

produced per unit area (P<0.05) (Table 1). Svea was most aggressive towards the clover followed by Adda, Salten and Fylking. The biomass production of the different components reflects the population size and were all, except for root dry matter, significantly influenced by the companion grass (Table 1). The total dry matter produced by the clover in a mixture with Svea was just over a third of that produced with Fylking. There were significant differences between grass companions in both tiller density (P<0.05) and shoot dry matter (P<0.001) (Table 3). Salten had significantly fewer tillers than the other three species. The shoot dry matter of Salten and Fylking was, however similar and significantly less than that of Adda and Svea, which produced greatest dry matter. Regression analyses revealed that number of growing points of the clover (r = -0.74; P<0.005) and total dry matter (r = -0.65; P<0.05) (both root and shoot DM) was significantly correlated with the shoot dry matter yield of the companion grass. The only significant correlation with grass tiller number was found for number of clover seedlings.

The results confirm other findings that severe competition exists between clover and grass at very early stages of growth (e.g. Collins *et al.*, 1996). We found that both morphological development and biomass production of the clover was greatly influenced by the grass companion. Even though tiller density differed significantly between the grass associates it only affected the number of clover seedlings that had established in the sward. The growth and development of the clover plants were, on the other hand, greatly influenced by the shoot yield of the companion grass. This may reflect both contrasting canopy architecture and growth habit of the grasses. The ryegrass caused greatest suppression to clover. It had the same tiller number as timothy but much higher shoot yields and thus larger leaf canopy. In contrast, smooth meadow grass was the most favourable grass companion. It is well documented that meadow grass establishes slowly in the northern environment (e.g. Helgadóttir, 1989) and its rhizomatous growth leads to an open sward. Both of these characters will favour clover growth. It is expected that the competitive effects of the contrasting grass associates will influence the winter survival of the clover. This will be presented in a subsequent paper.

ACKNOWLEDGEMENTS

This work is a part of the research project Application of legumes for feed and industry, which is supported by the Icelandic Research Council and the Agricultural Productivity Fund.

REFERENCES

Chestnutt, D. M. B. and J. Lowe, 1970. Review of agronomy of white clover/grass swards. In: White Clover Research (ed. by Lowe, J.), Occasional Symposium of the British Grassland Society No. 6, 191-213.

Collins, R. P., M. Fothergill and I. Rhodes, 1996. Interactions between seedlings of perennial ryegrass and white clover cultivars in establishing swards. Grass and Forage Science, 51: 163-169.

Helgadóttir, A, 1989. Breeding herbage species for northern areas. 2. Variety trials with smooth meadow grass (Poa pratensis L.). Acta Agriculturae Scandinavica, 39: 255-268.

Rhodes, I., 1981. The physiological basis of variation in the yield of grass/clover mixtures. In: Plant Physiology and Herbage Production (ed. by Wright, CE), Occasional Symposium of the British Grassland Society No. 13, 149-161.

Rhodes, I. and W. Harris, 1979. The nature and basis of differences in sward composition and yield in ryegrass white clover mixtures. In: Changes in Sward Composition and Productivity (ed. by Charles, AH and Haggar, RJ), Occasional Symposium of the British Grassland Society No. 10, 55-60.

Stomatal conductance of three white clover cultivars overwintered in the Alpine area of North-Eastern Italy

C. CORAN, S. VENERUS, M. SCIMONE AND G. PARENTE

SAASD–Settore Agricoltura–Aziende Sperimentali e Dimostrative, Pordenone, Italy

SUMMARY

The surviving plants of 3 white clover cultivars (Huia, AberHerald, Oboe) sown in 1994 at Tarvisio (756 m a.s.l., mean annual rainfall 1442 mm, mean annual temperature 7,8 °C) have been investigated by a steady-state porometer (LI-COR, inc.1600) during the growing period of year 1999.

Total stomatal conductance (g_l) of about 20 leaves per cultivar (5 leaves per cultivar per plot on 4 replicates) have been measured in 3 sunny days, 1 month after each cut. The differences in g_l among the 3 cultivars - which demonstrate a higher value for AberHerald than Oboe and Huia - are significant only for data of the second day (P<0,05).

In order to confirm that the individual clovers existing in every plot belong to the same cultivar and are not native wild ones, stolon weight (mg cm^{-1}) and leaf area (cm^2 per leaf) of each cultivar have been measured. Data have been compared with data registered in the previous years and a good similarity resulted.

Moreover, from a correlation between mean leaf area of each cultivar and the corresponding stomatal conductances, it seems that cultivar with smaller leaves (AberHerald) has higher stomatal conductance.

Keywords: leaf area, porometer, RWC, stolon, stomatal conductance, white clover

INTRODUCTION

White clover (*Trifolium repens* L.) is an important forage species for its high nutritive quality, its ability to fix atmospheric nitrogen, and its wide adaptation to local soil and climatic conditions (Malinowski *et al.*, 1998). However, since there is considerable genetic variation in winter hardiness in white clover (Collins and Rhodes, 1995), a strong interest is dedicated to the knowledge of morphological and physiological aspects of white clover growth in cool and wet regions of Europe.

Stomatal conductance is an important physiological aspect in studies of crop biomass production where it is important to maximize water-use efficiency.

Differences in white clover cultivars responses for stomatal conductance can be related to different assimilation rates and yield as it happens for other crop species (Cornish *et al.*, 1991). Moreover, plants characterised by small leaves have frequently been reported to have higher stomatal conductance and net photosyntetic rates, expecially in crop species (e.g. Egli *et al.*, 1970; Hiebsch *et al.*,1976).

In this paper the results of differences in stomatal conductance among cultivars are reported and the inverse relationship between leaf gas exchanges and leaf size is presented.

MATERIALS AND METHODS

The experiment concerned the survived plants of three white clover cultivars, sown at Tarvisio (a site located in an alpine valley, North-Eastern Italy, 756 m.a.s.l.) in 1994: Huia, a medium-leaf cultivar, AberHerald, a small/medium-leaf cultivar and Oboe, a large-leaf ladino-type cultivar.

The experimental design was a split-plot with 4 replicates of the three white clover cultivars in pure stands.

A Li-Cor Model 1600M stady state porometer (Li-Cor, Inc.) was used to determine stomatal conductance of the lower leaf surface of about 5 leaves per plot (together with photosynthetic active radiation, leaf and air temperature and relative humidity). The measures were made in in 3 sunny days from 11.00 to 13.00 hours, 1 month after each cut, on healthy, fully expanded trifoliate leaves under no or limited shading by adiacent leaves.

Ten terminal, fully expanded leaves per plot were harvested, kept moist in a plastic bag and then photocopied as soon as possible, in order to measure the individual leaf area using a leaf area meter (Li-Cor 3000).

The relative water content RWC was determined using the method of Barrs and Weatherley (1962).

In order to confirm that the individual clover survivors in every plot belong to the same cultivar and are not native wild ones, stolon specific weight (mg cm⁻¹) of each cultivar has been measured.

Differences among cultivars were analysed using a one-factor analysis of variance and a Duncan's multiple range test was used to separate means at 0.05 level of significance.

RESULTS

Differences among cultivars in specific stolon weight were significant and comparable with those of previous years. Average values were: 10.13 mg cm⁻¹

(AberHerald), 8.45 mg cm^{-1} (Oboe), and 7.08 mg cm^{-1} (Huia). Differences were significant at P<0.05 between AberHerald and Huia only.

During the growing season from July to October a decrease in the stomatal conductance was observed; in any case, the AberHerald average values in the three sampling days were higher than those of the other cultivars, but these differences resulted statistically significant for the second day only (P<0.05) (Fig. 1).

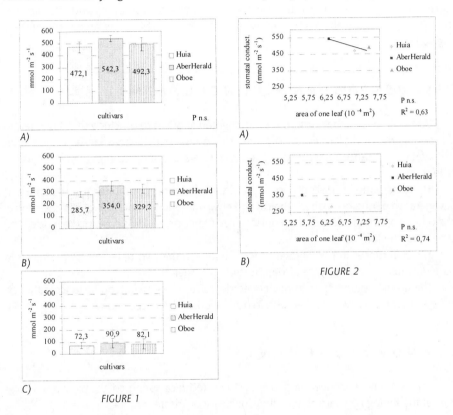

FIGURE 1

FIGURE 2

FIGURE 1. *AVERAGE STOMATAL CONDUCTANCE BETWEEN WHITE CLOVER CULTIVARS (WITH STANDARD DEVIATIONS) IN THREE DATES:*
A) MEANS OF 27/07/1999.
B) MEANS OF 10/09/1999.
C) MEANS OF 07/10/1999.

FIGURE 2. *CORRELATION BETWEEN AVERAGE INDIVIDUAL LEAF AREA AND STOMATAL CONDUCTANCE G$_L$ OF THREE WHITE CLOVER CULTIVARS:*
A) POROMETER MEANS OF 27/07/99 AND AREA MEANS OF 04/08/99.
B) POROMETER MEANS OF 10/09/99 AND AREA MEANS OF 25/08/99.

Differences among cultivars RWC values were not significant, but average data of 27/07/99 differed significantly from data of 07/10/99, showing an increase respectively of 3.69% for Huia, 8.25% for AberHerald, 7.51% for Oboe.

No significant differences were detected among cultivars for the individual leaf area, even if AberHerald always showed lower values than the other ones.

Correlation between mean individual leaf area of each cultivar and the corresponding stomatal conductance was estimated: stomatal conductance was strongly and negatively associated with leaf size, expressed as average leaf area (Fig. 2).

DISCUSSION AND CONCLUSIONS

Results based on the parameters investigated allow us to conclude that AberHerald is probably the best adapted to cold climate among the cultivars analysed. The higher stomatal conductance suggests also that AberHerald possibly has higher yield than the other two cultivars.

The third sampling did not show significant differences probably because at the end of vegetative period both physiological and environmental factors influenced the control of stomatal opening stronger than during growth period and this could have hidden the genetic factors effect.

The differences in percentage of RWC between the two dates seem to indicate a state of water stress in July, as also indicated by Turner (1990).

The strong negative correlation between leaf size and stomatal conductance, although not significant, was evidenciated also in other works (Mencuccini and Comstock, 1999).

ACKNOWLEDGEMENTS

This experiment has been carried out with the technical support of the plant physiology staff of the Biology Department of the University of Trieste.

REFERENCES

Barrs, H. D. and P. E. Weatherley, 1962. A re-examination of the relative turgidity technique for estimating water deficits in leaves. Australian Journal of Biology Science, 15: 413-428.

Collins, R. P. and I. Rhodes, 1995. Stolon characteristics related to winter survival in white clover. Journal of Agricultural Science, 124: 11-16.

Cornish, K., J. W. Radin, E. L. Turcotte, Z. Lu and E. Zieger, 1991. Enhanced photosynthesis and stomatal conductance of Pima cotton (*Gossypium barbadense L.*) bred for increased yield. Plant Physiology, 97: 484-489.

Egli, D. B., J. W. Pendleton and D. B. Peters, 1970. Photosynthetic rate of three soybean communities as related to carbon dioxide level and solar radiation. Agronomy Journal, 62: 411-414.

Hiebsch, C. K., E. T. Kanemau and C. D. Nickell, 1976. Effects of soybean leaflet type on net carbon dioxide exchange, water use and water-use efficency. Canadian Journal of Plant Science, 56: 455-458.

Malinowski, D. P., D. P. Belesky, J. Fedders, 1998. Photosyntesis of white clover (*Trifolium repens L.*) germoplasms with contrasting leaf size. Photosynthetica, 35 (3): 419-427.

Mencuccini, M. and J. Comstock, 1999. Variability in hydraulic architecture and gas exchange of common bean (*Phaseolus vulgaris*) cultivars under well-watered conditions: interactions with leaf size. Australian Journal of Plant Physiology, 26: 115-124.

Turner, L. B., 1990. Water relations of white clover (*Trifolium repens L.*): water potential gradients and plant morphology. Annals of Botany, 65: 285-290.

Effect of cutting regime and grass mixtures on white clover under subarctic conditions

M. JØRGENSEN AND K. RAPP

Norwegian Crop Research Institute, Holt Research Centre, N-9292 Tromsø, Norway

SUMMARY

A new white clover cultivar, Norstar, with excellent winter hardiness and good yield potential has been released (1999) for northern and upland parts of Norway. In a field experiment in Tromsø (69° 39'N), the dry matter (DM) yield and persistence of Norstar in mixtures with different grass species was studied. The plots were subjected to simulated grazing or cut for silage, and fertilised with a yearly total of 60kg Nha⁻¹. DM yields of the clover and grass components were determined during three growing seasons. The different grass mixtures had no direct impact on DM yield of clover, but in the first year the clover proportion of the total grass/clover yield was lower in mixture with timothy/ meadow fescue than in mixture with smooth meadow grass. However, in the following years the clover proportion of the former mixture increased, whereas it declined in the mixture containing smooth meadow grass. In 1999, the clover content in both mixtures was about 30%. Cutting regime had no influence on clover yield in either of the mixtures. Simulated grazing depressed the grass yield in white clover/timothy/meadow fescue mixtures, but not in white clover/smooth meadowgrass mixtures.

Keywords: cutting regime, DM yield, grass mixture, persistence, white clover

INTRODUCTION

The new white clover cultivar, Norstar, bred from material collected in mid Norway (Rennebu 62°N), is winterhardy and relatively high yielding (Rapp, 1996). With this new cultivar, white clover can be grown in the upland and northern parts of Norway, where the imported cultivars are not sufficiently winterhardy. Due to the long and cold winters, perennial ryegrass is not a feasible companion grass for white clover in most parts of Norway, and the performance of white clover with other grass species is less studied. Timothy and meadow fescue are the most commonly used grass species for seed mixtures for leys in Norway. In grassland for grazing purposes, smooth meadow grass is an important species. In this experiment we studied the effect of timothy/meadow fescue or smooth meadow grass and cutting regime on DM yield and persistence of white clover.

MATERIALS AND METHODS

A field experiment was established in 1996 on a sandy loam soil in Tromsø (69°39′N). The average temperature and precipitation (1961-1990) during the growing season (May-September) in Tromsø is 8.6°C and 368 mm. White clover (Norstar) was sown in monoculture and in mixtures with smooth meadow grass (Lavang) or with timothy (Engmo) and meadow fescue (Salten). The grass mixtures were also sown without clover. All plots were fertilised with 60 kg N, 32 kg P and 124 kg K ha⁻¹ per growing season. Two cutting treatments were used: silage cut (two cuts per growing season) and simulated grazing (three cuts, the plots being cut when the grass height was 20-30cm). For silage the first cut was made at the booting stage of timothy. The last cut was made at the end of August in both treatments. DM yield and clover content were measured in all treatments.

RESULTS AND DISCUSSION

There were no significant differences in overwintering and total plant cover between the two mixtures during the three years. Cutting regime had no effect on plant cover. In spring, the grass cover was higher and the clover cover lower when white clover was in mixture with timothy/meadow fescue than with smooth meadow grass in 1997 (Table 1). However, in the following years there were no differences between the two treatments.

TABLE 1. SPRING COVER OF SOWN GRASSES AND WHITE CLOVER IN THE TWO SEED MIXTURES; A) WITH SMOOTH MEADOWGRASS, B) WITH TIMOTHY/MEADOW FESCUE, DURING THREE YEARS. MEANS OF 2 CUTTING TREATMENTS AND 3 REPLICATES, (N=6) ± S.E.

	Cover of sown grasses %		Clover %	
Year	a	b	a	b
1997	55 ±4.6	80 ±7.1	21 ±5.4	8 ±1.9
1998	59 ±4.5	67 ±3.8	19 ±2.4	22 ±2.5
1999	50 ±4.9	58 ±5.1	36 ±2.0	36 ±4.2

The highest DM yield was obtained in white clover/timothy/meadow fescue mixtures cut for silage (Fig. 1). Simulated grazing reduced the total DM yield of white clover/timothy/meadow fescue mixture with 31%, but did not reduce the yield of white clover/smooth meadowgrass mixtures. Neither cutting regime nor grass mixture had any effect on clover yield (Fig. 1). In 1997, the clover proportion of the yield was higher in white clover/smooth meadowgrass mixtures than in mixtures of white clover/timothy/meadow fescue (Table 2). However, in the following years, the clover proportion of the white clover/smooth meadowgrass mixture decreased, whereas it slightly increased in the white clover/timothy/meadow fescue mixture.

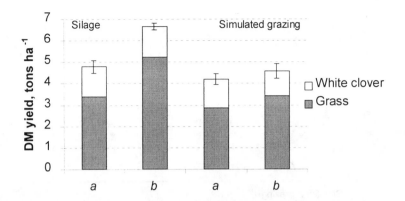

FIGURE 1. TOTAL DM YIELD OF GRASS AND CLOVER IN SEED MIXTURES; A) WHITE CLOVER/SMOOTH MEADOWGRASS, B) WHITE CLOVER/TIMOTHY/MEADOW FESCUE. THE MIXTURES WERE CUT FOR SILAGE (2 CUTS) OR SUBJECT TO SIMULATED GRAZING (3 CUTS). MEANS OF 3 YEARS AND 3 REPLICATES (N=6). BARS INDICATE S.E OF THE TOTAL GRASS/CLOVER YIELDS.

TABLE 2. TOTAL GRASS/CLOVER YIELD AND PER CENT WHITE CLOVER IN TWO SEED MIXTURES DURING THREE YEARS. MEANS OF TWO CUTTING TREATMENTS AND 3 REPLICATES (N=6) ±S.E.

| Years | White clover with smooth meadowgrass | | White clover with timothy and meadow fescue | |
	Total yield $t\,ha^{-1}$	White clover %	Total yield $t\,ha^{-1}$	White clover %
1997	3.28 ±0.30	46 ±6	4.60 ±0.40	18 ±3
1998	5.41 ±0.21	22 ±2	6.84 ±0.61	20 ±2
1999	4.80 ±0.41	30 ±2	5.39 ±0.53	31 ±3

Timothy, which dominated in the mixture, has an upright growth form with a large part of its leaves in the higher layers of the canopy, especially when it reaches the reproductive phase (Jørgensen and Junttila, 1994). It may therefore have shaded clover in the first year. However, frequent or early cutting is reported to reduce the competitive ability and persistence of timothy (Menzi, 1988), and this may have reduced the competition towards white clover.

The seasonal variation of white clover and grass yields is shown in Figure 2. In the silage cut, the white clover yields had more fluctuating yields when mixed with timothy/meadow fescue than with smooth meadowgrass. When subject to simulated grazing, the clover yields in each harvest were similar in both mixtures except for in 1997. Under this cutting regime, the clover yields were generally lower in the first cut in early summer than in the subsequent harvests.

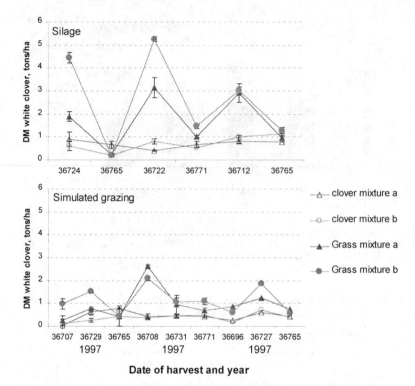

FIGURE 2. SEASONAL VARIATION OF YIELD OF WHITE CLOVER AND GRASS IN TWO SEED MIXTURES, A) WHITE CLOVER/SMOOTH MEADOWGRASS, B) WHITE CLOVER/TIMOTHY/ MEADOW FESCUE, CUT FOR SILAGE (2 CUTS PER YEAR) OR SIMULATED GRAZING (3 CUTS PER YEAR). MEANS OF 3 REPLICATES ±S.E.

CONCLUSIONS

Neither cutting regime nor grass mixture affected the total dry matter production of white clover in this experiment. Smooth meadowgrass is more tolerant to frequent cutting, but it spreads slowly and reaches maximum yields two to three years after establishment. Competition from this species towards white clover may therefore increase in the coming years.

ACKNOWLEDGEMENTS

The authors would like to thank Lars Svenson for technical assistance. The Norwegian Crop Research Institute funded this work.

REFERENCES

Jørgensen, M. and O. Junttila, 1994. Competition between meadow fescue (*Festuca pratensis* Huds.) and timothy (*Phleum pratense* L.) at three levels of nitrogen fertilization during three growing seasons. Journal of Agronomy and Crop Science, 173: 326-337.

Menzi, H., 1988. Einfluss von Witterung und Bestandesstruktur auf den Wachstumsverlauf von Weissklee (*Trifolium repens* L.) und die Ertragsbildung von Gras/Weissklee-Gemengen. Dissertation ETH Nr. 8702.

Rapp, K., 1996. Selection response for dry matter yield in white clover (*Trifolium repens* L.) using different selection methods. Norwegian Journal of Agricultural Sciences, 10: 265-280.

Patterns of white clover behaviour under mixed and mono grazing over seven years

T. NOLAN[1], J. CONNOLLY[2] AND M. WACHENDORF[3]

[1]Teagasc, Athenry, Co. Galway, Ireland
[2]National University of Ireland, Dublin, Belfield, Dublin 4, Ireland
[3]University of Kiel, Germany

SUMMARY

The effects of cattle, sheep and mixed cattle + sheep grazing on the evolution of white clover in a permanent pasture were measured from 1990 to 1996. An area of semi-natural pasture was divided into five blocks each with three plots (30 m x 20 m). Grazing treatments (cattle - eight 18-month old steers, sheep - 22 yearling dry sheep, mixed - 4 steers + 11 sheep) were randomly allocated within block. Grazings were for short periods of 3-4 days, at about 21-day intervals. Prior to grazing clover contribution to total vegetation dry mass was measured.

Clover content was consistently about three times higher in cattle (14%) than in sheep (5%) grazed plots with mixed grazing (9%) generally intermediate. Mixed-grazing clover content was closer to cattle levels in the first four years and to sheep levels in other years. Clover content generally declined in all treatments towards the end of the experiment, the decline being greater for mixed than cattle or sheep grazing. Within years, relativities in clover content between grazing regimes at the start of the grazing season, generally persisted throughout the year. The impact of climate on pasture dynamics will be examined.

Keywords: cattle, mixed grazing, sheep, sward dynamics, time, white clover

INTRODUCTION

Grasslands, comprising about 80% of all arable land in Ireland, are by far the most important component in Irish agriculture land use. The need to develop predictable methodology to establish and maintain clover in pastures is driven by EU concerns with extensification and environmental protection through a reduction in the use of artificial fertilisers. Some results of an experiment on the effects of cattle, sheep and mixed cattle + sheep grazing on the evolution of white clover in a permanent pasture are presented for the years 1990 to 1996. See Nolan and Connolly (1989) for production benefits of mixed grazing.

MATERIALS AND METHODS

The experimental location was Teagasc Research Centre, Athenry (53°17'N 8°47'E). Soil was a loam/rendzina with pH 7.0. Elevation was 40 m above sea level. In spring 1970 a permanent pasture containing an initial clover DM content of about 5% was selected. The area was divided into five blocks each with three plots and sheep, cattle and sheep + cattle grazing treatments were randomly allocated within each block. Plot size was 30 m x 20 m. All grazings were for short intense periods of 3-4 days, at about 21 day intervals (Table 1), using eight 18-month old steers, 22 yearling dry sheep and or a mixture of 4 steers + 11 sheep respectively. In 1994 the protocol was changed so that each grazing method was randomly allocated in four blocks with two blocks grazed at 3 week (Short) intervals and two blocks at 4 week (Long) intervals, which were lengthened to 4 and 5 week intervals respectively from July, to simulate different rotational grazing speeds. This aspect is not considered here. Artificial N application was 51 kg ha^{-1} in spring. Measurement of clover DM contribution was based on clipping five randomly selected 0.1 m^2 areas within each plot before each grazing.

TABLE 1. DATES OF GRAZING FOR 1990 TO 1996 (JANUARY 1ST = DAY 1).

Grazing	1	2	3	4	5	6	7	8
1990	185	204	232	253	276			
1991	84	112	140	168	196	232	275	324
1992	100	132	160	199	237	279		
1993	96	140	172	207	242	291		
1994	101	122	143	172	199	227	255	291
1995	96	117	138	159	187	215	243	
1996	110	131	162	190	218	253	287	

RESULTS AND DISCUSSION

In each year the mean percentage clover DM contribution to total DM was highest for cattle grazing, intermediate for mixed and lowest for sheep grazing (Table 2). Averaged over all years, the % clover DM contributions to total DM were 13.5, 9.3 and 4.8 for cattle, mixed and sheep grazing, respectively. These results confirmed earlier findings based on a four-year experiment with a ryegrass/white clover reseeded pasture (Nolan, 1995). For cattle the 1995 figure (7.8%) was comparatively very low and clover contributions for the sheep and mixed treatments during the final three years were reduced.

Clover percentage contributions to total DM were converted to the log scale for analysis (to correct for nonnormality and heteroscedasticity) and the SEDs and tests of significance are presented for that scale only in Table 2. In all years cattle grazing resulted in significantly ($p < 0.05$) higher annual clover proportions compared with sheep grazing.

Mixed grazing generally had a lower annual clover proportion than for cattle grazing, significant in 1993, 1994 and 1995. The overall clover proportion for mixed grazing was higher than for sheep grazing, significant in 1990 to 1993. Clover proportions in mixed grazing was closer to cattle grazing in the first four years and to sheep grazing in the final three years.

TABLE 2. PERCENTAGE WHITE CLOVER CONTRIBUTION TO TOTAL DRY MATTER (DM) FOR CATTLE, SHEEP AND MIXED CATTLE + SHEEP GRAZING FOR 1990 TO 1996. THE ANALYSIS WAS CARRIED OUT ON THE LOG SCALE AND THE SED AND TESTS OF SIGNIFICANCE ARE PRESENTED FOR THAT SCALE ONLY. MEANS WITH DIFFERENT SUPERSCRIPTED LETTERS ARE SIGNIFICANTLY DIFFERENT AT THE 5% LEVEL OR LESS.

	Year	Cattle	Mixed	Sheep	SED
% clover	1990	14.3	13.3	6.7	
	1991	15.1	12.3	4.2	
	1992	18.4	14.9	7.3	
	1993	13.5	9.8	4.4	
	1994	14.0	5.3	2.4	
	1995	7.8	3.1	3.3	
	1996	11.5	6.5	5.2	
Log(% Clover)	1990	2.46^a	2.48^a	1.69^b	0.22(
	1991	2.50^a	2.17^a	0.86^b	0.26$
	1992	2.67^a	2.49^a	1.55^b	0.231
	1993	2.60^a	2.28^b	1.48^c	0.125
	1994	2.37^a	1.38^b	0.53^b	0.416
	1995	1.42^a	0.75^b	0.44^b	0.243
	1996	2.13^a	1.22^{ab}	0.96^b	0.448

TABLE 3. F VALUES AND SIGNIFICANCE OF GRAZING REGIME, GRAZING DATE AND THEIR INTERACTION FOR LOG (%CLOVER IN TOTAL DM) IN 1990 TO 1996 EXCLUDING 1993.

Year	Grazing regime		Grazing date		Regime x Date	
	F value	P value	F value	P value	F value	P value
1990	8.36	0.011	16.27	<.001	1.51	0.178
1991	21.02	<.001	30.82	<.001	2.17	0.016
1992	13.65	0.003	31.48	<.001	1.18	0.324
1993	16.75	<.001	7.03	<.001	1.68	0.107
1994	9.84	0.013	12.27	<.001	1.62	0.099
1995	8.57	0.017	39.71	<.001	1.31	0.238
1996	3.82	0.085	8.58	<.001	0.31	0.985

Within years a repeated measures analysis was performed to assess the effect of grazing date. A split-plot analysis was used, the validity of which for the repeated measures data was checked before proceeding. F values and their significance for grazing treatments, dates of grazing and the interaction between these two factors for the analysis of log (% clover DM in total DM) for each year are shown in Table 3. Generally Treatment and Date were significant but not their interaction. Clover content generally was at a maximum in the July and August period for all years. Results for a typical year (1993) are shown in Fig. 1. On the percentage scale (Fig. 1 (a)) there was a clear increase in the difference among treatments with advancing grazing date but with treatments generally preserving their relative order of clover contribution. On the log scale (Fig. 1 (b)) the mean response lines are roughly parallel across grazing dates and this holds for all years. This suggests that the proportional difference between treatments in clover percentage contribution remains broadly constant with grazing date. Thus, if clover percentage content for the cattle grazing treatment was twice as high as for mixed grazing early in the season it tended to be about twice as high throughout. For all years the relativity obtaining in early grazing season was broadly maintained throughout the grazing season. This suggests a great importance of early season clover content. In addition, relative differences between grazing treatments at the end of the grazing season were broadly reflected in clover differences in spring of the following year, again suggesting a relationship over time in differentials. This work will be continued with modelling of the evolution of clover contents as affected by climatic variation (see Table 4 for a typical pattern for several meteorological variables).

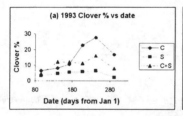 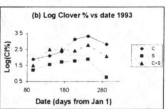

FIGURE 1. CLOVER CONTRIBUTION WITH TIME IN 1993. SHOWN ARE CLOVER CONTRIBUTION FOR CATTLE, SHEEP AND MIXED GRAZING, (A) % CLOVER CONTENT AND (B) LOG(CLOVER %).

TABLE 4. MEAN DAILY TEMPERATURE > 5° (°C), MEAN DAILY RADIATION (J CM⁻²) AND MEAN DAILY PRECIPITATION (MM) IN SIX GRAZING PERIODS FOR 1993. DAYS ARE FROM JANUARY 1 IN PERIOD 1.

Period	Length (days)	Mean daily temp. >5° (°C)	Mean daily radiation (J cm⁻²)	Mean daily precipitation (mm)
1	95	7.3	776	1.8
2	45	9.5	1400	2.7
3	32	12.7	1291	4.3
4	35	14.1	1450	1.7
5	35	13.6	1670	1.1
6	49	10.9	1011	2.6

CONCLUSIONS

1. There are distinct and persistent differences between grazing regimes in their impact on clover contribution. The ranking of clover contents (cattle > mixed > sheep) which appeared in 1970 persisted through to 1996. Clover content under mixed grazing tended to be closer to cattle grazing at the start and to sheep grazing towards the end of the experiment.
2. There was a general decline in clover contents towards the end of the experiment, in particular in 1995, and this appeared to be greatest for mixed grazing.
3. Within-year relativities in clover content between grazing regimes which existed at the start of the grazing season persisted throughout the year.
4. There was an indication that differences in clover content between treatments at the end of grazing persisted through to the following Spring.

REFERENCES

Nolan, T. and J. Connolly, 1989. Mixed vs. Mono grazing by steers and sheep. Animal Production, 48: 519-533.

Nolan, T., 1995. Mixed Animal Species Grazing. In: Jeffrey, D. W., Jones, M. B. and McAdam, J. H. (eds) Irish grasslands - their biology and management, 73-84. Dublin. Royal Irish Academy.

The effects of stolon morphology on the winter survival of white clover in a cool climate

R.P. COLLINS[1], Á. HELGADÓTTIR[2] AND I. RHODES[1]

[1]IGER, Plas Gogerddan, Aberystwyth, Ceredigion SY23 3EB, Wales/UK
[2]RALA, Keldnaholt, 112, Reykjavik, Iceland

SUMMARY

This experiment was carried out in order to clarify the role of stolon morphology in determining the winter survival and subsequent spring growth of white clover under UK conditions. Four divergent selection lines differing in combinations of stolon diameter and abundance (length per unit ground area) were created from within a single population. These were: 'Thick Sparse' (TKSP); 'Thin Sparse' (TNSP); 'Thick Profuse' (TKPR) and 'Thin Profuse' (TNPR). A field experiment was established in which the lines were grown with perennial ryegrass. Detailed measurements were made on the material removed from the field plots in December (beginning of winter) and March (end of winter/beginning of spring). In December, the lines differed substantially in morphology, particularly in terms of specific stolon weight (SSW) related to stolon diameter, stolon diameter, stolon abundance and growing point number. By March, some loss of stolon had occurred in all lines. There was no clear effect of SSW on this process: lines with similar values in December had contrasting values of stolon loss in March. Neither was there a relationship between values of stolon abundance in March and spring yield. It appeared that the capacity of lines to produce yield in spring was less dependent on the length of stolon present than on other factors, such as the size of leaves produced and the number of growing points per unit stolon length.

Keywords: morphological variation, selection lines, spring yield, white clover, winter survival

INTRODUCTION

White clover populations originating in the northernmost parts of Europe are characterised by thin stolons, short internodes and small leaves (Aasmo Finne, 2000; Helgadóttir et al., 2000), whereas those from warmer climates generally have thicker stolons, longer internodes and larger leaves (Williams, 1987). In parallel to this morphological variation, the cold tolerance of white clover populations decreases considerably along a geographical cline from northern to southern Europe (although altitudinal clines are also superimposed on this gradation) (Williams, 1987). However, the adaptive significance of observed differences in stolon characteristics is unclear. For example, research by Frankow-Lindberg (1999) showed no clear pattern in values of specific stolon weight (SSW) stolon dry weight per unit stolon length, a quantity which reflects stolon diameter between 'adapted' and 'non-adapted' selections within clover cultivars growing in Sweden. The results of Collins *et al.* (1991), and Collins and Rhodes (1995), however, showed that populations with higher values of SSW suffered less winter damage in UK conditions than those with thin stolons. This was considered to be related to the higher levels of carbohydrate reserves present during the winter in stolons with high values of SSW (Collins and Rhodes, 1995).

In order to try and clarify the role of stolon morphology in the overwintering and subsequent spring growth of white clover in UK conditions, a programme of selection has been carried out at IGER, Aberystwyth in which lines divergent for combinations of stolon diameter and abundance (stolon length per unit ground area) were bred (Collins *et al.*, 1997). These selection lines were created from within a single baseline population. This process has enabled confounding effects due to differences in geographic origin to be removed in studies investigating the influence of differences in stolon morphology on winter survival and spring growth.

The present experiment analysed changes in the morphological characteristics of four divergent selection lines during winter in a cool, maritime climate, and sought to relate these to the subsequent production of leaf material in spring.

MATERIALS AND METHODS

Four divergent selection lines were created after two generations of selection within a single population of white clover which had been collected in alpine Switzerland (Collins *et al.*, 1997). The stolon morphology of these lines differed in terms of diameter and abundance (stolon length x stolon number). The lines created were: 'Thick Sparse' (TKSP); 'Thin Sparse' (TNSP); 'Thick Profuse' (TKPR) and 'Thin Profuse' (TNPR).

Field plots containing these lines in binary mixtures with two perennial ryegrass cultivars were established in 1995 at IGER, Aberystwyth. The experiment was subsequently managed under a cutting regime. In December 1999 (beginning of winter) and March 2000 (end of winter/beginning of spring), vegetation cores were removed from the plots and analysed for a range of characters. These included: number of terminal and axillary growing points; stolon length and weight/ground area; stolon diameter measured on ten randomly chosen lengths of stolon within each sample; and leaf plus petiole weight (in March only). From these primary data other variables could be calculated, such as: number of growing points/stolon length; SSW; leaf plus petiole weight/growing point; and leaf plus petiole weight/stolon length. In addition, stolon carbohydrate contents were measured on both sampling dates, but these results are not yet available. The data were analysed for each sampling date separately by two-way ANOVA in a randomised-block design, with perennial ryegrass cultivar and clover selection line as factors.

RESULTS AND DISCUSSION

Perennial ryegrass cultivar had an effect on certain clover characters; these were chiefly related to growing point number. However, in order to simplify the presentation of results for this paper, data for clover selection lines were averaged over the two grasses (Table 1).

TABLE 1. MORPHOLOGICAL CHARACTERS OF FOUR WHITE CLOVER SELECTION LINES (SEE TEXT FOR DESCRIPTION OF ABBREVIATIONS) MEASURED IN FIELD PLOTS IN DECEMBER 1999 AND MARCH 2000. DATA FOR SELECTION LINES ARE AVERAGED OVER TWO COMPANION CULTIVARS OF PERENNIAL RYEGRASS. N.S.= NOT SIGNIFICANT; *= P<0.05; *** = P<0.001

Line		TKSP	TNSP	TKPR	TNPR	s.e.d.	sig.
Character							
Total no. growing points							
(m^{-2})	Dec.	3396	4768	3263	4917	283	***
	March	2826	3678	2434	3966	317	***
Stolon length							
$(m\ m^{-2})$	Dec.	58.2	85.8	86.5	120.1	5.6	***
	March	56.0	71.4	62.8	98.9	9.4	***
Stolon weight							
$(g\ m^{-2})$	Dec.	106.3	85.8	112.7	117.1	6.7	***
	March	59.4	46.6	53.1	59.7	-	n.s.
Specific stolon weight							
$(g\ m^{-1})$	Dec.	1.82	0.99	1.30	0.98	0.05	***
	March	1.07	0.65	0.86	0.60	0.04	***
Stolon diameter							
(mm)	Dec.	2.78	1.96	2.58	2.01	0.09	***
	March	2.59	1.92	2.39	1.93	0.07	***
Growing points/stolon length							
(m^{-1})	Dec.	59.2	56.7	37.3	41.1	4.4	***
	March	53.2	52.4	39.2	40.7	5.1	*
Leaf + petiole weight							
$(g\ m^{-2})$	March	26.6	20.9	21.2	25.7	-	n.s.
Leaf + petiole weight/growing point							
(mg)	March	9.32	5.59	8.63	6.51	0.66	***
Leaf + petiole weight/stolon length							
$(mg\ cm^{-1})$	March	4.9	2.9	3.4	2.6	0.5	***

The selection lines differed significantly in all the characters measured in December. The TNPR line had the highest number of growing points per unit ground area and greatest stolon abundance. The line that contrasted most with TNPR in December was TKSP; this had a much lower number of growing points and the lowest stolon abundance. As expected, the SSW of the 'thick' lines was much greater than that of the 'thin' ones. Patterns in SSW were reflected in the direct measurements of stolon diameter. In March there were again many differences in stolon morphology between the lines. TNPR still had the highest number of growing points per unit ground area and the greatest stolon abundance.

It was evident that all lines except TKSP lost a considerable amount of their stolon over the winter. However, the presence of thick stolons was insufficient on its own to protect plants from loss of stolon length due to winter damage. This was exemplified by the observation that the greatest proportional loss of stolon abundance over the winter was found in TKPR, which suffered a reduction of more than 27%. In contrast, TKSP lost only 3.8%. There were differences in SSW and stolon diameter between the TKSP and TKPR lines in December, but these appear to be insufficient to account for such a large discrepancy in stolon survival. The 'thin' lines, TNSP and TNPR, lost respectively only 16.8% and 17.7% of their stolon abundance over winter, despite having thinner stolons than TKPR. These results suggest that possession of thick stolons does not, *per se*, confer a greater ability on white clover lines to survive winter in a cool climate without loss of stolon.

Differences between the lines in stolon abundance in March did not, however, translate into differences in spring yield, as the results for leaf plus petiole weight per unit ground area demonstrate. The number of growing points per unit stolon length, combined with the amount of leaf produced by each growing point provide a breakdown of the components of spring yield. The number of growing points per unit stolon length is approximately inversely related to internode length, as every node has the potential to produce an axillary bud: the 'sparse' lines thus appeared to have shorter internodes than the 'profuse' ones. Leaf plus petiole weight per growing point would positively reflect leaf size: in this case the 'thick' lines had larger leaves than the 'thin' ones. Consequently, in terms of spring yield, lack of stolon abundance in spring could be overcome by plants that produced larger amounts of leaf per unit stolon length, either through having short internodes, large leaves, or both. Internode length and leaf size were not directly measured in this experiment, but glasshouse experiments have shown that the 'thick' lines produce large leaves (Collins *et al.*, 1998).

Previous studies showing superior stolon abundance in spring under UK conditions in populations with values of SSW may have provided only circumstantial evidence of a relationship between these characters (Collins *et al.*, 1991). The results of the present experiment indicate no such relationship. However, winter conditions during the course of this experiment were much warmer than average, and might not have provided a sufficiently robust test of the hypothesis that SSW and survival are positively linked.

ACKNOWLEDGEMENTS

We gratefully acknowledge the assistance of Sonia Venerus and Josep Leto. The visit of SV to IGER was funded as a short-term scientific mission by COST.

REFERENCES

Aasmo Finne, M., 2000. Genetic variation in a Norwegian germplasm collection of white clover (*Trifolium repens* L.). In: Lowland Grasslands of Europe – Utilisation and Development (eds. G. Fisher and B. E. Frankow-Lindberg). REU Technical Series. (in press).

Collins, R. P. and I. Rhodes, 1995. Stolon characteristics related to winter survival in white clover. Journal of Agricultural Science, 124: 53-62.

Collins, R. P., M. J. Glendining and I. Rhodes, 1991. The relationship between stolon characteristics, winter survival and annual yields in white clover (*Trifolium repens* L.). Grass and Forage Science, 46: 51-61.

Collins, R. P., M. T. Abberton, T. P. T. Michaelson-Yeates and I. Rhodes, 1997. Response to divergent selection for stolon characters in white clover (*Trifolium repens*). Journal of Agricultural Science, 129: 279-285.

Collins, R. P., M. T. Abberton, T. P. T. Michaelson-Yeates, A. H. Marshall and I. Rhodes, 1998. Effects of divergent selection on correlations between morphological traits in white clover (*Trifolium repens* L.). Euphytica, 101: 301-305.

Frankow-Lindberg, B. E., 1999. Effects of adaptation to winter stress on biomass production, growth and morphology of three contrasting white clover cultivars. Physiologia Plantarum, 106: 196-202.

Helgadóttir, Á., P. Marum and R. P. Collins, 2000. Breeding white clover cultivars for northern marginal environments. In: Proceedings of Meeting of COST 814 Programme, Pordeneone. This volume.

Williams, W. M., 1987. Adaptive variation. In: White Clover (eds. M. J. Baker and W. M. Williams). CAB International, Wallingford, UK, 299-321.

COST 814: Biocontrol links to New Zealand

S. L. GOLDSON[1], M. R. MCNEILL[1], J. R. PROFFITT[1], C. B. PHILLIPS[1]
AND J. R. CARADUS[2]

[1] AgResearch, PO Box 60, Lincoln, New Zealand
[2] AgResearch Grasslands, Private Bag 11008, Palmerston North, New Zealand

SUMMARY

Recently, a new and very severe pest of white clover (Trifolium repens), known as Sitona lepidus (syn. S. flavescens) has established in New Zealand; the weevil larvae feed on the plants' rhizobial nodules and small roots. Given the dependence of New Zealand's pastoral economy on low-input, plant-based nitrogen fixation, any threat to clover immediately causes very serious concern. Sitona lepidus may be more of a problem in New Zealand's agricultural ecosystem, in part, because natural enemies are absent.

Two years ago, a biological control programme was commenced by the Biocontrol and Biosecurity Group of AgResearch based at Lincoln, New Zealand. Amongst other initiatives, a significant development in the programme occurred in 1999, when links were established with Dr Rosemary Collins (IGER, Aberystwyth) through Dr Mike Hay at AgResearch Grasslands, New Zealand. With the help of Dr Collins, AgResearch contacted nine COST 814 researchers, who generously took the time to collect weevils from their white clover research plots and forward them to New Zealand (in alcohol). These weevils were then dissected and searched for parasitoids. Results have revealed unidentified braconid parasitoids from Wales, Sweden, Finland, France, Norway and Italy. Also, there is now the opportunity to extract the DNA from these European weevils and compare it to that of New Zealand's S. lepidus population. This is starting to allow the definition of the geographic origin of the New Zealand population and could assist in the selection of appropriate biocontrol agents.

In 2000, it is planned to maintain the links with the nine researchers who have been collecting the weevils, but the next phase of this programme will involve laboratory assessment of live material to evaluate the performance of the various species and ecotypes of the parasitoids. It is hoped to do this with the generous co-operation of IGER in Britain and the USDA, ARS European Biological Control Laboratory in France.

Keywords: biological control, Microctonus sp., New Zealand, Sitona lepidus, white clover

BACKGROUND

Sitona lepidus Gyllenhal Gyllenhal (syn. *S. flavescens* (Marsham)) (Coleoptera: Curculionidae), is thought to be of European origin and is found as far north as 66-67°N in Finland (Markkula and Koppa, 1960); indeed the species is distributed throughout palaearctic regions (Dieckmann, 1980) and North America where it established in the 1870s (Bright, 1994). Weevils of the genus *Sitona* Germar (Curculionidae: Brachycerinae: Entimini) have been identified as one of the most common pests of pasture legumes in Europe (Murray, 1991). While *S. lepidus* feeds on a large number of legume species, it has been shown to exhibit a strong preference for white clover (*Trifolium repens*), strawberry clover (*T. fragiferum*) and alsike clover (*T. hybridum*) (Byers and Kendall, 1982). The larvae of *Sitona* spp. are the most damaging stage of the life cycle. First instar larvae of *S. lepidus* feed on the root nodules of clover plants, while larger larvae feed on progressively larger roots (Byers and Kendall, 1982). Such larval feeding can cause significant damage to clover plants as a result of direct damage and also facilitates penetration of fungal disease via the feeding lesions (Newton and Graham, 1960).

In England *Sitona* spp. (mainly *S. lepidus* and *S. lineatus* (L.)) have been identified as pests of white clover in pastures (Clements and Murray, 1991), with *S. lepidus* being reported in one study as the dominant *Sitona* species on this legume (Murray and Clements, 1994). In general, adult *S. lepidus* are not thought to pose a threat to established swards, although significant damage has been observed to occur locally, particularly in late winter when overwintering adults respond to temporary increases in temperature and feed on still dormant clover (P. J. Murray pers. comm.). It is thought that feeding by weevils at this time of year may reduce the competitive ability of clover in a mixed sward, and lead to a decline of the legume component (Murray and Clements, 1993). In Northern Ireland, regular pesticide application to ryegrass/white clover sward more than trebled the white clover content in two years, compared to untreated pasture (Mowat and Shakeel, 1988). In the USA, *S. lepidus* is considered to be a minor pest of clover species in the eastern United States (R. A. Byers, pers. comm.).

S. lepidus was first recognised in New Zealand in March 1996, when teneral adults were found in dairy pasture in the Waikato area of the North Island (37°40'S, 175°30'E) (Barratt *et al.*, 1996). By this time the insect was found to be widely established throughout the northern part of New Zealand's North Island making eradication impossible (Barker *et al.*, 1996). Since then the weevil has been spreading at c. 35 km year⁻¹ (Willoughby and Addison, 1997) and, given its Northern Hemisphere distribution, there is every reason to expect it to spread throughout New Zealand. Soon after the weevil's discovery, severe damage to white clover was recognised in infested pastures; this arose from very high populations of all stages compared to those reported in Europe and the USA. The white clover all but disappeared and there were associated symptoms of nitrogen-deficiency. This resulted in increased costs through the need for nitrogen fertiliser application and lowered milk solids production (Eerens *et al.*, 1998). *S. lepidus* thereby became and, remains, a threat to the profitability of pastoral farming in New Zealand as farmers very much rely on white clover for both its nitrogen fixing capability and high nutritional value (Caradus *et al.*, 1996; Ulyatt *et al.*, 1977). The severity of the impact of *S. lepidus* in New Zealand is consistent with New Zealand's experience with several other exotic pest species including *Sitona discoideus* in lucerne (Goldson *et al.*, 1985). It may be conjectured that in general, New Zealand's pest problems arise from a lack of *in situ* natural enemies of exotic pests and, possibly, something to do with the paucity of species diversity of its agricultural ecosystems. New Zealand's pastoral grasslands represent a very incomplete transplant of the European grassland ecosystems and thus may offer niche availability to invading species.

In view of the severity of threat posed by the clover root weevil, a multifaceted research programme was initiated in October 1996 to find practical pest management options based on adequate biological and ecological knowledge. Part of this involved a search for suitable biological control agents as described in this contribution.

THE BIOLOGICAL CONTROL PROGRAMME

There are no reports on the use of parasitoids for the biological control of *S. lepidus* in the literature. *Microctonus hyperodae* (Hymenoptera: Braconidae), a South American parasitoid that usefully controlled Argentine stem weevil (*Listronotus bonariensis* (Kuschel)) (Goldson *et al.*, 1998), has been found to be ineffective against *S. lepidus* (Barratt *et al.*, 1997a). Similarly, neither have New Zealand populations of *M. aethiopoides* Loan shown any potential against *S. lepidus* (Barratt *et al.*, 1997a), in spite of this parasitoid having at least 13 known hosts in New Zealand (Barratt *et al.*, 1997b).

In 1998, the AgResearch Biocontrol and Biosecurity Group based at Lincoln, New Zealand began to develop an overseas programme to attempt to locate suitable biocontrol agents. A significant part of this programme arose through initial contact with Dr Rosemary Collins (IGER at Aberystwyth) who met the AgResearch biocontrol group via Dr Mike Hay of AgResearch Grasslands. During discussion with Dr Collins it was recognised that members of the COST 814 were possibly in a position to be able to help in the location of appropriate control agents for *S. lepidus*. As a result, AgResearch contacted and later supplied nine groups with a motorised suction device (McCulloch blowervac) and associated collecting weevil equipment. This was combined with the earnest request that during their regular visits to the clover plots, could the participants please spend 5-10 minutes with the machine to suck up any plant litter. It was further asked that this then be searched in the laboratory to extract any insects that looked like weevils or beetles and that these be forwarded to New Zealand (in alcohol). On arrival in New Zealand, the weevils were dissected and searched for the larvae of parasitoid natural enemies.

RESULTS

Overall, the results from the co-operative programme have been very useful; the details are given in Table 1 and Fig. 1. In 1999, c.1400 *Sitona* sp. were sent from Europe to New Zealand. Sixty eight percent of these were found to be *S. lepidus*; other species included *S. hispidulus*(15%), *S. puncticolis*(11%), *S. lineatus*(5%) and *S. sulcifrons*(2%). This bias towards *S. lepidus* is consistent with what would have been expected from white clover plots (e.g. Byers and Kendall, 1982).

TABLE 1. DETAILS OF *SITONA LEPIDUS* RECOVERY BY COST 814 MEMBERS.

Collector	Country	Location	Collection date	Nos. of *S. lepidus* dissected	Parasitised	% parasitism
R. Collins and	Wales	Plas Gogerddan	27 Jul 99	71	No	
M. Fothergill		Aberystwyth	10 Oct 99	93	Yes	4%
		Bronydd Mawr	20 Oct 99	130	No	
F-L. Bodil	Sweden	Uppsala	21 Jul 99	23	Yes	17%
P. Nykanen-Kurki	Finland	Mikkeli	24 - 30 Jun 99	30	No	
			12 - 23 Jul 99	216	Yes	2.5% - 15.6%
			16 and 26 Aug 99	12	No	
J-B. Cliquet	France	St Pierre sur Dives	5 Jul 99	5	No	
C. Robin	France	Mirecourt	1 Jun 99	7	Yes	14%
			29 Jun 99	9	Yes	11%
			9 Aug 99	13	No	
			13 Oct 99	8	Yes	12%
T. Nolan	Ireland	Newfort	20 Jul and 4 Aug 99	17	No	
P. Marum	Norway	Loken	12 Aug 99	5	No	
		Apelsvohh	13 Aug 99	4	No	
		Apelsvohh	21 Sep 99	13	Yes	23%
S. Venurus	Italy	Pordenone	5-Aug-99	16	Yes	19%
		Taruisio	25 Aug 99	2	No	
A. Elgersma	The Netherlands	Wageningen	29 Jul 99	2	No	

Dissection of the remitted *S. lepidus* revealed unidentified braconid parasitoid larvae in weevil populations from Wales, Sweden, Finland, France, Norway and Italy (Table 1). These larvae have been tentatively identified as a *Microctonus* sp. (near *aethiopoides*). However, the biotype of *M. aethiopoides* established in New Zealand, has been found to be unable to develop in *S. lepidus* (Barratt *et al.*, 1997a; McNeill *et al.*, 2000).

There is now the opportunity to extract the DNA from the weevils forwarded by COST 814 scientists and compare it to that of the New Zealand population. This may allow definition of the geographic origin of the New Zealand population and greatly assist in the selection of appropriate control agent ecotypes. Given the wide distribution of the parasitoids, care must be taken to choose biological control agents compatible with New Zealand's population of *S. lepidus*.

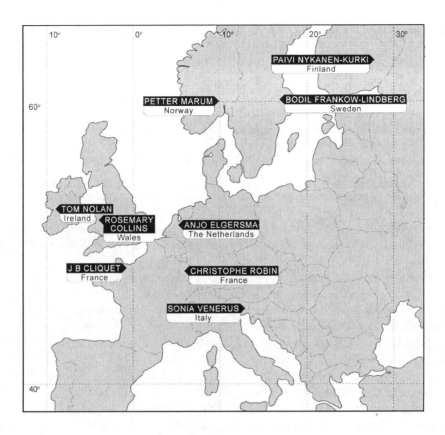

FIGURE 1. COLLECTION SITES OF *SITONA LEPIDUS* BY COST 814 MEMBERS.

In the summer of 2000 it is hoped to maintain the links with the nine COST 814 researchers who have been involved in collecting the weevils. It is planned that the next phase of the programme will involve laboratory testing of live material forwarded by COST members to evaluate the performance of the various species and ecotypes of the parasitoids. At this stage, this will be done with IGER in North Wyke, England and the USDA, ARS European Biological Control Laboratory in Montpellier, France.

ACKNOWLEDGEMENTS

This research has been carried out with the financial support of the New Zealand wool, meat, dairy and game industry boards of New Zealand, the New Zealand Foundation for Research, Science and Technology, AGMARDT and the C.

Alma Baker Trust. Thanks to Rachel Cane for technical assistance in the identification of parasitoids.

REFERENCES

Barker, G. M., P. J.Addison, A. C. Firth and B. I. P. Barratt, 1996. *Sitona lepidus* Gyllenhal newly established in New Zealand: assessment of distribution in the North Island. Proceedings of the 49th New Zealand Plant Protection Conference: 266-269.

Barratt, B. I. P., G. M. Barker and P. J. Addison, 1996. *Sitona lepidus* Gyllenhal (Coleoptera: Curculionidae), a potential clover pest new to New Zealand. New Zealand Entomologist, 19: 23-30.

Barratt, B. I. P., A. A.Evans and C. M Ferguson, 1997a. Potential for biocontrol of *Sitona lepidus* Gyllenhal by *Microctonus* spp. Proceedings of the 50th New Zealand Plant Protection Conference: 37-40.

Barratt, B. I. P., A. A. Evans, C. M. Ferguson, G. M. Barker, M. R. McNeill and C. B. Phillips, 1997b. Laboratory nontarget host range of the introduced parasitoids *Microctonus aethiopoides* and *M. hyperodae* (Hymenoptera: Braconidae) compared with field parasitism in New Zealand. Environmental Entomology, 26: 694-702.

Bright, D. E., 1994. Revision of the genus *Sitona* (Coleoptera:Curculionidae) of North America. Annals of the Entomological Society of America, 87: 277-306.

Byers, R. A. and W. A. Kendall, 1982. Effects of plant genotypes and root nodulation on growth and survival of *Sitona* larvae. Environmental Entomology, 11: 440-443.

Caradus, J. R., D. R. Woodfield and A. V. Stewart, 1996. White clover: New Zealand's competitive edge. pp. 1-6, in D.R. Woodfield (ed.) Proceedings of a joint symposium, Lincoln University, New Zealand, 21-22 November, 1995. Agronomy Society of New Zealand Special Publication No. 11, Grassland Research and Practice Series No. 6.

Clements, R. O. and P. J. Murray, 1991. Pest and disease damage to white clover at widespread sites in England and Wales. Proceedings of the British Grassland Society Symposium Strategies for Weed, Disease and Pest Control in Grassland, 10.21-pp.10.22.

Dieckmann, L., 1980. Beiträge zur Insektenfauna der DDR: Coleoptera-Curculionidae (Brachycerinae, Otiorhynchinae, Brachyderinae). Beiträge zur Entomologie, 30: 145-310.

Eerens, J. P. J., B. E. Willoughby, F. Kettlewell, S. Hardwick and S. Bay, 1998. The clover root weevil in northern pastures: on-farm observations of its impact on white clover. Proceedings of the New Zealand Grassland Association Conference, 60: 287-290.

Goldson, S. L., C. B. Dyson, J. R. Proffitt, E. R. Frampton and J. A. Logan, 1985. The effect of *Sitona discoideus* Gyllenhal (Coleoptera:Curculionidae) on lucerne yields in New Zealand. Bulletin of Entomological Research, 75: 429-442.

Goldson, S. L., J. R. Proffitt and D. B. Baird, 1998. Establishment and phenology of the parasitoid *Microctonus hyperodae* Loan in New Zealand. Environmental Entomology, 27: 1386-1392.

Markulla, M. and P. Köppä, 1960. The composition of the *Sitona* (Col. Curculionidae) population on grassland legumes and some other leguminous plants. Annals Entomologicae

Fennici, 26: 246-263.

McNeill, M. R., B. I. P. Barratt and A. A. Evans, 2000. Behavioural acceptability of *Sitona lepidus* (Coleoptera: Curculionidae) to the parasitoid *Microctonus aethiopoides* (Hymenoptera: Braconidae) using the pathogenic bacterium *Serratia marcescens* Bizio. Biocontrol Science and Technology (in press).

Mowat, D. J. and M. A. Shakeel, 1988. The effect of pesticide application on the establishment of white clover in a newly-sown ryegrass/white clover sward. Grass and Forage Science, 43: 371-375.

Murray, P. J., 1991. Pests of white clover. Proceedings of the British Grassland Society Symposium: Strategies for Weed, Disease and Pest Control in Grassland, pp. 8.1-8.7.

Murray, P. J. and R. O. Clements, 1994. Investigations of the host feeding preferences of *Sitona* weevils found commonly on white clover (*Trifolium repens*) in the UK. Entomologia Experimentalis et Applicata, 71: 73-79.

Murray, P. J. and R. O. Clements, 1993. *Sitona* damage to clover in the UK. in Prestidge, R.A. (ed.) 260-264, Proceedings of the 6th Australasian Conference on Grassland Invertebrate Ecology, AgResearch, Hamilton.

Newton, R. C. and J. H. Graham, 1960. Incidence of root-feeding weevils, root rot, internal breakdown and virus and their effects on longevity of red clover. Journal of Economic Entomology, 53: 865-867.

Ulyatt, M. J., J. A. Lancashire and W. T. Jones, 1977. The nutritive value of legumes. Proceedings of the New Zealand Grassland Association, 38: 107-118.

Willoughby, B. and P. J. Addison, 1997. Assessment of the dispersal of *Sitona lepidus* (clover root weevil) in the North Island of New Zealand. Proceedings of the 50th New Zealand Plant Protection Conference: 33-36.

The spring growth of survivor populations of white clover cv. AberHerald collected in northern Europe

R. P. COLLINS[1], M. FOTHERGILL[1], Á. HELGADÓTTIR[2] AND I. RHODES[1]

[1]IGER, Plas Gogerddan, Aberystwyth, Ceredigion SY23 3EB, Wales/UK
[2]RALA, Keldnaholt, 112, Reykjavik, Iceland

SUMMARY

The growth characteristics of 'survivor' populations from three sites participating in the multi-site COST 814 experiment investigating 'Overwintering and Spring Growth of White Clover', together with the original 'Baseline' population, were compared at two temperatures. Analysis of variance revealed the presence of interactions between temperature treatment and population for certain morphological characters, suggesting that there were differences between the populations in terms of their phenotypic plasticity. Principal Components Analysis was used to summarise the large amount of data generated by the experiment. The results showed that (1) temperature treatment had a large effect on overall plant morphology; (2) the populations fell into distinct groups, with some evidence of divergence from the Baseline.

Keywords: genetic shift, morphology, temperature, white clover

INTRODUCTION

The use of two cultivars of white clover (AberHerald and Grasslands Huia) in a common experiment across twelve contrasting European sites has presented the COST 814 sub-group investigating 'Overwintering and Spring Growth of White Clover' with unique and valuable genetic resources, because the seed provided to each site was from the same original seed stock. After three years growth as part of the common experiment, random vegetative samples of survivor plants were collected from each site and sent to IGER, Aberystwyth, where they were propagated so that polycross seed could be produced for each site x cultivar combination. It was considered that survivor genotypes would possess the characteristics necessary for persistence at their collection site, i.e. would have adapted to local conditions as a result of natural selection. The variability and high degree of out-breeding in white clover strongly favour genetic shifts in response to natural or artificial selection pressures (Gibson and Hollowell, 1966).

The experiment described here investigated the morphological responses to two low temperature regimes of three survivor populations of AberHerald, together with the unselected, Baseline population. In this way, the relative effects of adaptation (genetic shifts in the morphology of the survivor populations) and acclimation ('plastic' or phenotypic responses induced by the temperature treatments) could be determined.

MATERIALS AND METHODS

Material for this experiment was obtained from a spaced plant nursery at IGER, Aberystwyth. This contained 40 genotypes of AberHerald survivors from each site participating in the COST 814 multi-site programme, together with the Baseline. These plants had been grown from polycrossed seed. The survivor populations chosen were from Switzerland (Zürich), Germany (Kiel) and Sweden (Uppsala). On 7 January 2000, two stolon cuttings, each with a terminal bud, were collected from 20 genotypes of the chosen survivor populations, plus the Baseline. These were allocated to either of two temperature treatments: A (11/8°C day/night) or B (8/4°C day/night). The temperature treatments were imposed in growth cabinets under a 12h daylength and an average photosynthetic photon flux density of 500 ìmol m^{-2} s^{-1}. These temperatures are typical of those occurring in spring in Aberystwyth. The cuttings were planted into deep trays, with enough space around each one to allow adequate room for unimpeded stolon extension, and to allow individuals to be readily identified. On Day 1, a dot of red acrylic paint was placed on a standard internode on every cutting. They were then left to grow, with water supplied as required.

After five weeks in the growth cabinets a number of morphological measurements were carried out on each cutting. First, the length of stolon between the marked node and the youngest identifiable node was measured, and all the leaves and branches produced after the paint mark were counted. Each leaf was scored according to the Carlson scale of leaf development (Carlson, 1966). After scoring, a metamer (modular unit comprising fully-expanded leaf, internode and axillary bud (Marshall, 1996)) on every marked stolon was identified and dissected into its components. The diameter of the dissected internode was measured using calipers; the area of the dissected leaf was obtained using a leaf area meter (Delta-T, UK), and the length of its associated petiole was measured. Dry weights of these components were obtained.

Data from the cabinets were analysed together by ANOVA, which calculated the effects of temperature treatment, population and their interaction. Subsequently, Principal Components Analysis (PCA) was carried out using mean values of all the variables measured in each population at both temperatures.

RESULTS

A large number of variables were obtained from the measurements, both directly and from calculations involving the primary data. Predictably, temperature treatment had a highly significant effect on all these variables, so that in all populations plants at the higher temperature were larger and more branched.

Averaged over temperature, there were no significant differences between the populations for any plant character. However, significant interactions between population and temperature treatment were evident for some characters. Significant interactions were found in several variables related to leaf production rate, so these were combined by calculating 'Total Carlson Score x Metamer Leaf Area'. This gave a measure of plant 'leafiness'. There was also an interaction for metamer internode diameter. Results for these two variables are presented in Table 1. At the lower temperature, values of 'leafiness' for the three survivor populations were similar and were all significantly lower than the Baseline value. However, at the higher temperature the German and Swedish populations were much more productive than the Baseline and Swiss material. In the case of internode diameter, there was greater variation between the populations at the lower temperature. Again, the German and Swedish populations seemed to respond differently to the Baseline and Swiss plants. The latter tended to produce thinner stolons at the lower temperature.

TABLE 1. TOTAL CARLSON SCORE X METAMER LEAF AREA (CM²) AND METAMER INTERNODE DIAMETER (MM) OF FOUR POPULATIONS GROWN FOR FIVE WEEKS AT TWO TEMPERATURES UNDER CONTROLLED CONDITIONS. TEMP. A = 11/8°C; TEMP. B = 8/4°C. *P<0.05.

Population		Baseline	Switzerland	Germany	Sweden
		Total Carlson Score x Metamer Leaf Area (cm²)			
Temperature	A	66.2	65.6	81.8	88.7
	B	40.3	30.1	32.4	30.9
s.e.d.		8.7			
Significance		*			
		Metamer Internode Diameter (mm)			
Temperature	A	3.1	2.9	2.9	3.1
	B	2.5	2.4	2.7	2.9
s.e.d.		0.1			
Significance		*			

The results of PCA are shown in Fig. 1. The first two axes explained 91% of the total variation in the experiment. The PC 1 axis comprised a number of morphological characters (no. of branches, metamer wt., metamer leaf area, total Carlson score, no. of fully-expanded leaves), and it clearly separated the population groups according to temperature treatment. PC 2 was composed chiefly of internode length and diameter. This axis divided the populations into distinct groups according to site. At the lower temperature the Baseline and Swiss populations, and the German and Swedish populations appeared to form separate groups; at the higher temperature the Baseline was separated from the survivor populations.

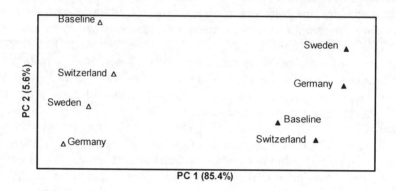

FIGURE 1. PRINCIPAL COMPONENTS ANALYSIS USING 23 GROWTH CHARACTERS MEASURED ON 'SURVIVOR' POPULATIONS FROM THREE SITES, PLUS THE UNSELECTED BASELINE POPULATION OF WHITE CLOVER CV. ABERHERALD. PLANTS WERE GROWN AT TWO TEMPERATURES UNDER CONTROLLED CONDITIONS. TEMP. A = 11/8°C (△); TEMP. B = 8/4°C (▲).

DISCUSSION

The results suggest that even a relatively small increase in the growth of temperature can have a large influence on the growth and morphology of white clover populations. The presence of interactions between growth temperature and population for certain characters indicates that some populations were more phenotypically plastic than others, although this was evident in different characters for different populations. PCA is a useful way of summarising the results of experiments such as this, in which many variables are generated for several populations. In this instance, the distinct grouping of the populations within each temperature treatment suggests that differentiation between the Baseline and some survivor populations has occurred. It is interesting to note the similarity of morphology in the Baseline and Swiss populations at the lower temperature, particularly as the cultivar AberHerald has been developed from material collected in the same region as the Swiss site.

Survivor populations offer opportunities for research and development in many areas. For example, they could be used to: (a) determine the extent of change in the population structure of white clover cultivars when utilised in a range of environments, including some for which they were not specifically bred; (b) identify morphological/physiological characters of adaptive value in particular climatic conditions, thus assisting plant breeders to formulate selection criteria for the genetic improvement of white clover; (c) quantify the agronomic and ecological consequences of changes in population structure; (d) provide genetic resources which can be incorporated into breeding programmes to improve white clover for use in cool areas of Europe. The research reported in this paper hints that populations from certain sites form groups with similar morphological responses to low temperatures. Clearly, however, a larger number of survivor populations would need to be investigated before definite patterns in morphology emerged.

REFERENCES

Carlson, G. E., 1966. Growth of clover leaves – developmental morphology and parameters at ten stages. Crop Science, 6: 293-294.

Gibson, P. B. and E. A. Hollowell, 1966. White clover. US Department of Agriculture Handbook 314. US Government Printing Office, Washington DC, USA.

Marshall, C., 1996. Sectorality and physiological organisation in herbaceous plants: an overview. Vegetatio, 127: 9-16.

Combining data on clover overwintering across 12 sites. A time-based modelling strategy

J. CONNOLLY AND M. WACHENDORF

Department of Statistics, University College Dublin

S U M M A R Y

Data on the evolution of two white clover varieties (cv AberHerald and cv Huia) in mixed clover-grass swards was available at twelve sites in Europe from experiments conducted for several years under a common protocol. Swards were measured up to seven times over winter and up to seven times over the growing season. In the overwintering period detailed morphological measurements were taken on the clover at each sampling time and, during the growing season, the clover contribution to total available biomass was recorded. The strategy underlying the combined analysis of these complex data centred on three principles (a) partition of the annual cycle into a number of functional periods whose duration at each site was defined in terms of local conditions (b) modelling sward development in each functional period using Internal, initial within-site biological variables and across-site external variables. (c). Linking models across functional periods through reverse direction modelling. The analysis used a mixed models technique in recognition of the complex error structure of the data. The models derived accounted for most of the variation in observed sward clover content across sites and over years. Some problems of statistical analysis and presentation of model results are discussed.

Keywords: modelling, model presentation, multi-site analysis, white clover

I N T R O D U C T I O N

Multi-site experiments are relatively rare (e.g. Reader *et al.*, 1994) but are more common in plant breeding where cultivars have to prove themselves across a range of different environments (e.g. Talbot and Verdooren, 1996). The analysis of the data for the common experiment performed across twelve European sites over several years (Wachendorf, 2000) provide a rare challenge in deriving relationships from a complex body of data. The modelling strategy, statistical modelling issues and presentation of models for these data are discussed. We develop perspectives relevant to evaluating data covering several phases of the annual cycle of plant communities. The basic randomised-block design design was repeated at each of 12 experimental sites (Wachendorf *et al.*, 2000) had two clover cultivars as treatments and four blocks. Clovers were grown with a companion ryegrass. Morphological, chemical and yield measurements were taken at several stages of the annual cycle for two years.

PRINCIPLES OF MODELLING STRATEGY

The modelling strategy had three main elements: (a) the selection of functional periods based on the annual growth cycle of the clover-ryegrass community rather than calendar date, (b) modelling within each functional period, incorporating initial within-site biological variables and across-site variables (c) linking the models of functional periods through reverse direction modelling, taking as the response variable for a functional period the biotic explanatory variable(s) of the succeeding period.

Division of annual cycle into functional periods

The data from these experiments used different time phases of differing lengths at each site rendering a calendar approach to comparing sites unrealistic. Breaking the annual cycle into functional periods determined by a common phase of the life cycle of the plants than date serves a double purpose. Modelling sward development within each period reduced the modelling difficulty and was conceptually simplified by comparing a common biological phase across all sites. The four functional periods were (Fig. 1),

Growing Season - from the first to the last growing season cut;

Start of Growth - final morphological measurement to the first growing season cut;

Dormancy - first to the last morphological measurement;

End of growth - last growing season cut to the first morphological measurement.

Internal, initial within site biological variables and across site external variables

Modelling in each functional period used internal biological variables describing the initial status of the sward for each plot at the start of the functional period and external climatic variables that characterised growing conditions at different sites and are measured as constant for all plots within a site at any time. Plant growth and interaction in a community during a functional period is a resultant of initial system state and ongoing external forces. Thus, the variation among sites and within site initial state could be integrated in a single model of facets of the system for the period. To include both variable types is not be realistic for a single experiment. Yet, such models could lead to a wider understanding of the role of both types of explanatory variables in the development of clover/ryegrass communities and the degree to which variation in their behaviour is linked to unpredictable elements of the environment.

Internal variables characterise the initial sward state for each plot in a modelling period. Each plot is a community whose evolution may be affected by initial conditions that may differ among identically treated plots. The use of initial conditions in assessing growth is not widespread. Connolly, Wayne and Bazzaz (in review) have stressed the need to allow for initial biological conditions in modelling competitive effects to avoid the possibility of bias.

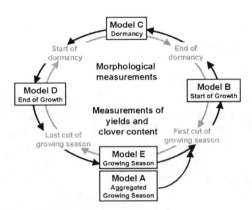

FIGURE 1. FUNCTIONAL PERIODS - MODELLING SCHEME

Linking through reverse direction modelling

To develop a series of interlinked models describing sward evolution through the annual cycle required that modelling proceed in a reverse direction. The explanatory variables for one functional period become the output variables to be modelled in the preceding period. A large number of candidate variables was available at the start of each functional period for inclusion as explanatory variables, particularly when detailed morphological measurements were available. These included; Mass variables (clover DM, DM of stolons, petioles, buds and nodal roots), Clover Morphological variables (number of terminal buds, total buds, nodal roots and tap roots leaf area, stolon length,), Clover Chemical variables (TNC and WSC of stolons), Grass variables (grass DM, number of tillers) and Combined variables (clover DM as % of all DM). Also available were meteorological variables for each modelling period; mean and cumulative temperature, radiation and precipitation. In model selection variables were included or excluded on the basis of their contribution to the explanatory power of the model. Only a few biological variables were necessary in the models and so the chain of explanation over functional periods was based on only these few variables. The meteorological variables are not subject to this recursive modelling scheme since these meteorological processes were not predictable from one period to the next.

Statistical modelling issues

Statistical issues arising in modelling these data are: (a) Complex error structure, (b) Transformation of variables and (c) Errors in explanatory variables. The fitting strategy was generally standard although a few points bear comment. Could the external variables explain most of the variation associated with site and year? All sites used AberHerald as one of two clover cultivars and most sites used Huia as the other. Clover cultivar was in all models and its interaction with internal or external variables were all possible terms for inclusion in the models.

Complex error structure

The multi-site and multi-year structure of the study suggests a complex error structure. Random components considered were: plot within site, site by year, and year to year variation associated with each plot. As data for two consecutive years only were available for most plots compound symmetry was assumed for the repeated measures.

Transformation of variables

Three variables were transformed before inclusion in the models. Clover content (CL) (g 100 g^{-1} DM) was measured as a percentage of dry matter but whether as a response or explanatory variable the logit of clover content, log (CL/(100-CL)), was used. This was to avoid heteroscedasticity in response, interactions induced by scale rather than biology and to ensure that predicted clover contents lie in the range 0 to 100%. The log of leaf area was a better explanatory variable than leaf area, suggesting that a fixed proportional increase in leaf area, rather than a fixed absolute increase, produced a constant effect on the response. Log tiller number was analysed to eliminate difficulties with heteroscedasticity. The inverse of tiller density was a better explanatory variable than tiller density, perhaps reflecting the common experience in competition models that response is inversely related to the density of competitors (Connolly, 1986). In one case the log of tiller number was used as explanatory variable as it fitted better.

Errors in explanatory variables

Imprecision in measuring an explanatory variable leads to biased estimation of the regression coefficient (Carroll *et al.*, 1995). Morphological variables (e.g. leaf area) which are based on subsamples from plots may not precisely measure the true plot value. Preliminary analysis of the variation in a variable among within-plot subsamples compared with its variation among plots will provide a basis for deciding whether the variable was measured sufficiently well to lead to negligible bias.

Presentation of results

A difficulty with statistical modelling of the type used here is that the final model may contain many terms, sometimes interacting with each other. The terms in the model may be variables (e.g. leaf area, average precipitation) or factors (e.g. site or clover variety). The model expressed as estimates of multiple regression coefficients may be difficult to appreciate and interpret, even for one familiar with multiple regression, particularly if transformations are used. A graphical or tabular approach greatly facilitated the interpretation of the various terms in the model.

The broad principle underlying the presentation of any model term is that predictions are initially made from the model for the term in question on the scale of the analysis, (e.g. logit of clover content predicted from log(leaf area)) and then these predictions are back-transformed to the natural scale in which the biologist most readily thinks (e.g. clover %) and plotted against the explanatory variable, again on the natural scale (e.g. leaf area). There were different types of model terms, factors and variables or not involved in interactions and variables not appearing in quadratic form and interactions of three types, factor by factor, factor by variable and variable by variable.

CONCLUSIONS

The modelling strategy was successful in developing a series of biologically meaningful linked models, that included the effects of within site and across site explanatory variables. The models gave insight into the annual evolution of the clover-ryegrass community across a wide range of sites/environmental conditions. The methods of presentation allowed a relatively simple appreciation of the behaviour of community dynamics across four linked functional periods.

REFERENCES

Carroll, R. J., D. Ruppert and L. A. Stefanski, 1995. Measurement error in nonlinear models. Chapman Hall, p. 305.

Connolly, J., 1986. On difficulties with replacement-series methodology in mixture experiments. Journal of Applied Ecology 23:125-137.

Connolly, J., P. Wayne and F. A. Bazzaz (in review). Interspecific Competition in Plants: How Well Do Current Methods Answer Fundamental Questions?

Reader, R. J., S. D. Wilson, J. W. Belcher, I. Wisheu, P. A. Keddy, D. Tilman, E. C. Morris, J. B. Grace, J. B. Mcgraw, H. Olff, R. Turkington, E. Klein, Y. Leung, B. Shipley, R. Vanhulst, M. E. Johansson, C. Nilsson, J. Gurevitch, K. Grigulis and B. E. Beisner, 1994. Plant competition in relation to neighbor biomass - an intercontinental study with *Poa pratensis*. Ecology, 75: (6) 1753-1760.

Talbot, M. and L.R. Verdooren, 1996. Meta-analysis and crop variety trials. In (eds: J Connolly & D Williams) Proceedings of EU HARMA VII Concerted Action Workshop, University College Dublin, Dublin p. 1-6.

Wachendorf, M., 2000. A model approach to climatic, geographic and edaphic determinants of overwintering of white clover. This volume.

An integrated approach to introgression breeding for stress tolerance in white clover

M.T. ABBERTON, A.H. MARSHALL, T. MICHAELSON–YEATES, A. WILLIAMS, W. THORNLEY, W. PREWER, C. WHITE AND I. RHODES

IGER, Aberystwyth, Ceredigion, SY 23 3EB, UK

SUMMARY

Interspecific hybrid and backcross plants have been produced between white clover (*Trifolium repens* L.) and a related species *Trifolium ambiguum* Bieb. Plants of the second backcross generation, with white clover as recurrent parent, combined the stoloniferous growth of white clover with the possession of a small amount of the rhizome typical of *T. ambiguum*. Plants with rhizomes were significantly more tolerant of drought than white clover itself. This work is now being extended to assess field performance of the hybrids and to locate molecular markers for the gene(s) controlling the rhizomatous trait. Yields and clover contents of second-generation backcross plants are comparable to those of white clover after the first harvest year under a cutting management. Amplified fragment length polymorphisms (AFLPS) have been used to locate markers in backcross progenies segregating for the presence of rhizomes.

Keywords: introgression, molecular markers, stress, Trifolium ambiguum, white clover

INTRODUCTION

White clover (*Trifolium repens* L.) is a highly heterozygous out breeding allotetraploid (2n=2x=32) that shows great variation, genotype x environment interactions and phenotypic plasticity.

However, there is only limited variation within the white clover gene pool for several agronomically desirable traits such as tolerance of drought. An approach to address this problem is the use of interspecific hybrids. In particular we have made crosses between white clover and the long-lived perennial *Trifolium ambiguum* Bieb. (Meredith *et al.*, 1995) This species has underground rhizomes (as opposed to the stoloniferous growth of white clover) that are believed to be largely responsible for its good tolerance of drought (Taylor and Smith, 1998).

We have shown that backcrosses with white clover as recurrent parent produces plants that have both rhizomes and stolons (Abberton *et al.*, 1998b). Plants of the second backcross generation allocate only a small fraction of their dry weight to rhizomes and yet show considerably enhanced drought tolerance (Marshall *et al.*, 2001).

This material is being analysed physiologically, agronomically and using molecular techniques in an integrated approach to germplasm improvement (Abberton *et al.*, 1998a).

It has been showed that the agronomic capabilities of this material are not compromised by limitations in nitrogen fixation, despite the different requirements of *T. ambiguum* from white clover in terms of nodulating rhizobia (Patrick *et al.*, 1994; Patrick and Lowther, 1995).

FIELD STUDIES

Although *T. ambiguum* is very persistent it establishes poorly and is not vigorous or competitive. Field experiments analysing growth with *Lolium perenne* as a companion grass under a cutting management show that the performance of the backcross 2 (second cycle of backcross progeny-BC2) plants is superior to that of the backcross 1 (first cycle of backcross progeny-BC1) and is beginning to approach that of the white clover. The BC2 plants are considerably more drought tolerant than white clover. This experiment is continuing and further experiments will assess the agronomic performance of the backcross plants under grazing.

TABLE 1. TOTAL DRY MATTER YIELD (KG/HA) AND CLOVER CONTRIBUTION IN THE FIRST HARVEST YEAR.

T. repens	9389	64%
T. ambiguum	2932	1%
Backcross 1	5851	41%
Backcross 2	7329	58%

Assessment of reproductive characteristics and seed yield shows that the fertility of the backcross plants is lower than for white clover. Although both white clover and the *T. ambiguum* line used are tetraploid there may well be some degree of meiotic irregularity and this is an area of research that we are currently pursuing.

MOLECULAR MARKERS

The use of molecular markers is an approach to increasing the speed and precision of a programme of recurrent selection and introgression. The targeting of markers flanking areas of the genome responsible for large amounts of the variation in quantitative or qualitative traits increases the response to selection and reduces linkage drag. It can thus decrease the number of selection cycles required to incorporate the gene(s) of interest within a background of predominantly pre-existing elite material (Webb and Abberton, 1998).

In order to develop marker-assisted approaches to the introgression of the rhizomatous trait from *T. ambiguum* into white clover we have generated molecular markers using a bulk segregant Amplified Fragment Length Polymorphism (AFLP) approach. AFLP markers are produced by the digestion of genomic DNA by two restriction enzymes and the subsequent amplification of the fragments produced by the polymerase chain reaction (PCR). Amplified fragments were visualised by silver staining following resolution on a polyacrylamide gel. The segregation of bands on these gels can be compared with the segregation of plants for presence/absence of the rhizomatous traits. Three second generation backcross families were analysed and in each family DNA from plants with rhizomes was bulked together and DNA from plants.

We have identified markers that discriminate between rhizomatous and non-rhizomatous plants. Differences between bulked DNA of the two plant types were found in three segregating families. These preliminary results need confirmation on DNA from individual plants and can then be converted to probes for a restriction fragment length polymorphism (RFLP) analysis.

FUTURE STUDIES

Field experiments at IGER, Aberystwyth are continuing to assess the performance of the hybrid material in subsequent years. In addition, the grazing tolerance of the backcross families will be tested and the drought tolerance of the material assessed in the field using shelters. Clonal genotypes of the two backcross generations and parents will be assessed for persistence and productivity at three sites within Europe (in Sweden, Norway and The Netherlands) from spring 2000 and subsequently at other sites across Europe. In 2001, similar experiments will be established at three sites within the UK.

Cytological analysis to confirm the stability of these hybrids at the chromosomal level will be carried out in parallel with molecular marker studies. For the latter, the next stage will be the confirmation of the putative markers by studies of individual plants and their incorporation into selection programmes across a wide range of material.

ACKNOWLEDGEMENTS

This work is financially supported by the UK Biotechnological and Biological Sciences Research Council and the Ministry of Agriculture Fisheries and Food.

REFERENCES

Abberton, M. T., T. P. T. Michaelson-Yeates, J. H. MacDuff, A. H. Marshall and I. Rhodes, 1998a. New approaches to legume improvement for sustainable agriculture. In: B.Boller and F.J. Stadlemann (eds). Breeding for a Multi-Functional Agriculture. Proc. Of the 21st Meeting of the Fodder Crops and amenity Grasses Section of EUCARPIA, Switzerland 1997 pp. 91-93 FAL. Reckenholz, Zurich.

Abberton, M. T., T. P. T. Michaelson-Yeates, A. H. Marshall, K. Holdbrook-Smith and I. Rhodes, 1998b. Morphological characteristics of hybrids between white clover, Trifolium repens L., and Caucasian clover, Trifolium ambiguum M. Bieb. Plant Breeding, 117, 491-493.

Marshall, A. H., M. T. Abberton, T. P. T. Michaelson-Yeates, I. Rhodes and T. A. Williams, 2000. Drought tolerance of interspecific hybrids between Trifolium repens and Trifolium ambiguum. Proceedings of XIX International Grassland Congress Universidade de Sao Paolo, 2001 (in press)

Meredith, M. R., T. P. T. Michaelson-Yeates, H. J. Ougham and H.Thomas, 1995. Trifolium ambiguum as a source of variation in the breeding of white clover. Euphytica, 82, 185-191.

Patrick, H. N. and W. L. Lowther, 1995. Influence of the number of rhizobia on the nodulation and establishment of Trifolium ambiguum. Soil Biology Biochemistry, 27, 717-720.

Patrick, H. N., W. L. Lowther and K.D. Trainor, 1994. Inoculation for successful establishment of Caucasian clover. Proceedings of the New Zealand Grassland Society 56, 101-105.

Taylor, N. L. and R. R. Smith, 1998. Kura Clover (Trifolium ambiguum M.B.) Breeding, Culture, and Utilisation. Advances in Agronomy 63, 154-179.

Webb, K. J. and M. T. Abberton, 1998. Molecular genetics of white clover. In: Crop development for Cool and Wet Cimate of Europe. Proceedings of COST 814 Workshop. Pamplona, Spain, 1998 (in press).

Genetic Resources of Trifolium in The Netherlands

L.J.M. VAN SOEST AND N. BAS

Centre for Genetic Resources, The Netherlands (CGN), Plant Research International, P.O. Box 16, Wageningen, The Netherlands

SUMMARY

The Centre for Genetic Resources the Netherlands (CGN) is the national genebank of the Netherlands and maintains collections of horticultural and agricultural crops. It presently conserves 21.000 accessions of 20 different crops in its genebank facilities.

More recently, foddercrops including clovers received much attention and several expeditions were organised to collect material (van Soest and Dijkstra,1998).

Keywords: agricultural crops, genetic resources, Trifolium repens

COLLECTIONS MAINTAINED IN THE GENEBANK

The *Trifolium* collection includes 202 accessions, 147 accessions of red clover (*T. pratense*) and 55 accessions of white clover (*T. repens*).

124 ecotypes of *T. pratense* were collected during a rescue operation in The Netherlands in 1985 and 1986. Besides these Dutch ecotypes, the red clover collection includes another 23 accessions of cultivars, tetraploid breeding lines and accessions collected in 1997 in Uzbekistan.

TABLE 1. TRIFOLIUM COLLECTIONS MAINTAINED BY CGN.

Population type	T. pratense	T. repens	Total
Ecotypes (wild)	129	33	162
Landraces	4	1	5
Advanced cultivars	11	20	31
Breeding lines	3	1	4
Total available	**147**	**55**	**202**
Needs multiplication*	12	39	51
Total collection	**159**	**94**	**253**

* material not yet available

The *T. repens* collection consists of old cultivars, ecotypes recently sampled in old pastures in The Netherlands and material collected in 1997 in Uzbekistan.

The clover collection of CGN will be enlarged in the near future with another 29 ecotypes of T. repens from the Netherlands and 22 accessions collected in 1999 in Central Asia, including material of *T. pratense* (12) and *T. repens* (10). This material will be regenerated in 2000 and 2001.

COLLECTING OF CLOVERS

Several collecting missions were organised in the Netherlands and Central Asia (Uzbekistan and Kyrgyzstan) in the period 1985 to 1999. In Central Asia the missions were organised in co-operation with the national genebank of Uzbekistan and the Vavilov Institute of Plant Industry (VIR) of St. Petersburg, Russia (van Soest *et al.*, 1998; van Soest, 1998).

The following collecting missions have been organised since 1985:
The Netherlands (1985/86); 124 accessions of red clover collected in all 12 provinces (Fig.1)
Uzbekistan (1997); 3 accessions of white clover and 5 of red clover;

FIGURE 1. COLLECTING SITES OF T. PRATENSE, SAMPLED IN ALL 12 PROVINCES OF THE NETHERLANDS.

The Netherlands (1997/98); 51 accessions of white clover and 3 of red clover Uzbekistan/Kyrgyzstan (1999); 10 accessions of red clover and 12 of wild clover.

REGENERATION

The multiplication of clovers is conducted in spatial isolated field plots of winter rye orTriticale. The distance between the plots is 50 m. After sowing in late summer the material is kept for vernalisation in an unheated greenhouse during winter. In April of the following year the clovers are transplanted in the isolated field plots. The plotsize is approximately 10 m². Seeds are harvested in August and after cleaning and drying samples are taken for germination tests. Before entering in the genebank the samples need to have a germinability above 85 %.

DOCUMENTATION, STORAGE AND UTILISATION

The collections are documented for passport data in the data management system GENIS, based on Oracle software.

Data can also be found on CGN's website (http://www.cpro.dlo.nl/cgn/).

The material is stored under long term storage conditions (-20°C) in the genebank facilities of CGN and freely availble to *bona fide* users. However before receiving the material the user is requested to sign a 'Material Transfer Agreement' (MTA). More details on the MTA can be found on the website of CGN.

CONCLUSION

A broad genepool of *T. repens* and *T. pratense* including ecotypes collected in old pastures from the Netherlands and natural grasslands in Central Asia is available for evaluation and utilisation in the cool and wet regions of Europe.

REFERENCES

Soest, L. J. M. van and H. Dijkstra, 1998. Current status of CGN forages collection. In: Maggioni, L. *et al.* 1998. Report of a working group on Forages. Sixth meeting, 6-8 March 1997, Beitostølen, Norway. IPGRI, Italy: 78-80.

Soest, L. J. M. van, K. I. Baimatov and V. F. Chapurin, 1998. Multicrop collecting mission to Uzbekistan. Plant Genetic Resources Newsletter, 116: 32-35.

Soest, L. J. M. van, 1998. Report of the expedition to Uzbekistan - Itinerary, collected materials and data. Centre for Plant Breeding and Reproduction Research (CPRO-DLO), Centre for Genetic Resources, The Netherlands (CGN), Wageningen, The Netherlands: 34.

Coadaptation of white clover and its symbiont Rhizobium leguminosarum biovar trifolii

S. DALMANNSDÓTTIR[1], Á. HELGADÓTTIR[1] AND M. M. SVENNING[2]

[1]The Agricultural Research Institute, Keldnaholt, 112 Reykjavik, Iceland
[2]Deparment of Biology Faculty of Science, University of Tromsø, 9037 Tromsø, Norway

SUMMARY

White clover is an important pasture legume all over Europe. Environmental conditions vary and white clover varieties suitable for marginal conditions are now available. A possible coadaptation might exist between host and symbiont, and we wanted to test whether the geographical origin of host and symbiont influence the plant productivity at different temperatures and the nodule occupancy of different *Rhizobium* strains. White clover from Norway (HoKv9238) and Wales (AberHerald), and R.l.bv. *trifolii* strains from Northern Norway (8-9/20-15) and Wales (Sp-21) were used. White clover was grown under sterile conditions in modified Leonard jars in the phytotron at two different temperature regimes. Results from two comparable experiments indicate that HoKv9238 produces more biomass when inoculated with the Norwegian *Rhizobium* strain than with the strain from Wales. Competition studies for nodulation gave an indication about strain preference for the different plants. The results from analysed nodules indicate that AberHerald shows preference for the southern strain as 98% of AberHerald nodules were inoculated with the strain from Wales, but only 53% of HoKv9238 nodules were occupied by the Norwegian strain.

Keywords: *coadaptation, nodule occupancy, Rhizobium leguminosarum bv.trifolii, white clover*

INTRODUCTION

White clover forms nitrogen fixing-symbiosis with the soil bacterium *Rhizobium*. The nitrogen-fixing efficiency will influence plant production and the choice of *Rhizobium* strain/strains for a particular white clover cultivar, may determine its success in the field. Interaction between plants and *Rhizobium* strains has been shown to influence plant productivity significantly (e.g. Mytton and Livesey, 1983; Svenning *et al.*,1991). According to Mytton *et al.*, (1977) the plant genotype accounted for 74% of the phenotypic variance while Roskonthen (1989) stated that the *Rhizobium* strain was the most important factor. Adaptive influence of the indigenous plants on local *Rhizobium* populations has also been shown (Sherwood and Masterson, 1974). It has been observed that the white clover cultivars AberHerald and AberCrest were pale and unhealthy looking when grown under field conditions in more northerly regions than where they normally are grown (Ian Rhodes and Päivi Nykänen-Kurki, pers. comm.). This suggests that the N-fixation might have been ineffective. Further, AberHerald showed symptoms of N deficiency under controlled conditions when inoculated with *Rhizobium* strains from Northern Norway (Dalmannsdottir, 1996). The aim of these experiments was to study the coadaption of white clover and R.l.bv. *trifolii* related to geographical origin in order to enhance white clover production in northern areas. Firstly, we studied the effects of two different temperature treatments on the symbiotic performance of indigenous strains isolated from one geographic locality in association with host plants originating from contrasting climatic conditions. Secondly, we looked at the nodule occupancy of two different bacteria strains nodulating two cultivars of contrasting geographic origin.

COADAPTATION OF WHITE CLOVER AND RHIZOBIUM

Materials and methods

In the experiment we used an indigenous population from Norway (HoKv9238) and a cultivar bred at IGER, Wales, from material originating from Switzerland (AberHerald). Two *Rhizobium* strains, 8-9 and Sp-21, from Norway and Wales, respectively, were used for inoculation. White clover was propagated from sterile seeds. They were grown in Leonard jars in sterile sand:perlite mixture (50:50) in the phytotron at the University of Tromsø. The plants were inoculated with the two *Rhizobium* strains separately and grown at two different temperatures, 12°C and 18°C (20 plants per treatment). The plants were harvested after 6 weeks when the biomass of the plant, nodule number and nodule biomass were recorded. We then repeated the experiment with slight alterations. First of all, the plants were inoculated with a single *Rhizobium* strain as well as with a mixture of the two strains. The Norwegian Rhizobium strain 8-9 was replaced with strain 20-15, and we used different day and night temperatures with 12 hours daylength (12/9°C and 18/15°C). After two weeks the seeds had germinated well, but several weeks later some of the plants had not established in spite of normal pH levels of the soil. After 11 weeks only some of the plants within each treatment were growing adequately. The plants grown at 18/15°C were though harvested, and fresh and dry weight of shoot and root measured. Five plants were harvested for each treatment. Plants grown at 12/9°C were all very small and were kept at the same temperature for 6 more weeks before harvesting. Because of this, results can not be directly compared between the two temperature treatments.

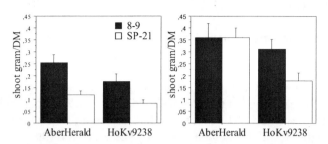

FIGURE 1. DRY MATTER PRODUCTION OF ABERHERALD AND HOKV9238 INOCULATED WITH TWO DIFFERENT RHIZOBIUM STRAINS, 8-9 AND SP-21. PLANTS WERE GROWN AT TWO DIFFERENT TEMPERATURES (12°C AND 18°C) AND HARVESTED AFTER 6 WEEKS. STANDARD ERRORS ARE SHOWN.

Results

The results of the first experiment (Fig. 1), show that HoKv9238 produced more dry matter when inoculated with the Norwegian *Rhizobium* strain (8-9) than with Sp-21 from Wales. AberHerald, on the other hand, produced more dry matter at 12°C in symbiosis with strain 8-9 but did not respond differently to the different rhizobia at 18°C. The results for root weight were similar to those for shoot weight. The nodule biomass was influenced more by the plant population than temperature or *Rhizobium* strain.

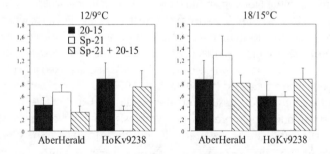

FIGURE 2. DRY MATTER PRODUCTION OF ABERHERALD AND HOKV9238 INOCULATED WITH TWO DIFFERENT RHIZOBIUM STRAINS, 20-15 AND SP-21. PLANTS AT 12/9°C WERE HARVESTED AFTER 17 WEEKS. PLANTS AT 18/15°C WERE HARVESTED AFTER 11 WEEKS. STANDARD ERRORS ARE SHOWN.

In the second experiment, AberHerald produced more biomass when inoculated with the Rhizobium strain from Wales at both temperatures. The Norwegian population, HoKv9238 produced most biomass with a mixture of the *Rhizobium* strains at 18/15°C, but at 12/9°C the biomass production of HoKv9238 was the same in symbiosis with strain 20-15 and with the mixture (Fig.2). Inoculation with strain Sp-21 gave low plant production.

NODULE OCCUPANCY

Materials and methods

Germinated sterile seeds of AberHerald and HoKv9238 were placed on agar slants in tubes and inoculated with a mixture of strain Sp-21 and strain 8-9. They were grown at room temperature and 20 plants were used for each treatment. At harvest, the roots were washed with tap water and then surface sterilised in 70% ethanol and 6% H_2O_2. Ten nodules were picked off each plant for nodule occupancy studies. *Rhizobium* was fingerprinted by the ERIC-PCR method (de Bruijn 1992, Versalovic 1991).

Results

About 50% of all the nodules were analysed, totally 117 nodules. Some of the nodules were small and did not give fingerprint results. AberHerald had 98% of nodules occupied by strain Sp-21 and 2% by strain 8-9, HoKv9238 had 47% of nodules occupied by strain Sp-21 and 53% by strain 8-9. Results indicate that AberHerald shows more preference for one strain than HoKv9238.

DISCUSSION AND CONCLUSION

In spite of difficulties encountered during the course of the two experiments, there are indications that HoKv9238, at low temperature, had higher dry matter production when nodulated with the Norwegian Rhizobium strain than the Welsh strain. According to Svenning et al. (1991) white clover from the north gave higher yields when nodulated with Rhizobium from the north than from the south. The mixed inoculum increased the dry matter of HoKv9238 more than that of AberHerald compared to single strain inoculum. In a field experiment in Iceland, where HoKv9238 was used, a mixed inoculum similarly had a positive effect on clover yield (Svenning *et al.*, 1997). The two experiments presented here gave partly contradictory results for AberHerald. In Exp.1, there was an obvious temperature effect indicating more efficient symbiosis with the Norwegian strain 8-9 at 12°C, but at 18°C the strains were equally efficient. In Exp.2, there was no such temperature effect. Strain Sp-21 was the most efficient at both temperatures. In the study on nodule occupancy where the plants were grown at room temperature, AberHerald seemed to have a high preference for the southernmost Rhizobium strain (Sp-21). Further work concerning coadaptation of white clover and Rhizobium should involve nodule occupancy studies of different climatic strains at low temperatures.

ACKNOWLEDGEMENTS

We thank the Icelandic Research Council, The Agricultural Productivity Fund and COST 814 for economic support.

REFERENCES

Dalmannsdottir, S., 1996. Virkning av temperatur paa vegetativ vekst hos kvitkløver (*Trifolium repens L.*). Cand.Scient. thesis. University of Tromsø, 80 pp.

de Bruijn, F. J., 1992. Use of repetitive (Repetitive Extragenic Palindromic and Enterobacterial Repetitive Intergenic Consensus) Sequences and the polymerase chain reaction to fingerprint the genomes of *Rhizobium meliloti* isolates and other soil bacteria. Applied and Environmental Microbiology, 58: 2180-2187.

Mytton, L. R., M. H. El-Sherbeny and D. A. Lawes, 1977. Specific and general effectiveness of *Rhizobium trifolii* populations from different agricultural locations. Plant and Soil, 73: 299-305.

Mytton, L. R. and C. J. Livesey, 1983. Specific and general effectiveness of *Rhizobium trifolii* populations from different agricultural locations. Plant and Soil, 73: 299-305.

Roskothen, P., 1989. Genetic effects on host x strain interaction in the symbiosis of *Vicia faba* and *Rhizobium leguminosarum*. Plant Breeding, 102: 122-132.

Sherwood, M. T. and C. L. Masterson, 1974. Importance of using the correct test host in assessing the effectiveness of indigenous populations of *Rhizobium trifolii*. Irish Journal of agricultural Research, 13: 101-108.

Svenning, M. M., 1991. Adaptation of white clover and *Rhizobium* to subarctic temperature and light conditions. Dr.scient. thesis, University of Tromsø.

Svenning, M. M., O. Junttila and B. Solheim, 1991. Symbiotic growth of indigenous white clover (*Trifolium repens*) with local *Rhizobium leguminosarum* biovar *trifolii*. Physiol. Plant., 83: 381-389.

Svenning, M. M., K. E. Eilertsen, J. Gudmundsson and P. Leinonen, 1997. Effect of inoculum composition on plant production and nodule occupancy in the field. In: Biological Nitrogen Fixation for the 21st Century (Elmerich C., Kondorosi A., Newton W.E. eds): 641.

Versalovic J, T. Koeuth and J. R. Lupski, 1991. Distribution of repetitive DNA sequences in eubacteria and applications to fingerprinting of bacterial genomes. Nucleic Acids Research, 19: 6823-6831.

Adaptation, forage potential and persistence of different alfalfa varieties in Italian alpine environments

R. PAOLETTI[1], F. GUSMEROLI[2], G. FALCHERO[3], G. RIGONI[4], M. C. ROSAFIO[1], G. P. DELLA MARIANNA[2], AND C. LOCATELLI[1]

[1] Experimental Institute of Fodder Crops (ISCF) – 26900 Lodi, Italy
[2] Fojanini Foundation for High Studies (FFHS) – 23100 Sondrio, Italy
[3] Mountain Community "Bassa Valle di Susa e Valcenischia" – 10053 Bussoleno (TO), Italy
[4] Mountain Community "Spettabile Reggenza dei Sette Comuni" – 36012 Asiago (VI), Italy

SUMMARY

Alfalfa (*Medicago sativa L.*) is a valuable forage for dairy farmers in N. Italy, either in lowland or in hill country. In the nineties, since the species was still almost unknown in our alpine districts, six trials, two in each region including a variable number of entries, were established in Lombardy, Piedmont and Venetia. Our main objective was to study the possibility of introducing alfalfa and at the same time to evaluate main Italian and foreign cultivars. The experimental design was a randomized complete block, 3-6 replicates and plot size ranged from 2.58 to 21 m². Ground cover in the establishment year, after the winter and in the autumn of each harvest year, DM yield (t ha⁻¹) in the second year, regrowth rate and persistency are here reported. Alfalfa proved to be adapted to the given alpine low- and medium-altitude locations. Among the tested cultivars the Italian "Lodi", "Luignano", "Garisenda", "Equipe" and some foreign genotypes, only, displayed to be high yielding and/or high persistent. Persistence was related not only to origin and dormancy but also to trial exposures and soil characteristics.

Keywords: adaptation, alfalfa, alpine environment, forage yield, persistence, variety

INTRODUCTION

Alfalfa (*Medicago sativa L.*) is a traditional performing forage crop in the Po Valley and other lowlands in N. Italy where it grows mainly in succession with maize for grain or silage and other cash crops. In the bordering hill countries alfalfa is also successfully grown. The species is still almost unknown, either in our alpine lowlands where the soils are basic or less acidic and well-drained, or at the medium-and medium-high-altitude alpine locations with good exposures and suited soils. In the main alpine districts the introduction of alfalfa, either pure or in association with perennial grasses, is considered by some advanced dairy farmers to be the key to provide hay and/or haylage in large quantities for feeding dairy cattle during the long winter season and in other periods when grazing is not possible. Therefore, since performing and persistent cultivars are needed for the establishment of efficient and long duration meadows, comparative variety trials, as for the Po Valley (Paoletti *et al.,* 1993 and 1997) and further to Bezzi *et al.* (1986) experiment, must be established at different locations. In this paper the results of a series of trials carried out in the nineties are summarized. The main objective was to study the possibility of introducing alfalfa and at the same time to test for their adaptabilty in different environmental conditions a number of commercial varieties of different origin with the addition of experimental types, for suggesting a recommended list to the interested alpine farmers. Most of the tested varieties, traditional or recently-released, are marketed in Italy and/or in other European countries.

MATERIALS AND METHODS

Our variety trials were carried out over a 4-year period in three different Italian alpine regions (Lombardy, Piedmont and Venetia). The six trials, two in each region, comprised a variable number (3 to 25) of Italian and foreign alfalfa cultivars, mostly marketed in N.Italy. The total number of cultivars on trial, including some experimental types, was 43 (Table 1). The experimental design was a randomized complete block, 3 to 6 replicates, and plot size ranged from 2.58 to 21 m^2. During 1993-1997 trials were established at five locations (1: Delebio, 217 m a.s.l., sandy soil, pH = 7.9 and 2: S. Giacomo di Teglio, 350 m, sandy soil, pH = 7.4 in N. Lombardy; 3 and 4: Dravugna, 1207 m, sandy-loam soil, pH = 6.2 in N. Piedmont; 5: Xebbo, 1150 m, humus light soil, pH = 5.2 and 6: Canove di Roana, 986 m, sandy-silt soil, pH = 5.8 on the Upland of the Seven Communes, Asiago in N. Venetia).

The preceding crops were natural / naturalized meadows or maize for silage (alpine lowland, only, location 1). Farmyard manure / slurry (trial grounds 1-2-3-4) or a compound N, P, K mineral fertilizer (locations 5 and 6) and lime (1-5-6) were applied prior to ploughing or to seeding. In early spring, starting in the second year, mineral fertilizers (P and K) were applied considering the different soil requirements. During establishment 50 kg N ha[-1] were applied to each plot.On average,three to five forage cuttings were taken at 10% bloom stage according to trial age and location characteristics. The following main data, recorded during a 4-year period, are reported in this short paper: establishment, ground cover percent, annual DM yield in the second harvest year, regrowth rate after cutting and persistency. Forage yields of the six trials were analysed within the Anova – 2 directive at P 0.05. As to quality parameters (NIRS), leaf/stem ratio and MFU content, the results will be published in the near future.

Cultivars and location No.*	Origin
Daisy[4] Pondus[2-5-6] Resis[4-5]	Denmark
Alizé[6] Diane[3-5] Esterel[3] Marina[3] Sitel[3]	France
Delta[3] Equipe[1-3-4-5-6] Garisenda[1-3-4-5-6] Giulia[3-6] La Rocca[3] Lodi[1-2-3-4-5-6] Luignano[3] Premariacco[3] Prosementi[3] Prospera[6] Robot[3-4-5-6] Selene[3] Triade[3] [4] Cascine[3]	Italy
Sygma[6]	Rumania
Alfagraze[3-4-5] Amerigraze[2-6] Bluegreen[3-6] Boreal[1-3-4-5] Capital[3-4-5] Eagle[3-6] Echo[3] Legend[3] Multiking 1[3-6] Natan[6] Pierce[6] 19308[5] 19414[5] 19426[5] 19427[5] 19429[5] 19430[5] 19501[5] 19503[5] 19504[5]	USA

*1 = Delebio and 2 = S.Giacomo T., Lombardy; 3 and 4 = Dravugna, Piedmont; 5 = Xebbo and   6 = Canove, Venetia.

RESULTS AND DISCUSSION

Establishment was good or satisfactory for all the alfalfa cultivars in the six trials at the five locations and initial ground cover, recorded in the autumn of the seeding year, was on average high (=87%). Mean forage potential in the second year of harvest was highest for the Lombard Location 1 (20.1 t ha^{-1} DM) followed by Location 4 in Piedmont (19.7 t ha^{-1}) and lowest for the Venetian Location 6 (11 t ha^{-1}) provided by 5 and 3 cuttings, respectively. Locations at higher altitudes (3 and 5) in Piedmont and Venetia showed an intermediate mean forage potential like Location 2 in the Lombard lowland (15 t ha^{-1}). Significant differences(P=0.05) emerged among the cultivars for five out of six trials (Table 2). Best performing cvs as "Diane", "Lodi", "Prosementi", "Echo", "Garisenda", "Sitel", "Delta", "Esterel" and "Giulia" provided over 21 t DM with 4-5 cuts. Total forage yields in the second year and per cut for the trial at Location 6 including 15 cultivars are presented in Figure 1. Regrowth rate after cutting proved to be highest for "Luignano", "Delta", "La Rocca" and "Lodi" reaching over 15 cm height 10 days from cutting. After four years of harvest final ground cover (persistence) decreased for most cultivars particularly in the regions Venetia and Lombardy (Table 2). The lowest values ranged from 3 to1 for a large number of cultivars. "Lodi" and "Luignano", only, displayed high ground cover values (=84% i.e. persistence index=5) followed by some other foreign more dormant (Bluegreen, Boreal, Capital, Eagle, Esterel, Legend and most experimental types) and few Italian (Delta, Garisenda, La Rocca) varieties. Remarkable differences emerged among tested cultivars for DM potential, regrowth rate after cutting and persistence in the given alpine environments. The forage yield in the second harvest year proved to be very high at the alpine lowland in Lombardy and also in Piedmont under favourable environmental conditions (soil and exposure). The performances of alfalfa different genotypes in these trials did not much differ from those recorded in the continental Po Valley. (Paoletti *et al.*, 1997). On the contrary, forage yields were much lower at locations with less favourable soil and exposure characteristics. Among the large group of Italian and foreign genotypes few cultivars showed to be persistent not only due to their origin and dormancy but mainly to soil and environmental conditions. Early semidormant and vigorous varieties such as "Lodi" seemed to be more adapted to the particular alpine environmental conditions.

TABLE 2. ANNUAL DMY (MEAN – MIN – MAX, T HA⁻¹) OF THE SIX TRIALS IN THE SECOND HARVEST YEAR AND CORRESPONDENT MIN AND MAX PERSISTENCE VALUES.

| Locations | No. cvs | Dry Matter Yield | | | F □ | Persistence □ | |
		Mean	Min	Max		Min	Max
Lombardy							
Loc 1	25	20.1	18.6	21.5	*	2	5
Loc 2	9	15.0	14.0	5.6	ns	2	4
Piedmont							
Loc 3	4	15.7	14.2	17.6	*	3	5
Loc 4	3	19.7	17.4	21.0	*	3	5
Venetia							
Loc 5	20	15.5	10.5	17.9	*	1	4
Loc 6	15	11.0	8.7	12.3	*	1	5

□ ns = non significant and * significant at $P □ 0.05$, respectively
□ 1=1-20%, 2=21-40%, 3=41-60%, 4=61-80%, 5=81-100%

CONCLUSIONS

The variety trials carried out at different regions and locations in N. Italy demonstrated that alfalfa may be successfully established even in some alpine environments. In fact, forage potentials of low- and medium-altitude, when pH was basic or less acidic, content of minerals sufficient or rich and field exposure and drainage adequate, proved to be comparable to those of the fertile Po Valley lowlands. At the other locations, under less favourable conditions, good or

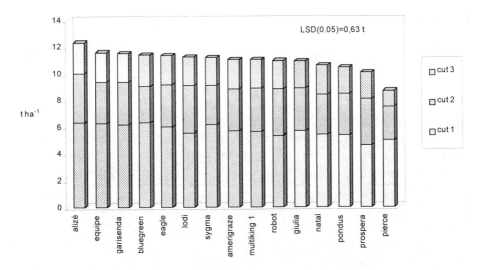

FIGURE 1. TOTAL DMY (T HA-1) OF 25 CULTIVARS AT LOCATION 6 (CANOVE,VENETIA) IN THE SECOND HARVEST YEAR.

satisfactory yields were obtained by applying lime and/or minerals according to oil analyses. With regard to variety performance among the many cultivars of different origins an acceptable number of Italian and foreign cultivars displayed a high forage potential during the first three years of harvest. On the contrary, only few Italian and foreign cultivars were persistent after four years of cutting. Therefore, new trials should be established in the near future to provide high performing and persistent varieties. For now some of the tested varieties, vigorous and sufficiently persistent, are available to our advanced alpine farmers. Alfalfa in pure stand or in association with one or two medium- or long-lived grasses is the key to secure a bulk of good hay or haylage for the long winter time in the Italian alpine regions. This crop should be recommended by our advisers taking into due account the given environmental conditions, management techniques and primarily the most adapted varieties on the market.

ACKNOWLEDGEMENTS

This work was funded by the MiPAF National Project "Gestione delle Risorse Prato-Pascolive Alpine". The Mountain Communities "Bassa Valle di Susa e Valcenischia"/"Spettabile Reggenza dei Sette Comuni" and the Fojanini Foundation for High Studies are gratefully acknowledged.

REFERENCES

Bezzi A., D. Orlandi and F. Clementel, 1986. Comportamento e produttività di cultivar foraggere in ambiente montano. L'Informatore Agrario XLII. 45: 43-46.

Paoletti R., E. Cervi-Ciboldi, C. Locatelli and N. Berardo, 1997. Forage production, quality and persistence of 25 lucerne (*Medicago sativa L.*) cultivars in the irrigated Lombard lowland. Rivista di Agronomia. 3: 1 Suppl. 197-201.

Paoletti R., C. Locatelli and L. Borrelli, 1993. Adaptation of Italian and foreign lucerne cultivars to the Po Valley light and acidic soils. Dry matter yield and persistency. Proceedings of the International Conference of the Eucarpia *Medicago* spp. Group, Lodi, 452-459.

Bio-agronomic evaluation of white clover cultivars at an alpine summer farm

R. PAOLETTI [1], G. FALCHERO [2], M. C. ROSAFIO [1], N. CASADEI [1]
AND C. LOCATELLI [1]

[1] Experimental Institute of Fodder Crops (ISCF) – 26900 Lodi, Italy
[2] Mountain Community "Bassa Valle di Susa e Valcenischia" – 10053 Bussoleno (TO), Italy

SUMMARY

White clover (*Trifolium repens* L.) is a valuable perennial legume for pasture and hay production in North Italy. The many attributes of the species are well known to our advanced mountain and lowland farmers. The objective of this investigation was to evaluate new cultivars in a representative grazing alpine environment. Five varieties provided by major seed companies ("Alice", "Barbian", "Huia","Milo" and "Rivendel") were established (mini- forage plots in a randomized complete block design, 3 replicates) at Chiet summer farm (2002 m a.s.l., Piedmont, NW Italy). Establishment, initial and final (persistence) ground cover, flowering earliness, DM yield, regrowth speed and susceptibility to diseases were recorded over a 5-year period. An additional forage sample was dried and then evaluated by NIRS. Main bio-agronomic traits, except quality parameters, are here presented. The trial has indicated that some adapted cultivars are available for regenerating alpine swards. Among the tested varieties "Milo" and "Alice" proved to be more persistent and higher yielding than the most widely used Huia. In the future, however, natural populations collected in the alpine swards should be used to avoid genetic shift and biodiversity reduction of the fragile rich alpine flora.

Keywords : alpine environment, cultivar, DM yield, persistence, white clover

INTRODUCTION

The white clover (*Trifolium repens* L.) Ladino type has been much appreciated by N. Italian farmers, particularly in the irrigated Po Valley, for more than hundred years till the eighties (Paoletti and Parente, 1991). At present the pure and clover – based meadows have almost disappeared being replaced by maize for silage, lucerne or soybean. However, white clover, either Ladino or Hollandicum type, is an important component of seeded swards. In the alpine area where edaphic, climatic and biological conditions are suitable white clovers of different leaf size can be found at different altitudes. Recently, some seed has been collected by the Lodi Institute from natural white clover populations spread in permanent alpine grasslands for direct seed multiplication or breeding purposes. Since large quantities of seed are not yet available for such different clover populations, a small number of cultivars of different origin recommended for the alpine sward regeneration was established (1994) in a representative alpine pasture land. The main objective was to assess their bio-agronomic characteristics in view of recommending the best-performing and adapted cultivars to farmers operating in our grazing districts. In some cases the introduction of adapted and high yielding varieties is the key to develop rapidly the grassland in most degraded swards and soils. Of course biodiversity in the specific alpine environments should be conserved by developing the original genotypes or releasing new varieties basing on white clover natural populations.

MATERIALS AND METHODS

Our experiment was conducted at Chiet summer farm located in the territory of the Lower Susa Valley (Piedmont, NW Italy) over a 5- year period. The field trial was established on a sandy loam soil (pH = 6,75, 1.78% humified organic matter, poor in nitrogen, potassium, magnesium and calcium) of a natural pasture at the altitude of 2002 m a.s.l.. Five cultivars of white clover were seeded by hand, namely "Alice", "Barbian", "Huia", "Milo" and "Rivendel", in summer 1994 at the rate of 7 kg ha^{-1}, in rows 12 cm apart; farmyard manure (25 t ha^{-1}) was incorporated when ploughing out the degraded pasture and nitrogen was applied at the rate of 50 kg ha^{-1} at seeding. The clovers were evaluated in a randomized-block design comprising three replicates. The mini-plot size was 0.5 m^2. Each year after establishment a compound mineral fertilizer was applied at the rate of 40-48-48 kg ha^{-1} of N,P,K and each year cut 1 (zero grazing) was taken at initial flowering and the regrowth was cut 45 days after (1996-1999). Establishment, initial and final (persistence) ground cover, flowering earliness according to Revaz (1970), DM yield, regrowth speed and susceptibility to diseases were recorded during the trial period. An additional forage sample was dried at 60°C, ground and then evaluated by NIRS. The following data are summarized in this paper: 1) establishment, 2) initial ground cover and persistence after five years, 3) earliness of flowering, 4) annual and total DM yield. Forage yields were analyzed within the Anova – 2 directive at P≤0.05.

RESULTS AND DISCUSSION

Establishment proved to be rather good for all the cultivars due to moderate precipitations and favourable temperatures soon after the seeding. Main recorded data concerning mean annual DMY, earliness of flowering, regrowth speed, initial ground cover in the first harvest year and final ground cover (persistence) are presented in Table 1 and annual DMY in Figure 1. Large and medium-large varieties ("Alice" and "Milo") on average overyielded significantly (P£0.05) the small-leaved cultivar "Huia" by providing during the growing season acceptable pure forage yields (1 to 1.3 t ha⁻¹ DM). Among the small-leaved varieties "Barbian" and "Rivendel" performed better than "Huia" displaying a higher forage potential. Regrowth speed in cm recorded 15 days after the first cutting was highest for "Milo" and "Alice", respectively. As to the flowering date "Alice" and "Milo" reached the 10% of flowered heads earlier (about five days) than the other three small-leaved cultivars i.e. between 20 and 25 July. Initial ground cover estimated before summer 1995 was satisfactory for all the cultivar ranging from 87 to 91 %. Persistence (final ground cover) in September 1999 showed to be highest for "Milo" followed by "Barbian" and "Huia" However, the figures did not differ significantly. Differences emerged among the tested cultivar of different origin for the main bio-agronomic characteristics. The forage yield level of all the clovers was moderate or low at the high altitude summer farm on the Alps. Persistence was quite good for the introduced cloves considering the high competition of some alpine species such as grasses and other dicotyledons and the paticular environmental situation of the field trial. In fact, the very low temperatures with much snow for more months a year on the soil did not affect negatively growth and health of the white clovers and the much appreciated qualitative parameters not reported in this paper.

TABLE 1. MEAN ANNUAL DMY (T HA⁻¹) WITH YIELD RANKING RELATIVE TO AVERAGE IN % REGROWTH SPEED (H). EARLINESS (E). INITIAL (I) AND FINAL GROUND COVER (F=PERSISTENCE) IN % OF 5 CVS (1995 – 1999).

Table 1. Mean annual DMY (t ha⁻¹) with yield ranking relative to average in % regrowth speed (H), earliness (E), initial (I) and final ground cover (F=persistence) in % of 5 cvs (1995 – 1999)

Cultivar	DMY	%	H	E*	I	F
Alice (UK)	1.0	111	15	73a	89	59
Barbian (NL)	0.9	100	12	73b	88	65
Huia (NZ)	0.6	67	7	73b	90	64
Milo (DK)	1.3	144	16	73a	87	67
Rivendel (DK)	0.8	89	8	73b	91	59
Average	0.9	100	12	73b	89	63
LSD (0.05)	0.3	-	4	-	n.s.	n.s.

*according to J.P.Revaz

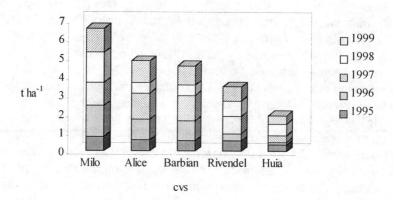

FIGURE 1. TOTAL AND ANNUAL DMY (T HA-1) OF THE FIVE VARIETIES - CHIET SUMMER FARM, 1995-1999.
LSD (0.05)=2 T.

CONCLUSIONS

From the reported results and considering some marketed varieties of white clover the following conclusions can be drawn:

at present a number of good cultivars, either large-or medium-and small-leaved and adapted to the alpine environmental conditions is available.

When reseeding of degraded pastures is necessary one or two clover varieties should be associated with high performing and persistent grasses to provide a bulk of high quality forage to be grazed and even cut for hay.

Persistency of the introduced clovers is acceptable because competition of native species, mainly grasses, and environmental factors, low temperatures and snow cover, are influencing their performance.

The absence of any disease during the trial means a healthy state and good adaptation of the cultivars.

The introduction of such genotypes should be careful and limited to the regeneration of the much degraded swards only, to protect the alpine valuable biodiversity and to avoid the risk of genetic shift.

The collection of white clover natural populations must be continued to provide through seed multiplication all the needed seed for the sward regeneration.

The breeding of new varieties for the alpine pastures basing it on the autochthonous materials may help to reach the target of developing our grazing areas without any sensible damage to the precious high altitude environment.

ACKNOWLEDGEMENTS

This experiment was funded by the MiPAF Project "Gestione delle Risorse Prato-Pascolive Alpine".

REFERENCES

Paoletti, R. and G. Parente, 1991. White Clover in Italy: role and prospects in the nineties. FAO Reur Technical Series 19, 129-141.

Revaz, J. P., 1970. La précocité des graminées fourragères. Revue Suisse d'Agriculture, 11, 3: 62-66.

Vegetative growth and frost hardiness of white clover (Trifolium repens L.) genotypes from Svaldbard, 80° N lat.

M. M. SVENNING, K. RØSNES, L. LUND AND O. JUNTTILA

Department of Biology, University of Tromsø, N-9037 Tromsø, Norway

SUMMARY

Vegetative growth and freezing tolerance of two genotypes of white clover (*Trifolium repens L.*) collected at Svaldbard (lat.78° 39' N, long. 16° 23' E) were studied in daylight phytotron at controlled temperature and humidity. For comparison, two genotypes of a new Norwegian cultivar Norstar and one genotype of the cultivar AberHerald were included in the experiments. The genotypes from Svalbard gave higher dry matter yields than the genotypes of Norstar, and one of them even exceeded AberHerald in dry matter production at the temperatures studied, constant 12°C and alternating 15/9 and 12/6°C (12/12 h). The genotypes from Svalbard were more freezing-tolerant than all the other genotypes. After a successive hardening treatment at 6°C and 0.5°C they obtained LT50 values of -16°C. Origin of these genotypes is not known, but due to their high productivity and freezing tolerance they may be useful for further breeding of white clover for marginal conditions.

Keywords: freezing tolerance, genotype, growth, temperature, white clover

INTRODUCTION

Cultivars developed for northern marginal conditions must posses a sufficient winter stability. Freezing tolerance is an important component in the winter stability. Previous studies with a number of white clover populations from various parts of Norway have shown that the most freezing-resistant populations were found in the northern coastal areas (Junttila *et al.*, 1990a, Røsnes *et al.*, 1993). These genotypes are, however, characterized by small leaflet size, short petioles and relatively low dry matter production (Junttila *et al.*, 1990b, Svenning *et al.*, 1997), and they are therefore not among the best suited for fodder production. White clover is growing wild all over the mainland of Norway, but not at Svalbard. However, the Russian mining settlements at Pyramiden, established in 1931, introduced livestock for food supply. Forage was imported from Russia. Currently, plants of white clover can be found at Pyramiden area, and they must have survived for some time under the extreme climatic conditions of Svalbard.Two white clover plants having relatively long petioles and large leaflets were brought from Pyramiden in 1998. Vegetative growth and freezing tolerance of these two genotypes have been studied under controlled conditions and compared to two randomly selected genotypes of Norstar and one genotype of the cultivar AberHerald.

MATERIALS AND METHODS

White clover plants with developed nodules were discovered in 1998 at Pyramiden, Svalbard (lat.78° 39' N, long. 16° 23' E). Two genotypes of white clover (Pyr-1 and Pyr-2) were collected by Bjørn Solheim and these were brought to the phytotron of the University of Tromsø (lat. 69°39' N, long. 18° 57' E). Plants were kept at 18°C under 24-h photoperiod and they were propagated by stem cuttings. Similarly, two randomly selected genotypes of cultivar Norstar (Norstar-1 and Norstar-2; from the population no. HoKv9262, origin 62° 50´ N, 08° 55´ E, Rindal, Møre og Romsdal, about 500 m a.s.l., Rapp, 1996), kindly provided by The Norwegian Plant Research Institute, Holt Research Centre, and one genotype of the cultivar AberHerald were also propagated by cuttings. During the experiment, plants were grown under natural long-day light conditions in April-May, 1999, at three different temperature treatments: constant 12°C, alternating 15/9°C, and 12/6°C (both 12/12 h). The air humidity was adjusted to give 0.5 kPa water vapour pressure deficit. Plants were watered daily and fertilized with a complete nutrient solution once a week. Five plants of each genotype were harvested at the beginning of the experiment and then after 2, 4 and 6 weeks. Except for the last harvest, plants were divided into stolons, petioles and leaflets (laminae) and dry weights were determined after drying for 24 h at 60°C. In addition, length of the longest stolon, area of two random, full-sized leaves, length of petioles for these leaflets, and length of two internodes were measured. Freezing tolerance was measured at the end of the growth period in the phytotron, and after a subsequent hardening periods for 2 weeks at 6°C at 0.5°C, using controlled freezing equipment (Junttila et al., 1990a).

RESULTS

The genotype of AberHerald had the longest petioles and twice as large leaflets as the other genotypes. Genotypes from Svalbard were comparable to the two genotypes of Norstar both in respect to leaflet size and petiole length. Compared to the other genotypes, AberHerald was characterized by very short internodes, approximately only 40 % of the internode length in one of the Svalbard genotypes (Pyr-2).

At the start of the experiment, plants of Norstar-1 were significantly (P=0.05) smaller than plants of Pyr-1 and AberHerald, and Norstar-1 plants had the lowest dry weight at every harvests. At the end of the experiment, both Norstar-1 and Norstar-2 had significantly (P<0.05) lower dry weights than the other genotypes. One of the genotypes from Svalbard, Pyr-2, had the highest dry matter production throughout the experiment, and after 6 weeks also the difference between Pyr-2 and AberHerald was statistically significant (Table 1). Dry matter production was enhanced with increasing temperature. No significant interaction between genotype and temperature was detected for dry matter production (Table 1).

TABLE 1. DRY WEIGHT OF TOP (G PLANT⁻¹) IN FIVE GENOTYPES OF WHITE CLOVER AFTER A GROWTH PERIOD OF 6 WEEKS AT INDICATED TEMPERATURES. GENOTYPE, $P=0.0001$; TEMPERATURE, $P=0.0001$; GENOTYPE X TEMPERATURE INTERACTION, N.S. $(P=0.25)$.

Genotype	Temperature, °C			Mean
	12/6	15/9	12	
Pyr-1	9.38	10.49	12.73	10.86
Pyr-2	9.19	11.91	13.62	11.57
Norstar-1	4.49	7.11	9.02	6.88
Norstar-2	7.26	10.08	11.04	9.46
AberHerald	9.56	10.84	11.80	10.73
Mean	7.98	10.09	11.64	

Pyr-2, the genotype with the highest dry matter yield, was characterized by the lowest proportion of leaflets, significantly ($P<0.001$) less than in the other genotypes. Also the difference between AberHerald and Norstar-1 was statistically significant ($P=0.05$). On the other hand, AberHerald had the highest proportion of petioles, 25.4 %, significantly ($P<0.001$) higher than in the other genotypes. The lowest values were obtained for Pyr-2 and Norstar-1. These genotypes had the highest proportion of dry weight in stolons, while the proportion of stolons was lowest in Pyr-1 and AberHerald (Table 2). Percentage of biomass of leaflets was not affected significantly by growth temperature, but proportions of biomass in petioles and stolons were significantly lower at 12/6°C that at the two other temperature treatments.

At the end of the growth experiment, freezing tolerance of the genotypes, expressed as a temperature for 50 % survival, LT50, varied from -3.7 to -7.5°C (Table 3). Treatments at 6 and 0.5°C enhanced hardiness in all genotypes. After hardening, AberHerald was the least and Pyr-2 the most freezing-tolerant genotype. Genotypes Norstar-1, Norstar-2 and Pyr-1 were intermediate to AberHerald and Pyr-2 (Table 3). Dry matter content in the stolons increased during hardening (Table 3). Generally, dry matter content was higher in the plants grown at 15/9°C than in those grown at 12/6°C, and after hardening at 0.5°C it was highest in the genotypes from Svalbard (Pyr-1 and Pyr-2). For the whole material, there was a significant ($P<0.001$) positive correlation between dry matter content and freezing tolerance.

TABLE 2. DISTRIBUTION OF THE DRY WEIGHT OF THE TOP BETWEEN LEAFLETS (LAMINA), PETIOLES AND STOLONS IN FIVE GENOTYPES OF WHITE CLOVER. RESULTS ARE MEANS (±SD) OF THREE GROWTH TEMPERATURES AFTER A GROWTH PERIOD OF 4 WEEKS. INTERACTION BETWEEN THE GENOTYPES AND GROWTH TEMPERATURE WAS NOT SIGNIFICANT. GENOTYPES, P<0.0001 FOR ALL COLUMNS.

| Genotype | DW, g | % of total DW | | |
		Leaflets	Petioles	Stolons
Pyr-1	5.14±1.01	43±1.9	23±2.3	34±1.2
Pyr-2	4.67±0.91	38±1.7	17±1.9	45±3.2
Norstar-1	3.05±0.94	43±4.2	18±1.3	39±4.6
Norstar-2	4.05±0.91	42±2.5	18±1.6	40±2.6
AberHerald	4.48±0.88	42±1.5	26±1.9	32±2.1

TABLE 3. FREEZING TOLERANCE (LT50, °C) AND DRY MATTER CONTENT (% OF FW) IN FIVE GENOTYPES OF WHITE CLOVER AS AFFECTED BY GROWTH TEMPERATURE AND HARDENING TREATMENT. PLANTS WERE GROWN FOR SIX WEEKS AT THE INDICATED TEMPERATURES IN 24-H PHOTOPERIOD. DURING HARDENING (2 WEEKS AT 6 °C, FOLLOWED BY 2 WEEKS AT 0.5°C) THE PHOTOPERIOD WAS 12 H. SEVEN TO EIGHT TEST TEMPERATURES WERE USED IN EACH TEST, AND EACH SAMPLE CONSISTED OF FIVE STOLON PIECES. NO HARDEN. : FREEZING TOLERANCE AT THE END OF GROWTH PERIOD IN THE PHYTOTRON.

| Genotype, Growth temp. | | LT50, °C | | | Dry matter content, % | | |
		No harden.	6°C	0.5°C	No harden.	6°C	0.5°C
Pyr-1	15/9	-5.7	-8.7	-13.9	19.0	21.7	22.4
	12/6	-4.4	-9.1	>-14	16.7	17.7	22.6
Pyr-2	15/9	-5.8	-9.9	-16.6	17.6	20.0	24.5
	12/6	-4.9	-9.8	-16.1	16.5	18.3	24.9
Norstar-1	15/9	-6.4	-8.7	-14.3	15.2	15.4	21.8
	12/6	-5.3	-8.7	>-14	14.9	16.5	17.8
Norstar-2	15/9	-7.5	-9.2	>-14	19.7	19.6	20.5
	12/6	-5.3	-8.5	-13.6	15.0	16.6	18.8
AberHerald	15/9	-4.9	-7.3	-12.6	18.5	22.4	23.8
	12/6	-3.7	-7.3	-12.1	16.7	16.8	20.3

DISCUSSION

The present results indicate that the genotypes from Svalbard combine a high growth potential (Table 1) with a relatively high level of freezing tolerance. After an artificial hardening treatment, these genotypes were hardy to about -16°C (Table 3). They were consistently more freezing-tolerant than the genotypes Norstar-1 and Norstar-2, but did not show as high level of hardiness as has been found in the most hardy genotypes from Northern Norway, about -20°C (Junttila et al., 1990a; Røsnes et al., 1993; Svenning et al., 1997). High level of freezing tolerance in the Svalbard genotypes suggests that they may have good capacity for over-wintering in Northern Norway.

In a recent study, Frankow-Lindberg(1999) concludes that adaptation of white clover to an long and cold winters results in a reduced stolon extension rate and internode length. The present results do not support such conclusion. Both the genotypes of Norstar and the genotypes from Svalbard, all of which are obviously well adapted to long winter, had significantly longer internodes than the less hardy cultivar AberHerald. Investigation of a number of white clover populations collected across Norway did not show any significant relationship between internode/stolon length and origin of the population (Junttila *et al.*, 1990b). Northern genotypes of white clover are generally characterized by small leaflet size, short petioles and low productivity (Ollerenshaw and Baker, 1981; Ollerenshaw and Haycock, 1984; Junttila *et al.*, 1990b). Caradus *et al.* (1989) describe frost-tolerant white clover as small-leaved and relatively prostrate. Thus, these characters are often correlated with high frost tolerance. However, although the genotypes from Svalbard had larger leaflets than the local populations from Northern Norway, their leaflet size was still not more than about 50% of leaflet size in AberHerald.

Significant differences were found between the studied genotypes concerning allocation of dry matter between stolons, petioles and leaflets (Table 2). Unfortunately, roots were not included in the study. According to Frankow-Lindberg (1999) root dry weight of total dry weight of the plant was 18-19 % for AberHerald and 26 % for a wild population of white clover from Uppsala area. Generally, low temperature enhances dry matter allocation to the roots, and partitioning between roots and shoots could be a character linked with adaptation to low-temperature growth conditions, but this aspect has not been thoroughly studied in white clover.

ACKNOWLEDGEMENTS

Thanks are due to Eli Robertsen and the staff at the phytotron of the University of Tromsø for technical assistance.

REFERENCES

Caradus, J. R., A. C. Mackay, J. Van Den Bosch, D. H. Greer and G. S. Wewala, 1989. Intraspecific variation for frost hardiness in white clover. Journal of Agricultural Science, Cambridge, 112: 151-157.

Frankow-Lindberg, B. E., 1999. Effects of adaptation to winter stress on biomass production, growth and morphology of three contrasting white clover cultivars. Physiologia Plantarum, 106: 196-202.

Junttila, O., M. M. Svenning and B. Solheim, 1990a. Effects of temperature and photoperiod on frost resistance of white clover (*Trifolium repens*) ecotypes. Physiologia Plantarum, 79: 435-438.

Junttila, O., M. M. Svenning and B. Solheim, 1990b. Effects of temperature and photoperiod on vegetative growth of white clover (*Trifolium repens*) ecotypes. Physiologia Plantarum, 79: 427-434.

Ollerenshaw, J. H. and R. H. Baker, 1981. Low temperasture growth in a controlled environment of *Trifolium repens* plants from northern latitudes. Journal of Applied Ecology, 18: 229-239.

Ollerenshaw, J. H. and R. Haycock, 1984. Variation in the low temperature growth and frost tolerance of natural genotypes of *Trifolium repens* L. from Britain and Norway. Journal of Agricultural Science, Cambridge, 102: 11-21.

Rapp, K., 1996. Selection response for dry matter yield in white clover (*Trifolium repens L.*) using different selection methods. Norwegian Journal of Agricultural Sciences, 10: 265-280.

Røsnes, K., O. Junttila, A. Ernstsen and N. Sandli, 1993. Development of cold hardiness in white clover in respect to carbohydrate and free amino acid content. Acta Agriculturae Scandinavica.Section B, Soil and Plant Science, 43: 151-155.

Svenning, M. M., O. Junttila and K. Røsnes, 1997. Hardening and dehardening in contrasting genotypes of white clover (*Trifolium repens L.*). Physiologia Plantarum, 101: 31-37.

Interaction between white clover (Trifolium repens L.) and different Rhizobium leguminosarum biovar trifolii strains in Icelandic soil

M. M. SVENNING[1], J. GUDMUNDSSON[2], I. L. FAGERLI[1] AND P. LEINONEN [3]

[1]Department of Biology, Faculty of Science, University of Tromsoe, 9037 Tromsoe, Norway
[2]Rannsoknastofnun Landbunadarins, Keldnaholt, 112 Reykjavik, Iceland
[3]Elomestari Oy, Partala, Fin-51900 Juva, Finland

SUMMARY

In a field experiment in Iceland white clover population HoKv9238, a selected population from a breeding programme in Norway, has been grown in combination with red fescue, cv. Leik. The white clover was inoculated with three strains of *Rhizobium leguminosarum* biovar *trifolii* as single strain inoculum or as mixed strain inoculum. During a four-year period clover and grass production were measured and the competition for nodule occupancy between the three strains of rhizobia, followed by a molecular fingerprint method. Population HoKv9238 made an effective and lasting symbiosis with the three strains of R.l.bv. *trifolii*. When mixed strain inoculum was used, one of the strains was dominating through the whole experimental period.

Keywords: competition, fingerprinting, Rhizobium, white clover

INTRODUCTION

White clover (*Trifolium repens*) is an important pasture legume in Europe. It is mainly used in combination with grass in grazing areas, as green manure and in bicropping systems. It is a perennial legume forming nitrogen-fixing symbiosis with *Rhizobium leguminosarum* biovar *trifolii* and by this supply themselves and other plants with nitrogen. The combination of good plant production during a short growing season at low temperatures as well as sufficient winter stability is necessary for agricultural purposes in subarctic climates. Plant material suitable for these conditions has been lacking, but an ongoing breeding program on white clover in Norway has resulted in promising material for cold climates (Rapp 1996). The new cultivars are bred on native populations and genotypes from coastal and inland regions in Norway.

The soil bacteria forming symbiosis with white clover is normally present in the soil and inoculation is not necessary except where pH is low or clover has been absent for a very long time. In parallel with the plant breeding, extensive studies of indigenous R.l.bv. *trifolii* populations has been accomplished and resulted in a selection of efficient strains for white clover. This material has been used in combination with white clover in an experiment to study the performance and persistence of the symbiosis in the field. The absence of indigenous rhizobia in Icelandic soil give an unique opportunity to follow the R.l bv. *trifolii* strains in a realistic field situation. Variability within a strain introduced into the field might occur (Gibson *et al.*, 1976, 1991). The introduced strains will therefore be comprehensive studied for symbiotic effectiveness and genetic stability after several years in the field.

MATERIALS AND METHODS

White clover population HoKv9238 (Holt Research Centre, Tromsø, Norway) and red fescue cv. Leik were grown in mould and sandy soils. At sowing the seeds were inoculated with R.l.bv. *trifolii*. The 3 strains used (strains 8-9, 20-15 and 32-28) are all isolated from the indigenous soil population in northern Norway. The three strains were inoculated as single strains or as a mix of the 3 strains. Control with no rhizobia treatment was included.

Inoculants for the field trials were standard peat-based inoculants prepared into sterile, finely-ground peat (Elomestari Oy, Juva, Finland). Inoculum was added to the seeds before sowing.

The plot size was 10m² and the experimental design was randomised block with 4 replicates. The field was established in 1994 and 20kgP ha⁻¹ was added in summer 1994.

The yield was measured by cutting in September each year after the establishment year. Clover and grass was separated before drying for weight measurements.

Whole plants were harvested in autumns 1995, 1996 and 1997, and spring 1996 and 1997 for nodule occupancy studies. The plant roots were washed with tap water and then surface sterilised in 70% ethanol and 6% H_2O_2. Ten nodules from each of 3 plants / plot and 3 plants from 3 or 4 replicates were harvested form the roots in 1995, 1996 and 1997. Totally 70-120 reisolates from each treatment were analysed for symbiont.

Nodule occupancy was studied by ERIC-PCR fingerprinting of reisolates from nodules or from nodule suspensions (de Bruijn 1992, Versalovic 1991).

RESULTS AND DISCUSSION

Clover and grass production were measured during 3 subsequent growing seasons, 1995, 1996 and 1997. Highest clover yield was obtained when the three R.l.bv. *trifolii* strains were used in a mixture for inoculation (Table 1). The higher clover yield in this treatment was specially expressed the first year, but there was also an effect on clover the third year. Strain 8-9 and strain 20-15 gave nearly the same clover yields while strain 32-28 gave the lowest clover yield. The first year after establishment, grass production was higher in the control plot than in the *Rhizobium*-treated plots. However, the second year it was higher grass production in the *Rhizobium*-treated plots than in the control plot, and mixed inoculum gave the highest production. The third year mixed inoculum gave lowest grass production and the control plot had an average production. The first year the grass in the control plots had little competition from the clover plants and without inoculum the clover plant had poor growth. The grass in the *Rhizobium*-treated plots had no advantage over the grass in control plot, it is likely that nitrogen transfer was low the first year. The second year the nitrogen transfer was possibly higher and gave a positive effect on grass production. Poor growth of clover in control the year before gave little transfer of nitrogen and from there little grass production the second year. The third year both grass and clover production were lower than the second year. For all treatments, the highest clover and grass production was found the second year.

TABLE 1. YIELD OF WHITE CLOVER AND GRASS IN PLOTS WITH DIFFERENT *RHIZOBIUM* INOCULUM. THE WEIGHT IS GIVEN IN HKG/HA (HECTO KILO/HECTARE).

Treatment	1995		1996		1997		Average for 3 years		
	Clover	Grass	Clover	Grass	Clover	Grass	Clover	Grass	Total
Strain 8-9	2.88	23.7	7.8	46.8	3.6	32.9	4.76	34.46	39.21
Strain 20-15	3.79	23.5	7.3	53.5	2.9	37.6	4.67	38.20	42.88
Strain 32-28	1.86	21.3	8.0	54.3	1.7	38.3	3.81	37.93	41.74
Mix	6.63	24.1	8.8	61.2	5.4	30.3	6.92	38.54	45.45
Control	1.19	28.1	6.0	36.7	1.8	34.1	3.00	32.97	35.97
Mean	3.27	24.1	7.6	50.5	4.6	36.4	4.61	34.42	42.7
Sd.e.	0.98	2.38	1.85	7.09	1.73	3.77	1.16	2.54	3.16
P-value	0.001	0.13	0.66	0.04	0.241	0.246	0.052	0.16	0.088

Reisolates of R.l.bv. *trifolii* were fingerprinted by ERIC-PCR and the strains could be identified after several years in the field. Changes in fingerprint patterns were not detected in the samples from mould soil. Genetic as well as phenotypic changes can occur in strains when introduced into soil. Gibson *et al.* (1991) did not observe changes in fingerprint profile of strains after 9 years in the field, but observed serological changes of the strains. In their study symbiotic effectiveness was very little or not influenced. In this experiment, plots inoculated with single strains had a dominance in the nodules of the strain used during 4 years (results not shown). In nodules of plants inoculated with all 3 strains (mix inoculum), strain 20-15 always occupied most of the nodules (Table 2). The bacteria have spread in the soil and inoculated the control plants where strain 20-15 also dominated in the nodules. The frequency of the other strains are higher in the control plots than the inoculated plots, but strain 20-15 is the most competitive in these conditions. Strain 32-28 occupied few nodules of plants treated with mix inoculum. On the other hand, strain 32-28 occupied nearly half of the nodules of the control plants in sandy soil (results not shown). It seems that the soil type might influence the dispersal of the bacteria and thereby the interaction between them. This will be investigated in further studies.

TABLE 2. PROPORTIONAL AMOUNT (IN %) OF 3 DIFFERENT *R.L.BV TRIFOLII* STRAINS IN NODULES OF WHITE CLOVER INOCULATED WITH A MIXTURE OF THE 3 STRAINS AND NODULE OCCUPANCY IN PLANTS WHERE NO INOCULUM WAS ADDED (CONTROL). THE SYMBIONT, *R.L.BV TRIFOLII* IS IDENTIFIED BY ERIC-PCR FINGERPRINTING.

Harvest	Mixed inoculum			Control		
	strain 8-9	strain 20-15	strain 32-28	strain 8-9	strain 20-15	strain 32-28
Autumn 1995	18	81	1	32	57	11
Spring 1996	22	78	0			
Autumn 1996	9	88	3	30	66	4
Spring 1997	33	66	1	36	58	6
Autumn 1997	9	91	0	27	65	9

After growing white clover/grass mixture for 4 years, the field was ploughed and barley was grown. The quantity of R.l.bv. *trifolii* was 10^4-$10^{5/}$ soil and strain 20-15 was found to still dominate in the nodules (Table 3).

TABLE 3. NODULE OCCUPANCY OF THE 3 *R.L. BV. TRIFOLII* STRAINS IN NODULES FORMED DURING MPN (MOST PROBABLY NUMBER) TESTS OF SANDY AND MOULD SOIL HARVESTED IN 1998, WHEN BARLEY WAS GROWN IN THE FIELD. THE VALUES ARE MEANS OF 3 PARALLELS.

Soil type	Strain 8-9	Strain 20-15	Strain 32-28	MPN
Mould	16.5	61.6	22.1	9×10^3-3×10^5
Sandy	6.9	68.4	13.2	4×10^4-3×10^5

ACKNOWLEDGEMENTS

We thank the Norwegian Research Council for financial support (Grant 111838/ 111). The research is part of NKJ(Nordic Joint Committee for Agricultural research) project no 95.

Karl Erik Eilertsen and Eli Robertsen are thanked for technical help.

REFERENCES

de Bruijn, F. J., 1992. Use of repetitive (Repetitive Extragenic Palindromic and Enterobacterial Repetitive Intergenic Consensus) Sequences and the polymerase chain reaction to fingerprint the genomes of *Rhizobium meliloti* isolates and other soil bacteria. Applied and Environmental Microbiology, 58: 2180-2187.

Gibson A. H., R. A. Date, J. A. Ireland and J. Brockwell, 1976. A comparison of competitiveness and persistence amongst five strains of *Rhizobium trifolii*. Soil Biology Biochemistry 8: 395-401.

Gibson A. H., D. H. Demezas, R. R. Gault, T. V. Bhuvaneswari and J. Brockwell, 1991. Genetic stability in rhizobia in the field. In The rhizosphere and plant growth. D.L. Keister and P.B. Cregan (Eds.) 141-148. Kluwer Academic Publishers, Dordrecht, The Netherlands.

Rapp K., 1996. Selection response for dry matter yield in white clover (*Trifolium repens L.*) using different selection methods. Norwegian Journal of Agricultural Sciences 10: 265-280.

Versalovic, J., T. Koeuth, J. R. Lupski, 1991. Distribution of repetitive DNA sequences in eubacteria and applications to fingerprinting of bacterial genomes. Nucleic Acids Research, 19: 6823-6831.

WORKING GROUP 3

N-Use Efficiency
Invited papers

The nitrogen cycle in the soil-plant system

G. HOFMAN[1], J. SALOMEZ[1], S. DE NEVE[1] AND O. VAN CLEEMPUT[2]

[1] Department of Soil Management and Soil Care
[2] Department of Applied Analytical and Physical Chemistry
Faculty of Agricultural and Applied Biological Sciences, Ghent University, Coupure 653, 9000 Ghent, Belgium

SUMMARY

Nitrogen is vital to the growth of plants and its supply has in most cases the largest effect on crop yield. In the soil-plant ecosystem, there are several N inputs and outputs. Moreover, nitrogen is subjected to various transformation processes, whereby the valency of N changes between N^{5+} (NO_3^--N) and N^{3-} (NH_4^+-N). All these factors and processes influence the amount of N present in the mineral N pool of the soil and thus the N available to the growing crop. The different factors and N transformation processes are discussed and as far as possible, a quantification is given. Uncertainties, various strategies and their influence on the N efficiency and on the reduction of environmental problems and further research topics are also indicated.

Keywords: environment, nitrogen, N processes

INTRODUCTION

Agriculture is subject to dramatic changes and hence faces a number of important new challenges. Examples of these changes and challenges include:

- a direct support to the farmers instead of a price policy for the products;
- set-aside and extensification of agricultural production;
- yield optimisation instead of maximisation of the production;
- more emphasis on the quality of the products;
- consumers' impact on production strategies;
- environmental concerns;
- sustainability of agricultural production;
- image of agriculture, etc.

These challenges require a mental change of the farmers and an adaptation of the production systems towards a more environmentally friendly and sustainable agriculture. In the framework of the final conference of COST 814 "Crop development for cool and wet regions of Europe", this contribution will focus on the N cycle in the soil-plant ecosystem, with special emphasis on environmental problems.

N cycle in the soil-plant system

Nitrogen is the nutrient which has, if no real constraints are present, the largest effect on crop yield and is therefore still used in large quantities in various areas of Western Europe. The increase of N efficiency and the minimisation of N losses to the environment are incentives to use nitrogen in a more proper way. Unfortunately, it is rather difficult to convince farmers of a limited N-application approach and so to obtain these goals, because nitrogen is liable to various and complex transformation processes which influence the mineral nitrogen pool. A simplified scheme of the factors influencing the soil mineral N pool is given in Fig. 1.

Although our knowledge of soil nitrogen dynamics has made significant progress in the last decades, it still remains difficult to quantify some of these factors and processes. This complicates an accurate estimate of the extent of the available soil mineral N pool and as a consequence the amount of N fertilisers to be applied. We will here discuss the different factors and processes having an impact on the size of the soil mineral N pool. Uncertainties will be mentioned as well as possible strategies to ensure an optimum use of this pool.

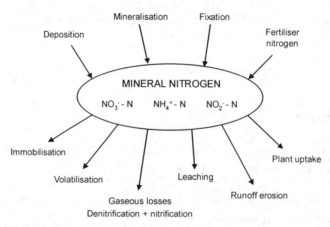

FIGURE 1. FACTORS INFLUENCING THE SOIL MINERAL N POOL.

Increase of the mineral N pool
N deposition

In a rural environment, with low-intensity farming, the total N deposition (dry and wet) is lower than 20 kg N ha[-1] (Campbell *et al.*, 1990). In the intensive farming regions of large parts of Europe, this deposition is of the order of 30-40 kg N ha[-1] or even more (Goulding, 1990; Van Breemen and Van Dijk, 1988). Measurements in Flanders, in a region with intensive pig breeding, showed a total N deposition of about 25 kg N ha[-1] in the late eighties (Demyttenaere, 1991) and were found to remain of the same order in the late nineties (Vervaet *et al.*, 1999). There is no doubt that agricultural activities are to a great extend responsible for this enhanced N deposition. Depending on the time of deposition, some of this nitrogen becomes available for plant growth. On the other hand, it has to be noticed that this deposition contributes to the further acidification of agricultural soils, to a decline in biodiversity and to eutrophication of nitrate-vulnerable zones. It can be expected that the total N deposition will decrease in the future by minimising the NH_3 losses from stables (green label) and when application of slurry on agricultural land will be done by direct incorporation. The effect of slurry injection on an enhanced denitrification has to be emphasised.

N mineralisation

The input of various kinds of organic materials, i.e. animal manures, composts, sludges, crop residues, green manures, etc. as well as the mineralisation of soil organic matter (SOM) influence the soil mineral N pool. The impact of organic material on the available mineral nitrogen depends on the one hand on the decay rate of that material, mainly influenced by its composition, and on the other hand on climatic and soil conditions (Palm and Sanchez, 1991; Vigil and Kissel, 1991; Honeycutt *et al.*, 1993; Breland and Hansen, 1996). Various simulation models are available to describe the release of mineral N from the input of organic material. De Neve (2000) describes such a model for vegetable crop residues. This model, coupled to the leaching model of Burns (1974) showed a quite good relationship between the measured and simulated mineral N amount in the soil as given in Fig. 2.

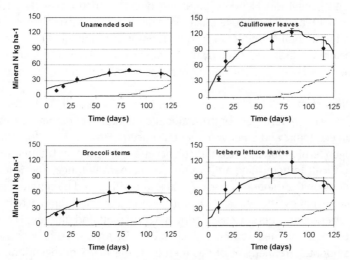

FIGURE 2. MEASURED (♦) AND SIMULATED (–) MINERAL N CONTENT OVER THE WHOLE SOIL PROFILE (0-120 CM) AND CUMULATIVE AMOUNTS OF N LEACHED BELOW 120 CM (- - -) ACCORDING TO MODEL CALCULATIONS. BARS REPRESENT ± 1 STANDARD DEVIATION ON MEASURED DATA (DE NEVE, 2000).

Depending on the history of the field and the variation in amount and composition of organic material applied in previous years, large differences in N mineralisation from SOM can be obtained (Table 1, Demyttenaere (1991)).

It should be emphasised that a lack of knowledge on mineralisaton from SOM and from incorporated organic material will result in an insufficient estimate of the available nitrogen. This was and is still the weakest point in N fertiliser advice systems. Research is still going on to predict the N mineralisation more precisely.

TABLE 1. N MINERALISATION (KG N HA^{-1} D^{-1}) DEPENDING ON FIELD HISTORY AND EARLIER INPUTS OF ORGANIC MATERIAL (OM) (DEMYTTENAERE, 1991).

	Yearly input OM	N mineralisation
agricultural land	Low	0.5 - 0.7
agricultural land	Moderate	0.9 - 1.1
agricultural land	High	1.1 - 1.3
grassland	Low	1.2 - 1.5

Biological nitrogen fixation

In intensive agricultural systems in the cool and wet regions of Europe, the impact of biological nitrogen fixation (BNF) is rather small. However, the trend towards extensification and the interest for organic farming will increase the contribution of N fixation in agricultural systems. Moreover, in some countries or regions, like The Netherlands and Flanders, there are restrictions on N fertiliser use. The Netherlands introduced the minerals accounting system (MINAS) (Ministry of Agriculture, Nature Management, and Fisheries, 1999), while in Flanders there are direct restrictions on N fertiliser use (Anonymous, 1999a). Since nitrogen fixation is not accounted for in these systems, its contribution to the total N budget in crop rotations is also not known. Research has to find out if the nitrate directive, set up by the European Commission (Anonymous, 1991), will still be achieved when introducing more nitrogen-fixing plants in the rotation.

N fertilisation

The efficient use of fertilisers, both organic and mineral, is of paramount importance from both an economic and an environmental concern. However, the formulation of a correct nitrogen fertilisation advice is difficult because the optimum N application rate is sometimes difficult to determine and is situated in a narrow range. The N fertilisation further depends on the mineral N pool, which is also influenced by different processes.

Until the seventies, the "classic" way of determining the optimum N rate was to make field experiments, thereby considering different plots and different N application rates on each plot. The mean optimum, obtained over several years, was used as the advised N amount. A refinement of this method is the ADAS nitrogen index method (Anonymous, 1994). On the basis of past management practices and of the crop previously grown, fields are rated with an index, ranging from 0 (low amounts of N_{min} expected) to 2 (high amounts of N_{min} expected). This gives an indication of expected N_{min} values, but the exact N_{min} amount is unknown. The recommended N rate further depends on soil type and the organic matter content of the soil. This type of advice method is useful in situations where soil sampling is not possible (i.e. presence of stones) or where the N_{min} at the start of the growing season is not likely to fluctuate among fields and years.

In all other situations a method which includes soil analysis and eventually an estimate of the total available mineral nitrogen pool is recommended (Neeteson, 1995). Several methods are described, going from the N_{min} method *sensu stricto*, still in use with some adaptations in several parts of Germany and The Netherlands (Zentralverband Gartenbau-Bundesfachgruppe Gemüsebau, 1995; Anonymous, 1998) over an N index method (Geypens *et al.*, 1994) towards an N balance sheet method (Hofman, 1983). The last two methods include an estimation of the mineralisable nitrogen.

Some of the actual nitrogen fertilisation recommendation systems focus on a dynamic optimisation of nitrogen supply like the KNS-system (Kulturbegleitende N_{miN} Sollwerte-System) in Germany (Lorenz *et al.*, 1985) and the NBS-system (N bijmestsysteem) in The Netherlands (Breimer, 1989) and in Belgium (Pannier *et al.*, 1996). These systems are based on the knowledge of the N uptake evolution by the crop during the growing period and on the necessary mineral nitrogen buffer in the soil to match the nitrogen requirements.

To assess the requirement for supplementary N application, plant monitoring can be used. Several non-invasive methods like the use of chlorophyll meters, chroma meters, measurements of chlorophyll fluorescence, light interception and crop reflection are available (Booij *et al.*, 1999). Invasive methods such as measurements of total N content and of nitrate-N concentration in petiole sap can be complementary to the N_{min} methods (Haase *et al.*, 1999).

At last, simulation models as a tool for N recommendations become more and more important because time and money are less and less available for field experiments.

Depletion of the mineral N pool
Nitrogen immobilisation
Immobilisation can be defined as the temporal disappearance of mineral nitrogen in soil microbial biomass and/or SOM. It mostly occurs when large amounts of material with low N and high C content (C/N rate > 25) start to decompose in the soil. When the rate of microbial activity subsides, a gradual release of the immobilised nitrogen will occur. This explains the temporary character of N immobilisation. In the soil-plant system, this immobilisation must be recognised because a temporary lack of available nitrogen can influence plant growth.

Ammonia volatilisation
Volatilisation of ammonia is one of the major environmental problems in agriculture. According to Bouwman *et al.* (1997), about 75% of the NH_3 emission can be contributed to anthropogenic sources, especially to agricultural activities. The draft protocol by the

Executive Body of the Convention on Long-range Transboundary Air Pollution of the EC sets reduction targets for ammonia by 17% compared to the levels of 1990. Because of the impact of this emission on public health and on the environment, various emission ceilings per country are proposed in Table 2 (Anonymous, 1999b). The first measure will be the reduction of ammonia emission during spreading of animal manure. A further reduction through construction of low-emitting animal houses will be the next step (Hendriks et al., 1999).

TABLE 2. EMISSION LEVELS (10^3 TONNES OF NH_3) AND REDUCTIONS (%) TO BE REACHED IN 2010 FOR AMMONIA ACCORDING TO THE DRAFT PROTOCOL OF THE EC (ANONYMOUS, 1999B).

	Emission levels 1990	Emission reduction
Austria	81	19
Belgium	107	31
Denmark	122	43
Finland	35	11
France	814	4
Germany	764	28
Greece	80	9
Ireland	126	8
Italy	466	10
Netherlands	226	43
Norway	23	0
Portugal	98	10
Spain	351	-1
Sweden	61	7
Switzerland	72	13
UK	333	11

Gaseous losses by denitrification and nitrification

Gaseous losses of nitrogenous compounds, i.e. NO_x, N_2O and N_2, occur by denitrification and as side products of nitrification. It has to be mentioned that also a-biological production of these compunds is possible. Biological and a biological processes of production and consumption of NO and N_2O are described by Davidson (1991).

Next to the fact that these losses create an economical loss, the production of NO_x and N_2O has harmful effects on the environment.

It is generally accepted that under upland conditions 1 to 2% of the applied N is emitted as N_2O. Eichner (1990) made a summary of fertiliser-derived N_2O emission data from 104 field experiments. She found that the average daily fertiliser-derived emission varied from 0.03 to 123 g N_2O-N ha^{-1}d^{-1}, or 0.01 to about 45 kg N_2O-N ha^{-1} y^{-1}. Our own long-term measurements of total denitrification losses (N_2O + N_2) on natural grasslands, fertilised permanent grassland and maize fields showed losses ranging between 0.01 and 0.03 kg N ha^{-1}d^{-1}, 0.09 - 0.13 kg N ha^{-1}d^{-1} and 0.02 till 0.07 kg N ha^{-1}d^{-1}, respectively (Vermoesen et al., 1996). Important factors driving these losses are sufficiently available nitrate and organic carbon, low oxygen content as well as management practices and other environmental factors (Table 3, Peoples et al., 1995).

	Organic matter	Well drained	Moderately well drained	Poorly drained
Sandy, sandy loam	< 2%	2 - 9	4 - 14	6 - 30
Loam, silt loam	2 - 5%	3 - 16	6 - 20	10 - 45
Clay loam, clay	> 5%	4 -20	10 - 25	15 - 55

Next to N_2O, nitrification and denitrification also produce nitric oxide (NO). Lloyd (1993) found that only small amounts of NO are produced during denitrification as the activity of the nitric reductase is higher than of the nitrous reductase. Therefore, NO volatilisation seems to be mainly due to nitrification (Whitehead, 1995). These losses are of the order of some kg NO-N ha^{-1} y^{-1}. Lee et al. (1997) mention a loss rate of 10 ng NO-N m^{-2} s^{-1} (= 3.15 kg NO-N ha^{-1} y^{-1}) from fertilised agricultural grasslands.

Until now, most of these measurements have been done under laboratory circumstances. It is important that in the coming years more measurements of gaseous losses are done in the field to evaluate the real value of these losses. Recently, a Photo Acoustic Infrared Gas Analyzer became available and this makes it possible to automatically determine the N_2O-emissions in the field. This is also possible for NO emissions with the chemiluminescence $NO-NO_2-NO_x$-analyser.

TABLE 4. LATENT MINERAL NITROGEN RESIDUE (KG NO_3-N ha^{-1}) OF SOME ARABLE CROPS AND OF FIELD-GROWN VEGETABLES (AFTER DEMYTTENAERE ET AL., 1989).

Crop	Depth (m)	Latent mineral N residue
winter-wheat	1.20	35
sugarbeets	1.20	25
maize	0.90	50
potatoes	0.75	75
spinach	0.30	75
blanching celery	0.60	90
pea	0.60	50
cauliflower	0.60	80
carrot	0.60	50
leek	0.60	90
bean	0.60	60
celeriac	0.90	50
cabbage	0.90	25
brussels sprouts	0.90	25

N leaching

In the cool and wet regions of Europe, leaching losses of NO_3-N mainly occur during winter and early spring. Besides weather conditions and soil characteristics, N losses throughout the rooting zone are highly influenced by the amount and distribution of residual mineral N in the soil profile. Even with an optimum N fertilisation, the latent mineral N residue (i.e. residual mineral nitrogen at harvest) will differ between crops.

This is due to variable rooting depth and root distribution, to differences in N demand near harvest time and to inefficient fertiliser distribution (Hofman *et al.*, 1990). In the context of a more severe nutrient management in the EU, although some figures are available (Table 4), it is important to characterise these latent mineral N residues for all crops. In the Action Manure Plan of Flanders a provisory residual NO_3^-- N amount of 90 kg N ha[-1] until a depth of 90 cm in autumn is accepted (Anonymous, 1999a). Taken into account the soil characteristics and the differences in latent mineral N residues between crops, a further differentiation of this maximum allowed residual nitrogen has to be envisaged.

N losses by run-off and erosion

In hilly regions large amounts of nitrogen (N) can be transported by surface runoff. Two important fractions can be distinguished: dissolved N and particulate N, i.e. N adsorbed on sediment particles. In general, only small amounts of dissolved N are found in runoff water, compared to other pathways of N losses. When rainfall occurs nitrate will be leached out, due to its high solubility. Therefore, the largest amounts of dissolved N will be found in subsurface runoff and groundwater, while the upper layer (0-5 cm) is depleted in soluble N. Furthermore, the rain dilutes the N concentration in runoff water. Analysis of water samples taken during runoff events, showed that at high sediment discharges (> 1000 g s[-1]) the nitrate concentration in the surface water was lower than the European Nitrate Directive of 11.3 mg NO_3 - N l[-1] (Anonymous, 1991), while at low discharges the nitrate concentration exceeded this threshold value (Fig. 3).

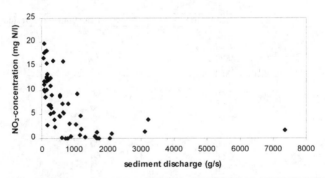

FIGURE 3. NITRATE CONCENTRATION OF SURFACE WATER IN RELATION TO SEDIMENT DISCHARGE DURING RUNOFF EVENTS.

On the other hand, large amounts of particulate N can be transported by erosion of arable land. Because N, especially organic N and NH_4^+, is adsorbed mainly on clay-sized particles, the eroded sediment is often enriched in N. This enrichment is due to the selective erosion of finer particles at low erosion intensities. Based on rainfall simulations, Sharpley (1985) found enrichment ratios for total N varying between 1.5 and 3. In small agricultural watersheds in southern Germany the enrichment ratios for total N varied between 0.5 and 5.85 (Weigand *et al.*, 1998).

N losses by surface and subsurface runoff can be reduced to a large extent by the use of grass filters (Daniels and Gilliam, 1996). Particulate N losses are reduced by deposition of soil particles, while dissolved N is removed by denitrification.

N uptake

Knowing the production and the N content, the total N uptake by the crop can be derived. This total N uptake is the basis for most N fertiliser advice systems. Therefore, a target potential yield and mean N concentrations in the different plant parts are needed. For crops with a N split application or for the use of the KNS or NBS system, the N uptake curve during the growing season is necessary.

CONCLUSIONS

The available nitrogen for crops is determined by the evolution of the mineral nitrogen pool in the soil profile. Factors and processes influencing this pool have to be better quantified to optimise yield and to minimise losses to the environment. New research topics arise by changes in agricultural production systems and by the implementation of legislation measures imposed by national and EU authorities.

REFERENCES

Anonymous, 1991. Council Directive 91/676/EEC of 12 December 1991 concerning the protection of waters against pollution caused by nitrates from agricultural sources. Official Journal of the European Communities, L373: 0001-0008.

Anonymous, 1994. MAFF reference book 209. H.M. Stationery Office, London, UK. 112 pp.

Anonymous, 1998. NMI praktijkgids bemesting. Wageningen, The Netherlands, 1-60.

Anonymous, 1999a. Decreet houdende wijziging van het decreet van 23 januari 1991 inzake de bescherming van het leefmilieu tegen de verontreiniging door meststoffen. Moniteur Belge-20-08-1999-Belgisch Staatsblad, 30967-30994.

Anonymous, 1999b. Draft protocol to the 1979 convention on long-range transboundary air pollution to abate acidification, eutrophication and ground-level ozone. Economic and Social Council of the United Nations, 71 pp.

Booij R., J.L. Valenzuela and C. Aguilera, 1999. Determination of crop nitrogen status using non-invasive methods. In: Haverkort A.J., MacKerron D.K.L. (eds.) Management of nitrogen and water in potato production, Wageningen Pers, The Netherlands: 72-82.

Bouwman, A.F., D.S. Lee, W.A.H. Asman, F.J. Dentener, K.W. Van der Hoek and J.G.J. Oliver, 1997. A global high-resolution emission inventory of ammonia. Global Biogeochemical Cyclus, 11: 561-587.

Breimer, T., 1989. Stikstofbijmeststysteem (NBS) voor enige vollegrondsgroentegewassen. IKC-

AGV, Lelystad, The Netherlands. 58 pp.

Breland, T.A. and S. Hansen, 1996. Nitrogen mineralization and microbial biomass as affected by soil compaction. Soil Biology and Biochemistry, 28: 655-663.

Burns, I.G., 1974. A model for predicting the redistribution of salts applied to fallow soils after excess rainfall or evaporation. Journal of Soil Science, 25: 163-178.

Campbell, G.W., D.H.F. Atkins, J.S. Bower, J.G. Irwin, D. Simpson and M.L. Williams, 1990. The spatial distribution of the deposition of sulphur and nitrogen in the UK. Journal of the Science of Food and Agriculture, 53: 427-428.

Daniels, R.B. and J.W. Gilliam, 1996. Sediment and chemical load reduction by grass and riparian filters. Soil Science Society of America Journal, 60: 246-25.

Davidson, E.A.,1991. Fluxes of nitrous oxide and nitric oxide from terrestrial ecosystems-Microbial production and consumption of greenhouse gases: methane, nitrogen oxides and halomethanes. In: Rogers J.E., Whitman W.B. (eds.) American Society of Microbiology, Washington, USA: 219-235.

Demyttenaere, P., 1991. Stikstofdynamiek in de bodems van de Westvlaamse groentestreek. PhD dissertation, Faculteit van de Landbouwwetenschappen, Gent. 203 pp.

Demyttenaere, P., G. Hofman, P. Verstegen, G. Vulsteke and M. Van Ruymbeke, 1989. Need for modifications of the mineral nitrogen valance in the vegetable area of West-Flanders, Belgium. Pedologie, XXXIX-3: 261-274.

De Neve, 2000. Modelling and non-destructive real-time monitoring of nitrogen mineralization from vegetable crop residues and from soil organic matter. PhD dissertation, Faculty of Agriculture and Applied Biological Sciences, Gent. 181pp.

Eichner, M.J., 1990. Nitrous oxide emissions from fertilized soils: summary of available date. Journal of Environmental Quality, 19: 272-280.

Geypens, M., H. Vandendriessche, J. Bries and G. Hendrickx, 1994. The N-index expert system, a tool for integrated N-management. 15th World Congress of Soil Science, 51: 165-173.

Goulding, K.W.T., 1990. Nitrogen deposition to land from the atmosphere. Soil Use and Management, 6: 61-62.

Haase, N.U., J.P. Goffart, D.K.L. MacKerron and M.W. Young, 1999. Determination of crop nitrogen status using invasive methods. In: Haverkort A.J., MacKerron D.K.L. (eds.). Management of nitrogen and water in potato production, Wageningen Pers, The Netherlands: 55-71.

Hendriks, J., A. Andries, D. Berckmoes and C. Vinckier, 1999. Estimation of a cost curve of an ammonia emission reduction plan for Flanders. In: KBTL (eds.) Regulation of animal production in Europe, Wiesbaden, Germany: 214-221.

Hofman, G., 1983. Minerale stikstofevolutie in zandleemprofielen. Dissertation for higher education, Faculteit van de Landbouwwetenschappen, Gent. 183 pp.

Hofman, G., P. Demyttenaere, M. Van Meirvenne, C. Ossemerct and M. Van Ruymbeke, 1990. Causes and consequences of differences in latent mineral N residues in the soil profile. Communications in Soil Science and Plant Analysis, 21: 1779-1791.

Honeycutt, C.W., L.J. Potaro, K.L. Avila and W.A. Halteman, 1993. Residue quality, loading rate and soil temperature relations with hairy vetch (Vicia villosa Roth) residue carbon nitrogen and phosphorus mineralization. Biological Agriculture and Horticulture, 9: 181-199.

Lee, D.S., A.F. Bouwman, W.A.H. Asman, F.J. Dentener, K.W. Van der Hoek and J.C.J. Oliver, 1997. Emissions of nitric oxide, nitrous oxide and ammonia from grasslands on a global scale. In: Jarvis S.C., Pain B.F. (eds.) Gaseous Nitrogen Emissions from Grasslands, CAB International, Wallingford, UK: 353-371

Lloyd, A., 1993. Aerobic denitrification in soils and sediments: from fallacies to facts. Trends in Ecology and Evolution, 8: 352-356.

Lorenz, H., J. Schlaghecken and G. Engl, 1985. Gezielten Stickstoffversorgung - das kulturbegleitende N_{min}-Sollwerte-System (KNS-System). Deutsche Gartenbau 13: 646-648.

Ministry of Agriculture, Nature Management, and Fisheries, 1999. Mineral policy in The Netherlands; Dutch policy to reduce undesired effect of mineral losses to the environment. Ministry of Agriculutre, Nature Mangement, and Fisheries, The Hague.

Neeteson, J.J., 1995. Nitrogen management for intensively grown arable crops and field vegetables. In: Bacon P.E. (ed.) Nitrogen fertilization in the environment. Marcel Dekker Inc., New York, USA: 295-325.

Palm, C.A. and P.A. Sanchez, 1991. Nitrogen release from the leaves of some tropical legumes as affected by their lignin and polyphonic contents. Soil Biology and Biochemistry, 23: 83-85.

Pannier, J., G. Hofman and L. Vanparys, 1996. Optimization of a nitrogen advice system: target values as a function of N-mineralization rates. In: Van Cleemput O., Hofman G., Vermoesen A. (eds.) Progress in Nitrogen Cycling Studies. Kluwer Academic Publishers, Dordrecht, The Netherlands: 353-358.

Peoples, M.B., J.R. Freney and A.R. Mosier, 1995. Minimizing gaseous losses of nitrogen. In: Bacon P.E. (ed.) Nitrogen Fertilization in the Environment, Marcel Dekker, New York, USA: 565-602.

Sharpley, A.N., 1985. The selective erosion of plant nutrients in runoff. Soil Science Society of America Journal, 49: 1527-1534.

Van Breemen, N. and H.F.G. Van Dijk, 1988. Ecosystem effects of atmospheric deposition of nitrogen in The Netherlands. Environmental Pollution, 54: 249-274.

Vermoesen, A., O. Van Cleemput and G. Hofman 1996. Long-term measurements of N_2O emission. Energy conversion Management, 37: 279-284.

Vervaet, H., P. Boeckx, O. Van Cleemput and G. Hofman, 1999. Mineral N deposition on a forest in an area of intensive animal breeding in Belgium. Abstracts 10th Nitrogen Workshop, Royal Veterinary and Agricultural University Copenhagen, Denmark, 1: 4.

Vigil, M.F. and D.E. Kissel, 1991. Equations for estimating the amount of nitrogen mineralized from crop residues. Soil Science Society of America Journal, 55: 757-761.

Weigand, S., W. Schimmack and K. Auerswald, 1998. The enrichment of ^{137}Cs in the soil loss from small agricultural watersheds. Zeitschrift für Pflanzenernährung und Bodenkunde, 161: 479-484.

Whitehead, D.C., 1995. Grasland Nitrogen. CAB International, Wallingford, UK. 397 pp.

Zentralverband Gartenbau-Bundesfachgruppe Gemüsebau, 1995. Gemüse aus kontrolliertem Integriertem anbau in der Bundesrepublik Deutschland. Kulturspezifische Richlinien (Produktrichtlinien) für den Integrierten Anbau van Gemüse in der Bundesrepublik Deutschland. 46 pp.

Physiological and genetic bases of variation for nitrogen use efficiency in grain maize

A. GALLAIS[1,2], P. BERTIN [1] AND B. HIREL[3]

[1] Station de Génétique Végétale du Moulon, INRA-UPS-INA.PG, Ferme du Moulon, 91190 Gif/Yvette, France
[2] INAPG, 16 rue Claude Bernard, 75231 Paris Cedex 05, France
[3] Unité de Nutrition Azotée des Plantes, INRA, Route de St-Cyr 78026 Versailles Cedex, France

S U M M A R Y

To avoid pollution by nitrates and to maintain a sufficient net income, the farmer must optimize the use of nitrogen from fertilizer. Development of varieties with improved nitrogen use efficiency may be a way to reach both objectives. In this paper we present and discuss our results on the study of genetic variability of nitrogen use efficiency in maize at low and high nitrogen (N) input. Genotype x nitrogen interaction was present for grain yield. Kernel number was the yield component which was the most affected both by nitrogen stress and by the genotype x nitrogen interaction. The responsiveness of yield was mainly explained by the responsiveness of kernel number. At low N input, leaf senescence and anthesis-silking interval were negatively correlated to yield whereas nitrogen nutrition index was positively correlated. The results indicate that the limiting steps in nitrogen metabolism are different at low and high N input. More Quantitative Trait Loci for morphological traits, grain yield and its components were detected under high nitrogen input compared to high N input, whereas for N-content, the reciprocal was observed. Several coincidences with gene-encoding enzymes involved in nitrogen and carbon assimilation (glutamine synthetase, ADPGlucose-pyrophophorylase, sucrose phosphate synthase, sucrose synthase and invertase) and Quantitative Trait Loci for grain yield and its components were observed. All coincidences were consistent with the expected physiological function of the corresponding enzyme activities. Results show that in maize, the nitrogen use efficiency can be improved by developing specific varieties for low and high N input. Abbreviations: N, nitrogen; N+ (N-), high (low) nitrogen input; NUE, nitrogen use efficiency; ASI, anthesis-silking interval; QTL, quantitative trait locus; GS, Glutamine Synthetase.

Keywords: genetic variation, maize, nitrogen fertilization, nitrogen use efficiency, Quantitative Trait Loci

INTRODUCTION

Nitrogen (N) fertilization has been a powerful tool for increasing yield, especially in cereals. However, for maize, except for the case of fertilizing irrigation, in contrast to wheat, N fertilizer is provided only once at sowing. Consequently, under some specific environmental conditions in certain parts of Europe, this agronomic practice can lead to groundwater pollution by nitrates, particularly with silage maize when slurry is used. Because N fertilizers have been, up to now, relatively cheap in comparison to other inputs, and because of the expected economic benefits from a maximized crop yield, no intensive studies were developed to optimize the use of mineral N. Nowadays, the situation is changing since the farmer must actively contribute to the protection of the environment. Furthermore, as a consequence of the agricultural policy, the use of N fertilizer must be optimized to ensure sufficient income. Both objectives can be reached by developing specific farming techniques and by selecting varieties which are more efficient in terms of N absorption and N metabolism.

For grain maize, nitrogen use efficiency (NUE) can be defined (after Moll *et al.*, 1987) as the ratio of grain yield to the quantity of N provided both by the soil and by the fertilizers. Since N concentration in the soil is not always precisely known, but is fixed for a given year and field, NUE in an environment can be measured by the yield itself, i.e. the silage dry-matter or grain yield. NUE for grain yield is a product of several components: where NUpE is the N uptake efficiency, NUtE the N utilization efficiency, $NUtE_G$ for grain, $NUtE_S$ for silage, and $NUtE_{BG}$ for total biomass at grain harvesting. For a given N level, NUpE can be also estimated by N-yield. Note that NUtE for biomass is the inverse of the N content. Thus, NUtE for grain production is equal to the ratio of harvest index to N content, which is equivalent to a carbon/N (C/N) ratio. In theory, to fully estimate NUE, it would be more accurate to consider total plant biomass. However, in practice, only aerial biomass is taken into account because root biomass cannot be easily measured in the field.

To investigate whether it is justified to breed for NUE, at a given level of N fertilization, it is first necessary to study genetic variation for NUE and then determine related traits which can be used as selection criteria. Genetic variability can then be evaluated by two complementary experiments:

- at a given level of nitrogen fertilization, the variety with the best NUE being that exhibiting the best yield.

- at varying levels of N fertilization, to test genetic variation in responsiveness; the interest of such protocol will be to show whether it is necessary to select specific genotypes for low or high N-input. The test of responsiveness is not necessary if the aim is to improve yield for a given level of fertilization.

In the present paper, our recent findings on the physiological and genetic basis of NUE in grain maize are described and discussed with respect to published results. We have developed a two-year experiment using 99 recombinant inbred lines (RILs) crossed to the same tester. The RILs were grown under high (N^+) or low N input (N^-) (Bertin,

1997; Bertin and Gallais, 2000). Such genetic material was chosen in order to detect some chromosome segments, i.e. Quantitative Trait Loci (QTL), involved in the genetic variation of the studied traits. The studied traits at flowering and harvesting time included dry matter production, yield of the different plant parts as well as their relative N content. In addition, for 80 of these lines, a number of physiological traits related to N metabolism were studied on young plants (6-7 leaf stage). These plants were grown under hydroponic conditions on a nutrient solution containing a high level of inorganic N as a form of nitrate. Shoot total N nitrate and carbohydrate content (glucose, fructose) were determined. In leaves, nitrate reductase (NR) and glutamine synthetase (GS) activities were measured in the 80 selected lines. For QTL detection, we used a genetic map composed of 152 RFLP markers (Causse *et al.*, 1996). These RFLP markers included probes for genes involved in C and N metabolism such as nitrate reductase (NR), cytosolic glutamine synthetase (GS1), ADPGlucose-pyrophophorylase (ADPGppase), sucrose phosphate synthase (SPS), sucrose synthase (SuS) and invertase (Inv). Except for the work recently published by Agrama *et al.* (1999), this is the first report describing the detection of QTLs for NUE based on both agronomic and physiological studies.

Genetic variation for NUE and correlated traits
Effect of nitrogen stress on means

In our experiment, N stress reduced grain yield by about 40%. Kernel number was the yield component which was the most affected, a finding consistent with the results of Reed (1988), Below (1995) and Uhart and Andrade (1995). Thousand-kernel weight was moderately affected (10%) by a strong N stress. N uptake was also strongly reduced (by 50% at flowering and 42% for grain, 51% for stem at grain harvesting). NUE was increased following a N stress by 72% at flowering and by 27% at harvesting. This corresponds to the well-known decrease in NUE when the level of fertilization is increased. One of the more specific changes from flowering to harvesting is the N translocation from stover to grain. While in our conditions, on the average of two years and for 99 genotypes, the change in stover dry matter does not appear very important (+1%), N content in stover was reduced by 35% under both N rate conditions. This result indicates that there is a specific translocation of N from stover to grain. The amplitude of such a phenomenon is dependent on both the post-anthesis N-uptake and N stress conditions. In our experimental conditions, relative N translocation from stover to grain was similar under high or low N input. Genetic variability of this phenomenon will be important to consider.

The decrease in kernel number is due to ovule abortion just after fertilization since the number of ovules is only slightly affected by N deprivation (Below, 1995; Lemcoff and Loomis, 1986; Uhart and Andrade, 1995). Such abortion could be the consequence of a lack of photosynthesis products in plants applied with a low level of N. However, the reduction in post-anthesis growth (29%) was much greater than the reduction of vegetative growth (14%). This could be explained by a very high sink demand in both carbohydrates and N compounds, with respect to the available plant resources just after fertilization.

This imbalance may, therefore, lead to ovule abortion in a genotype-dependent manner. A high N content in developing embryos suggests that they require a high level of N metabolites for their development (Czyzewicz and Below, 1994).

Variation in NUE and existence of genotype x nitrogen interaction

Genetic variance for NUE, i.e. grain yield, was observed at both levels of N fertilization. From high to low N input, it can increase or decrease according to climatic conditions. Environmental variation was always increased, due to the appearance of soil heterogeneity. Consequently, yield heritability was lower at low N input compared to high N input. Then, as already observed by Presterl (1996), the expected response to selection will therefore be lower at low N input. As already reported by Jackson et al., (1983), we observed, that NUpE was more variable in N^+ than in N^-. It was the opposite for NUtE. Regardless of both plant developmental stage and N fertilization, the genetic correlation between NUpE and NUtE was never significant. Both parameters were equally related to NUE either at low or high level of N fertilization. Therefore, from a breeding point of view, such a result shows that it will be necessary to improve both parameters simultaneously.

Genotype x nitrogen level (G x N) interaction significantly affected yield representing about 20 to 30% of total genetic variation (the sum of the genetic variance across the two N feeding conditions and the G x N interaction). Although relatively low, this genetic variation may be significant if we consider that RILs were used in this experiment. This means that the genetic correlation between two N conditions is generally relatively high (0.75 in our experiment). Such results were also obtained by several other groups using an even more diverse plant material (Beauchamp et al., 1976, Pollmer et al., 1979, Balko and Russell, 1980a; Reed et al., 1980, Russell, 1984, Moll et al., 1987, Landbeck, 1995).

Kernel number was also greatly affected by the G x N interaction whereas thousand-kernel weight was not modified. Such interaction was even more consistent according to the year than for grain yield. Furthermore, responsiveness (which is another expression of the interaction) for yield was highly and positively correlated to the responsiveness for kernel number ($r = 0.85**$). This underlines the role of ovule abortion in the yield responsiveness to N fertilization. The absence of G x N interaction for vegetative traits indicates clearly that observed interaction for yield is due to grain development.

Two genotypic behaviours explain part of G x N interaction for grain yield. First, it seems that low-yielding genotypes at low N input were the most responsive to high N input. However, they were not among the most productive at high N input. Therefore, responsiveness of grain yield or kernel number was negatively related to traits in N^- such as grain yield or kernel number ($r = -0.70**$). Secondly, the differences between high potential genotypes were reduced at low N input due to a curvilinear relationship between yield at low N input and yield at high N input. These characteristics illustrate the adaptation of modern varieties to high N-input (Castleberry et al., 1984, and Russell, 1985). Other factors can contribute to explain G x N interaction. In particular, several traits measured in N⁻ were negatively correlated to yield responsiveness (N content at flowering, N nutrition index (NNI), N uptake at harvest, post-anthesis N uptake). Therefore, G x N interaction appears to be essentially due to the variation to N⁻ adaptation rather than to the variation in N⁺ adaptation.

Traits related to NUE or its components

It was easier to explain the variability of grain yield at low N input than at high N input. Vegetative development appeared generally favourable for grain yield at high and low N input. This was related both to the size of the photosynthetic source (leaf area) and the size of the sink (ear), and even for a given earliness. At low N input three inter-related traits were highly correlated to grain yield and kernel number: NNI (positively), leaf senescence (negatively), and ASI (negatively). NNI is the ratio of actual N content to optimum N content (Lemaire and Gastal, 1997) corresponding to the maximum yield for the minimum N content. Measured at flowering, it was positively related to nitrogen accumulated at this time and negatively related to leaf senescence three weeks later. The role of leaf senescence at low N input was also pointed out by Bänziger et al. (1997a,b) and by Presterl et al. (1996). Furthermore, Ma and Dwyer (1998) showed that a modern stay-green hybrid had a greater NUE at low N input than an old hybrid exhibiting early senescence.

It appears that NNI, at low N-input, has a physiological meaning, already detectable at the early stages of flowering and fully revealed at maturity. NNI is related to the potential leaf photosynthetic activity. With active chloroplasts, N content will be higher because leaf senescence is delayed. Then, if at flowering the flux of photosynthates is limited in N⁻, this can lead to kernel abortion at the top of the ear just after fertilization. Resistance to abortion could be due to the ability to remobilize N stalk reserves. Such a hypothesis is supported by the conclusions of Uhart and Andrade (1995), Reed et al. (1988) and Czyzewicz and Below (1992), showing that N is necessary for kernel development. However, such effects of NNI and senescence are expected to be weak or absent under a favourable environment. This could explain some inconsistent results on the correlation between yield and senescence (Presterl et al., 1996).

Anthesis-silking interval also seems to reflect a particular physiology. When maize plants are subjected to some stresses such as drought or N deficiency, an increase in ASI is observed (Edmeades et al., 1993; Lafitte and Edmeades, 1995). The consequence could be a deficit in ovule fertilization in monogenotypic stands (a single-cross hybrid for example). However, in spite of the presence of pollen, a significant positive correlation between ASI and grain yield is observed at low N input (Lafitte and Edmeades, 1995; Bertin and Gallais, 2000). Therefore, genotypes for which ASI does not increase, may be more efficient in terms of N assimilation and management thus leading to a greater yield in N⁻. It is well known that a short ASI is related to a prolific physiology. At the extreme, true prolificacy leads to protogyny whereas non-prolific maize shows protandry. Prolific genotypes exhibit two favourable traits: i) they show a high degree of translocation from the stover to the grain, a characteristic which favours yield under stress conditions.

This may explain why, with such material, NUtE is more important than NUpE, in contrast to non-prolific maize (Jackson *et al.*, 1986) ii) Bertin *et al.* (1976) and Boyat and Rautou (1977) showed that they have a greater inducible leaf nitrate reductase activity at lower light intensity. Therefore, in such genotypes, it is logical to think that remobilisation could co-exist with post-anthesis N absorption.

Differences in NUpE in adult plants might be related both to the quantity and quality of the root system. Although previous experiments have shown a great variability in the architecture of the root system (Hébert *et al.*, 1992), up to now, no direct relationship with NUpE could be found. The whole plant NUpE, measured by N uptake, corresponds to the product of biomass x N content. However, its main component is represented by N grain yield due to the high contribution of the grain to the whole plant N-content. NUpE variation depends on the correlation between yield and N-content. At flowering, in N⁻, such correlation was strongly negative whereas, in N⁺, no such strong negative correlation was observed. We observed a strong reduction in genetic variance in N uptake at flowering from N⁺ to N⁻. Until flowering, maize functions like forage grasses, for which negative correlation between dry-matter yield and protein content is well established (Lemaire and Gastal, 1997). At harvest, correlation between yield and N content was lower. Therefore, the reduction in NUpE variance from N⁺ to N⁻ was not so evident. In addition, the absence of variation in N uptake at flowering in N⁻ means that N source (i.e. in the soil) was a limiting factor. In contrast when soil N is high, genetic differences in N uptake can be revealed. As a consequence, vegetative development was more related to NUpE in N⁺ than in N⁻. Post-anthesis N absorption was also highly related to NUpE in N⁺, leading to an increase in kernel weight.

As expected, NUtE was highly negatively correlated to the N content ($r_p = -0.88**$ in N⁺ and $r_p = -0.90**$ in N⁻) and positively correlated to the harvest index ($r_p = 0.75**$ in N⁺ and $0.60**$ in N⁻). It was negatively correlated to NNI ($r_p = -0.80**$) and also negatively correlated to N-quantity in the stover. To increase NUtE, it is necessary to decrease N content and to increase harvest index. These results are close to those of Di Fonzo *et al.* (1982) which showed that in N⁻, grain yield was correlated to the N harvest index.

Relationships with physiological traits at young stage

No significant relationship was observed with nitrate reductase activity (NRA) and grain yield, whatever the level of N input. This does not support the results of Feil *et al.* (1993) who found a significant correlation. The impact on grain yield of variation of nitrate reductase activity is still a matter of debate. Hageman (in Sherrard *et al.*, 1986) showed that a selection based on high and low NRA has a consequence on the leaf area (the larger leaves exhibiting a higher NRA) and therefore could affect dry-matter production and grain yield. Moreover, a study (Cacco *et al.*, 1993) performed on US varieties showed that at low N input modern varieties exhibit a higher NRA than old varieties. In the same study, SPS activity appeared to be higher at high N input. This later result suggests that under such conditions the efficiency of carbon metabolism is also improved. More difficult to understand is the decline in glutamate deshydrogenase (GDH) activity at low N input. It could be the consequence of a better adaptation to stress of modern varieties. In our study we did not observe any relationship between GDH activity and grain yield.

Nitrate content in young plants was positively correlated to grain yield and to NUpE at low or high N input. This may be related to vegetative development and may reflect the ability of a given genotype to absorb and store more or less N. Such stored N will be further remobilized to the kernels. Although not fully understood this process is controlled in part by the enzyme glutamine synthetase (GS) (Masclaux *et al.*, 2000). In our study, at low N input, a positive relationship between GS activity and grain yield, NUtE and kernel number was observed. A favourable effect of GS activity at high N input on N translocation from stover to grain was also detected. Interestingly, we found that the carbohydrate content in young plants was negatively related to NNI and NUpE at high N input. Leaf carbohydrate content mirrors the efficiency to export photosynthates, a high content reflecting a lower efficiency. Consequently, this will be unfavourable on NNI, leaf area duration and NUpE.

Then, it appears that the ideotype for grain production can be summarized as follow: the plant must absorb as much N as possible before flowering and store it in stover. After fertilization, stored N must be efficiently remobilized (translocated) to the ear to be further used for grain development. Since carbohydrates are required to produce inorganic N molecules, an active photosynthesis must be maintained as long as possible, thus delaying leaf senescence. In contrast, with maize silage it is necessary to have a high protein content in the whole plant and the stover in particular. However, it is also necessary to have a high grain contribution. Therefore, N translocation must also be active in maize silage in order to maximize N grain content. Thus, to maintain a high N content in the stover, it will be necessary to have efficient N absorption and reduction after flowering. Of course, N absorption after flowering will depend on its availability, the efficiency with which it is taken up by the roots and leaf photosynthetic activity. The N reduction is under the control of nitrate reductase activity which is progressively inhibited during the filling period, thus explaining N translocation from the stover to the grain. Therefore, for maize silage, to increase both N absorption and stover N content it will be necessary to select genotypes able to maintain a high level of NR activity during the grain filling period.

All these different parameters are always associated to a high glutamine synthetase activity. Thus, to increase grain yield, it could be efficient to select for glutamine synthetase activity. For silage maize, post-flowering absorption may also be important to consider in order to have a sufficient protein content in the stover. Whether it is possible to have simultaneously during the filling period, N absorption, nitrate reduction and N remobilization is still unclear. However, for grain or for silage production we found that genetic variability exists for different traits related to NUE. It appears therefore possible to improve NUE at different levels of N fertilization. Nevertheless, genotypes adapted to high N input will not necessarily be adapted to low N input. In the future, with molecular markers of the detected QTLs or direct markers of the involved genes, marker-assisted selection can be developed to obtain maize varieties, either specifically or more generally adapted to various levels of N fertilization.

DISCUSSION

As already observed by Rizzi *et al.* (1993) and Di Fonzo *et al.* (1982), our results show that N metabolism variation is different at low or high N input. Limiting factors are different in N^+ and in N^-. One of the most spectacular results is that only traits measured in N^- explain the responsiveness for grain yield. It can therefore be concluded that genes involved in the genetic variability at low N input are probably different from those expressed at high N input. It can also be concluded that at low N input variation in NUtE is more important than variation in NUpE, the opposite being observed at high N input. Therefore, the use of molecular markers should be an efficient tool to verify whether specific loci are involved in the genetic variability (QTLs) at low or high N input.

Identification of QTLs
QTLs for yield, its components and morphological traits
For yield, its components (kernel number and kernel weight), and morphological traits (plant height, leaf area, flowering date), QTLs appear to be organised in clusters. These clusters were approximately the same under both N fertilization conditions. However, fewer QTLs were detected at low N input than at high N input. In particular, for yield and kernel number, QTLs detected at low N input were a subset of those detected at high N input. This result is quite different from that of Agrama *et al.* (1999) who found specific QTLs for low N input. This can be explained by either a greater environmental variation at low N input or by a scaling effect (lower performance at low N input). However, the fact that for common QTLs the allelic effects were similar in N^+ and in N^- is not in favour of such a scaling effect.

The QTLs being grouped in clusters can be due to pleitropy and linkage. Indeed, co-locations correspond to parental associations of traits, which could be in favour of linkage. In addition, these clusters seem to have a physiological meaning, which could be in favour of pleiotropy. Such distribution of QTLs was also pointed out by Khavkin and Coe (1997). They underlined that clusters are located within chromosome zones where genes involved in the regulation of growth and development are present (homeobox genes).

Whether or not there are specific QTLs to N^- remains to be determined, since for several traits, there was no QTL x N interaction although specific QTLs were detected in N^+. Only some QTL x N level interactions were detected (only 4 out of about 20 different QTLs detected for yield and its components). However, for QTLs showing a significant interaction with N level, we observed some co-locations which may have a biological meaning :

- on chromosome 6 the zone showing QTL x N interaction for yield was near a QTL for NNI in N^- in 1994. NNI was shown to be highly related to yield in N^-.

- on chromosome 6 and chromosome 8 the zone involved in the interaction is close to the SPS gene. The enzyme plays an important role in both the synthesis and export of sucrose in the leaf (see below). Therefore, its activity could be very important for the tolerance to N stress.

- interactive QTLs on chromosome 6 and 8 were also detected by the QTL responsiveness for yield and kernel number.

Then, our conclusion is that genetic variation is differently expressed at low and high N input. This is in good agreement with what has been observed at the phenotypic level (Laffite and Edmeades, 1994; Di Fonzo *et al.*, 1992; Bertin and Gallais, 2000).

QTLs for NUE components

Unlike for yield and its components, for grain or stover N content more QTLs were detected in N⁻ compared to N⁺. However, QTLs detected in N⁻ for N content co-located very often with QTLs involved in vegetative development, grain yield or its components in N⁺. The examination of allele effects showed (as expected on the basis of a N dilution effect) that favourable alleles for yield or morphological traits in N⁺ corresponded to unfavourable alleles for N content in N⁻. As a consequence, QTLs for N uptake were mainly detected at high N input, whereas QTLs for NUtE were mainly detected at low N input. QTLs for N uptake co-located with QTLs for whole plant or grain yield whereas QTLs for NUtE co-located very often with QTLs for N content. Note that the two QTLs for NNI detected at low N input co-located with QTLs for NUtE. Therefore, considering the various QTLs detected in this experiment, a greater variation of N uptake under high N input seems to occur as well as a greater variation of N utilization at low N input. These results are consistent with those of Bertin and Gallais (2000) and Di Fonzo *et al.* (1982) at the phenotypic level. In both studies it was shown that variation in NUtE plays a more important role than NUpE in N⁻, the reverse being observed in N⁺. In N⁺, the variation was mainly due to the ability of the plant to grow whereas in N⁻, due to a limitation in N absorption, variation in growth was more dependent on the N metabolic use.

Co-localisations with QTLs for physiological studies

Most of the QTLs detected in young developing plants correspond to clusters observed at the adult stage. Many co-localisations tend to confirm the observed correlation with nitrate content, sugar content and GS activity. QTLs for nitrate content co-located positively (with allele effects of the same sign), with QTLs for grain yield and kernel number on chromosome 2 and 5, and with QTL for N uptake on chromosome 2. This result tends to confirm that nitrate uptake at vegetative stage was favourable to N uptake efficiency in adult plants and for grain yield regardless of the N fertilization level. On chromosome 2 we found a negative co-localisation (with allele effects of opposite sign), with QTL for N transfer. This could be the result of a negative correlation between N transfer and N uptake during the grain filling period.

QTLs for soluble sugar content (glucose and fructose) co-located negatively with several QTLs: QTLs for yield on chromosome 1 and chromosome 8, QTLs for N transfer on chromosome 1, 8 and 9 (mainly under high N input), and 5 QTLs for NUtE. This negative association is quite consistent with the negative correlation observed at the phenotypic level between grain yield and sugar content at young stage. A high sugar content at young stage could reflect the inability of the plant to export sugars from the leaf to the ear.

For GS activity, five QTLs co-located positively to QTLs for yield or its components were identified: 3 on chromosome 1, 1 on chromosome 4 and 1 on chromosome 5. Such co-locations are consistent with the role of cytosolic GS, during N remobilization. GS activity is expected to influence kernel number as well as kernel weight. We already found that both agronomic traits can be affected by the intensity of N translocation just after fertilization and during the grain filling period, thus assessing the role of cytosolic GS during these two processes.

Co-localisations with some genes involved in N or C-metabolism

After QTL detection, it is necessary to further identify the corresponding genes. To do this, adaptation to N stress or utilization of N is a good model because the N assimilatory pathway is well characterized. Moreover, cDNAs encoding enzymes or proteins involved in the pathway (nitrate and nitrate reductase, glutamine synthetase, asparagine synthetase, nitrate transporter) can be used as probes to locate the corresponding genes on a RFLP map. In parallel, as C-metabolism is also involved in the response of plant to nitrogen, the same approach can be used to locate genes encoding enzymes involved in C metabolism (ADPGppase, SPS, SuS, Inv).

Nitrate reductase (NR) and glutamine synthetase (GS). QTLs for yield and its components co-located with four loci for NR or for cytosolic Glutamine Synthetase (GS1). On chromosome 1, a QTL affecting kernel number in N^+ and kernel weight at both low and high N input coincided with NADH-NR and NAD(P)H-NR locus. A QTL for yield and grain number in N^+ coincided also with the GS1 locus (2-year experiment). On chromosome 4 a QTL for kernel weight co-located with NADH-NR and GS1-4 loci, which are very close to each other. On chromosome 5, a QTL for kernel weight and yield at both N^+ and N^- coincided with *GS1* locus. Interestingly, at each of these three loci a co-localisation with GS activity was also observed. Considering the role of GS1 during leaf N remobilization, the triple coincidence GS1 structural gene, QTL for GS activity and QTL for yield, in three independent sites could not be due to chance, like the coincidence between two other QTLs for GS activity and QTLs for yield or its components. Therefore, GS genes on chromosomes 1, 4 and 5 are likely to be good candidate genes corresponding to QTLs influencing yield. On chromosome 10 there was also an interesting coincidence between the GS locus and QTLs for senescence. Glutamine synthetase enzyme being involved in the N remobilization during senescence, such co-localisation is quite logical. The absence of QTL for GS activity could mean that it corresponds to another type of GS, not expressed in a young stage.

ADPGppase. This enzyme catalyses starch synthesis from ADP-glucose. Coincidence was observed on chromosome 3 between the sh2 locus, encoding ADPGppase (Chourey and Nelson, 1976) and a QTL for N content and kernel number at N^+. Coincidences with

ADPGppase genes were also observed on chromosome 4 and chromosome 8 for QTLs of vegetative development (mainly leaf area) at N^+ and N^-. Several coincidences between such genes and QTLs for kernel number were also observed. Goldman *et al.* (1993) have also found a QTL co-locating with the gene sh2 and affecting both starch content and protein content of the grain. The coincidence between ADPGppase genes and QTLs for kernel number could be the consequence of a relationship between abortion just after fertilization and availability of soluble sugars. Note that, on chromosomes 1 and 3, the effect of the QTL on kernel number per plant in N^+ was opposed to its effect on N content in N^-. More generally, all QTLs for N content in N^- co-located with QTLs for plant development, kernel number or grain yield in N^+. This means that the effect on N metabolism of the sh2 locus could be the result of a dilution effect. Furthermore, Giroux *et al.* (1996) have shown that some sh2 mutants can increase both seed weight and starch content. The non detection in this zone of a QTL affecting kernel weight can be due to a purely statistical problem due to a negative correlation between kernel weight and kernel number. Consequently, the sh2 locus appears to be a good candidate gene corresponding to a QTL for both yield and N utilization.

Sucrose Phosphate Synthase (SPS). A clear co-location was observed on chromosome 6 between the SPS locus and a QTL for grain yield in 1995 (or on average of both years), and a QTL for senescence. Note also that such a chromosome zone was also found to be involved in the interaction with the level of N fertilization. On chromosome 8, a second locus-encoding SPS was also identified. Again, in the same chromosome zone there was a QTL for yield in 1995 affecting the kernel number per plant. The SPS locus was detected in the same zone of the QTL detected for yield responsiveness yield and kernel number. Similar observation was made by Causse *et al.* (1995) since they found a co-localisation between the two SPS genes and the QTLs for growth in young plants. The coincidence between the SPS locus and QTLs for yield, kernel number per plant and senescence in N^+ is of particular interest. Such an enzyme is not only involved in leaf sucrose synthesis but plays also an important role in the export of sucrose towards the other parts of the plant such as the ear (Prioul, 1995). Furthermore, the role of carbohydrate metabolism during leaf senescence is well known.

Sucrose synthase (SuS) and invertase. On chromosome 9 a clear coincidence was observed between the SuS locus and two QTLs detected in N^+, one affecting yield in 1995, the other affecting senescence. Three coincidences were observed with the invertase genes: on chromosome 2 with a QTL affecting kernel weight either at N^+ and N^-, on chromosome 5 with QTLs involved in vegetative development and grain yield, and on chromosome 10 with QTLs of vegetative development detected only in N^+. Therefore, the two invertase genes are also good candidate genes corresponding to QTLs for yield or kernel weight.

CONCLUSIONS

QTL studies tend to confirm that variation in NUtE was greater than variation in NUpE in N-. The opposite was observed in N+: QTLs detected in N- were related to NUtE traits and QTLs detected in N+ were more related to NUpE traits. However, it is difficult to conclude whether there are specific QTLs for either low or high N imput conditions. The same loci appear to be involved either at low or high N input, but they are differently expressed according to the level of N fertilization. Different genes were identified as candidates corresponding to QTLs for yield or its components. To validate these different candidate genes, further studies are necessary. Regardless of N fertilization, to have a good NUE for grain production, it appears essential to have genotypes with high N uptake efficiency at flowering, low kernel abortion just after fertilization, non-senescent leaves (associated to high NNI at flowering) and with efficient N translocation. All these different parameters are always associated to a high glutamine synthetase activity. Thus, to increase grain yield, it could be efficient to select for glutamine synthetase activity. For silage maize, post-flowering absorption may also be important to consider in order to have a sufficient protein content in the stover. Whether it is possible to have simultaneously during the filling period, N absorption, nitrate reduction and N remobilization is still unclear. However, for grain or for silage production we found that genetic variability exists for different traits related to NUE. It appears therefore possible to improve NUE at different levels of N fertilization. Nevertheless, genotypes adapted to high N input will not necessarily be adapted to low N input. In the future, with molecular markers of the detected QTLs or direct markers of the involved genes, marker-assisted selection can be developed to obtain maize varieties, either specifically or more generally adapted to various levels of N fertilization.

REFERENCES

Agrama, H.A.S., A.G. Zacharia, F.B. Said, and M. Tuinstra, 1999. Identification of quantitative trait loci for nitrogen use efficiency in maize. Molecular Breeding, 5: 187-195.

Balko, L.G. and W.A. Russell, 1980a. Effects of rates of nitrogen fertilizer on maize inbred lines and hybrid progeny. I. Prediction of yield response. Maydica, 25: 65-79.

Balko, L.G. and W.A. Russell, 1980b. Effects of rates of nitrogen fertilizer on maize inbred lines and hybrid progeny. II. Correlations among agronomic traits. Maydica, 25: 81-94.

Bänziger, M., F.J. Betran and H.R. Lafitte, 1997a. Efficiency of high-nitrogen selection environments for improving maize for low-nitrogen target environments. Crop Science, 37: 1103-1109.

Bänziger, M. and H.R. Lafitte, 1997b. Efficiency of secondary traits for improving maize for low-nitrogen target environments. Crop Science, 37: 1110-1117.

Beauchamp, E.G., L.W. Kannenberg and R.B. Hunter, 1976. Nitrogen accumulation and translocation in corn genotypes following silking. Agronomy Journal, 68: 418-422.

Below, F. E., 1995. Nitrogen metabolism and crop productivity. In Handbook of plant and crop physiology. Ed. Mohammad Pessarakli, Marcel Dekker Inc. New York, pp. 275-301.

Bertin, G., A. Panouillé and S. Rautou, 1976. Obtention de variétés de maïs prolifiques en épis, productives en grain et à large adaptation écologique. Ann. Amélior. Plant., 26: 387-418.

Bertin, P., 1997. Bases génétiques et physiologiques de la valorisation de la fumure azotée chez le maïs. Thèse, Univ. Paris Sud, Orsay, France.

Bertin, P. and A. Gallais, 2000. Physiological and genetic basis of nitrogen use efficiency in maize. I. Agrophysiological results. Maydica

Boyat, A. and P. Robin, 1977. Relations entre productivité, qualité du grain et activité nitrateréductase chez les céréales. Ann. Amélior. Plant., 27: 389-410.

Cacco, G., M. Saccomani and G. Ferrari, 1993. Changes in the uptake and assimilation efficiency for sulfate and nitrate in maize hybrids selected during the period 1930 through 1975. Physiol. Plant., 58: 171-174.

Castleberry, R. M., C. W. Crum and C. F. Krull, 1984. Genetic yield improvement of US maize cultivars under varying fertility and climatic environments. Crop Science, 24: 33-36.

Causse, M., S. Santoni, C. Damerval, A. Maurice, A. Charcosset, J. Deatrick and D. de Vienne, 1996. A composite map of expressed sequences in maize. Genome, 39: 418-432.

Causse, M., J. P. Rocher, A. M. Henry, A. Charcosset, J. L. Prioul and D. de Vienne, 1995. Genetic dissection of the relationship between carbon metabolism and early growth in maize, with emphasis on key-enzyme loci. Molecular Breeding, 1: 259-272.

Cheikh, N. and R. J. Jones, 1994. Disruption of maize kernel growth and development by heat stress. Role of cytokinin/abscisic acid balance. Plant Physiology, 106: 45-51.

Chourey, P. S. and O. E. Nelson, 1976. The enzymatic deficiency conditioned by the shrunken-1 mutations in maize. Biochem. Genet., 14: 1041-1055.

Czyzewicz, J. R. and F. E. Below, 1994. Genotypic variation for nitrogen uptake by maize kernels grown in vitro. Crop Science, 34: 1003-1008.

Di Fonzo, N., M. Motto, T. Maggiore, R. Sabatino and F. Salamini, 1982. N uptake, translocation and relationships among N related traits in maize as affected by genotype. Agronomie, 2: 789-796.

Edmeades, G.O., J. Bolanos, M. Hernandez and S. Bello, 1993. Causes of silking delay in a lowland tropical maize population. Crop. Science, 33: 1029-1035.

Feil, B., R. Thiraporn and P. Stamp, 1993. In vitro nitrate reductase activity of laboratory grown seedling as an indirect selection criteria in maize. Crop Science, 33: 1280-1286.

Gan, S. and R. M. Amasino, 1995. Inhibition of leaf senescence by autoregulated production of cytokinin. Science, 270: 1986-1988.

Giroux, M. J., J. Shaw, G. Barry, B. G. Cobb, T. Greene, T. Okita and L. C. Hannah, 1996. A single gene mutation that increases maize seed weight. Proc. Natl. Acad. Science, 93: 5824-

Goldman, I. L., T. R. Rocheford and J. W. Dudley, 1993. Quantitative loci influencing protein and starch concentration in the Illinois long term selection maize strain. Theoretical and Applied Genetics, 87: 217-224.

Hébert, Y., Y. Barrière and J. C. Bertholleau, 1992. Root lodging resistance in forage maize : genetic variability of root system and aerial part. Maydica, 37: 173-183.

Jackson, W. A., W. L. Pau, R. H. Moll and E. J. Kamprath, 1986. Uptake, translocation and reduction of nitrate. In. C.A. Neyra Ed. "Biochemical Basis of Plant Breeding". C.R.C. Press. Florida, pp. 73-108.

Khavkin and E. Coe, 1997. Mapped genomic locations for developmental functions andQTLs reflect concerted groups in maize (Zea mays L.). Theoretical and Applied Genetics, 95: 343-352.

Lafitte, H. R. and G. O. Edmeades, 1994. Improvement for tolerance to low soil nitrogen in tropical maize. II. Grain yield, biomass production, and N accumulation. Fields Crop Research, 39: 15-25.

Lafitte, H. R. and G. O. Edmeades, 1995. Association between traits in tropical maize inbred lines and their hybrids under high and low soil nitrogen. Maydica, 40: 259-267.

Landbeck, M. V., 1995. Untersuchungen zur genetischen verbesserung der anbaueigung von körnermais unter produktionsbedingungen mit verringerter sticksoffversorgung. Dissertation, Univ. Hohenheim, 109 pp.

Lemaire, G. and F. Gastal, 1997. N uptake and distribution in plant canopies. In. "Diagnosis ofthe nitrogen status in crops". G. Lemaire, Ed. Springer. Verlag, Berlin-Heidlberg, 3-43.

Lemcoff, J.H. and R.S. Loomis, 1986. Nitrogen influences in yield determination in maize. Crop Science, 26: 1817-1022.

Ma, B. L. and L. M. Dwyer, 1998. Nitrogen uptake and use in two contrasting maize hybrids differing in leaf senescence. Plant and Soil, 199: 283-291.

Masclaux, C., M. H. Valadier, N. Brugière, J. F. Morot-Gaudry and B. Hirel, 2000. Characterization ofthe sink/source transition in tobacco (Nicotiana tabacum L.) shoots in relation to nitrogen management and leaf senescence. Planta (In press).

McCullough, P. Girardin, M. Mihajlovic, A. Aguilera and M. Tollenaar, 1994. Influence of N supply on development and dry-matter accumultion of an old and a new maize hybrid. Canadian Journal of Plant Science, 74: 471-477.

Moll, R. H., E. J. Kamprath and W. A. Jackson, 1987. Development of nitrogen efficient prolific hybrids of maize. Crop Science 27: 181-186.

Pollmer, W.G., D. Eberhard, D. Klein and B.S. Dhillon. 1979. Genetic control of nitrogen uptake and translocation in maize. Crop Science 19: pp. 82-85.

Presterl, T., G. Seitz, M. Landbeck and H. H. Geiger, 1996. Breeding strategies for the improvement of nitrogen efficiency of European maize under low input conditions. In "Genetics, Biotechnology and Breeding of Maize and Sorghum", Proceedings XVII Conference Eucarpia "Section Maize and Sorghum", Ed. A.S. Tsaftaris, 59-64.

Prioul, J. L., 1995. Corn: distribution of photoassimilates and source-sink relationship. In: Photoassimilates Distribution in Plants and Crops. Ed. E. Zankski, A.A. Schahher, I.N.C. Marcel Dekker, New York, 905 pp.

Reed, A. J., F. E. Below and R. H. Hageman, 1980. Grain protein accumulation and the relationship between leaf nitrate reductase and protease activities during grain development in maize. I. Variation between genotypes. Plant Physiology, 66: 164-170.

Reed, A. J., G. W. Singletary, J. R. Schussler, D. R. Williamson and A. L. Christy, 1988. Shading effects on dry matter and nitrogen partitioning, kernel number, and yield of maize. Crop Science

Rizzi, E., C. Balconi, L. Nembrini, F. M. Stefanini, F. Coppolino and M. Motto, 1993. Genetic variation and relationships among N-related traits in maize. Maydica, 38: 23-30.

Russell, W. A., 1984. Further studies on the response of maize inbred lines to N fertilizer. Maydica, 29: 141-150.

Russell, W. A., 1985. Comparison of the hybrid performance in maize inbred lines developed from the original and improved cycles of BSSS. Maydica, 30: 407-419.

Sherrard, J. H., R. J. Lambert, F. E. Below, R. T. Durand, M. J. Messmer, M. R. Willman, C. S. Winkels and R. H. Hageman, 1986. Use of physiological traits, especially those of nitrogen metabolism for selection in maize. In "Biochemical basis of plant breeding". Vol. II. Nitrogen metabolism. Ed. C.A. Neyra, CRC Press, Florida. 109-130.

Uhart, S. A. and F. H. Andrade, 1995. Nitrogen deficiency in maize. II. Carbon-nitrogen interaction effects on kernel number and grain yield. Crop Science, 35: 1384-1389.

N-Use Efficiency
Offered papers

N - leaching from maize plots in comparison with leaching from grassland plots

P. RAMSPACHER

Joanneum Research, Institute of Hydrogeology and Geothermics (IHG), Elisabethstraße 16, A-8010 Graz, Austria

S U M M A R Y

In order to determine differences in nitrate leaching between grassland and maize, a series of percolation water, sampled by use of suction cups, was analysed according hydrochemical composition. Nitrate load calculations were carried out based on percolation water quantities registrated at lysimeters, as well as on nitrate concentrations from percolation water. Because of fertilizing maize in a single distribution in springtime, there was a uniform nitrate peak registered in June and July causing very high leaching rates during that time and also due to precipitation events during that period. Additionally, intensive leaching from maize as well as from grassland could be observed in early springtime as a result of washing-out of nitrate during the snow-melting season, which was accumulated in the soil from mineralisation processes. Under certain circumstances in maize trials NO_3-leaching rates up to 50% of N fertilization could be registered. At grassland trials N leaching was much less compared to maize trials. Results from grassland show that leaching did not exceed 2.5% of total N distributed to the different plots.

Keywords: grassland, maize, nitrate leaching

I N T R O D U C T I O N

Within the project "Ammonium thiosulphate (ATS) as an environmentally friendly tool for reducing N inputs" (Contract number: N. AIR – CT94 – 1953) field trials (1995-1997) were carried out in order to study the inhibiting effect of ATS on the balance of nitrogen. Different field experiments were established comparing conditions in maize monoculture with conditions in permanent grassland. This paper includes results from this project regarding nitrate leaching from maize and grassland, applying different fertilizers (SL=slurry, SMF=solid mineral fertilizer) at different application rates.
Investigation sites:
Gumpenstein (northern part of Styria): permanent grassland
Wagna (southern part of Styria): maize monoculture

MATERIALS AND METHODS

In order to calculate nitrate leaching quantities, percolation water was sampled by use of ceramic suction cups from different depths. Percolation water sampling during the vegetation period was carried out at intervals of about one week. Water samples were analysed according to hydrochemical composition. Nitrate load calculations were carried out based on percolation water quantities registered at nearby lysimeters, as well as on nitrate concentrations from percolation water.

Sampling depth at grassland trials: 0.5 m

Sampling depth at maize trials: 0.7 m

Meteorological conditions (figs. 1 and 2)

Wagna:	1996: 964 mm	105% of mean long term value
	1997: 685 mm	75% of mean long term value
Gumpenstein:	1996: 1137 mm	112% of mean long term value
	1997: 1354 mm	134% of mean long term value

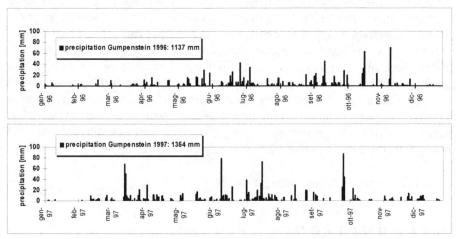

FIGURE 1. GUMPENSTEIN – DAILY AMOUNT OF PRECIPITATION (1996 – 1997).

RESULTS

N leaching mainly occurs as nitrate leaching depending on a number of different factors as for example soil characteristics, meteorological conditions, quantity of fertilizer, fertilizer application procedure as well as mineralisation processes in the soil. Because of fertilizing maize in a single distribution in springtime, there was a uniform nitrate peak registered in June and July causing very high leaching rates during that time and also due to precipitation events during that period. As can be seen from cumulation curves in Fig.3, nitrate leaching from maize plots in 1997 was much less than in 1996. This result

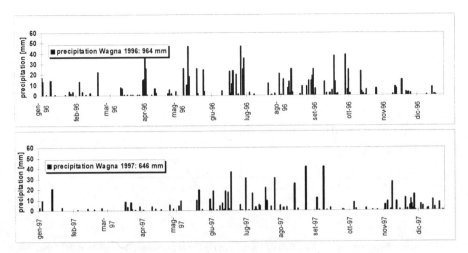

FIGURE 2. WAGNA - DAILY AMOUNT OF PRECIPITATION (1996 – 1997).

can be explained by the fact, that in 1997 there was much less precipitation than in 1996 available, causing less leaching. Intensive leaching from maize could be observed in early springtime before distribution of fertilizer as a result from washing out nitrate during snow-melting season, which was accumulated in the soil from mineralisation processes. Under certain circumstances at maize trials NO_3-leaching rates up to 50% of N fertilization were registered (Table 1).

TABLE 1. MAIZE TRIALS WAGNA - PRECIPITATION, GROUNDWATER RECHARGE AND CALCULATED NO_3- LOADS FROM SELECTED PLOTS.

	Precipitation (mm)	Tot. Groundwater Recharge (mm)	Recharge % of Prec.	Recharge Feb. - Oct. (mm)	Recharge Feb. - Oct. % of Tot. Rech.
1996	964	491	52	318	65
1997	685	172	25	112	65
NO3 - load (kg/ha) from the observation period Feb. - Oct.								
	contr. plot + ATS	contr. plot - ATS	SL 90 kg + ATS	SL 90 kg - ATS	SMF 210 kg + ATS	SMF 210 kg - ATS	SL 150 kg - ATS	SMF 150 kg + ATS
1996	115	83	37	199	494	372	148	232
1997	19	13	6	34	63	32	83	68
N - leaching in % of total N applied								
1996	-	-	9	50	50	40	22	35
1997	-	-	1,5	9	7	3,5	12	10

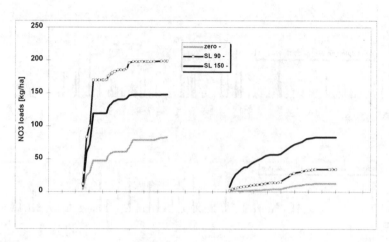

FIGURE 3. MAIZE TRIAL WAGNA, CUMULATION CURVES – NITRATE LEACHING FROM SLURRY PLOTS 1996/1997.

Meteorological conditions for the grassland trials were completely different to maize trials. In fact with intensive rainfall in 1997 at these trials nitrate leaching in 1997 was much higher than in 1996. As already registered at maize trials, in early springtime, increasing nitrate leaching could be observed before fertilization due to increased mineralization processes in the soil as well as due increasing infiltration caused by snow-melting water recharge. In the grassland trials fertilized with slurry, N leaching was much less compared to maize trials (Fig.4).

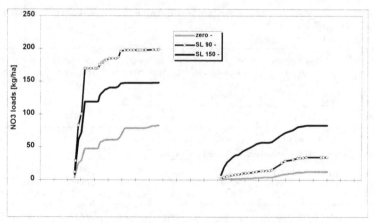

FIGURE 4. GRASSLAND TRIAL GUMPENSTEIN, CUMULATION CURVES – NITRATE LEACHING FROM SLURRY PLOTS 1996/1997.

Results from grassland show, that leaching did not exceed 2,5% of total N distributed to the different plots. At a percentage of 75% of all grassland trials, nitrate leaching was less than 1% compared to the quantity of N fertilized. As Table 2 is showing, nitrate leaching also is depending on the N source applied. In maize trials as well as in grassland trials increasing rates of leaching could be observed after applying solid mineral fertilizer. Fertilizing procedure in grassland (3 distributions) additionally was effecting lower leaching rates in comparison with leaching from arable land, which was fertilized in only one distribution.

TABLE 2. NO$_3$- LOADS FROM SELECTED PLOTS COMPARING MAIZE TRIALS WITH GRASSLAND TRIALS.

	Annual NO$_3$-load [kg/ha]			
	Maize SL90 +ATS	Maize SL90 -ATS	Grassl. SL90 +ATS	Grassl. SL90 -ATS
1996	36.8	198.6	4.4.	5.2
1997	14.8	92.3	6.6.	2.3
	Maize SMF210 +ATS	Maize SMF210-ATS	Grassl.SMF210 +ATS	Grassl.SMF210-ATS
1996	491.1	371.8	8.2	8.4
1997	190.7	86.5	22.7	16.5

REFERENCES

Final consolidated report, „Ammonium thiosulphate (ATS) as an environmentally friendly tool for reducing N inputs" (Contract number: N. AIR – CT94 – 1953), 01 Jan.1995 – 30 Jun. 1998.

Protection of ground water in three water catchment areas

H. S. OESTERGAARD

The Danish Agricultural Advisory Centre The National Department of Plant Production Udkaersvej 15, Skejby, DK-8200 Aarhus N

SUMMARY

The aim of the project is to demonstrate how the Environmental Protection Plan can be applied to reduce nitrate leaching in nitrate-sensitive areas.

On the basis of cultivation data for 1998 and 1999 the leaching of nitrate and the economic consequence have been calculated for the present farming methods as well as two alternative cultivation systems.

The results of the model calculations show that given the present land use the average nitrate concentrations are 18, 12 and 17 mg N litre^{-1} in the 3 catchment areas. If alternative A is applied, calculations show that nitrate leaching is reduced to 14, 10, and 13 mg NO_3-N litre^{-1}. Grass combined with reduced nitrogen fertilization (alternative B) will reduce nitrate leaching to 6, 5, and 7 mg NO_3-N litre^{-1}.

The economic consequences of the yield reductions are determined by the price of grain, the production costs, and the possibilities of subsidies. The calculations show that from an economic view a better result will be obtained by replacing the present cultivation method with alternatives A and B. It is important that the results only show what is happening in the field, and not how the gross margin is changed and the effect on the prices of property, etc.

Keywords: economy, environmental protection, nitrate leaching

INTRODUCTION

In certain parts of the country ground water is particularly sensitive to nitrate leaching from the root zone. In such areas it may be necessary to introduce extraordinary changes in the agricultural practice to reach a reduction in the concentration of nitrate in the run-off water from the root zone to the ground water. In order to reach such a reduction it is necessary to be able to calculate both the leaching and the economic consequences of changes in agricultural practice.

Purpose

The purpose of the project is to demonstrate how the Environmental Protection Plan can be applied to secure groundwater quality and to demonstrate the application of the plan in practice.

MATERIALS AND METHODS

The Department of Plant Production and the plant production centres in Aalborg and on Djursland have carried out a project in three nitrate-sensitive water catchment areas.

Calculation of nitrate leaching

The calculation of nitrate leaching is based on the model Simmelsgaard II (Simmelsgaard, S.E., 1997). The model is a so-called empiric type of model based on empirically found correlations between measured leaching results and cultivation conditions.

The model includes the importance of soil type, run-off areas, crop type, and amount of nitrogen applied. Leaching is calculated as follows:

$$\text{EKSP}(1{,}136 - 0{,}0628 \times \text{CLAY PCT.} + 0{,}00565 \times \text{N-level} + \text{Crop value}) \times \text{Percolation}^{0.416}$$

where the N-amount is the average of N applied in the rotation (fertilizer + farmyard manure), the loam percentage is from the 0-25 layer, and the crop value is determined by the combination of crop and autumn growth. The model has been modified by the Department of Plant Production in order to apply it in the project and make it possible to calculate the consequences of time of sowing, soil treatment, and grazing.

Economic calculations

The purpose of the economy model is to be able to estimate the economic consequences that changes in the agricultural practices can cause, especially the economic consequences of changes in crop distribution, use of cover crops, as well as reduction of nitrogen amounts. It is important to note that only changes in income from field production are calculated. Especially on cattle farms changes in the field can have an effect on the income in the cowshed which is often much higher than in the field. When considerable changes are made in the field, such as changes of feed production, it is important to assess the effects derived in the cowshed. In the same way only changes in gross margin of cultivation is calculated without taking into consideration if the value of land or property changes by applying the 5-year arrangements where farmers are committed to a certain given agricultural practice.

RESULTS

On the basis of cultivation data for 1998 for each farm the plant production advisers have calculated the leaching of nitrate for the present farm practice as well as drafting two action plans with the purpose of reducing leaching primarily by applying the Environmental Protection Plan. For each alternative the economic result is compared with the present practice.

Nitrate leaching

Table 1 shows the result of the leaching calculations for the three areas. The result shows an estimate of nitrate leaching of about 70 kg N ha^{-1} for North Jutland A and Djursland, and only 44 kg N ha^{-1} for North Jutland B. North Jutland A is primarily a cattle area, Djursland is primarily dominated by pig farms, while North Jutland B is not a typical area, as most of the area is fallow land. The nitrate concentration in the run-off water varies in the calculations from 14 to 22 mg NO_3-N litre^{-1}. In alternative A as well as alternative B leaching is reduced considerably. This means that according to the model calculations the concentrations in the run-off water vary from only 8 to12 mg NO_3-N litre^{-1} in alternative B.

TABLE 1. KEY FIGURES FOR NITROGEN SUPPLY AND NITRATE LEACHING.

Area	N supply					N surplus	NO₃ leaching	NO₃ concentration
	Mineral fertilizer kg N ha^{-1}	Animal manure kg N ha^{-1}	Manure, grazing kg N ha^{-1}	N2-fix. and dep. kg N ha^{-1}	Supply tot. kg N ha^{-1}	kg N ha^{-1}	kg N ha^{-1}	mg N l^{-1}
North Jutland A, 283 ha								
Present practice	101	111	17	38	267	108	69	20
Alternative A	86	87	9	28	211	73	52	15
Alternative B	52	87	9	29	177	52	32	9
North Jutland B, 133 ha								
Present practice	90	18	2	30	141	53	44	14
Alternative A	92	18	3	19	132	54	36	12
Alternative B	55	18	3	19	95	35	24	8
Djursland, 433 ha								
Present practice	90	94	0	27	211	95	70	22
Alternative A	67	95	0	30	193	79	48	16
Alternative B	63	88	0	33	183	71	37	12

The way to reduce nitrogen leaching in North Jutland A has primarily been to reduce the application of nitrogen by 40 percent on part of the area, while on Djursland the means was an increase of the area with grass. While the amount of nitrogen in fertilizer has decreased, the amount of animal manure is almost the same in the two alternatives as in the present practice. Calculations show that it is possible to reduce nitrogen leaching to a low level although almost the same amount of manure has been spread.

Economic calculations

The economic calculations of the project only express the effects of changes in cultivation practice, and calculations have only been made on the changes in gross margin.

In general, these calculations show (Table 2) that a minor advantage in managerial economy has been obtained by changing the practice as suggested in the two alternatives. The difference in income is up to 500 DKK ha⁻¹.

Especially on cattle farms, it must be taken into consideration that the gross margin represents only the income in the field. If the changes of the production in the field effects the income in the stable, e.g. milk yield, the economical calculations are irrelevant, as the gross margin in the cowshed is far higher than in the field. Changes in the peak period by changing from winter crops to spring crops may have a negative effect on the working rhythm in the cowshed.

TABLE 2. KEY FIGURES FOR THE ECONOMIC CONSEQUENCES OF DIFFERENT AGRICULTURAL PRACTICES IN THE 3 AREAS.

	Gross yield $DKK\ ha^{-1}$	Unit costs $DKK\ ha^{-1}$	Costs for machinery $DKK\ ha^{-1}$	Gross margin $DKK\ ha^{-1}$
North Jutland A, 283 ha				
Present practice	9118	2983	3100	3035
Alternative A	8719	2605	3020	3094
Alternative B	8684	2469	2933	3282
North Jutland B, 133 ha				
Present practice	5969	1331	2417	2221
Alternative A	6063	1301	2342	2420
Alternative B	5984	1151	2116	2716
Djursland, 433 ha				
Present practice	6821	1704	3212	1905
Alternative A	7165	1641	3284	2240
Alternative B	7093	1577	3060	2455

CONCLUSION

The project shows that it is possible to reduce nitrogen leaching in the three areas considerably even though animal production is maintained. In order to reduce leaching to under 11 mg NO_3-N litre⁻¹ water in the run-off groundwater the cultivation in the field must be changed radically with almost 100 percent autumn growth with grass or crops undersown with grass, and nitrogen application must be reduced.

The project proves it is possible to apply the measures of the Environmental Protection Plan with reduced N application and crops undersown with ryegrass for this purpose. However, the tools of the Environmental Protection Plan with perennial grass, 0 N and perennial grass, and 80 N have not been applied. The tools used have been chosen from estimates by local advisers. The tools of the Environmental Protection Plan to prolong the period of cultivation of grasslands would however be effective in reducing nitrogen leaching on cattle farms.

The Environmental Protection Plan with reduced application of nitrogen demands that the norms for the nitrogen requirement of crops and the demanded utilization of nitrogen in livestock manure makes it possible that all animal manure can be spread on the fields of the property. In recent years the norms have been reduced and as a result of the Water Environmental Plan II the norms are reduced by 10% from 1999, and at the same time the demanded utilization percentage for animal manure has increased. This makes it difficult to apply the measures of the Environmental Protection Plan with reduced nitrogen application on farms with a livestock intensity matching the harmonization demands. The project also shows that leaching may be affected by smaller changes in cultivation methods, such as soil treatment, time of sowing, and grazing intensity in the autumn period.

The economic consistency calculations of the alternatives in comparison with the present practice show that on average a slight increase has been obtained in the gross margin of both alternatives seen as an average of the farms in the three water catchment areas. However, this is only the case, if the calculations used are not based on derived negative economic consequences of other operations on the farm. Increases of grain price and other price relations may change the calculations considerably. The economic calculations do not take into consideration how the introduction of the 5-year measures of the Environmental Protection Plan will effect the prices of land and property.

REFERENCES

Simmelsgaard, S.E., 1997. Soil Use and Management, Vol. 13, 1-8.

Evaluation of the data set of the Hungarian N-fertilization field trials with winter wheat, 1960-1995

P. CSATHÓ

Research Institute for Soil Science and Agricultual Chemistry, Hungarian Academy of Sciences, H-1022 Budapest, Herman O. u. 15, Hungary

SUMMARY

As a first attempt, the data set of N fertilization trials with winter wheat has been established. Altogether 66 long-term field trials were found in the literature, with several hundred individual trials. The 1 to 10 years of the long-term field trials were taken into the data set, and the winter wheat yields were averaged within that period. Among the N treatments, the one providing the maximum economic yield (~95% of maximum yields) was taken into account. The correlation between soil organic matter (OM) values and responses to N was also investigated. The main findings are considered as basics for a new, environmentally friendly, sustainable N fertilizer recommendation system. Evaluating the results of the Hungarian 1 to 10 years-old field nitrogen trials with winter wheat, there were drawn conclusions as follows: 1) As a result of N application, surpluses in winter wheat were between 0.8 to 1.5 t ha^{-1}. At lower soil OM contents the surpluses were higher, and the amount of N needed for maximum economic yields were also higher. 2) The soil OM values indicated the natural N- supplying power of the different soils moderately. 3) Connection between soil OM content of N-control (PK) plots and the responses to N, expressed in relative yields (100Yield in PK plot/Yield in NPK plot,%) could be described by a Mitscherlich-like equation, modified by Bray (1944): / Y' = 100 (1-10^{-cx}) /, where x = soil OM content in the N-control (PK) plots; Y' = relative yield in the trials, having "x" soil OM contents in the N-control plots; and c = proportionally constant (Mitscherlich's "working factor").

Keywords: field trials, nitrogen, responses to N, soil OM, winter wheat

INTRODUCTION

In Hungarian agriculture winter wheat is one of the two most important crops in Hungary. For that reason the synthesis of the national field trial series of winter wheat is especially important.

Soil organic matter content and turnover both have a special role from either agronomic or environmental points of view (Kádár, 1992; Németh, 1996; Németh *et al.,* 1997-98; Várallyay *et al.,* 1980). As a first attempt, the data set of N fertilization trials with wheat has been established.

MATERIALS AND METHODS

The N supply of the control plots of the Hungarian field trials was estimated by the organic matter (OM) content, according to Tyurin (1951).

A database of the results of 1- to 10- year old Hungarian nitrogen fertilization field trials found in literature was compiled. In all trials by- products were removed from the fields. Soil characteristic data of PK (N-control) treatments, grain yield data of PK and also PK + N treatments giving maximum economic yields (about 95% of the maximum yields) were collected. The results were classified according to the soil OM groups.

RESULTS AND DISCUSSION

The correlation between soil OM content and responses to N application was examined on the data set of Hungarian field trials with winter wheat, carried out between 1960 and 1995 (Table 1).

TABLE 1. CORRELATION BETWEEN SOIL OM CONTENT AND RESPONSES TO N APPLICATION IN HUNGARIAN FIELD TRIALS WITH WINTER WHEAT, SET UP BETWEEN 1960 AND 1995.

Soil organic matter (OM) groups,%	Number of trials (n)	K_A*	Soil organic matter (OM) content,%	N dose, kg ha^{-1}**	Grain yield on PK plots (N-control)	Relative yield,% (PK/NPK)	Surplus, t ha^{-1} (NPK-PK)
< 1.0	4	28	0.74	143	1.88	57	1.50
1.01-2.00	19	38	1.56	105	2.26	63	1.34
2.01-3.00	22	43	2.73	119	3.02	82	0.78
3.01-4.00	17	45	3.61	86	2.91	76	0.79
> 4.01	4	47	4.48	79	3.78	81	0.89
Mean (Total)	66	41	2.60	105	2.75	74	0.99

* upper limit of plasticity, according to Arany (similar to the US plasticity index); ** The N amount needed for maximum economic yield (~ 95% of maximum yield)

Evaluating the results of the Hungarian 1- to 10-year-old field nitrogen trials with winter wheat, conclusions were drawn as follows: 1) As a result of N application, surplusses in winter wheat grain yields were between 0.8 to 1.5 t ha^{-1} (Table 1). 2) The soil OM values indicated the natural N-supplying power of the different soils quite adequately, i.e. on soils with higher OM contents responses of wheat to N application were diminished. 3)As an effect of increasing soil OM content, the amount of N needed for maximum economic yields (~ 0.95 x maximum yields) of winter wheat also diminished significantly.

The connection between the OM content of the N-control (PK) plots and the responses to N, expressed in relative yields (100 Yield in PK plot/ Yield in NPK plot, %) could be described by a Mitscherlich-like equation, modified by Bray (1944): / Y' = 100 (1-10^{-cx}) / , where x = OM content in the N-control (PK) plots; Y' = relative yield in the trials, having "x" OM contents in the N-control plots; and c = proportionally constant (Mitscherlich's "working factor"). The value of "c" was 0.27528 in the data set of Hungarian wheat field N trials.

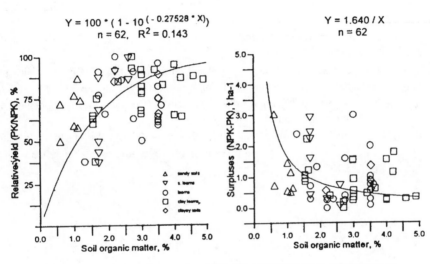

FIGURE 1. CORRELATION BETWEEN SOIL OM CONTENTS AND RESPONSES TO N APPLICATION IN HUNGARIAN FIELD TRIALS WITH WINTER WHEAT, 1960-1995.

CONCLUSIONS

The new N supply categories for Hungarian soils, expressed in OM contents, are sometimes lower than those in former fertilizer advisory systems (Csathó, et al., 1998, 1998a). Using the new OM content categories can help in establishing a new, environmentally friendly N fertilizer advisory system.

ACKNOWLEDGEMENTS

This research was financially supported by the Hungarian National Scientific Research Fund (OTKA) under Grant No. T30180.

REFERENCES

Csathó, P., T. Árendás and T. Németh, 1998. New, environmentally friendly fertiliser advisory system, based on the data set of the Hungarian long-term field trials set up between 1960 and 1995. Communications in Soil Science and Plant Analysis, 29: 2161-2174.

Csathó, P., T. Árendás and T. Németh, 1998a. New, environmentally friendly fertilizer recommendation system for Hungary. In: Codes for good agricultural practice and balanced fertilization. Proc. Int. Symp. CIEC, PFS and Workshop IMPHOS, IPI, Pulawy, Poland. (Ed.: Fotyma, M.) Bibliotheca Fragmenta Agronomica, 3 : 225-230.

Kádár, I., 1992. Principles and methods of plant nutrition. (In Hungarian). RISSAC - Akaprint. Budapest. 398 pp.

Németh, T., 1996. Organic matter and nitrogen turnover of soils. (In Hungarian). RISSAC – Alfaprint. 392 pp.

Németh, T., G. J. Kovács and I. Kádár, 1987-1988. Examination of NO_3., SO_4^{2-} and salt leaching in a long-term field trial with fertilizers. (In Hungarian). Agrokémia és Talajtan, 36-37: 109-126.

Tyurin, I. V., 1951. K metodike analiza dlja szravnitelnogo izucsenija szosztava pocsvennogo gumusza. Trudü Pocsvennogo Instituta. A. N. Sz. Sz. Sz. R.

Várallyay, G., I. Szücs, A. Murányi, K. Rajkai and P. Zilahy, 1980. Map of soil factors determining the agroecological potential of Hungary II (in Hungarian). Agrokémia és Talajtan, 29: 35-76.

Reed canarygrass fertilised with several rates of N

A. PARTALA[1], T. MELA[1] AND C. ERIKSSON[2]

Agricultural Research Centre of Finland (MTT)
[1] Plant Production Research, Crops and Soil
[2] Data and Information Services
FIN-31600 Jokioinen, Finland

SUMMARY

Reed canarygrass (*Phalaris arundinacea L.*) is harvested for bioenergy and for paper industry in May as a dead, dry and nutrient-poor material. The study was carried out to determine the influence of N rate on dry matter (DM) yield, N offtake and soil mineral N of reed canarygrass (RCG) in a delayed harvest system. The study was conducted in both a heavy clay soil and in an organic soil with four annual nitrogen fertiliser rates (0, 50, 100 and 150 N kg ha^{-1}). On the three years study, one year after the first fertiliser application the mean DM yield was 5930 kg ha^{-1} in clay soil and 6630 kg ha^{-1} in organic soil and there were no differences between fertiliser rates. The amount of nitrogen removed with the harvested DM yield was 30 kg ha^{-1} in clay soil and 47 kg ha^{-1} in organic soil. The second and third fertiliser application increased the DM yield approximately 1000 kg ha^{-1} per each nitrogen increment of 50 kg ha^{-1} in clay soil. In contrast, in the organic soil the mean DM yield was not dependant on the fertiliser rate, because of the higher nitrogen mineralisation rate than in the clay soil. Three years after the first N application the mineral N content of organic soil (0-25 cm) was a maximum 13 kg ha^{-1} higher than without N fertilisation. The soil mineral N increase without DM yield increase obviously means both an economic and an environmental risk. The results showed that the DM yield of RCG responded strongly with the high rates of N fertiliser in clay soil. When RCG is grown in organic soil with high nitrogen mineralisation rate both the need for N fertilisation and the fertilisation costs are decreased.

Keywords: bioenergy, biomass, N fertilisation, Phalaris arundinacea L.

INTRODUCTION

The best time to harvest reed canarygrass for bioenergy and for paper industry could be May. In the delayed-harvest system both the quality and economic demands for the produced biomass are reached as the drying of the nutrient-poor grass is unnecessary as well as the undesirable effects of mineral substances on pulp and combustion processes are avoided (Mela *et al.*, 1994). Moreover the yield can remain fairly constant for at least 6 years under delayed harvest without the need for re-establishment (Pahkala and Pihala, 2000). Despite the advantages noticed following the new harvesting regime, few studies have been reported for reaching accurate fertiliser recommendations in long-term cultivation. Fertiliser rate of 200 kg ha[-1] has been observed to be economically too high in the delayed harvest of RCG (Pahkala and Pihala, 2000; Landström *et al.*, 1996).

The study was carried out to determine the soil and crop factors influencing the N fertiliser demand of reed canarygrass ley in the delayed harvest system.

MATERIALS AND METHODS

Field experiments

Two field experiments were carried out at Jokioinen, southwestern Finland between May 1995 and May 1998, one in a heavy clay and the other in an organic soil. The heavy clay topsoil, 0-25 cm, contained about 70% clay, 0.32% N, 3.9% org. C and had a pH(H_2O) of 5.9. The organic soil, 0-25 cm, contained about 74% clay in its mineral fraction, 1.14% N, 17.9% org. C and had a pH (H_2O) of 5.3. Besides soil types, age and variety of reed canary grass were different in the experiments. Reed canary grass was sown in clay soil in 1992 (cv. Venture) and in organic soil (cv. Palaton) in 1994.

Four rates of fertiliser (0, 50, 100 and 150 kg N ha[-1]) were given annually (1995-1997) to the plots (15m²) after the harvesting in May. The crop was harvested in May (1996-1998) with a harvest machine (Haldrup forage plot harvester). The DM yield and total N of shoot material harvested in May 1996 and 1998 were measured. After the harvest the soil samples, composing of about 16 sub-samples, were taken for mineral N measurements to the depth of 25 cm from each plot. Inorganic forms of N were extracted from the soil with 2M potassium chloride (KCl) and determined colorimetrically with a Skalar Autoanalyzer.

Statistical methods

In field experiments of clay and organic soil the experimental design was a randomized complete block design, where four nitrogen fertiliser rates were randomized to four plots within each block separately. Furthermore, repeated measurements were made from each plot in two or three years. In the statistical analyses the data of the two field experiments were combined. When analysing dry matter yield, soil mineral N and N offtake the following mixed model was used:

$$Y_{ijkl} = \mu + E_i + b_{j(i)} + F_k + EF_{ik} + e_{ijk} + S_l + ES_{il} + f_{ijl} + FS_{kl} + EFS_{ikl} + g_{ijkl}$$

where Y_{ijkl} is the response for experiment i, block j, fertiliser rate k and year l; μ is the overall mean; b is the random block effect; E, F and S are the fixed effects of experiment, fertiliser and year, respectively; EF, ES and FS are the two-factor interactions of the fixed effects and EFS is the three-factor interaction; e, f and g are the random error terms. The random variables $b_{j(i)}$, e_{ijk}, f_{ijl} and g_{ijkl} are assumed independent and normally distributed with zero means and variances σ^2_b, σ^2_e, σ^2_f and σ^2_g, respectively. The response variable N offtake was distributed non-normally and therefore a logarithmic transformation was made to its values prior to analysis. Furthermore, N offtake was measured in two years and the error vectors $g_{ijk} = (g_{ijk1}, g_{ijk2})$ were assumed independent and multivariate normal with zero means and unstructured covariance matrices Σ. In the analysis of yield measured in three years a corresponding distributional assumption for $g_{ijk} = (g_{ijk1}, g_{ijk2}, g_{ijk3})$ was employed. The models were fitted by using the residual maximum likelihood (REML) estimation method. The degrees of freedom were approximated by a Satterthwaite procedure (Verbeke et al., 1997). Accordances of the data with the distributional assumptions of the models were checked by graphic plots. The residuals were checked for normality using box plot (Tukey, 1977). In addition, the residuals were plotted against the fitted values. Planned comparisons between means were made by two-sided t-type tests or 95% confidence intervals (95% CI). If the 95% CI does not include zero the difference between means is statistically significant at the 5% level. In the analyses the MIXED (Littell et al., 1996), UNIVARIATE and PLOT procedures (SAS, 1990) of the SAS/STAT software were used.

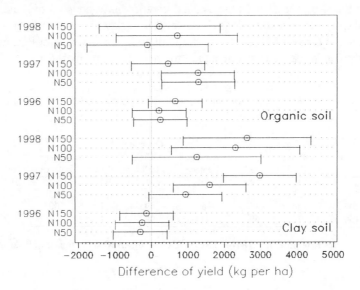

FIGURE 1. DIFFERENCES OF MEAN DM YIELDS AND 95% CONFIDENCE INTERVALS (KG HA⁻¹) IN CLAY AND ORGANIC SOIL IN SPRING HARVEST 1996-98. THE DM YIELD IN EACH N FERTILISER RATE (N50 = 50 KG HA⁻¹, N100 = 100 KG HA⁻¹ AND N150 = 150 KG HA⁻¹) DIFFERS SIGNIFICANTLY (P<0.05) FROM THE DM YIELD FROM THE UNFERTILISED RCG, IF THE CONFIDENCE INTERVAL IS NOT CROSSING THE ZERO LINE IN X-AXES.

RESULTS AND DISCUSSION

Dry matter yield and N offtake

In May 1996 one year after the first fertiliser application the mean DM yield was 5,930 kg ha[-1] in clay soil and 6,630 kg ha[-1] in organic soil and indicated no differences between fertiliser rates. The nitrogen removed from the field with the harvested yield was in clay soil 30 kg ha[-1] and in organic soil 47 kg ha[-1]. In May 1997 the DM yield with the two highest fertiliser rates was significantly higher than without fertilisation in clay soil, while in the organic soil there was not any differences (Fig. 1). Because the values of crop N concentrationsare missing from May 1997, the N offtakes could not be calculated. The third DM yield in May 1998 indicated in clay soil the dependence on the fertiliser rate; with the two highest fertiliser rates the yield as well as the N-offtake was higher than without fertilisation. The third yield of RCG without fertilisation (3,560 kg ha[-1]) was only about 57% of that received with N apply of 150 kg ha[-1] (6,200 kg ha[-1]). Whereas in organic soil the third DM yield was not dependent on the fertiliser rate, being between 6,200 and 7,000 kg ha[-1]. Despite the DM yield respond to the fertiliser rate was different in clay and organic soil, the N-offtakes responded in a similar way; N-offtakes were significantly higher with the two highest fertiliser rates compared to the unfertilised RCG in both soil types. Despite this the N removed with the yield was much higher in organic soil (varied from 59 to 91 kg ha[-1]) than in clay soil (varied from 18 to 40 kg ha[-1]) (Table 1). Therefore the N-balance, calculated as the difference between input of N as a fertiliser and offtake of N as a harvested yield, was higher in clay soil at each fertiliser rate. In organic soil the excess of N seemed to accumulate N to the shoots of RCG, which can have a negative influence to the quality of the harvested raw material.

TABLE 1. N-OFFTAKES WITH THE HARVESTED CROP AND AVERAGE N-BALANCE CALCULATED AS THE DIFFERENCE BETWEEN INPUT AS A FERTILISER AND OFFTAKE AS A DM YIELD (KG HA[-1]) OF RCG IN 1996 AND 1998.

Input	Clay soil Offtake 1996	1998	Average Balance	Organic Soil Offtake 1996	1998	Average Balance
0	32	18	-25	41	59	-50
50	27	25	24	50	71	-10
100	30	35[**]	67	49	91[**]	30
150	32	40[**]	114	48	91[**]	80

[**] In this N-fertiliser rate the N-offtake significantly differs (P<0.01) from the offtake of unfertilised RCG.

Soil mineral N

The mean mineral N in the soil (0-25 cm) ranged between 8 and 13 kg ha[-1] in clay soil in May 1996-1998, indicating not any significant differences between fertiliser treatments. In organic soil the mean mineral N ranged between 15 and 39 kg ha^{-1} during the same period. In organic soil the trend of mineral N was increasing by the fertiliser rate in May 1997 and 1998. With the two highest fertiliser rates the soil mineral N was significantly higher than without fertilisation, increasing about 3.5 kg ha^{-1} and 7 kg ha^{-1} with each apply of 50 kg ha^{-1} fertiliser N in spring 1997 and 1998, respectively (Fig. 2). Despite the soil mineral N increased with the high rates of added N the DM yield did not increase. The increase of mineral N without yield increase is a risk for N leaching during heavy rains. Therefore the high rates of fertiliser N in organic soil were overestimated and a waste of money, too.

CONCLUSIONS

The results showed that the yield of RCG corresponded strongly on the high rates of N fertilisation in clay soil. When RCG is grown in organic soil with high nitrogen mineralisation rate both the need for N fertilisation and the fertilisation costs are decreased. However, over-fertilisation in organic soil can cause a risk for N leaching as well as a decreased quality of raw material.

REFERENCES

Landström, S., L. Lomakka and S. Andersson, 1996. Harvest in spring improves yield and quality of reed canary grass as a bioenergy crop. Biomass and Bioenergy, 11(4): 333-341.

Littell, R. C., G. A. Milliken, W. W. Stroup and R. D. Wolfinger, 1996. SAS System for Mixed Models, Cary, NC: SAS Instiute Inc., NC, USA, 633 pp.

Mela, T., A. Hatakka, M. Hemming, J. Janson, M. Järvenpää, B. Lönnberg, L. Paavilainen, K. Pahkala, A. Pehkonen and A. Suokannas, 1994. Production of agrofibre and its suitability for paper manufacture. In: Hennink S et al (eds.) Alternative Oilseed and Fibre Crops for Cool and Wet Regions of Europe pp 85-90: COST 814, Workshop held in Wageningen (The Netherlands), April 7-8, 1994. Brussels.

Pahkala, K. and M. Pihala, 2000. Different plant parts as raw material for fuel and pulp production. Industrial Crops and Products, 11: 119-128.

SAS Institute Inc. (1990) SAS® Procedure Guide, Version 6, Third edition, Cary, NC. USA, 705 pp.

Tukey, J. W. (1977) Exploratory Data Analysis. Reading, MA: Addison-Wesley, 688 pp.

Verbeke, G. and G. Molenberghs (Editors) Lecture notes in statistics 126. Linear mixed models in practise: a SAS-oriented approach. Springer-Verlag, New York, Inc., 306 pp.

Effect of nitrogen and water supply on the photosynthetic activity of *Miscanthus sinensis* under field conditions

L. G. ANGELINI, N. OGGIANO AND M. MAFFEI

Dipartimento di Agronomia e Gestione dell'Agroecosistema, University of Pisa, Pisa, Italy

SUMMARY

Although C4 plants are considered to have higher conversion efficiency and productivity than C3 plants, this advantage may not be realized under sub optimal conditions. Therefore the effects of irrigation and nitrogen fertilization on photosynthetic capacity were studied and the correlation occurring between leaf nitrogen and CO_2 assimilation examined. A long period of nitrogen stress (imposed to the miscanthus crop for three years) associated with soil water limitation, caused a significant decline of net photosynthesis. The photosynthetic capacity was reduced mainly through the use of nitrogen, as it appeared strongly dependent on specific leaf nitrogen (SLN), especially for low values of this parameter.

Keywords: fertilization, irrigation, Miscanthus sinensis, nitrogen, photosynthesis

INTRODUCTION

Miscanthus sinensis cv. 'Giganteus' (Andersson) is a perennial C4 grass with high biomass per area production in European climatic conditions (Beale and Long, 1995; Ercoli *et al.*, 1999; Ceccarini *et al.*, 1999). It is suitable for production of energy because of its high growth rate and crop yield. The financial viability of energy crops is dependent not only upon the production of high yields of harvested dry matter, but also upon minimizing the level of inputs, especially fertilizers. C4 crops exhibit a higher nitrogen-use efficiency than C3 crops (Long, 1983; Dalianis *et al.*, 1995) and hence require lower nitrogen inputs (Beale *et al.*, 1996). Few data are available on the capacity of *M. sinensis* cv. 'Giganteus' to maintain an adequate photosynthetic capability without nitrogen fertilizer (Himken *et al.*, 1997). Furthermore, summer drought plays one of the major role in limiting growth in Mediterranean area (Petrini *et al.*, 1996) and water stress may cause severe alterations in leaf metabolism affecting photosynthetic CO_2-uptake.

Little is known on the factors that limit photosynthesis in *Miscanthus sinensis* and the mechanisms this plant puts into action under conditions of nitrogen and water deficit. Therefore the aim of this research was to study CO_2 and water vapour exchanges in a 3-

year-old crop of *Miscanthus sinensis*, with and without nitrogen fertilization and with and without irrigation.

The effects of water deficit on photosynthesis were assessed during the growing season, evaluating light-saturating CO_2-uptake rate (Amax), transpiration rate (E), stomatal conductance (gs), and water use efficiency (WUE). To relate photosynthetic capacity to resource availability, the following indices were used: specific leaf nitrogen (SLN), nitrogen use efficiency (NUE), chlorophyll use efficiency (CUE). In order to better understand how nitrogen deficit affects maximum photosynthetic capacity, the correlation between leaf nitrogen content and CO_2 assimilation was studied.

MATERIALS AND METHODS

Field experiments were conducted at the Experimental Station of Rottaia (Pisa, Central Italy, 43° 39' N; 10° 19' E; 1 m o.s.l.); soil physical and chemical properties were: sand 33.9%; silt 20.8%; clay 45.3%; organic matter 2.15%; pH 7.2; total nitrogen 0.12%; assimilable P_2O_5 73 ppm; exchangeable K_2O 165 ppm.

A split-plot design was used with two irrigation regimes (H0 and H100) as main plots, and two nitrogen levels (N0 and N1), as subplots, replicated three times. Irrigation treatments were unirrigated (rainfed) and irrigated, designed so that rainfall plus irrigation replaced 100% estimated evapotranspiration. Water was distributed by drip irrigation. More details about the potential evapotranspiration estimation and the irrigation method are available in Ercoli *et al.*, 1999. Nitrogen treatments were 0 and 200 kg N ha⁻¹. Nitrogen was applied as urea. Fertilizer was distributed pre-sowing at a rate of 87 kg P ha⁻¹ and 83 kg K ha⁻¹. Miscanthus was grown in 0.50 m wide rows, at a density of 4 plants m⁻². On individual attached leaves photosynthetic capacity and stomatal conductance were measured on five dates during the growing cycle. Gas exchange characteristics were measured using a portable open differential system (ADC LCA-4, Hoddesdon, UK). Measurements were made at midday under light-saturating conditions (photon flux ³1800 mmol m⁻² s⁻¹) on each of the dates. After the gas exchange measurements, leaves were excised and dried at 50°C. Nitrogen concentration was determined by Kjeldahl procedure and SLN for each sample was calculated as the product of leaf nitrogen percentage and specific leaf dry weight. Chlorophyll content was determined according to Moran and Porath (1980).

RESULTS

Gas exchanges

Both nitrogen and water regimes had a significant effect on net photosynthesis during the overall cycle. Net photosynthesis significantly decreased ($P < 0.05$) under nitrogen shortage, with an average diminution of 25% at each of the dates considered.

Irrigation also affected CO_2 assimilation rate which increased in fertilized as well as in non-fertilized plants (Table 1). Net photosynthesis was always higher when nitrogen was applied under both water regimes. Higher values of net photosynthesis were found under non-limiting water and nitrogen conditions, whilst the lowest values were observed in plants grown without nitrogen and irrigation (H0 N0, Table 1). The CO_2 assimilation rate during the growing season displayed an increasing trend till the half of July, and this behaviour was observed in all treatments (Table 1). Subsequently a progressive decline was registered.

TABLE 1. EFFECT OF NITROGEN SUPPLY AND WATER REGIME ON NET PHOTOSYNTHESIS (AMAX), TRANSPIRATION RATE (E), STOMATAL CONDUCTANCE (GS), WATER USE EFFICIENCY (WUE), LEAF NITROGEN CONTENT (LN), SPECIFIC LEAF NITROGEN (SLN) AND NITROGEN USE EFFICIENCY (NUE) OF M. SINENSIS CV. 'GIGANTEUS' MEASURED ON FIVE DATES AT MIDDAY UNDER LIGHT SATURATING CONDITIONS (PHOTOSYNTHETIC ACTIVE RADIATION ^{3}1800 MMOL M^{-2} S^{-1}).

	H0		H100		Significance		
	N0	N1	N0	N1	N	W	NxW
Date 23/6							
Amax μmol CO_2 $m^{-2}s^{-1}$	21.44 ± 2.26	23.03 ± 1.02	26.61 ± 0.08	35.15 ± 1.79	**	**	**
E mmol H_2O $m^{-2}s^{-1}$	10.02 ± 0.26	9.70 ± 0.08	10.76 ± 0.52	10.96 ± 0.11	n.s.	*	**
gs mol H_2O $m^{-2}s^{-1}$	0.484 ± 0.06	0.451 ± 0.08	0.527 ± 0.02	0.564 ± 0.02	n.s.	**	*
WUE mmol CO_2/mol H_2O	2.12	2.37	2.47	3.21	**	**	**
LN mmol N g^{-1}	1.31 ± 0.07	1.49 ± 0.08	1.27 ± 0.01	1.54 ± 0.06	n.s.	n.s.	n.s.
SLN g N m^{-2}	1.36 ± 0.28	1.33 ± 0.11	1.28 ± 0.05	1.59 ± 0.13	*	n.s.	n.s.
NUE μmol CO_2/mmol N s^{-1}	0.22 ± 0.04	0.24 ± 0.01	0.29 ± 0.01	0.31 ± 0.04	n.s.	n.s.	n.s.
Date 07/7							
Amax μmol CO_2 $m^{-2}s^{-1}$	19.90 ± 0.33	29.58 ± 1.47	27.29 ± 1.09	35.04 ± 2.26	**	**	n.s.
E mmol H_2O $m^{-2}s^{-1}$	8.78 ± 0.06	8.80 ± 0.47	9.12 ± 0.57	9.56 ± 0.10	n.s.	*	n.s.
gs mol H_2O $m^{-2}s^{-1}$	0.435 ± 0.01	0.500 ± 0.01	0.482 ± 0.05	0.497 ± 0.03	*	n.s.	n.s.
WUE mmol CO_2/mol H_2O	2.27	3.36	2.66	3.66	**	**	**
LN mmol N g^{-1}	1.11 ± 0.07	1.44 ± 0.09	1.42 ± 0.02	1.40 ± 0.05	n.s.	n.s.	n.s.
SLN g N m^{-2}	1.30 ± 0.46	1.51 ± 0.06	1.58 ± 0.11	1.47 ± 0.07	n.s.	n.s.	n.s.
NUE μmol CO_2/mmol N s^{-1}	0.22 ± 0.04	0.27 ± 0.01	0.22 ± 0.01	0.33 ± 0.04	**	n.s.	n.s.
Date 14/7							
Amax μmol CO_2 $m^{-2}s^{-1}$	19.67 ± 1.47	33.89 ± 0.63	31.87 ± 0.73	36.33 ± 2.60	**	**	**
E mmol H_2O $m^{-2}s^{-1}$	8.74 ± 0.46	9.31 ± 0.13	9.71 ± 0.22	10.23 ± 0.21	n.s.	*	n.s.
gs mol H_2O $m^{-2}s^{-1}$	0.419 ± 0.01	0.507 ± 0.01	0.470 ± 0.03	0.532 ± 0.04	**	**	n.s.
WUE mmol CO_2/mol H_2O	2.25	3.64	3.28	3.55	**	**	**
LN mmol N g^{-1}	1.01 ± 0.08	1.31 ± 0.05	1.50 ± 0.07	1.64 ± 0.01	*	*	n.s.
SLN g N m^{-2}	1.09 ± 0.03	1.32 ± 0.09	1.62 ± 0.15	1.59 ± 0.05	n.s.	*	n.s.
NUE μmol CO_2/mmol N s^{-1}	0.27 ± 0.01	0.32 ± 0.04	0.28 ± 0.04	0.36 ± 0.03	**	n.s.	n.s
Date 25/7							
Amax μmol CO_2 $m^{-2}s^{-1}$	17.18 ± 3.00	23.27 ± 0.50	18.57 ± 0.66	30.75 ± 1.41	**	**	**
E mmol H_2O $m^{-2}s^{-1}$	9.45 ± 0.15	9.25 ± 0.13	8.12 ± 0.28	9.85 ± 0.44	*	n.s.	**
Gs mol H_2O $m^{-2}s^{-1}$	0.467 ± 0.01	0.309 ± 0.01	0.262 ± 0.01	0.423 ± 0.01	n.s.	n.s.	**
WUE mmol CO_2/mol H_2O	1.82	2.52	2.29	3.12	**	**	n.s.
LN mmol N g^{-1}	0.93 ± 0.09	1.30 ± 0.05	1.14 ± 0.07	1.28 ± 0.01	n.s.	n.s.	n.s.
SLN g N m^{-2}	1.01 ± 0.05	1.44 ± 0.02	1.14 ± 0.09	1.37 ± 0.07	**	n.s.	n.s.
NUE μmol CO_2/mmol N s^{-1}	0.24 ± 0.01	0.23 ± 0.03	0.23 ± 0.04	0.31 ± 0.01	n.s	n.s	n.s
Date 23/8							
Amax μmol CO_2 $m^{-2}s^{-1}$	12.59 ± 2.67	13.06 ± 1.70	13.76 ± 0.59	20.53 ± 0.21	**	**	**
E mmol H_2O $m^{-2}s^{-1}$	8.41 ± 0.31	7.87 ± 0.06	7.30 ± 0.13	9.27 ± 0.53	**	**	**
gs mol H_2O $m^{-2}s^{-1}$	0.357 ± 0.02	0.273 ± 0.01	0.230 ± 0.01	0.401 ± 0.01	**	**	**
WUE mmol CO_2/mol H_2O	1.50	1.66	1.89	2.22	*	*	n.s.
LN mmol N g^{-1}	0.80 ± 0.08	1.03 ± 0.05	1.05 ± 0.07	1.08 ± 0.03	n.s.	n.s.	n.s.
SLN g N m^{-2}	0.86 ± 0.04	1.20 ± 0.01	1.17 ± 0.04	1.13 ± 0.08	**	n.s.	n.s.
NUE μmol CO_2/mmol N s^{-1}	0.20 ± 0.01	0.15 ± 0.04	0.16 ± 0.04	0.25 ± 0.01	n.s	n.s	n.s

Data are the means±standard deviations of ten replicates. **, * and n.s.: significance at P<0.01, P<0.05 and not significant respectively.

The transpiration rate was affected significantly by water supply till the second half of July. Hereby the nitrogen fertilization played a significant role in increasing the rate of water transpired, mainly in well watered plants (Table 1).

Stomatal conductance did not change under nitrogen and water limitation for the most part of the growing cycle, although a slight increase was observed when nitrogen and water were applied (Table 1). This parameter decreased after the middle of July, with the increase of air temperature and vapour pressure deficit (VPD) and a strong correlation between gs and VPD was found (Fig. 1).

The ratio between CO_2 assimilation and water transpired, i. e. water use efficiency, was significantly affected by nitrogen and water supply. WUE values were always higher when nitrogen was applied both in dry and wet conditions. The lowest value was observed under water and nitrogen shortage in every survey (Fig. 1). The analysis of variance showed that WUE was not significantly affected by the interaction of the two main treatments in data collected after the middle of July.

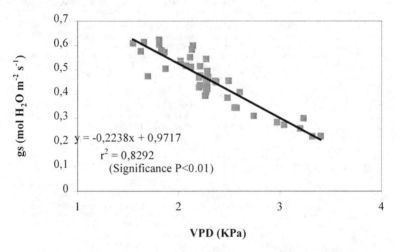

FIGURE 1. THE RESPONSE OF THE STOMATAL CONDUCTANCE (GS) TO VARIATION IN VAPOUR PRESSURE DEFICIT (VPD) OF M. SINENSIS CV. 'GIGANTEUS'. DATA COLLECTED BETWEEN 23 JUNE AND 23 AUGUST.

Leaf nitrogen content and nitrogen use efficiency

N-fertilization affected the nitrogen content positively on both weight basis (LN, mmol N g^{-1}) and on an area basis (SLN, g m^{-2}). During the whole cycle LN content of the fertilized treatment was 12% to 25% higher than that of the zero-N treatment. Similarly SLN increased up to 31% with nitrogen supply.

The efficiency of nitrogen use (NUE) was also positively affected by nitrogen application, with increases ranging from 8% to 36% in fertilized plots. For high values of NUE, always realized in N-fertilized plots, plants also displayed high photosynthetic rates peak values of NUE corresponding to peak values of Amax (Table 1). In order to better understand how nitrogen deficit affects leaf photosynthesis, the correlation between SLN and Amax was analysed. Data collected showed that net photosynthesis of *Miscanthus sinensis* was highly correlated to specific leaf nitrogen, and CO_2 assimilation increased with increasing SLN. The fitted logistic function that relates CO_2 assimilation data and SLN was a second order polynomial (Fig. 2). According to this relationship Amax plateaued at a value of 28 μmol CO_2 m^{-2} s^{-1} when SLN corresponded to 1.69g m^{-2}.

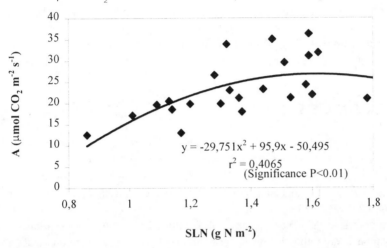

$$y = -29{,}751x^2 + 95{,}9x - 50{,}495$$
$$r^2 = 0{,}4065$$
(Significance P<0.01)

SLN (g N m^{-2})

FIGURE 2. THE RESPONSE OF THE LIGHT SATURATED ASSIMILATION RATE (AMAX) TO VARIATION IN SPECIFIC LEAF NITROGEN (SLN) OF M. SINENSIS CV. 'GIGANTEUS'. DATA COLLECTED BETWEEN 23 JUNE AND 23 AUGUST.

The interaction between nitrogen fertilization and water supply did not ever affected LN, SLN, NUE indices significantly. Basically nitrogen content was higher when nitrogen was applied only in the non-irrigated plots. Differences between N treatments decreased in the irrigated plots, as well as differences in the water regimes, when nitrogen was applied.

Total leaf chlorophyll
Leaf chlorophyll content was not significantly affected by either nitrogen or water treatments, nor by their interaction, even if in N0 H0 treatment the chlorophyll content was slightly lower. The chlorophyll use efficiency (μmol CO_2 g chl^{-1}) followed the same pattern.

CONCLUSIONS

The study of the photosynthetic activity in *Miscanthus sinensis* showed that a long period of nitrogen stress (imposed to the miscanthus crop for three years) caused a significant decline of net photosynthesis and related parameters during the overall growing cycle. The midday net photosynthesis decrease seems related to both gs values reduction and SLN lower content. In fact Amax displayed a close correlation with leaf nitrogen and CO_2 assimilation decreased as SLN declined below 1.69 g m^{-2}. At higher values of SLN photosynthetic capacity was less responsive to SLN.

Nitrogen shortage reduced CO_2 uptake of the mesophyll and disturbed the photosynthetic machinery mainly through the use of nitrogen, which is in most part used to synthesize phosphoenolpyruvate carboxylase. In C4 plants this enzyme is 10% of soluble leaf proteins (Long, 1983); consequently in many cases, as in miscanthus, the photosynthetic capacity appears strongly dependent on specific leaf nitrogen (SLN).

REFERENCES

Beale, C. V., and S. P. Long, 1995. Can perennial C4 grasses attain high efficiencies of radiant energy conversion in cool climates? Plant, Cell and Environment, 18: 641-650.

Beale, C. V., D. A. Bint and S. P. Long, 1996. Leaf photosynthesis in the C4-grass Miscanthus x giganteus, growing in the cool temperate climate of southern England. Journal of Experimental Botany, (47) 295: 267-273.

Ceccarini, L., L. Angelini and E. Bonari, 1999. Caratteristiche produttive e valutazione energetica della biomassa di Miscanthus sinensis 'Anderss', Arundo donax L. e Cynara cardunculus L. in prove condotte nella Toscana litoranea. In: Proceedings of XXXIII S.I.A. Conference, Padova, pp. 20-25 September 1999.

Dalianis, C. D., C. A. Sooter and M. G. Christou, 1994. Growth, biomass productivity and energy potential of giant reed (Arundo donax) and elephant grass (*Miscanthus sinensis* "giganteus"). In: Proceedings European Conference on Biomass for Energy, Environment, Agriculture and Industry, Wien, Austria, 3-5 October 1994.

Ercoli, L., M. Mariotti, A. Masoni and E. Bonari, 1999. Effect of irrigation and nitrogen fertilization on biomass yield and efficiency of energy use in crop production of Miscanthus. Field Crops Research, 63: 3-11.

Himken, M., J. Lammel, D. Neukirchen, U. Czypionka-Krause and H. W. Olfs, 1997. Cultivation of Miscanthus under West European conditions: seasonal changes in dry matter production, nutrient uptake and remobilization. Plant and Soil, 189: 117-126.

Long, S. P., 1983. C4 photosynthesis at low temperatures. Plant, Cell and Environment, 6: 345-363.

Moran, R. and D. Porath, 1980. Chlorophyll determination in intact tissues using N,N dimethylformamide. Plant Physiology, 65: 478-479.

Petrini, C., R. Bazzocchi, E. Bonari, L. Ercoli and A. Masoni, 1996. Effect of irrigation and nitrogen supply on biomass production from Miscanthus in northern-central Italy. Agricoltura Mediterranea, 126: 275-284.

The ageing of grass-clover sward and its effect on nitrogen balance in the rumen of sheep

J. VERBIC, D. BABNIK, M. RESNIK, J. VERBIC AND V. KMECL

Agricultural Institute of Slovenia, Hacquetova 17, 1000 Ljubljana, Slovenia

SUMMARY

Protein degradability (EPD), microbial protein synthesis in the rumen (MPS) and nitrogen excretion in sheep were continuously measured during the first growth of the grass/clover sward. MPS was estimated on the basis of urinary purine derivatives excretion and EPD by means of the nylon bag technique. The concentration of crude protein (CP) in forage decreased between 21 April and 8 June from 187 to 78 g kg^{-1} dry matter (DM); EPD decreased from 710 to 610 g kg^{-1}; MPS from 21 to 15 g N kg^{-1} DM intake; and ammonia concentration in rumen fluid decreased from 400 to 125 mg NH$_3$-N l^{-1} during the experiment. The needs of rumen microbes for N were only fully covered at the beginning of the experiment by N being released directly from the forage. Later, MPS exceeded the supply of rumen degradable N (RDN), indicating that a considerable amount of endogenous N was transferred to the rumen and incorporated into microbial protein. Urinary N excretion decreased from 23.4 to 7.6 and N excreted in faeces decreased from 7.6 to 5.8 g sheep^{-1} day^{-1}. It was concluded that in diets composed of fresh forage RDN could be efficiently captured into the microbial biomass. However, extensive N excretion can not be avoided if the metabolizable protein supply exceeds the requirements of animals.

Keywords: grasslands, microbial protein synthesis, nitrogen excretion, protein degradation, ruminants

INTRODUCTION

In ruminants, significant losses of N may arise due to the imbalance between the N which is released during microbial decomposition of protein in the rumen and the capability of rumen microbes to incorporate it into microbial protein. A surplus of rumen degradable protein is inevitably lost, mainly in the form of urea in the urine. Due to the action of urease which appears in the faeces, urea is converted into ammonia and is lost into the atmosphere from the soil–plant–animal cycle. Due to the relatively high N: C ratio an extremely high N excretion can be expected in diets which are composed of grassland forage. The objective of this experiment was to quantify the effect of the ageing of grass-clover forage on protein degradability and microbial protein yield in the rumen and to discuss the possible consequences for nitrogen excretion in ruminants.

MATERIALS AND METHODS

First-growth of grass/clover sward was used in the experiment. The proportion of clover (*Trifolium pratense* and *Trifolium repens*) ranged from 0.10 to 0.25 of herbage DM. The following grasses were represented: *Phleum pratense* (0.46), *Lolium perenne* (0.25), *Festuca pratensis* (0.25), *Dactylis glomerata* (0.03) and *Festuca rubra* (0.01). Herbage was mown daily from 17 April until 11 June. During the experiment DM yield increased linearly from 1,300 to 10,000 kg ha^{-1}.

Protein degradabilities were determined using the nylon bag technique as described by Ørskov (Ørskov *et al.*, 1980). Fresh samples were weighed into nylon bags and incubated in the rumen of three sheep for 3, 6, 12, 24, 48 and 72 h. Data of protein degradabilities were fitted to the equation $p = a + b (1 - e^{-ct})$ (Ørskov and McDonald, 1979). Effective degradabilities (EPD) of protein were calculated as $EPD = a + bc/(c + k)$ (Ørskov and McDonald, 1979) where a, b and c represent parameters from the estimated degradation curve and k fractional outflow rate, which was fixed to 0.05 h^{-1}. Samples of rumen fluid were taken 4 h after the morning feeding.

Nitrogen excretion and organic matter digestibility were measured by the total collection method. Four wethers which were kept in metabolism cages were used. They were fed experimental feed in two equal meals at the level of 1,120 g DM day^{-1}. The quantity of urine and faeces was measured daily. Samples from three consecutive days were pooled to determine the concentration of nitrogen and organic matter. The presumption that faeces was excreted with a delay of 24 h was taken into account, i.e. the sample collected at the given time was attributed to feed consumed between 36 h and 12 h earlier. Microbial protein synthesis was estimated by means of urinary purine derivative excretion as described by Chen (Chen *et al.*, 1991).

RESULTS AND DISCUSSION

With advancing maturity the concentration of CP in herbage decreased from 187 to 78 g kg^{-1} DM. During the same period EPD decreased from 710 to 610 g kg^{-1} (Fig. 1). Consequently, the amount of RDN declined from 21 to 8 g N kg^{-1} dry matter intake (Fig. 2). MPS in the rumen decreased from 22 to 15 g N per kg of dry matter intake as the season progressed.

From Fig. 2 it can be seen that at the early maturity level the nitrogenous substrates for microbial protein synthesis were fully supplied by RDN. However, as the season progressed, microbial protein synthesis exceeded RDN supply. Up to 7 g N kg^{-1} DMI had to be recycled into the rumen from metabolism in the very late stages of growth.

Using a similar methodology, Verbic *et al.* (1999) found out that a certain amount of N can also be recycled from the metabolism in the case of hay while a surplus of RDN was characteristic for silages.

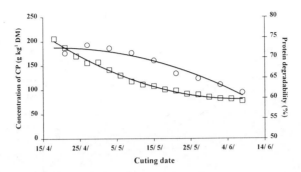

FIGURE 1. CONCENTRATION OF CRUDE PROTEIN (CP,□) AND PROTEIN DEGRADABILITY IN THE RUMEN (○) OF GRASS-CLOVER HERBAGE.

Feeding high-protein diets in the early growth stages was accompanied by high rumen ammonia concentration and high urinary N output (Fig. 3). With advancing maturity both ammonia concentration as well as urinary N excretion decreased. The decrease in faecal N output, which represented 0.23–0.43 of total N excretion, was less pronounced.

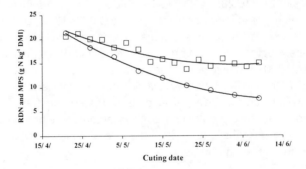

FIGURE 2. CONCENTRATION OF RUMEN DEGRADABLE N (RDN,○) AND MICROBIAL PROTEIN SYNTHESIS (MPS,□) DURING THE AGEING OF GRASS-CLOVER HERBAGE (IN G N KG⁻¹ DRY MATTER INTAKE).

Urinary N output should be discussed in the light of the understanding that, besides the surplus of RDN, any protein supplied in excess of animal requirements can also be an important source of urinary N losses. Without any doubt, this was also the case in the present experiment in which average daily gains were only about 0.03 kg day⁻¹. According to AFRC (1992), about 1.5 g N can be retained in the fleece and the body at given weight gains and a similar value was also obtained from the experimental data (1.6 g N day⁻¹). However, the supply of metabolizable protein to the animal even at the latest growth stages of grass did not fall below the amount equivalent to 14 g N day⁻¹ and thus exceeded the animal requirements several times. From N excretion data (Fig. 3) it seems that equilibrium between protein supply and protein requirements in low-productive sheep was achieved after 15 May when crude protein concentration in herbage declined below 110 g kg⁻¹ dry matter.

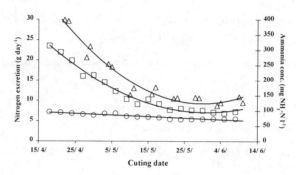

FIGURE 3. RUMEN AMMONIA CONCENTRATIONS (△) AND DAILY URINARY (□) AND FAECAL (○) N EXCRETION IN SHEEP GIVEN GRASS-CLOVER HERBAGE AT VARIOUS STAGES OF MATURITY.

It can be concluded that in diets composed from fresh forage RDN could be efficiently captured into the microbial biomass. The efficiency of microbial protein synthesis in the rumen varied from 21.7 to 28.9 g N kg⁻¹ digestible organic matter intake (DOMI) which is considerably higher than in hay or silages (16.7 to 20.0 g N kg⁻¹ DOMI; Verbic, 1999, unpublished results). Values for fresh forage were close to specific value for the first growths of temperate grasses and legumes (27.2 g N kg⁻¹ DOMI) as proposed by Australian workers (CSIRO, 1990), but higher than the average value used in French protein system (20.2 g g N kg⁻¹ DOMI, INRA, 1989). A balanced or even deficient RDN supply (Fig. 2) indicates that, in ruminants which are given diets composed from fresh forage, extensive N excretion should not be a problem unless the metabolizable protein supply exceeds the animal requirements. The latter is often the case when low-production animals are kept on high-protein grasslands forage.

ACKNOWLEDGEMENTS

The research was supported by the Ministry of Science and Technology and by the Ministry of Agriculture, Forestry and Food of the Republic of Slovenia.

REFERENCES

AFRC, 1992. Nutritive requirements of ruminant animals: Protein. Nutrition Abstracts and Reviews Series B, 62: 787-835.

Chen, X. B., E. R. Ørskov and F. D. DeB. Hovell, 1991. The use of intragastric infusion in studies on excretion of purine derivatives as a measure of microbial protein supply in ruminants. In: Eggum, Boisen, B., S., Borsting, C., Danfær, A., Hvelplund, T. (Eds.), Protein Metabolism and Nutrition. Proceedings of 6th International Symposium on Protein Metabolism and Nutrition, Vol. 2, Herning, 9-14 June 1991, National Institute of Animal Nutrition, Foulum, 67-70.

CSIRO, 1990. Feeding standards for Australian Livestock - Ruminants. CSIRO, Melbourne. 266 pp.

INRA, 1989. Ruminant nutrition. Recommended allowances and feed tables. INRA, Paris. 389 pp.

Ørskov, E. R., F. D. DeB. Hovell and F. Mould, 1980. The use of nylon bag technique for the evaluation of feedstuffs. Tropical Animal Production, 5: 195-213.

Ørskov, E. R., I. McDonald, 1979. The estimation of protein degradability in the rumen from incubation measurements weighted according to rate of passage. Journal of Agricultural Science, Cambridge, 92: 499-503.

Verbic, J., E. R. Ørskov, J. Zgajnar, X. B. Chen and V. Znidaršic-Pongrac, 1999. The effect of method of forage preservation on the protein degradability and microbial protein synthesis in the rumen. Animal Feed Science and Technology, 82: 195-212.

Nitrogen content and nitrogen export in a wide range of Lolium perenne varieties

A. DE VLIEGHER, L. CARLIER, C. VAN WAES AND J. VAN WAES

Ministry of Small Enterprises, Traders and Agriculture, Agricultural Research Centre,
Dep. Crop Husbandry and Ecophysiology, Burg. Van Gansberghelaan 109, 9820 Merelbeke,
Belgium

SUMMARY

Fertilizer nitrogen is still a major factor for profitability in meat and milk production. Differences in N export between species or between varieties could be of importance in minimising the risk of N-leaching. N efficiency is calculated as N_{output} x 100 x (N fertilizer$_{input}$)$^{-1}$. The purpose of this study was the examination of differences in relative ADM yield, N content and N export in a wide range of 40 varieties of *Lolium perenne* at two locations in Belgium: a sandy loam and a sandy soil. Diploid and tetraploid varieties as well as early and late varieties are represented in this comparison. The trials were cut 4-6 times a year during 3 years after the sowing year.

Keywords: exportation, Lolium perenne, nitrogen, varieties

INTRODUCTION

It is well known that all the grass varieties do not react in the same way to nitrogen in terms of dry matter yield, nitrogen content and nitrogen export. *Lolium perenne* is the dominating grass species in Belgian cultivated grassland. Maybe differences between varieties of this species in N content and N export should receive more attention in the perspective of efficient N use for grass production and the restriction of the amount of leachable N in the soil at the end of the growing season.

Baert *et al.* (1999) and De Vliegher *et al.* (1999) published results of genotype variation in nitrogen use efficiency at two levels of nitrogen fertilisation .The purpose of this study was to examine the differences in relative DM yield, N content, N export in a range of 40 listed or candidate varieties of Lolium perenne at two locations in Belgium.

MATERIALS AND METHODS

In 1995, 40 varieties of *Lolium perenne* were established in a complete block design with 4 replicates in Merelbeke (sandy loam) and in Geel (sand). Diploid (28), tetraploid (12), early (9), intermediate (15) and late (16) varieties were involved. In the 3 following years, the level of N input by mineral fertilisers was 425 kg ha^{-1} year^{-1}. This experiment was executed during 3 growing seasons with 5-6 cuts annually.

RESULTS

A very large quantity of the applied nitrogen is exported by harvesting the grass under mowing conditions: 88% in Merelbeke and 104% in Geel. In Geel the N output exceeded the N input by mineral fertiliser, especially in the first harvest year, because there was a supplementary uptake of mineralised soil nitrogen (Table 1).

TABLE 1. DM YIELD, N CONTENT AND N EXPORT OF 40 VARIETIES OF LOLIUM PERENNE IN 1996-1998 IN TWO LOCATIONS IN BELGIUM.

characte-ristic		Merelbeke (sandy loam)				Geel (sand)			
		1996	1997	1998	cycle	1996	1997	1998	cycle
DM yield kg/ha	average	14531	13253	15320	**14368**	17212	14686	12597	**14832**
	stand.dev.	369	485	565	**396**	498	863	666	**516**
	range	1416	1998	2705	**1867**	2250	3596	2788	**2142**
N content g/kg	average	24,7	23,9	28,6	**25,7**	32,4	25,4	31,9	**29,9**
	stand.dev.	0,5	0,7	0,9	**0,5**	0,9	0,7	1,0	**0,7**
	range	2,2	2,8	4,7	**2,4**	3,1	3,5	5,6	**3,8**
N export kg/ha	average	360	316	437	**371**	557	373	402	**444**
	stand.dev.	9	10	13	**8**	18	17	21	**11**
	range	34	44	76	**46**	66	59	79	**40**

The range in nitrogen export within the 40 varieties was on average 40-46 kg N ha^{-1} year^{-1} and corresponds to 10% of the mineral N-input. Within a year the differences could increase to 79 kg N ha^{-1}. Although there is no difference in the level of N export between the early, intermediate and late groups, the range for the early and intermediate types varies between 11 and 30 kg N ha^{-1} year^{-1} and the variation between the late varieties is much higher: there are candidate varieties with a very low and with a very high N output (Table 2).

TABLE 2. DM YIELD, N CONTENT AND N EXPORT OF THE DIFFERENT TYPES OF LOLIUM PERENNE IN 1996-1998 IN TWO LOCATIONS IN BELGIUM.

characte-ristic		Merelbeke (sandy loam) type			Geel (sand) type		
		early(9)	interm.(15)	late(16)	early(9)	interm.(15)	late(16)
DM yield kg/ha/year	average	14443	14284	14404	14908	14828	14793
	stand.dev.	191	306	537	404	535	578
	range	526	1068	1867	1117	1707	2142
N content g/kg	average	25,6	25,8	25,7	29,8	30,0	29,9
	stand.dev.	0,4	0,4	0,5	0,5	0,8	0,7
	range	1,2	1,3	2,3	1,4	2,7	3,0
N export kg/ha/year	average	371	370	372	443	445	444
	stand.dev.	4	7	11	11	10	11
	range	11	20	46	30	27	40

There is not a good correlation between N output and N content but the range in N content in Geel is very large: 5.6 g N kg⁻¹DM.

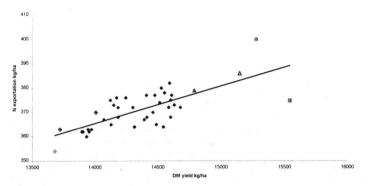

FIGURE 1. RELATIONSHIP BETWEEN DM YIELD AND N EXPORTATION ON A SANDY LOAM SOIL (MERELBEKE) HARVEST 1996-1997-1998.

The correlation between N export and DM yield is good (Merelbeke $R^2 = 0.54$, Geel $R^2 = 0.55$)(Figs 1 and 2). In general, high-yielding varieties export large quantities of nitrogen. As a result, breeding for high nitrogen efficiency (or export) can be achieved by breeding for high DM yield.

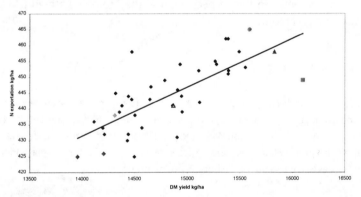

FIGURE 2. RELATIONSHIP BETWEEN DM YIELD AND N EXPORTATION ON A SANDY SOIL (GEEL). HARVEST 1996-1997-1998.

The correlation between the N export in the 2 locations is not promising (Fig. 3) given the perspective that breeders select mostly in one location. However, some varieties combine in both locations a high DM yield with a substantial or high nitrogen content and can be integrated in a specific selection programme for nitrogen efficiency.

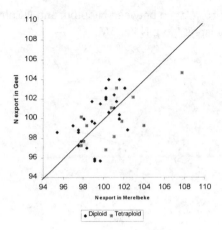

FIGURE 3. RELATIONSHIP BETWEEN N EXPORT IN MERELBEKE (SANDY LOAM) AND GEEL (SAND) IN 1996-1998.

CONCLUSION

In general, breeding for dry matter yield is breeding for nitrogen efficiency. The correlation between the N export in the 2 locations is not promising. However, some varieties have potential in this respect because they combine a high DM yield with a substantial or high N content.

REFERENCES

Baert, J., A. De Vliegher, D. Reheul and A. Ghesquiere, 1999. Nitrogen use efficiency of grass varieties at high and low level of applied nitrogen. Cost 814 meeting , Melle, june 1999: 41-50.

De Vliegher, A., L. Carlier, C. Van Waes and J. Van Waes, 1999. Varietal differences in yield and nitrogen efficiency in Lolium perenne. Proceedings Meeting 22th Eucarpia Fodder Crops and Amenity Grasses Section, Saint Petersburg, 5 pp. (in press).

Root distribution and N-acquisition efficiency of maize genotypes

K. R. VÉGH[1] AND T. SZUNDY[2]

[1] Research Institute for Soil Science and Agricultural Chemistry of the Hungarian Academy of Sciences, 1525 Budapest, Hungary
[2] Agricultural Research Institute of the Hungarian Academy of Sciences, 2452 Martonvásár, Hungary

SUMMARY

In field conditions N-recovery often depends on root density in the soil volume.

The vertical root distribution and nitrogen use efficiency of six maize genotypes were studied in a field experiment with three nitrogen fertilizer rates (0.140 and 250 kg N ha^{-1} in loam soil). Shoot biomass, leaf area and nutrient content were determined in early vegetative growth, at flowering and during grain filling. At the same time root depth profiles were determined by a core break method. Water dynamics in the soil profile were simulated by the SOIL water and heat model. Simulation outputs were compared to measured soil moisture and nitrogen distribution data. The vertical distribution of root length density significantly differed for the maize genotypes in the soil profile. Simulation outputs were in reasonable agreement with the moisture data measured in the field. Using root distribution data in the simulation the differences in N-acquisition efficiency partly can be explained, but in low and high N supply additional factors, as high differences in shoot N demand, biomass allocation and physiological nitrogen use efficiency in plant tissues are involved.

Keywords: maize genotypes, N-fertilization, root distribution, water supply

INTRODUCTION

The interactions between water availability and nitrogen supply are of particular importance for maize yield. In a soil with limited nutrient supply uptake is strongly affected by root density. Dynamic studies on the accumulation and partition of nitrogen in plant tissues have showed the highest N uptake rate before and during flowering. N uptake rate of high-yielding genotypes remains high during the early period of maturation as well (Osaki *et al.*, 1995). Deeper root extension helps plant to cope with its water and nitrogen demand during temporary drought by exploiting water stored and N accumulated in the deep soil horizon. In periods of insufficient precipitation topsoil dries out and the availability of soil nutrients decreases and, root activity ceases in the nutrient-rich upper soil layers. Additionally maize genotypes may differ in exploitation efficiency and, in physiological efficiency in nutrient use (Végh *et al.*, 1997, 1998). In this research the vertical root distribution, the efficiency in nitrogen acquisition and utilization in the physiology of six maize genotypes were studied.

MATERIALS AND METHODS

Two maize hybrids (Norma and Mv 444) and their parental inbred lines (N-A, N-B, 444-A and 444-B) were grown in a field experiment on a loam soil. Three nitrogen fertilization rates were applied: 0.140 and 280 kg ha^{-1} N. Soil physical properties, water retention characteristic curve, saturated conductivity and particle size distribution for the different layers were determined from soil cores. Soil moisture content was sampled five times during the growing season at 0-100 cm soil depth. Vertical root distribution was determined when flowering started, by using the core-break method, and plant shoots where sampled. Leaf area, shoot dry mass and nitrogen content were measured. The interactions of root activity and water availability were studied by simulating water transport in the layered soil profile by using the SOIL water and heat model (Jansson, 1991).

RESULTS

Significant genotype differences were detected for root length density (Lv) in the 0-100 cm soil profile (p<0.001). Relative root length density was calculated by the comparison of the Lv values of the genotypes to the maximum value, which was achieved by inbred N-A. The influence of genotype on the root length depth distribution was significant in N1, N2 and N3 plots (p<0.001).

N uptake differed significantly for the genotypes (p=0.024) and was affected by N rates (p=0.032). N-A had the highest root density in the plough layer and it had high compensatory root growth on low N supply (Végh *et al.*, 1998). The hybrids had higher root densities in the subsoil (Table 1) and could exploit its available water content and, in N3 plots, the available nitrogen as well, which had been accumulated in the deeper soil horizon (Fig. 1). Model predictions were compared to the field measurements. Simulation of soil moisture dynamics was in good agreement with the moisture data measured in the field. The model simulated daily values of water storage of the plough layer and the subsoil. The daily values of plant available water stored in the soil was estimated as the difference of actual water storage and water storage at wilting point in the different layers. During flowering and early grain filling stage water content in the plough layer fell below the wilting point, and plants were dependent on the water content of the subsoil (Fig. 1).

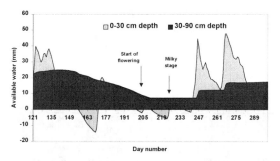

FIGURE 1. PLANT AVAILABLE WATER STORAGE IN THE PLOUGH LAYER AND THE SUBSOIL DURING THE VEGETATION PERIOD.

To achieve high yield, nitrogen should be actively absorbed through roots during maturation (Osaki *et al.*, 1995). It means that genotypes heaving higher root density in the subsoil during the dry periods could accumulate more nitrogen in shoot and grains. Both the genotype and N fertilization (Table 1) affected the distribution ratio of the root length in the subsoil (the vertical distribution of relative root length density). Hybrids had deeper root systems than their parental lines. N uptake were the highest for the hybrids, Norma and Mv 444, in the N3 treatment (100% in Table 2). Male parents, 444-B and N-B had the shortest root system with the highest root uptake efficiency (NRE, mg shoot N per root length), while the root system of female parents were much longer. Hybrids had an extended root system and high root uptake efficiency. NUE (g dry matter of shoot per mg N uptake of total plant) was different for the genotypes and decreased as NRE increased with increasing N-rates. Genotype Mv 444 had the highest NUE in unfertilized plots and it markedly decreased with fertilization.

TABLE 1. RELATIVE (%) ROOT LENGTH DENSITY AND ITS VERTICAL DISTRIBUTION IN THE SOIL PROFILE.

Genotype	Lv_{rel} (%) in the 0-100 cm profile			Lv_{rel} (%) in the subsoil		
	N1	N2	N3	N1	N2	N3
Norma	60	75	56	37	38	43
N-A	100	75	75	23	28	38
N-B	25	28	17	26	38	26
Mv 444	71	56	42	44	32	39
444-A	44	22	22	25	49	15
444-B	31	30	18	26	52	38

CONCLUSIONS

The root system of the high-yielding hybrids proliferated in the subsoil and acquired water stored and nitrogen accumulated in the deeper layers when the plough layer dried out during flowering and early grain filling stage. Both higher root density (characteristic for female parents) and root uptake efficiency (characteristic for male parents) were shown for the hybrids. High physiological efficiency in nitrogen use of the hybrids decreased with increasing N availability.

TABLE 2. RELATIVE N UPTAKE, ROOT UPTAKE EFFICIENCY (NRE) AND N-USE EFFICIENCY (NUE) OF THE GENOTYPES DURING FLOWERING.

Genotype	Rel. N-uptake (%)			NRE_{rel} (%)			NUE_{rel} (%)		
	N1	N2	N3	N1	N2	N3	N1	N2	N3
Norma	46.3	45.9	100.0	23.0	17.8	53.2	81.2	76.1	50.9
N-A	43.2	57.3	48.8	12.8	24.3	19.4	74.1	70.4	63.7
N-B	32.7	28.1	51.2	39.0	29.4	90.8	60.3	73.9	54.0
Mv 444	30.7	57.3	75.6	13.0	30.6	44.7	100.0	68.3	37.8
444-A	29.5	29.5	59.8	10.7	10.3	11.2	68.5	62.4	45.0
444-B	36.8	33.9	36.6	35.3	33.7	100.1	67.9	62.9	48.3

ACKNOWLEDGMENTS

Research work has been supported by the Hungarian National Research Found (OTKA No. T 17832 and T 25399).

REFERENCES

Jansson, P. E., 1996. Simulation model for soil water and heat conditions. Description of the SOIL model. Deptartment of Soil Sciences Swedish Agricultural University, Uppsala, 80 pp.

Osaki, M., T. Shinano, M. Matsumoto, J. Ushiki, M. M. Shinano, M. Urayama and T. Tadano, 1995. Productivity of high-yielding crops V. Root growth and specific absorption rate of nitrogen. Soil Science Plant Nutrition, 41: 635-647.

Végh, K. R., T. Szundy and T. Tischner, 1997. Adaptive strategies of maize genotypes to low phosphorus supply. In: T. Ando (Ed.) Plant Nutrition - for Sustainable Food Production and Environment. Kluwer, 329-330.

Végh, K. R., T. Szundy, K. Rajkai and T. Tischner, 1998. Roots, phosphorus uptake and water use efficiency of maize genotypes. Acta Agron. Hung., 46: 35-43.

Effects of water and nutrient supply on the N-acquisition efficiency of spring barley

K. R. VÉGH

Institute for Soil Science and Agricultural Chemistry of the Hungarian Academy of Sciences, Budapest, Hungary

S U M M A R Y

Effects of soil fertility level on the N-acquisition and N-use efficiency of two spring barley cultivars were studied. Cv. Sk 1775 and cv. Golf plants were grown on three levels of macro- and micro-nutrient fertilization and two soil moisture levels in soils with different texture. Root capacity for nitrogen acquisition from the soil (characterized by root length: L, specific root surface area: SRA, and nitrogen root uptake efficiency: NRE), and nitrogen utilization efficiency in plant tissues (characterized by N-use efficiency: NUE) were studied. Cv. Sk 1775 appeared to have high ability to compensate low nutrient supply by growing longer roots with low energy cost. Golf, with a shorter root system but by maintaining higher uptake efficiency, acquired more N from the clay. Plants produced the longest root system in sandy soil, whereas root uptake efficiency was the highest in the moist, fertilized loam.

Keywords: barley cultivars, fertility levels, N-uptake rate, root length, soils

I N T R O D U C T I O N

Nitrogen efficiency of a plant is reflected by its growth and yield in various soil nitrogen conditions. The combined influences of soil fertility - including nitrogen availability - and soil moisture are major environmental variables in crop growing areas. There are soils very rich in macro- and micro-nutrients, and similar-textured soils with very low nutrient supply, both with a long agricultural history. Additionally, barley cultivars may differ in their ability to adapt to low nutrient supply in different moisture regimes.

The objective of this work was to study nitrogen efficiency of two spring barley cultivars as affected by soil fertility in soils with different texture.

M A T E R I A L S   A N D   M E T H O D S

Two varieties of spring barley (SK 1775 and Golf) were grown in a pot experiment in heavy clay soil on 3 fertilization (F1, F2, F3), and 2 soil moisture (W1 = pF:3.7, W2 = pF: 2.0) levels. Sk 1775 was also grown in light-textured sandy soil and a loam, under the same nutrient and moisture treatments. Fertility levels were set by adding 2 rates of a complete nutrient solution containing macro- and micro-nutrients. Unfertilized control (F1) soils had very low nutrient content. Moisture content was adjusted to that of the soils at pF 2.0 (=W2) and pF 3.7 (=W1) pressure head, and maintained by daily watering to a given weight during the experiment. 30-day old plants were harvested, root systems were washed from the soil and the fresh and dry mass of roots and shoots were measured. Root length was determined by a line intersect counting method (Tennant, 1975). Specific root surface area (RSA) was estimated on the basis of the fresh mass, mean diameter and length of root system assuming roots to be cylindrical and smooth. N-content of the samples was determined after wet digestion by dead-stop titration. Root nitrogen uptake efficiency (NRE) and physiological nitrogen use efficiency (NUE) for the two cultivars grown in different soil fertility and moisture regimes were evaluated.

RESULTS

Root length was significantly affected by soil texture ($p < 0.001$) and by plant variety ($p < 0.001$) (Tables 1 and 2). Effects of soil fertility on root length depended upon soil moisture content. In heavy clay significant differences between root length values were obtained in F1 and F3 treatments in moist soil. While the root system of Sk 1775 became much longer in the favorable conditions of moist, nutrient-rich clay soil, Golf had a more economic biomass partition and much shorter root system, than in drought conditions. The root system of Sk 1775 was much longer than that of Golf in each treatment (Table 1). Specific root surface area (SRA), i. e. the root surface area per unit root mass reflects both the root fineness and water-and nutrient-absorbing surface of a plant. It characterizes the quantity of biomass allocated to the resource-acquiring organ, the root system. SRA values were similar for the two varieties in dry clay but differed significantly in moist soils. Sk 1775 needed increased root proliferation on the highest soil fertility level to reach a high biomass accumulation and yield. This was associated with lower nitrogen uptake efficiency of its roots compared to Golf. Nitrogen uptake efficiency (NRE, mg shoot N per root length) offers an indication of root activity in nitrogen uptake. Golf showed significantly higher efficiency in N uptake than Sk 1775 ($p < 0.001$) reflected in NRE values. Its root N efficiency significantly increased as a consequence of increasing moisture and nutrient supply with little change in the size of the root system. NRE for SK 1775 was the highest in moist loam on the highest fertility level. Nitrogen use efficiency (NUE, g dry matter of shoot per mg N uptake of total plant) was not affected by nutrition level, because in different rates the whole scale of macro- and micro-nutrients was applied on the different fertility levels. As N supply increased together with the other nutrients, its effects on metabolic activity in the plant tissues interacting with the other nutrients, could not be seen clearly. As an important factor, P availability may highly affect both root and shoot growth, and nitrogen root uptake efficiency as well (Végh 1991). Values of NUE for Sk 1775 were similar in every soil type and fertility conditions, showing that N utilization efficiency was not altered by the changing conditions.

CONCLUSIONS

The comparison of N efficiency of spring barley cultivares showed that developing a finely divided, long root system (associated with low root uptake efficiency of Sk 1775) was less successful in nutrient and water deficient conditions than the greater uptake efficiency of Golf. The maximum value of NRE was reached in the moist loam with a high nutrient-supplying capacity, while due to the restricted root growth in the heavy clay soil and the low nutrient capacity in the sand root uptake efficiency proved to be lower. Soil moisture conditions played an important role in N efficiency of the two barley cultivars.

ACKNOWLEDGEMENTS

Research work has been supported by the Hungarian National Scientific Research Found (OTKA No. T 17832 and T 25399).

REFERENCES

Szlovák, S., 1986. The effect of nitrogen doses and different water supply upon nitrogen utilization of maize. Acta Agron. Hung., 35: 239-265.

Tennant, D., 1975. A test of modified line intersect method of estimating root length. Journal of Ecology, 63: 995-1001.

Végh, K. R., 1991. Effect of soil water and nutrient supply on root characteristics and nutrient uptake of plants. In: B.L. McMichael and H. Persson (eds.) Plant Roots and their Environment. Elsevier, Amsterdam, 143-148.

Effects of reduced nitrogen application rates on forage maize production under marginal climatic growth conditions

R. WULFES[1], F. TAUBE[2] AND H. OTT[1]

[1] Department of Agriculture, University of Applied Sciences Kiel, Germany
[2] Department of Grass and Forage Science, University of Kiel, Germany

SUMMARY

Two field experiments with five years of measurements were carried out to investigate the consequences of reduced nitrogen application rates on yield and quality parameters of forage maize (*Zea mays* L.) under marginal climatic growth conditions in northern Germany. Application of mineral N fertilizer ranged from 0 to 190 kg N ha^{-1}. In all N treatments 30 kg N ha^{-1} were included as subsurface fertilizer. Furthermore, some treatments received slurry at 80 or 160 kg N ha^{-1}. Genotypic differences in N response was tested with eight maize cultivars. Above 60 kg N ha^{-1}, no significant increase in the yield of dry matter (DM), net energy of lactation (NE$_L$) and starch was observed. Nitrogen uptake and crude protein (CP) content increased over the whole range of treatments, whereas NE$_L$ content and starch content were not significantly influenced. Additional slurry application did not affect DM yield compared with mineral N treatments, but decreased N uptake and CP content. The genotypic variability in DM yield reduction without N against the high N level ranged between 16% and 36%. Typical low-input and high-input cultivars may be classified. The results showed that under marginal climatic conditions and long-termed slurry application, the actual N fertilizer response on yield parameters was very low but increased with experimental time. The amount of N fertilization may be reduced to under 100 kg N ha^{-1}, but the genotypic variability in N response should be considered.

Keywords: forage maize, forage quality, maize cultivars, nitrogen, nitrogen utilization, slurry

INTRODUCTION

From an economic and ecological point of view, forage maize is destined to be integrated in semi-intensive forage production systems because of high nitrogen use efficiency (Taube *et al.*, 1997). Numerous investigations on maize have dealt with yield responses to N treatments, usually conducted under optimal climatic growth conditions (Muchow and Sinclair, 1995). Little is known about N effects on yield and quality of forage maize under sub optimal climatic conditions (Greef *et al.*, 1999), especially in a long-term perspective. Therefore, the objectives were to study the effect of reduced nitrogen application rates on yield and quality parameters of forage maize under sub-optimal climatic growth conditions in northern Germany. Special attention is given to slurry application, nitrogen-genotype interactions and long termed effects.

MATERIALS AND METHODS

Two field experiments with five years of measurements (1993 to 1997) were carried out in a randomized complete block design with four replications at a loamy sand site in Ostenfeld near Kiel in Schleswig-Holstein. In experiment I, the mineral N treatments were 0, 30, 60, 90, 110, 150 and 190 kg N ha^{-1}. Additionally in the 30 and 110 kg N treatment slurry was applied with 80 and 160 kg N to a total N amount of 110 and 190 kg N ha^{-1}. The maize cultivar (*Zea mays* L.) Alarik (early maturity class) was sown with a crop density of 9 plants m^{-2} in each year. In experiment II, eight cultivars of maize (early maturity class: Alarik, Kid, Naxos, Jericho, Helix, Pirat; early-mid maturity class: Helmi, Magda) were sown with a crop density of 9 plants m^{-2}. They received 0.50 and 150 kg mineral N ha^{-1}. In all N treatments (Exps. I and II), 30 kg N ha^{-1} were included as subsurface fertilizer. Dry matter (DM) yield and forage quality (crude protein [CP], starch, net energy of lactation [NE$_L$]) were analyzed by NIRS.

RESULTS AND DISCUSSION

In experiment I, significant effects due to N application rate were observed mainly in the yield parameters, whereas the quality parameters NE$_L$-content and starch content were not affected by nitrogen application rates (Table 1). On average over five years, above 60 kg N ha^{-1} (N60) no significant increase in DM-yield, NE$_L$-yield and starch yield was observed. The decrease in DM yield without nitrogen fertilizer was only 25%, due to high nitrogen mineralization in the soil (82 kg N ha^{-1} yr^{-1} in N0), so the mean apparent nitrogen utilization rate decreased from 64% (N30) to 34% (N190) (data not presented). The CP content increased with nitrogen application about 20 g kg^{-1} DM because of increased N uptake and stable DM yield. There was a strong interaction between nitrogen fertilization and year, because of decreased soil N mineralization with experimental time. Especially in the unfertilized treatments the DM yield decreased from 8.3 t ha^{-1} (1993) to 6.4 t ha^{-1} (1997), whereas in the same time the N uptake decreased from 120 kg ha^{-1} to 51 kg ha^{-1}. As a consequence, the apparent N utilization rate increased during experimental time especially in the highly fertilized stands (N150: 14% [1993] to 65% [1997]), while the CP-content decreased strongly about 20 (N150) to 30 (N60) g kg^{-1} DM.

The combination of mineral (30 kg N ha^{-1} subsurface) and organic N fertilizer to a total amount of 110 and 190 kg N ha^{-1} showed no different effect on DM and NE$_L$ yield compared with pure mineral N-fertilization, but N uptake and CP content was reduced if slurry was added (data not presented). Therefore, with 110 kg N ha⁻¹ only half of the apparent N utilization rate was calculated for the slurry N component compared with pure mineral N fertilizer, while at the high N level no differences were measured between mineral and organic N utilization rate. The response of the organic N component on DM-yield increased with experimental time.

The results of experiment II showed significant genotype by N interactions for DM yield, NE_L yield, CP content and starch content. Nitrogen uptake and NE_L concentration was not affected. The N response on DM yield varied with genotype, particularly at high N levels (Table 2). Without N fertilization, the DM yield was reduced between 16 % (cv. Jericho) and 36% (cv. Magda) compared with the high N level; reduction from 150 to 50 kg N ha⁻¹ reduced DM yield between 3% (cv. Jericho) and 18% (cv. Magda). Therefore, typical low-input and high-input cultivars may be classified. CP content varied between cultivars mainly at the high N level, whereas the greatest differences in starch content occurred at low N level.

TABLE 1. EFFECT OF MINERAL NITROGEN FERTILIZATION ON YIELD AND FORAGE QUALITY PARAMETERS OF FORAGE MAIZE (MEAN OF 5 YEARS, LOAMY SAND SITE).

N-fertilizer[4] kg N ha⁻¹	DM[1] t ha⁻¹	NE_L[2] GJ ha⁻¹	Starch t ha⁻¹	Nitrogen kg N ha⁻¹	DM[1] g kg⁻¹	NE_L[2] MJ kg⁻¹ DM	Starch g kg⁻¹ DM	CP[3] g kg⁻¹ DM
0	7.8ᶜ	49.4ᶜ	1.71ᵇ	82ᶠ	303ᵇ	6.36	219	65ᵉ
30	9.2ᵇ	59.3ᵇ	2.17ᵃᵇ	101ᵉ	325ᵃ	6.41	233	68ᵈᵉ
60	10.5ᵃ	67.0ᵃ	2.46ᵃ	121ᵈ	321ᵃᵇ	6.36	229	72ᵈ
90	10.9ᵃ	70.0ᵃ	2.64ᵃ	133ᶜᵈ	311ᵃᵇ	6.41	233	78ᶜ
110	10.9ᵃ	69.8ᵃ	2.59ᵃ	139ᵃᵇᶜ	317ᵃᵇ	6.39	231	80ᵇᶜ
150	11.4ᵃ	73.1ᵃ	2.65ᵃ	150ᵃ	315ᵃᵇ	6.40	224	84ᵃᵇ
190	10.8ᵃ	68.8ᵃ	2.38ᵃ	147ᵃᵇ	304ᵇ	6.36	211	87ᵃ
LSD₀.₀₅	1.1	7.0	0.59	13	20	n.s.	n.s.	5

[1]dry matter, [2]net energy of lactation, [3]crude protein, [4]included 30 kg N ha⁻¹ subsurface fertilizer. Means with the same letter are not significantly different. LSD = least significant difference with p<0.05. n.s. = p>0.05.

TABLE 2. INFLUENCE OF GENOTYPE ON THE EFFECT OF NITROGEN FERTILIZATION ON DRY MATTER YIELD, CP-CONTENT AND STARCH CONTENT OF 8 MAIZE CULTIVARS (MEAN OF 5 YEARS, LOAMY SAND SITE).

N-fertilizer[3] kg ha⁻¹		0	50	150	0	50	150	0	50	150
	Maturity	DM[1]-yield			CP[2]			Starch		
Cultivar	class	--------t ha⁻¹---------			------g kg⁻¹ DM-----			------g kg⁻¹ DM------		
Alarik	early	9.4ᵇᴬ	11.1ᵃᴬ	11.7ᵃᴮ	65ᶜᴬᴮ	73ᵇᴬ	83ᵃᴮ	247ᵃᴬ	219ᵃᴬᴮ	241ᵃᴬ
Kid	early	8.8ᵇᴬ	11.1ᵃᴬ	12.6ᵃᴬᴮ	68ᵃᴬ	71ᵇᴬ	83ᵃᴮ	240ᵃᴬ	262ᵃᴬ	254ᵃᴬ
Naxos	early	9.3ᵇᴬ	10.6ᵇᴬ	12.4ᵃᴬᴮ	64ᶜᴬᴮ	72ᵇᴬ	81ᵃᴮᶜ	289ᵃᴬ	263ᵃᴬ	263ᵃᴬ
Jericho	early	9.5ᵇᴬ	11.0ᵃᵇᴬ	11.3ᵃᴮ	67ᶜᴬ	74ᵇᴬ	95ᵃᴬ	271ᵃᴬ	266ᵃᴬ	224ᵃᴬ
Helix	early	10.1ᵇᴬ	11.9ᵃᴬ	13.3ᵃᴬ	60ᶜᴮ	68ᵇᴬ	81ᵃᴮᶜ	224ᵃᴬᴮ	233ᵃᴬᴮ	215ᵃᴬ
Pirat	early	9.6ᵇᴬ	11.1ᵃᴬ	13.3ᵃᴬ	62ᵇᴬᴮ	68ᵇᴬ	84ᵃᴮ	226ᵃᴬᴮ	225ᵃᴬᴮ	262ᵃᴬ
Helmi	mid-earl.	8.9ᶜᴬ	11.3ᵇᴬ	13.5ᵃᴬ	60ᶜᴮ	69ᵇᴬ	78ᵃᴮᶜ	177ᵇᴮ	211ᵃᴬᴮ	243ᵃᴬ
Magda	mid-earl.	8.9ᶜᴬ	11.4ᵇᴬ	13.9ᵃᴬ	61ᶜᴮ	69ᵇᴬ	76ᵃᶜ	167ᵇᴮ	194ᵃᵇᴮ	253ᵃᴬ
Mean		9.3	11.2	12.8	63	71	83	230	234	245
LSD₀.₀₅ cv. x N		1.7			6			65		

[1]dry matter, [2]crude protein, [3]included 30 kg N ha⁻¹ subsurface fertilizer. Means with the same letter are not significantly different (capital letters: within N-treatment, small letters: within cultivars). LSD = least significant difference with p<0.05.

CONCLUSIONS

Under practical farm conditions, especially in regions of intensive forage production, the long-term slurry application increased the soil N content, which covered the actual N fertilizer effect on forage maize. Under marginal climatic conditions, the amount of N fertilization may be reduced to under 100 kg N ha[-1], but the genotypic variability in N response should be considered. At a location with high N status, the N utilization rate of organic and mineral N may be calculated with nearly the same amount. Experiments concerning the N effect on yield and quality parameters of forage maize should be established for a long time and should consider the genotypic variability in N response.

REFERENCES

Greef, J. M., H. Ott, R. Wulfes and F. Taube, 1999. Growth analysis of dry matter accumulation and N uptake of forage maize cultivars affected by N supply. Journal of Agricultural Science, Cambridge, 132: 31-43.

Muchow, R.C. and T. S. Sinclair, 1995. Effect of nitrogen supply on maize yield: II. Field and model analysis. Agronomy Journal, 87: 642-648.

Taube, F., M. Wachendorf, J. M. Greef and R. Wulfes, 1997. Perspektiven semi-intensiver Produktionssysteme in Milchvieh-/Futterbauregionen Norddeutschlands (Perspectives of Semi-Intensive Production Systems for Dairy Farms in Northern Germany). Berichte über Landwirtschaft, 75: 586–603 (In German with English and French abstracts).

Nitrogen use of grass in Iceland in relation to soil and climate

H. BJÖRNSSON

Agricultural Research Institute, Keldnaholti, 112 Reykjavík, Iceland

SUMMARY

Under good conditions the marginal increase for fertilizer nitrogen in grass yield is around 67%. Values below 60% are indicative of poor growing conditions. Grass growth is related to temperature, especially winter temperature. Results are presented from a long-term experiment on permanent grass, 1954 to 1996. The soil is rich in organic matter as is typical for soils of volcanic origin. On average 84 kg N ha⁻¹ year⁻¹ were harvested from nitrogen sources that are independent of N application, mainly rhizospheric biological fixation. This is about twice the amount commonly found in Icelandic experiments. This fixation is most likely the fertility process that varies with winter temperature. The fate of the one-third of fertilizer nitrogen that is not recovered in yield is not known although there is some indication of accumulation in soil on plots fertilized with nitrogen.

Keywords: andosols, fixation, nitrogen mineralization, permanent grassland, temperature

INTRODUCTION

Icelandic agriculture is primarily based on permanent grassland on soils of volcanic origin, andosols, or on histosols, in a cool temperate oceanic climate. The three factors, permanent grass, andosols and humid climate, all support a continuous accumulation of soil organic matter. Of importance is the tendency of andosols, rich in allophane clay, to accumulate more organic matter than other mineral soils. The C/N ratio is usually also high (Shoji *et al.*, 1993).

Grass takes up fertilizer N efficiently when applied in spring under good conditions and application late in the growing season also gives good results (Björnsson and Hermannsson, 1989, Björnsson, 1998a, b). Published values on marginal N uptake commonly range from 55 to 75% of the N applied (for a sample of references see Björnsson *et al.*, 1975). Two-thirds can be anticipated under good conditions and values below say 60%, if evaluated with good accuracy, should be regarded as indicators of N losses such as denitrification under wet soil conditions (Björnsson, 1979, 1998 b), although immobilization is also a possibility.

RESULTS

Grass growth in relation to temperature

Grass growth in Iceland is strongly related to temperature. Table 1 shows the effect of mean temperature, September to June, on grass growth the following summer, adjusted for dates of cut that summer and previous summer (Björnsson and Helgadóttir, 1988). The yield data are annual means, 1951 to 1983, of long-term experiments from four experimental stations. At two of the stations the experimental period was split in two, thus allowing a fertility increase in time. Without adjustments the regression coefficient is 786 kg ha^{-1}°C^{-1}. Unexpected is that winter temperature is more strongly related to grass growth than is summer temperature. In contrast to the onset of spring, summer temperature is rather less variable and a simple linear regression is insufficient to model its effect. Results from nitrogen experiments alone (Table 1) indicate that plots without N application respond to temperature, although N response also increases as temperature increases. The periods effect was nonsignificant for the 0N treatment and the response to fertilizer N decreases with time at two stations.

TABLE 1. REGRESSION OF GRASS YIELD ON MEAN TEMPERATURE SEPTEMBER TO JUNE AT FOUR EXPERIMENTAL STATIONS IN ICELAND 1951 TO 1983 (FROM BJÖRNSSON AND HELGADÓTTIR, 1988).

	Mean fertilizer N kg ha^{-1}	Mean yield DM t ha^{-1}	Regression, DM kg ha^{-1} °C^{-1} coefficient	standard error
All experiments	95	5.1	735	92
Nitrogen experiments	100	5.2	842	111
Without nitrogen	0	2.8	617	99
Nitrogen response			171	55

Long term nitrogen experiment

Results are presented from a long-term experiment with comparison of nitrogen fertilizers, 1954 to 1996, at the experimental station Skriduklaustur in eastern Iceland. The presentation is restricted to the nitrogen levels 0, 75 and 120 kg N ha^{-1} year^{-1}, nitrogen applied in spring as ammonium nitrate and other nutrients nonlimiting. Yield results are restricted to 27 of the 43 experimental years when nitrogen analyses are available.

The site is on a deep andic gleysol that was drained with open ditches before 1950. It was cultivated without ploughing in 1951 and has remained a permanent pasture since. The experiment is located near a ditch and the drainage conditions are optimal. Some soil properties have been determined a few times. Results presented here are from a detailed soil sampling following the termination of the experiment in 1996 (Thorvaldsson, G., T. Gudmundsson and H. Björnsson, in preparation). Table 2 shows results that relate to soil organic matter for the three treatments, each value a mean from three plots. Block differences were eliminated for the calculation of standard deviations. These soil properties do not vary at deeper horizons for the treatments selected.

Mean values for 10-60 cm depth are bulk weight 0.75 g cm^{-3}, 10.4% loss on ignition and the carbon and nitrogen content is 41 and 3.1 g kg^{-1} respectively. The values below the surface horizon are typical for Icelandic andosols (Arnalds *et al.*, 1995). The high organic matter contents in the surface layer may indicate that the soil had peaty characters prior to drainage. On the contrary, comparisons with earlier analyses (Helgason, 1975) indicate that a surface layer, rich in organic matter, is developing.

TABLE 2. VALUES IN TWO SURFACE HORIZONS FOR SOIL PROPERTIES RELATED TO ORGANIC MATTER.

Fertilizer	Bulk weight g cm^{-3}		Loss on ignition %		C g kg^{-1}		N g kg^{-1}		N kg ha^{-1}
N kg ha^{-1}	0-5 cm	5-10cm	0-5 cm	5-10cm	0-5	5-10	0-5	5-10	0-10
0	0.50	0.69	29.0	13.7	134	55	9.6	4.4	3900
75	0.48	0.71	32.0	13.0	154	52	11.5	4.3	4300
120	0.48	0.70	31.3	14.7	146	61	11.2	5.0	4400
Standard deviation	0.028	0.036	1.6	2.0	10.6	8.8	0.70	0.73	

Table 3 shows yield and nitrogen contents and uptake presented as means and standard deviations of annual values for the 27 years when nitrogen has been determined. In the later years the experiment was cut only once per season in eight years. Yield and N uptake are shown for 1st cut and for the total of the season and nitrogen concentration is shown for both cuts. The mean yield for 27 years is very close to the mean for the whole experimental period of 43 years. Yield in the 0N treatment is large compared to the 2.8 t ha^{-1} reported in Table 1. That value is based on this and six other experiments that yielded about half as much for 0N. The annual variation in yield or N uptake, as expressed in the standard deviations, is increased by the irregularities in the number of cuts. The profile of treatment yields over years shows nearly parallel variations and the response to N fertilizers is little variable. This can be expressed as pairwise coefficients of correlation between vectors of yield or N uptake. They are >0.90, except for total N uptake where the correlation of 0N with the 75N and 120N treatments is somewhat less. The N content in yield decreases significantly as yield increases, except for the 0N treatment. The coefficients are -0.3, -1.0 and -1.1 g N kg^{-1} for an increase in DM yield of 1.0 t ha^{-1} for the 0N, 75N and 120N kg ha^{-1} treatments respectively, and the standard error of coefficients is 0.3. This relationship may partially explain the effect of temperature on yield response to nitrogen (see previous section).

The marginal increase in N uptake for increased N fertilization is uneven for the two intervals. Of course, experimental error may be causing the low yield of 75 kg ha^{-1} relative to the other two treatments. Otherwise, the 69% for an increase from 75 to 120 kg ha^{-1} indicates optimal conditions for the utilization of nitrogen. It is known that white clover sometimes contributed significantly to the 0N-treatment. Assuming 67% utilization of 75 kg N ha^{-1} this contribution is 14 kg N ha^{-1} and the remainder, 83 kg N ha^{-1}, is the estimated contribution of other N sources to the N uptake, equal at all N levels. Over the 43 years' duration of this experiment this quantity is equivalent to 80 to 90% of the nitrogen presently found in the top 10 cm of the soil profile. More nitrogen is required in order to sustain this uptake, a 50% increase to 125 kg N ha[-1] year[-1] is a cautious estimate of annually available soil nitrogen.

TABLE 3. YIELD, NITROGEN IN YIELD AND MARGINAL NITROGEN UPTAKE FOR INCREASED N APPLICATION.

Fertilizer N kg ha[-1]	DM yield t ha[-1]		Nitrogen g kg[-1]		Nitrogen uptake kg ha[-1]		Marginal N-uptake
	1st cut	total	1st cut	2nd cut	1st cut	total	
A. Mean values							
0	3.36	4.86	19.5	21.7	65	97	
75	4.63	6.24	21.9	21.0	100	133	48 %
120	5.06	6.89	25.0	21.9	125	164	69 %
B. Standard deviations							
0	1.25	1.17	1.7	3.3	23	23	
75	1.24	1.43	1.8	3.1	25	31	3.6
120	1.25	1.32	2.2	3.2	23	25	3.2

DISCUSSION

What are the sources of nitrogen and what is the fate of the nitrogen that is not recovered in yield? Soil N mineralization and atmospheric N compounds are the common answers to the first question. Nitrogen in precipitation is usually found to be <1 kg N ha[-1], and assuming the dry deposition of N resources to be of the same magnitude, the atmospheric contribution of nitrogen compounds can be neglected. The experiment is on a drained soil and, at least initially, net mineralization of organic matter would be expected. A preliminary comparison with earlier soil measurements, however, does not indicate a decline in soil organic matter, but rather the opposite. No decline of this N source with time has been observed. The remaining alternative is fixation of atmospheric N by soil microbia. This activity has especially been studied in warm climates. In temperate climates it has been estimated in the long-term Rothamsted experiments. In the Broadbalk wheat experiment the biological fixation is estimated >30 kg N ha[-1] year[-1] since 1843 and in the wilderness area the accumulation of organic matter since 1882 corresponds to a minimum of 39 kg N ha[-1] year[-1] (Dart, 1986). The values reported for Rothamsted are of the same magnitude as found in Icelandic experiments, except for the experiment discussed here where it is twice as much.

One might expect less fixation in the cooler and shorter summers of Iceland than in England. The relationship between temperature and grass growth reported is best explained as an effect on biological N fixation, perhaps because length of summer is correlated with winter temperature. This fixation appears to be rather little affected by N-application. Icelandic agriculture has for thousand years depended on cutting fields that have received no fertilizers. N fixation is probably responsible for maintaining their fertility.

The fate of nitrogen not recovered in yield is a more difficult question. Release from grass roots and soil microorganisms would increase N response in the second and later years compared to the first experimental year. This is not the case, the nitrogen is not recovered. Denitrification and leaching are probably responsible when the recovery is significantly less than two-thirds. Under good conditions they should be minimal, at least in the growing season. An alternative explanation is the accumulation of soil organic matter. The results on soil nitrogen in Table 2 indicate a limited accumulation of organic matter on plots receiving nitrogen, although in small amounts compared to the nitrogen not accounted for.

REFERENCES

Arnalds, O., C. T. Hallmark and L. P. Wilding, 1995. Andisols from four different regions of Iceland. Soil science society of America Journal, 59: 161-169.

Björnsson, H., F. Pálmason and J. Sigvaldason, 1975. Soils, fertilization and grassland production (In Swedish). Nordisk jordbrugsforskning, 57: 169-174.

Björnsson, H., 1979. Utilization of fertilizer nitrogen in Icelandic grassland experiments (In Swedish). Nordisk Jordbrugsforskning, 61: 273-274.

Björnsson, H., 1998a. Application of nitrogen fertilizers in autumn. In: Ecological Aspects of Grassland Management. Proceedings of the 17th General Meeting of the European Grassland Federation. Debrecen, Hungary, Agricultural University Debrecen May 18-21, 1998 (G. Nagy og K. Petö eds.): 639-642.

Björnsson, H., 1998b. Fertilizer application in late summer and autumn (In Icelandic). Rádunautafundur 1998, 141-154.

Björnsson, H. and Á. Helgadóttir, 1988. The effect of temperature variation on grass yield in Iceland, and its implications for dairy farming. In: The Impact of Climatic Variations on Agriculture. Vol. 1 Assessments in Cool Temperature and Cold Regions (M. L. Parry, T. R. Carter and N. T. Konijn editors). Kluwer Academic Publishers Group, Dordrecht: 445-474.

Björnsson, H. and J. Hermannsson, 1989. Pasture production and quality in a cool oceanic climate. XVI International Grassland Congress, Nice, France: 1453-1454.

Dart, P. J., 1986. Nitrogen fixation associated with non-legumes in agriculture. Plant and Soil, 90: 303-334.

Helgason, B., 1975. Changes in the base status and soil organic matter content resulting from long-term use of three nitrogen fertilizers (Tables and summary in English) . Íslenzkar landbúnadarrannsóknir, 7: 8-19.

Shoji, S., M. Nanzyo and R. A. Dahlgren, 1993. Volcanic ash soils. Genesis, properties and utilization. Elsevier, Amsterdam. 288 pp.

Research on diagnostic tools of nitrogen status of winter wheat

N. MAES, B. HALLAUX, J.L. HERMAN AND J.P. DESTAIN

Agricultural Research Centre (C.R.A.) - Department Crop Production, 5030 Gembloux, Belgium

SUMMARY

In order to adjust fertilizer N advice to cereal needs, trials testing different parameters able to be correlated with the N status of winter wheat were conducted since 1998 in two main agricultural regions of Belgium: Loam region and Condroz (clay and loam soils).

The parameters were: total N content of the crop (dynamic of N uptake and critical curve), nitrate content of basal stem, and chlorophyll content. Moreover, different measurements related to chlorophyll and photosynthesis activity were made on fresh material or directly in the field: chlorophyll meter and laser chlorophyll fluorescence.

Generally, all measurements and tools showed satisfactory correlations with levels of available nitrogen for crop (mineral soil N + fertilizer N). Tested tools are suitable in order to detect a nitrogen deficiency early. However, site and climate were able to affect widely these tools and the choice of reference values must always be adapted. Nevertheless, by combining the estimated N balance sheet method with the most relevant diagnostic tools, it seems possible to better fine-tune N fertilization of winter wheat and to reach both economic (quantity and quality of harvest) and environmental (lowering residual N in soil) objectives.

Keywords: diagnostic tools, N balance, nitrogen fertilization, N status, winter wheat

INTRODUCTION

As far as nitrogen fertilization of winter wheat is concerned, different aims of research are followed at the Department Crop Production of CRA: the improvement of the prediction of mineral nitrogen provided by the soil and of the knowledge of the needs of crops (forecast nitrogen balance method), numerous studies of the N status of plants and choice on type of split application. In this paper, the use of diagnostic tools of N status of winter wheat will be discussed.

In Belgium, fertilizer nitrogen of winter wheat is split applied at growth stages 25, 30 and 37-39 (Bodson *et al.*, 1994; Destain *et al.*, 1997). The total fertilization rate can be estimated with good precision at the end of the winter with a nitrogen balance method. The utilisation of a diagnostic tool would allow us to modulate the last split application. Indeed, from GS 32, it is possible using these tools to discriminate crops on the basis of their nitrogen uptake.

MATERIALS AND METHODS

Four trials with 5 rates of N fertilization of winter wheat were conducted in 2 locations differing by soil and climate in Belgium during 1998 and 1999. Diagnostic tools of N status of crops investigated were: N content and critical curve with determination of a nitrogen nutrition index (NNI), Nitrate content in basal stem sap, chlorophyllmeter measurement and chlorophyll fluorescence. Most of measurements were made at GS 30, 32, 37, 39 and 50. Details on the measurements are as follows:

- critical curve of nitrogen is plotted according to Justes (1993) and Gate (1995). This curve represents the evolution of N concentration in the aerial biomass related to the evolution of the optimal biomass during the all vegetative period. The curve allows to calculate a nutritional nitrogen index (NNI) defined as the ratio between N concentration observed and the value on the curve for the biomass considered. According to Justes (1993), a N deficiency is suspected when the value of NNI falls below 0.9.

- regular measurements of nitrate concentration are taken between GS 31 and 39. Nitrate content of sap in basal stem is considered as a good indicator of N availiability for the plant. This parameter is used in the commercial Jubil method (INRA-ITCF - France). A total N rate is proposed, based on the forecast balance sheet method, 40 kg N is subtracted from this amount and reserved for the late application. Based on critical values, the decision of applying or not the third split dressing is taken.

- by chlorophyllmeter technic (N-Tester of Hydro-Agri), a measurement of chlorophyll colour at two wavelengths is made directly in the field at different growth stages (GS 32, 37, 39 and 45) on the last unfurled leaf.

- the principle of chlorophyll fluorescence is the following: lighting green plants with UV and analyzing the fluorescence reemitted in the blue (F440), green (F520), red (F690) and far red (F740) wave lengths. It is possible to find a good relation of the values obtained (ratios F440/F690 and F440/F740) with growth conditions and differing stress sources (Heisel et al., 1997; Lichtenthaller and Miehé, 1997).

TABLE 1. CORRELATIONS (R) BETWEEN THE LEVEL OF N APPLIED FOR THE TWO FIRST DRESSINGS AND VALUES OBTAINED BY MEASUREMENTS WITH DIFFERENT TOOLS (AT GS 39).

	SITE A 1998	SITE B 1998	SITE A 1999	SITE B 1999
Nutritional N Index	0.91***, n=30	0.89***, n=14	0.89***, n=15	0.92***, n=20
Nitrate content in basal stem sap	-	-	0.96**, n=6	0.97**, n=6
Chlorophyll meter	0.87***, n=60	0.94***, n=20	0.94***, n=20	0.83***, n=15

RESULTS AND DISCUSSION

After two years of experimentation it appears that tools employed from GS 32 are able to discriminate plants which were conducted with different rates of N (Table 1). Environmental effect (site and year) can affect the relevance of the tool.

For the NNI, if on one hand a value <1 always shows a N deficiency during vegetative development, on the other hand, a value ≥1 can lead to a later N deficiency in the case where the third split dressing is not applied. Moreover, the NNI is not predictive of the potential yield as a site effect is predominant. Using this index simultanously with a yield index (ratio between observed yield for a treatment and maximum yield observed in the site) cannot eliminate the site effect (Fig. 1). Moreover, determination of this NNI is difficult in the practice as both determinations of biomass and N content are needed.

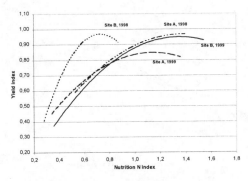

FIGURE 1. RELATION BETWEEN NNI AND YIELD INDEX (GS 39).

According to nitrate content in the sap of basal stem (Jubil method), a third split dressing is never applied (as observed values are above critical values). This conducts to a low protein content and N removed by the harvest without affecting yield as compared to «Livre blanc» method («Livre blanc» : annual publication of results and recommended information for winter wheat for farmers published by Agricultural University and Agricultural Research Centre of Gembloux) (Table 2).

TABLE 2. YIELD, PROTEIN CONTENT, N REMOVED AND N EFFICIENCY FOR TWO METHODS OF TUNING N FERTILIZATION.

Total N rate applied and splitting schedule (kg N/ha)	"Livre blanc" 57 - 64 - 65 = 186	Jubil 50 - 118 - 0 = 168
Yield (kg/ha)	9 413	9 470
Protein content (%)	11.6	10.6
N removed (kg N/ha)	164	152
Efficiency of N(kg/kg N)	19.5	24.7

Furthermore, one can suspect in the case where a high quality of grain is needed, ITCF has recently proposed to modify recommandation with new critical values (Anonymous, 2000).

Chlorophyllmeter values are highly correlated to N fertilizer level but with a strong pedoclimatic effect (Fig. 2). When using the chlorophyllmeter index at GS 39 (defined as the ratio between chlorophyllmeter value observed for the treatment and maximum chlorophyllmeter value for this site), 84% of the variation of yield index (ratio between yield observed for the treatment and maximum yield for the site) and 81% of the variation of a fertilization index (ratio between N needed -mineralization + fertilization- from this GS 39 to harvest and total N needed) can be explained (Figs. 3 and 4). To be a relevant tool, chlorophyll meter technic needs an interpretation in term of indexes, the advantages of this tool are to be found in the simplicity of use and the possibility of making numerous repetitions in order to take the field variability into account. Pratically, the need for non limiting N window on a small area in the field establishing the chlorophyllmeter value maximum of the site, is requested.

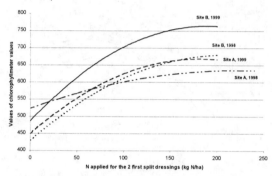

FIGURE 2. RELATION BETWEEN N RATE AND CHLOROPHYLL METER MEASURES (GS 39).

With regards to chlorophyll fluorescence, ratios blue to red (F440/F690) and far red (F440/F740) at GS 39 are negatively correlated to the total N applied for the two first split dressings and not depending on the year and site (Figs. 5 and 6). However, a lack of measurements leads to dubiousness over the relevance of this tool. At GS 50, the reliability of these ratios seems poor. Generally, these ratios are influenced by stress sources before that N deficiency signs occur. Although actually measurements are made on fresh leaves in the laboratory, possibilities of working in the field can be studied (portable system).

CONCLUSIONS

To be able to assess the N status of the plant, a diagnostic tool must detect a deficiency early and its reference values must be stable in time and space while interpretation in term of phytotechnic parameters is possible. Moreover, this tool can be easily used and must lead to an economic return. Taking account of results obtained these two last years, chlorophyllmeter measurements have been shown to satisfy these criteria best.

Although, interpretation of values collected in field in terms of indices such as a fertilization index, is necessary. It is the reason why it seems essential that the use of such diagnostic tools will be combined with a network of reference plots, as a basis of N advices well adapted to site and year.

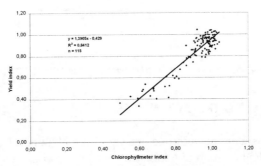

FIGURE 3. RELATION BETWEEN CHLOROPHYLL METER INDEX AND YIELD INDEX (GS 39).

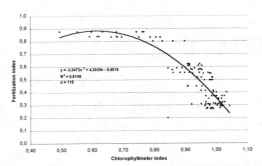

FIGURE 4. RELATION BETWEEN CHLOROPHYLL METER INDEX AND FERTILIZATION N INDEX (GS 39).

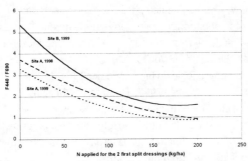

FIGURE 5. RELATION BETWEEN N RATE AND CHLOROPHYLL FLUORESCENCE (RATIO BLUE TO RED F440/ F690) (GS 39).

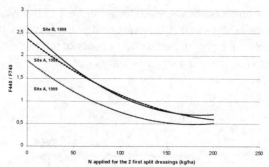

FIGURE 6. RELATION BETWEEN N RATE AND CHLOROPHYLL FLUORESCENCE (RATIO BLUE TO RED F440/ F740) (GS 39).

ACKNOWLEDGEMENTS

This experiment has been carried out with financial support from the Research and Development Administration of Ministry of Small Enterprises, Traders and Agriculture. Thanks to the laboratory of applied optical group of CNRS of Strasbourg.

REFERENCES

Anonymous, 2000. Jubilâ Les points forts de la nouvelle version. Perspectives agricoles, n°256: 70-71.

Bodson, B., J. P. Destain and A. Iorgiu,1994. Study of the dynamic of uptake by winter wheat of split applied nitrogen and the role of each dressing to improve nitrogen balance and crop's economic optimum. 3rd ESA Congress, Padova (I), 448-449.

Destain, J. P., B. Bodson, J. L. Herman, E. François and J. Franc. 1997. Uptake and efficiency of split applications of nitrogen fertilizer in winter wheat. In «T. Ando et al., Plant Nutrition for sustainable food production and environnement», 633-634.

Heisel, F., M. Sowinska, E. Khalili, C. Eckert, J. A. Miehé and H. K., 1997. Laser-induced fluorescence imaging for monitoring nitrogen fertilising treatments of wheat, Lichtenthaler, Advances in Laser Remote Sensing for Terrestrial and Oceanographic Applications, R. M. Narayanan, J. E. Kalshoven, Jr., Editors, Proc. Of SPIE Vol 3059, p. 10.

Gate, P., 1995. «Ecophysiologie du Blé», Lavoisier, Paris, 429 pp.

Lichtenthaller, H. and J. Miehé, 1997. Fluorescence imaging as a diagnostic tool for plant stress, Elsevier Science Ltd. Trends in plant science Vol 2, N°8, 316-320.

Justes, 1993. " Diagnostic de la nutrition azotée du blé à partir de la teneur en nitrate de la base de tige, application au raisonnement de la fertilisation azotée ", thèse de doctorat à l'Institut National agronomique de Paris-Grignon, 227 pp.

Nitrogen use efficiency in tomato and potato as affected by water regime and N fertilisation

L. DALLA COSTA AND R. GIOVANARDI

DPVTA-Dipartimento Produzione Vegetale, Università di Udine, Italy

SUMMARY

An experiment was performed to compare nitrogen use in 2 solanaceae species in lysimeters of 0.8 m^2. Potato, grown in 1994 and 1996 and tomato grown in 1998 were fertilised with 0, 100, 200 kg ha^{-1} N as urea, and irrigated with 3 water regimes: $ET_{1.0}$, water stressed ($ET_{0.7}$), and over-irrigated (OW) consisting in surface irrigation (potato) with almost $ET_{1.2}$ and sub surface irrigation for tomato(watertable at 0.5 m). In tomato fertilisation with 200 kg ha^{-1} N was distributed as top dressing with urea; or via fertigation. After final harvest an over-irrigation simulating an intense rainfall max estimated NO_3-N losses a leachates.

Both crops showed higher ANR and better AE with abundant water availability during the whole crop cycle. The results on tomato indicated fertigation as best fertilisation system to allow the highest N uptake, increasing ANR. With good water availability, increasing N rate from 100 to 200 kg ha^{-1} caused a reduction in AE of 24% in tomato and of 30% in potato

The potential risk for NO_3-N losses with leaching was confirmed, especially at high fertiliser rates and when combined with low water availability during the crop cycle.

Over-irrigated in both years potato released the lowest amount of NO_3-N in the percolating water, as expected by the high NUE coefficients observed; tomato showed a lower concentration of NO_3-N (-50.1%) than potato. The NO_3-N content in leaching water of fertigation treatments was found similar to conventionally fertilised treatments.

Keywords: fertigation, irrigation, leaching nitrate, nitrogen, potato, tomato

INTRODUCTION

Modern crop production management involves optimising applied N and water so that neither is in excess, yield is maximised and leaching of N into the groundwater is minimised (Westermann et al.,1988). Nitrogen use efficiency of the crop, expressed by the parameters suggested by Craswell et al. (1984) allow comparisons among crops in their differential ability to rescue applied nitrogen (ANR) and to convert it in agronomic product (PE). The overall agronomic efficiency is depending on timing and rate of application of both N fertiliser and water (Joern and Vitosh, 1995). Low recovery of applied nitrogen raises the problem of the fate of applied N and the potential risk of groundwater pollution.

MATERIALS AND METHODS

The experiment was performed during three years in small-sized lysimeters (0.8 m² in surface and 0.7 m in depth), covered by a rain shelter.

Potato cv. Liseta was grown in 1994 and 1996, fertilised with 0, 100, 200 kg ha[-1] N, distributed as urea, and irrigated according to 3 water regimes: well-watered $ET_{1.0}$ (implying the restitution of ETm), water stressed ($ET_{0.7}$), and over-irrigated (OW), close to $ET_{1.2}$.

Tomato cv Rio Grande was planted in 1998, fertilised with 0, 100, 200 kg ha[-1] N distributed either as top dressing with urea splitt in 2 applications; or via fertigation splitted in 10 times. The 3 water regimes applied were: $ET_{1.0}$, water stressed $ET_{0.7}$, and over-watered (OW) feeding a subsurface water table set at 0.5 m depth.

N use efficiency (NUE) parameters were calculated according to Craswell et al. (1984): 1) Apparent Nitrogen Recovery (ANR), the increase of the above-ground N uptake compared to the unfertilised crop, per unit of N fertiliser applied, 2) Physiological Efficiency (PE), increase in yield dry weight per unit of N taken up, and their the product 3) AE, agronomic efficiency, which measures the increase in tuber yield of the fertilised crop compared to the unfertilised, again per unit of N fertiliser applied.

After final harvest an over-irrigation was performed on all crops simulating an intense rainfall and leachate was collected and analysed for NO_3-N content. The field design applied, a randomised block, with 2 replications was not organised as complete factorial.

RESULTS AND DISCUSSION

Yield results (Table 1) showed that both crops benefited from abundant irrigation (OW), and production was found higher than in $ET_{1.0}$. Irrigation in $ET_{1.0}$ was based on soil moisture content: the available water content (AWC) >60% was maintained through the season (ET1.0) and was considered close to optimum for both crops but was apparently allowing minor stress which hindered the best performance. Water-limiting treatments ($ET_{0.7}$) had a higher effect in potato (yield reduction of 17%) than in tomato (-13%). Yield reductions for potato were found to be comparable in the two years.

A positive effect of fertilization was evident for both crops: potato with an increase of 45% (D 0-200 N) in 1994 and 33% in 1996; in tomato 47% increase with conventional fertilization and 53% with fertigation.

The parameters used for NUE (table 2) displayed an more variable values for potato crop as regards Apparent Nitrogen Recovery in relation to the N rate applied than in tomato. N recovery is favoured by higher water availability in both crops. A remarkable increase in ANR was obtained modifying the way N was applied, namely, with split application (fertigation in tomato) as compared to top dressing. For both species higher rate of N distribution does not necessarily show lower ANR values as expected.

TABLE 1. YIELD DW (G M^{-2}) IN THE 3 EXPERIMENTS AS AFFECTED BY NITROGEN APPLICATION RATE (KG N HA^{-1}) AND WATER REGIME. TREATMENT 200F INDICATES FERTIGATION.

	Potato 1994			Potato 1996			Tomato 1998			
	0 N	100N	200N	0 N	100N	200N	0 N	100N	200N	200 F
ET$_{1.0}$	637 d	904 c	1040bc	583de	842b	836b	472e	667d	870b	978a
ET$_{0.7}$	529 e	619 d	982bc	490e	642cde	793bc	390e	609d	718cd	700cd
OW	682 d	1073 b	1351a	725bcd	996a	1053a	411e	725cd	790bc	1033a

Concerning agronomic efficiency of nitrogen fertilizer, lower variability in AE values were found in tomato in relation to the N rate applied. Higher values of agronomic efficiency were favoured by higher water availability in both crops. Increasing N application rate from 100 to 200 kg ha^{-1} causes a parallel decrease in AE from 29.7 kg tuber DW kg^{-1} N applied to 20.7 kg kg^{-1} N in potato, and from 25.8 to 19.5 kg fruit DW kg^{-1}N in tomato. A limited increase in AE was obtained modifying the way N was applied, with split application (fertigation in tomato) as compared to top dressing.

TABLE 2. NITROGEN USE EFFICIENCY PARAMETERS IN THE 3 EXPERIMENTS AS AFFECTED BY NITROGEN APPLICATION RATE (KG N HA^{-1}) AND IRRIGATION REGIME: ANR (E1), PE (KG KG^{-1}) AND AE (KG KG^{-1}). TREATMENT 200F INDICATES FERTIGATION.

	Potato 1994		Potato 1996		Tomato 1998		
	100N	200N	100N	200N	100N	200N	200 F
ANR							
ET$_{1.0}$	0.75	0.40	0.55	0.53	0.46	0.49	1.07
ET$_{0.7}$	0.24	0.41	0.40	0.49	0.65	0.53	0.93
OW	1.00	0.65	0.55	0.51	0.58	0.59	1.15
PE							
ET$_{1.0}$	36	52	49	23	43	41	24
ET$_{0.7}$	40	54	34	31	32	31	17
OW	42	52	55	34	54	32	27
AE							
ET$_{1.0}$	27	20	26	13	20	20	26
ET$_{0.7}$	9	23	15	15	21	16	15
OW	39	33	27	16	32	19	31

As regards water use efficiency (Table 3) referred to total biomass and to yield (data not shown) showed in general an increase with increasing rates of N applied, except in 1996 for potato (significant interaction year X N).

The modality of N fertilizer distribution (top dressing of fertigation in tomato) displayed a remarkable effect in increasing WUE.

Increasing N-NO$_3$ concentration in leachate after harvest was observed (Fig. 1) with high N fertilization rates, especially when final yield was lower (potato, 1996). Higher N-NO$_3$content occured in the leachate of water-limited treatments. Increased risk of high N-NO$_3$ concentration was found in the potato crop, in comparison with tomato, and lower risk of after-harvest N leaching in crops grown with better water management.

TABLE 3. WATER USE EFFICIENCY (G TOTAL DRY WEIGHT L⁻¹) IN THE 3 EXPERIMENTS AS AFFECTED BY NITROGEN APPLICATION RATE (KG N HA⁻¹) AND IRRIGATION REGIME. TREATMENT 200F INDICATES FERTIGATION.

	Potato 1994			Potato 1996			Tomato 1998			
	0 N	100N	200N	0 N	100N	200N	0 N	100N	200N	200F
$ET_{1.0}$	3.64cd	3.86cd	4.44bc	2.65cd	3.17abc	3.22ab	1.84f	2.31cd	2.7abc	2.99a
$ET_{0.7}$	6.55a	5.35b	4.65bc	2.21d	2.81bc	3.27ab	2.1def	2.89ab	2.78ab	3.08a
OW	1.88f	2.41ef	3.12de	2.79bc	2.96bc	3.55a	1.69f	2.21de	2.3cde	2.45bcd

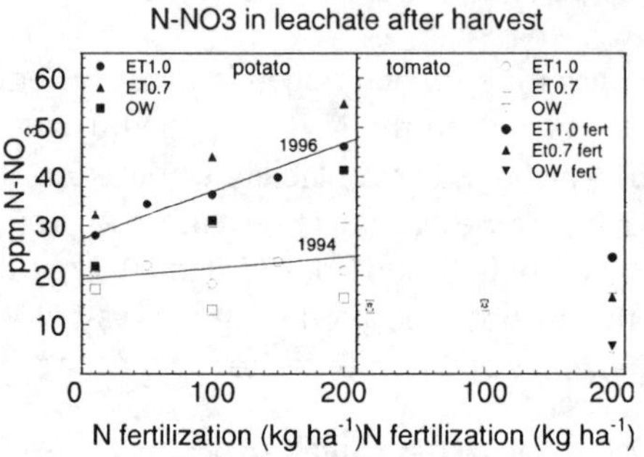

FIGURE 1. NO₃-N CONTENT (PPM) IN LEACHING WATER AFTER THE POST-HARVEST OVER-IRRIGATION: RESULTS OF THE 3 EXPERIMENTS AS AFFECTED BY NITROGEN APPLICATION RATE (KG N HA⁻¹) AND IRRIGATION REGIME.

CONCLUSIONS

Both crops showed, in the environmental conditions studied, similar requirements in terms of water supply and nitrogen nutrition. They displayed however appreciable differences in yield responses to the factors studied, in nitrogen recovery, and in agronomic efficiency.

The final over-irrigation produced a leachate with reasonably low concentration of N-NO₃ even with high fertiliser rates for both crops, but lower in case of tomato. However the higher risk of nitrate losses was confirmed in crops grown in unfavourable conditions of water supply.

REFERENCES

Craswell, E.T., 1984. In Advances in Plant Nutrition (Ed. Tinker P. B.). New York: Praeger Publ. pp. 1-56.

Joern, B. C. and M. L.Vitosh, 1995. Influence of applied nitrogen in potato: II. Recovery and partitioning of applied nitrogen. American Potato Journal, 72: 73-84.

Westermann, D. T., G. E. Kleinkopf and L. K. Porter, 1988. Nitrogen fertilisers efficiencies on potatoes. American Potato Journal, 65: 377-386.

N-efficiency under arable land and grassland measured by gravitation lysimeters

W. HEIN AND G. EDER

Bundesanstalt für Alpenländische Landwirtschaft (BAL) Gumpenstein, Irdning, Austria

S U M M A R Y

The changing of the animal manure system from farmyard manure to slurry happened in the 60's caused by economic factors. Slurry was applied to crops and grassland, sometimes in high amounts. In the beginning of the 90's when the biological organic farmers gained importance the farmyard system recovered.

At the BAL Gumpenstein a research project was started in 1992 to answer a lot of questions concerning the different animal manure systems. Cattle slurry, composted farmyard manure and farmyard manure were compared with each other and tested in exact field trials on grassland, arable land and in lysimeters.

The lysimeters contain 9 chambers with the following variants: 2 variants of silage maize on the level of manure from 3 LU, treated with cattle slurry (180 kg ha^{-1} y^{-1}) and composted farmyard manure; 2 variants of winter-rye on the level of 2 LU, treated with cattle slurry (120 kg ha^{-1} y^{-1}) and composted farmyard manure; clover-grass without animal manure; green fallow-land; 3 variants of permanent grassland on the level of 3 LU, treated with cattle slurry, composted farmyard manure + liquid manure and farmyard manure + liquid manure.

For measuring the amounts of nutrient leaching losses gravitation lysimeters are used in this project. The results show the concentration of nitrate in the seepage water and the whole nitrogen leaching losses during the years 1993 to 1999. The nitrate concentration varies from year to year depending on the precipitation. The legal limit for drinking water of 50 mg l^{-1} was overstepped only once with the average concentration for winter did rye in the year 1998, treated with slurry. Neither with silage maize nor with any variant of grassland the average nitrate concentration come to the legal limit. This is a good example of nitrogen leaching losses under arable land being much larger than under grassland. The soil under grassland is protected all year round with plant cover and its roots are able to take up water and nutrients for most of the year.

Keywords: animal manure system, arable land, cattle slurry, composted farmyard manure, grassland, nitrogen leaching losses

INTRODUCTION

Several institutions for agricultural research answered many questions concerning farmyard manure in the 50's and the years before (Sauerlandt, 1948; Franz, 1950). During the 60's many Austrian farmers changed their system of animal manure from farmyard manure to slurry because of its easier handling. Many scientific determinations were done to make the slurry system perfectly and to introduce it to the farmers effectively (Schmid, 1968; Schechtner, 1974; Hochkönig, 1981). Most of the buildings built at that time had a slurry system; cattle or pig slurry was given to different crops and grassland, even in high amounts. When the biological farmers grew more and more in numeber at the beginning of the 90's the farmyard manure system recovered (Bartussek, 1995).

For lack of scientific determinations as is which system is best the farmers are not sure what to do. Therefor the BAL Gumpenstein started a large project in the year 1992 to test three different systems of animal manure: untreated farmyard manure, composted farmyard manure and slurry, all manure coming from cattle. All kinds of animal manure were applied in exact field trials on grassland, arable land and in lysimeters.

MATERIALS AND METHODS

The main objective of the project is to compare the system of farmyard manure, composted farmyard manure and cattle slurry with each other to see the advantages and disadvantages of each system. The leaching losses of nutrients from the storage to the application are determined exactly and the influence of all different animal manure on the plants and the soil is analysed carefully.

The lysimeters are instruments for measuring the amounts of nutrient leaching losses in seepage water, especially the losses of nitrate. In this project the chambers that are treated with composted farmyard manure and slurry are of great interest.

The lysimeters consist of 9 chambers, filled with an eutric cambisoil with a pH-value of 5.8 and a humus content of 3.4%. The soil type is a sandy loam with 30% sand, 63% silt and 7% clay.

Two different crops and grassland are grown, the crops are silage maize on a level of 3 LU and winter rye on a level of 2 LU; the variants of grassland are clover-grass, green-fallow-land and permanent grassland. Clover-grass and green fallow-land are not manured, the permanent grassland is treated with cattle slurry, composted farmyard manure + liquid manure and farmyard manure + liquid manure.

The amount of nitrogen for silage maize is 180 kg ha^{-1} y^{-1}, the amount for winter-rye is 120 kg ha^{-1} y^{-1} with cattle slurry and the amount applied by composted farmyard manure is less.

The manure was given before sowing and only the slurry to silage maize was split up. The permanent grassland was manured on the level of mesure from 3 livestock units (LU).

RESULTS

The main results are presented in Table 1 and Fig. 1.

The seepage water is responsible for the transportation of the nutrients to the ground water and depends on many factors as the precipitation, the soil and the agricultural use.

TABLE 1. NO₃-N IN MG L⁻¹ (THE LIMIT OF 50 PPM NO₃ AGREES WITH 11.5 PPM NO₃-N).

		1993	1994	1995	1996	1997	1998	1999
Silage maize, cattle slurry 3 LU	maximum	14,74	15,70	9,75	11,68	17,61	17,79	9,63
	average	4,67	3,43	3,26	2,80	5,80	8,92	4,11
Silage maize, composted	maximum	6,85	2,97	3,45	6,23	11,68	15,51	8,05
farmyard manure 3 LU	average	1,47	1,08	1,22	2,13	6,57	8,18	3,99
Winter-rye, cattle slurry 2 LU	maximum	13,13	6,30	8,23	12,16	19,02	24,76	17,13
	average	3,08	2,66	3,72	5,85	8,03	13,01	4,47
Winter-rye, composted farmyard manure 2 LU	maximum	8,37	4,64	7,57	13,61	31,60	33,24	11,65
	average	2,91	2,36	4,99	10,80	8,93	9,65	4,05
Clover grass	maximum	15,43	0,97	0,71	2,96	4,50	6,83	1,03
	average	1,20	0,37	0,36	1,01	0,55	0,83	0,55
Green fallow land	maximum	8,28	3,38	0,39	1,95	3,60	1,10	1,02
	average	2,31	0,35	0,20	0,33	0,37	0,43	0,67
Grassland, cattle slurry 3 LU	maximum	3,56	0,78	0,37	1,58	1,08	0,77	1,79
	average	1,11	0,30	0,13	0,27	0,23	0,28	0,86
Grassland, composted farmyard manure + liquid manure 3 LU	maximum	2,94	1,54	0,69	1,18	2,12	1,14	2,04
	average	0,72	0,28	0,22	0,20	0,41	0,50	0,81
Grassland, farmyard manure + liquid manure 3 LU	maximum	1,36	0,62	0,27	1,12	0,94	0,97	0,54
	average	0,40	0,29	0,22	0,21	0,28	0,29	0,30

Table 1 shows the concentration of nitrate in the seepage water, the yearly average and the maximum value. The legal limit for nitrate in drinking water is 50 mg NO_3 l⁻¹, which is overstepped only once. Nitrite was hardly verifiable and the leaching of ammonium was less than 500 g NH_4-N ha⁻¹ y⁻¹, so only the losses of nitrate were determined. The amount of seepage water is bound up with the precipitation. The yearly precipitation varies from 836 mm in the year 1999 to 1,354 mm in the year 1997 and the yearly average is 1,010 mm, while the variation comes to 51%.

In Fig. 1 the amounts of NO_3-N that are eroded during the years 1993 – 1999 are presented. The difference between arable land and grassland is an important fact. Within the crops there is a difference between silage maize and winter rye because of the method of manuring. As long as the whole amount of manure is given to winter rye before sowing in autumn the N losses are higher than with silage maize when the amount of slurry is split up.

The differences between the individual years can be seen as well and especially year 1997 shows very high N losses caused by a high precipitation.

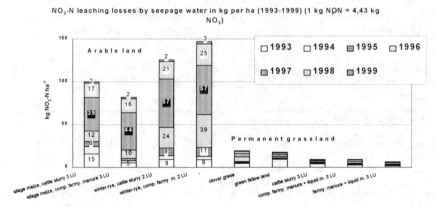

FIGURE 1. NO₃-N LEACHING LOSSES BY SEEPAGE WATER IN KG PER HA (1993 – 1999) (1 KG NO₃-N = 4,43 KG NO₃).

DISCUSSION AND CONCLUSIONS

Although the lysimeters were built and filled in the year 1992 there was no time for the soil to settle and so the results have to be viewed cautiously, especially for the year 1993. Therefore it is better to view the results from the year 1994 or 1995. The absolutely highest concentration of nitrate was found in winter rye in the year 1998 with 147 mg l⁻¹, treated by composted farmyard manure. The maximum value in 1997 of the same variant was 140 mg l⁻¹. The highest average concentration was found in the year 1998 with 57 mg l⁻¹ in winter rye treated with cattle slurry. Here the whole amount in one application before sowing was the problem. The value of 57 mg l⁻¹ in seepage water is above the legal limit, but all other average values are below it. Even the high amounts from 3 livestock units given to silage maize do not cause similar problems because during the vegetation period the plants use the nitrogen for growing.

Another fact can be seen well with this project, i.e. the big difference between arable land and grassland. The nitrogen leaching losses under arable land are larger than under grassland. So not even the manure on a level ofrom 3 LU to permanent grassland is a problem if the utilisation is adapted to the location and the intensity of farming.

REFERENCES

Bartussek, H., M. Tritthart, H. Würzl and W. Zoreta, 1995. Rinderstallbau. Leopold Stocker Verlag, Graz.

Franz, H., 1950. Neue Forschungen über den Rotteprozess von Stallmist und Kompost. Veröffentlichungen der Bundesanstalt für alpine Landwirtschaft Admont. Springer-Verlag. Wien.

Hochkönig, W., 1981. Wirtschaftlichkeit und Grenzen der Gülletechnik. Bericht über die 7. Arbeitstagung "Fragen der Güllerei", 29.9.-2.10.1981 in Gumpenstein, pp. 493-548.

Sauerlandt, W., 1948. Grundlagen der Bodenfruchtbarkeit. Humusdüngung und Bodengare. Metta Kinau Verlag Nachfolger, Lüneburg.

Schechtner, G., 1974. Aktuelle Fragen der Gülleanwendung auf dem Grünland. Bericht über die 6. Arbeitstagung "Fragen der Güllerei", 5.-7.6.1974 in Gumpenstein, pp.71-117.

Schmid, G., 1968. Gülleanwendung auf dem Ackerland. Bericht über die 5. Arbeitstagung "Fragen der Güllerei", 10.-12.9.1968 in Gumpenstein, pp. 147-160.

Optimizing N fertilization of fodder maize with respect to soil fertility, dry matter yield and limits to N residues at harvest

M. GEYPENS[1,2], J. MERTENS[1], L. VANONGEVAL[1] AND J. BRIES[1]

[1] Soil Service of Belgium, W. de Croylaan 48, B-3001 Leuven, Belgium
[2] Catholic University Leuven

SUMMARY

On dairy farms in the northern part of Belgium (Flanders), animal manure is the main nutrient source for fodder maize. On some maize fields, the excessive use of organic manure during the last two decades has led to an accumulation of young organic matter, a diminished N efficiency of the N fertilization and unacceptable nitrate losses to the environment. Since 1991, the organic and mineral fertilization of maize was more and more restricted through the Flemish manure legislation. Several experiments were carried out to determine the response of the fodder maize to these restrictions. Results of field experiments show that on fields with an 'organic manure history', N fertilization may be reduced substantially without any risk in reduction of the dry matter production. At the same time, N efficiency may be improved resulting in a reduction of the N residues in the soil profile at harvest. To realize this, N fertilization must be based on mineral N content of the soil in April and on the N delivery capacity during the growing season. As these factors may vary a lot between fields, a field-specific approach is needed.

Keywords: fodder maize, N fertilization, N-INDEX, N residue

INTRODUCTION

The Flemish Manure Decree, which is dealing with the maximal amounts of N and P_2O_5 applied to agricultural land as mineral or organic fertilizers, has changed the common fertilization practices in maize. The organic and mineral fertilization is restricted to the allowable fertilization rates for N en P at field level. Within these limitations, the N fertilization has to be such that the nitrate residue in the soil profile (0-90 cm) does not exceed 90 kg NO_3-N ha[-1] in the period between the first of October and the fifteenth of November (Bries et al., 2000). One of the main objectives of this regulation is to avoid nitrate pollution of the groundwater (EU nitrate directive). To reach these environmental objectives without reduction of crop yield, the N fertilization has to be optimized taking into account soil fertility and the availability of animal manure. Therefore, determining nitrogen composition of the manure and field-specific N recommendations will be necessary. In Belgium and the northern part of France, these field-specific N recommendations are based on the calculation of the N-INDEX of the field (Vandendriessche et al., 1996).

MATERIALS AND METHODS

N-INDEX is a calculated measure of available mineral N for a specific crop on a well determined field. Nitrogen-index is the sum of a maximum of 18 factors, some of which may be zero for some crops or situations (Vandendriessche et al., 1996):
N-INDEX = $x_1 + x_2 + ... + x_{18}$.

These factors may be divided in three groups:

- Factors which are determined by the amount of mineral N in the soil available for the crop and the amount of N, already taken up by the crop at the time the samples are taken. For maize, the amount of available mineral N in the soil is measured for the soil layers 0-30 and 30-60 cm.

- Factors determining the mineral N which will be supplied by the soil. The mineralization process is assessed by the summation of several subprocesses which will contribute to the total mineralization. Each subprocess is treated as a factor in the calculation of N-INDEX.

- The last factors taken into account are losses, e.g. leaching, volatilization, denitrification and run-off, resulting in a diminished availability of mineral N.

Based on this N-INDEX a N fertilizer recommendation is calculated which is generally formulated as: N recommendation = A - b x N-INDEX. The value of A and b for each arable crop are derived from field experiments.

The applicability of the N-INDEX is frequently tested in the past in short-and long term N fertilization trials on different soil types. On these field trials, several N rates were compared to the recommended N fertilization. Nitrogen was applied in mineral (ammonium nitrate) or organic form (cattle slurry). The cattle slurry was injected shortly before drilling the seed. Each treatment was replicated four times (split-plot design). The results of a long term (1995-1999) field trial on a loamy soil are summarised in Table 1.

RESULTS AND CONCLUSIONS

Table 1 shows that the dry matter yield is still relatively high (> 15 t ha^{-1}) on the plots where no fertilizer was applied during the previous 5 years. However, the yield on the fertilized plots is significantly higher. The optimal yield is reached on the plots with a N fertilization based on the N-INDEX. Mineral N fertilization above the recommended N rate did not necessary improve the dry matter production.

TABLE 1. RESULTS OF A N-FERTILIZATION TRIAL (R = RECOMMENDED N-RATE BASED ON N-INDEX) OF FODDER MAIZE ON A LOAMY SOIL IN BELGIUM (1995-1999).

year	N applied (kg N/ha)	yield (kg DM/ha)	
1995	0	17000	a
	83	17500	a
	139 (R)	17800	a
	195	16800	a
1996	0	14008	b
	71	15779	a
	105 (R)	16205	a
	104	15484	a
1997	0	14800	b
	78	15900	ab
	139 (R)	15600	ab
	183	16500	a
1998	0	13447	b
	86	19589	a
	127 (R)	20490	a
	200	20318	a
1999	0	15108	b
	112	21314	a
	176 (R)	21767	a
	200	21951	a

On fields with a high mineral N content before sowing or with a high N delivery capacity during the growing season, because of a regular and an abundant application of organic manure in the past, no fertilization is needed for an optimal dry matter production (see Fig. 2). This case proves the importance of the field-specific approach of the N-INDEX whereby the mineral N content in the soil profile as well as the N delivery capacity during the growing season is taken into account.

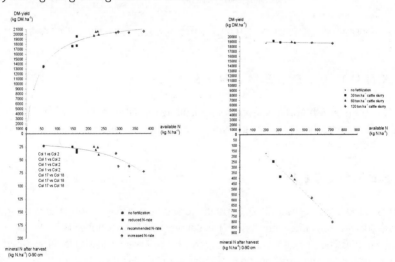

FIGURE 1 + 2. RELATION BETWEEN THE AVAILABLE N (= AMOUNT OF MINERAL N IN SPRING + MINERAL FERTILIZER N + EXPECTED NET N DELIVERY DURING GROWING SEASON) IN THE SOIL PROFILE AND THE DRY MATTER YIELD OF FODDER MAIZE AND MINERAL NITROGEN AT HARVEST ON A FIELD WITHOUT (FIG. 1) AND WITH (FIG. 2) AN ORGANIC MANURE HISTORY.

Fig. 3 shows that the mineral N-recommendation of 127 kg N ha⁻¹ can be replaced by:
- an application of 20 t ha⁻¹ cattle slurry + 63 kg N.ha⁻¹ (mineral fertilizer)

- an application of 40 t ha^{-1} cattle slurry

An application of 40 t ha^{-1} cattle slurry (available N = 140 kg N ha^{-1}) covers the N demand of the maize on this field (N recommendation = 127 kg N ha^{-1}). However, with this dose, a total of 264 kg N ha^{-1} is applied, exceeding the allowable fertilizer rate for animal manure (170 kg N ha^{-1}) in Flanders (Belgium). So, taking into account the plant available N in slurry, mineral N-fertilizer can be replaced by an equivalent dose of slurry. As total N application from animal manure should not exceed the allowable fertilizer rate for maize, N must be applied in an efficient way to obtain optimal yields.

The NO$_3$-N residues at harvest are significantly higher on the overfertilized plots (see Fig. 1). Thus, when more N is applied than recommended, the risks of nitrate leaching increase. Fig. 2 shows that the 'organic manure history' strongly influences the N residues, the N residues are very high (>150 kg N ha^{-1}), even on the unfertilized plots.

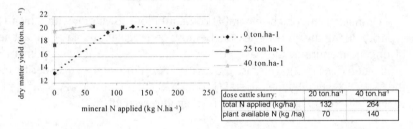

FIGURE 3. N-RESPONSE OF MAIZE ON DIFFERENT RATES OF N-FERTILIZER AND USE OF CATTLE SLURRY.

ACKNOWLEDGEMENTS

The ALT (Flemish Administration for Agriculture) and the Federal Ministry of Agriculture (Belgium) are greatly acknowledged for their financial support.

REFERENCES

Bries, J. and L. Vanongeval, 2000. Legislation on nutrient management in Flanders. Proceedings of the COST action 836, Integrated Research in Berries, 16-17th December 1999, Versailles, France

Vandendriessche, H., J. Bries and M. Geypens, 1996. Experience with fertilizer expert systems for balanced fertilizer recommendations. Commun. Soil Sci. Plant Anal., 27(5-8), pp. 1199-1209.

Evaluation of the data set of the Hungarian N-fertilization field trials with maize, 1960-1995. A preliminary study

P. CSATHÓ

Research Institute for Soil Science and Agricultural Chemistry, Hungarian Academy of Sciences, H-1022 Budapest, Herman O. u. 15, Hungary

SUMMARY

As a first attempt, the data set of N fertilization trials with maize (corn) has been established. Altogether 66 long-term field trials were found in the literature, with several hundred individual trials. The 1 to 10 years of the long-term field trials were taken into the data set, and the maize yields were averaged within that period. Among the N treatments, the one providing the maximum economic yield (~95% of maximum yields) were taken into account. The correlation between soil organic matter (OM) values and responses to N was also investigated. The main findings are considered as basics for a new, environmentally friendly, sustainable N fertilizer recommendation system. Evaluating the results of the Hungarian 1 to 10 years old field nitrogen trials with the, maize the drawn conclusions were as follows: 1) As a result of N application, surpluses in maize were between 0.9 to 2.0 t ha^{-1}. At lower soil OM contents the surpu ses were higher, and the amount of N needed for maximum economic yields were also higher. 2) The soil OM values moderately indicated the natural N- supplying power of the different soils. 3) Connection between soil OM content of N-control (PK) plots and the responses to N, expressed in relative yields (100Yield in PK plot/ Yield in NPK plot,%) could be described by a Mitscherlich-like equation, modified by Bray (1944):

/ $Y' = 100 (1-10^{-cx})$ /, where x= soil OM content in the N-control (PK) plots; Y' = relative yield in the trials, having "x" soil OM contents in the N-control plots; and c= proportionally constant (Mitscherlich's "working factor").

Keywords: field trials, maize, nitrogen, responses to N, soil OM

INTRODUCTION

In Hungarian agriculture maize is one of the two most important crops in Hungary. For that reason the synthesis of the national field trial series of maize is especially important.

Soil organic matter content and turnover both have a special role from either agronomic or environmental points of view (Kádár, 1992; Németh, 1996; Németh *et al.,*

1997-98; Várallyay *et al.,* 1980). As a first attempt. the data set of N fertilization trials with maize has been established.

MATERIALS AND METHODS

The N supply of the control plots of the Hungarian field trials was estimated by the organic matter (OM) content, according to Tyurin (1951).

A database of the results of 1- to 10- year old Hungarian nitrogen fertilization field trials found in the literature was compiled. In all trials by- products were removed from the fields. Soil characteristic data of PK (N-control) treatments, grain yield data of PK and also PK + N treatments giving maximum economic yields (about 95% of the maximum yields) were collected. The results were classified according to the soil OM groups.

RESULTS AND DISCUSSIONS

The correlation between soil OM content and responses to N application was examined on the data set of Hungarian field trials with maize, carried out between 1960 and 1995.

TABLE 1. CORRELATION BETWEEN SOIL OM CONTENT AND RESPONSES TO N APPLICATION IN HUNGARIAN FIELD TRIALS WITH CORN, SET UP BETWEEN 1960 AND 1995.

Soil organic matter (OM) groups,%	Number of trials (n)	K_A*	Soil organic matter (OM) content,%	N dose, kg ha^{-1}**	Grain yield on PK plots (N-control)	Relative yield,% (PK/NPK)	Surplus, t ha^{-1} (NPK-PK)
< 1.0	6	27	0.94	152	3.45	63	2.02
1.01-2.00	15	37	1.52	132	3.92	65	1.93
2.01-3.00	9	41	2.37	112	4.06	71	1.63
3.01-4.00	12	42	3.56	70	5.86	85	0.85
> 4.01	9	43	4.71	77	5.57	82	1.37
Mean (Total)	51	39	2.64	106	4.64	74	1.54

* upper limit of plasticity, according to Arany (similar to the US plasticity index); ** The N amount needed for maximum economic yield (~ 95% of maximum yield)

Evaluating the results of the Hungarian 1- to 10-year-old field nitrogen trials with maize, conclusions were drawn as follows: 1) As a result of N application. surpluses in maize grain yields were between 0.9 to 2.0 t ha^{-1} (Table 1). 2) The soil OM values indicated the natural N-supplying power of the different soils quite adequately, i.e. on soils with higher OM contents responses of maize to N application were diminished. 3) As an effect of increasing soil OM content, the amount of N needed for maximum economic yields (~ 0.95 x maximum yields) of maize also diminished significantly.

The connection between the OM content of the N-control (PK) plots and the responses to N, expressed in relative yields (100Yield in PK plot/ Yield in NPK plot,%) could be described by a Mitscherlich-like equation, modified by Bray (1944) : / Y' = 100 (1-10^{-cx}) /, where x= OM content in the N-control (PK) plots; Y' = relative yield in the trials, having "x" OM contents in the N-control plots; and c = proportionally constant (Mitscherlich's "working factor"). The value of "c" was 0.27675 in the data set of Hungarian maize field N trials.

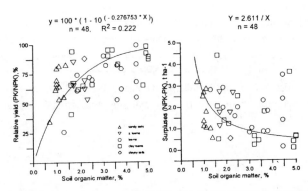

FIGURE 1. CORRELATION BETWEEN SOIL OM CONTENTS AND RESPONSES TO N APPLICATION IN HUNGARIAN FIELD TRIALS WITH CORN, 1960-1995.

CONCLUSIONS

The new N supply categories for Hungarian soils, expressed in OM contents, are sometimes lower than those in former fertilizer advisory systems (Csathó, *et al.*, 1998, 1998a). Using the new OM content categories can help in establishing a new, environmentally friendly N fertilizer advisory system.

ACKNOWLEDGEMENTS

This research was financially supported by the Hungarian National Scientific Research Fund (OTKA) under Grant No. T30180.

REFERENCES

Csathó, P., T. Árendás and T. Németh, 1998. New, environmentally friendly fertiliser advisory system, based on the data set of the Hungarian long-term field trials set up between 1960 and 1995. Communications in Soil Science and Plant Analysis, 29: 2161-2174.

Csathó, P., T. Árendás, and T. Németh, 1998a. New, environmentally friendly fertilizer recommendation system for Hungary. In: Codes for good agricultural practice and balanced fertilization. Proceedings of International Symposium CIEC, PFS and Workshop IMPHOS, IPI, Pulawy, Poland. (Ed.: Fotyma, M.) Bibliotheca Fragmenta Agronomica, 3: 225-230.

Kádár, I., 1992. Principles and methods of plant nutrition. (In Hungarian). RISSAC - Akaprint. Budapest. 398 pp.

Németh, T., 1996. Organic matter and nitrogen turnover of soils. (In Hungarian). RISSAC – Alfaprint. 392 pp.

Németh, T., G. J. Kovács, and I. Kádár, 1987-1988. Examination of NO_3^-, SO_4^{2-} and salt leaching in a long-term field trial with fertilizers. (In Hungarian). Agrokémia és Talajtan, 36-37: 109-126.

Tyurin, I. V., 1951. K metodike analiza dlja szravnitelnogo izucsenija szosztava pocsvennogo gumusza. Trudü Pocsvennogo Instituta. A. N. Sz. Sz. Sz. R.

Várallyay, G., I. Szücs, A. Murányi, K. Rajkai and P. Zilahy, 1980. Map of soil factors determining the agroecological potential of Hungary II. (In Hungarian). Agrokémia és Talajtan, 29: 35-76.

WORKING GROUP 4

Small grain cereals and pseudo cereals
Invited papers

Potential of pseudocereals for European agriculture

A. MUJICA[1], S. E. JACOBSEN[2] AND J. IZQUIERDO[3]

[1] Universidad Nacional del Altiplano, Escuela de Postgrado, Av. Del Ejercito 329, Puno, Peru
[2] International Potato Center (CIP), Apartado 1558, Lima 12, Peru
[3] FAO, Regional Office for Latin America and the Caribbean, P.O. Box 10095, Santiago, Chile

SUMMARY

Plant species of great importance for humans, with a high degree of adaptability to different agroecosystems, are found in the Andean region of South America. Among the grain crops are quinoa (*Chenopodium quinoa* Willd.), amaranth (*Amaranthus caudatus L.),* and *cañihua* (*Chenopodium pallidicaule* Aellen), sometimes called pseudocereals, and the South American lupin (*Lupinus mutabilis* Sweet). The term pseudocereals is not scientifically based, and preferably should be avoided.

The importance as human food and animal feed stems from the high nutritive value, mainly explained by an appropriate balance of essential amino acids. The species have evolved up to an altitude of 4,000 m asl in different environmental and soil conditions, with tolerance to various adverse abiotic factors such as drought, cold and salinity. They have developed morphological, anatomical, physiological, biochemical and phenological mechanisms, allowing them to produce under extreme conditions. The most versatile of the Andean crops, quinoa, is able to grow in environments from cold to hot climates, from loamy to sandy soils, from pH of 4.5 to 9, from dry until relatively humid areas, from sea level to 4,000 m asl, from short to long days, all of which explain its ·wide potential in the latitudes of Europe, as well as adaptation to different production systems.

The characteristics of quinoa give this crop a potential to be grown on marginal soils in a sustainable production system, such as on arid and semi-arid land, in cold areas and in saline environments where other crops are not suitable. New varieties even better than those already existing may be bred by means of appropriate selection and breeding for desired characters to be achieved from the enormous diversity and genetic variability of this species. Regarding the adverse biotic factors, work has commenced to introduce resistance towards the main disease downy mildew (*Peronospora farinosa*), and on IPM strategies towards the main pest, the cona-cona (*Eurysacca melanocampta*).

In the Andean region there is at least 3,000 accessions of quinoa and several hundreds of the other species, which makes it possible to select genotypes with specific characteristics for different climatic regions and uses.

Keywords: amaranth, cañihua, lupin, marginal environments, potential, quinoa

INTRODUCTION

Several species of great importance for human consumption, and with a wide adaptability, have originated in the South American Andes region. Among these crops are the Andean grain crops quinoa (*Chenopodium quinoa* Willd.) and amaranth (*Amaranthus caudatus* L.), which are also denominated pseudocereals, in addition to tarwi (*Lupinus mutabilis* Sweet) and *cañihua* (*Chenopodium pallidicaule* Aellen). These Andean grain crops are very important in the human consumption and animal feed of the region, having a high nutritive value mainly explained by an appropriate balance of amino acids, and adaptation to altitudes from sea level to 4,000 m, under very different environmental conditions. Quinoa and cañihua are able to tolerate adverse abiotic factors such as drought, frost and salinity, due to a large number of morphological, anatomical, physiological, biochemical and phenological mechanisms (Mujica and Jacobsen, 1999a), which allow these crops to be produced under extreme conditions.

The Andean grain crops are used for human consumption providing an almost complete food. Leaves are used as vegetables, inflorescences like broccoli (Mujica and Berty, 1997), and seeds are used in the elaboration of a range of dishes, in soups, salads, desserts, bread etc. The entire plant can be used as forage, and components of the seeds and other plant parts can be used industrially, such as the secondary metabolites (saponins, alkaloids), colourants, cellulose and fuel (Mujica *et al.*, 1999).

ADAPTATION

The Andean grain crops best known with respect to their potential for production in Europe are quinoa and amaranth, which have been tested with promising results, quinoa all over Europe and amaranth especially in the southern part. Lupin (*Lupinus albus, L. angustifolius, L. luteus*) is becoming a new crop of much interest in Europe and other parts of the world, mainly as a protein-rich fodder for pigs. However, little work has been done with the South American lupin, which is another species, with a very long growth season. Cañihua has been tested in some European countries, and may have a potential under cold conditions in the mountains of central Europe.

Quinoa is regarded as the Andean grain crop of most potential for European agriculture. The adaptation of quinoa ranges from cold and temperate areas to hot and humid tropical areas, and from loamy to sandy soils, with a pH of 4.5 up to 9, and from dry to humid areas. Quinoa has photoperiodic demands from short photoperiod to daylength-neutral types, which allows the wide distribution of quinoa in Europe, as well as adaptation to different production systems. There is a wide variability and genetic diversity in the more than 3,000 accessions, presently available in the genebanks of the region, which gives the possibility to select genotypes with adequate characteristics for different environments and uses (Mujica and Jacobsen, 1999b).

Quinoa has been shown to have all drought resistance mechanisms, such as escape, tolerance and avoidance, securing acceptable yields with only 25% of field capacity or even less water in the soil. Quinoa possesses high capacity to resist drought through reduction of the stomatal opening and a permanent low osmotic potential (Nuñez, 1999).

Quinoa resists frost down to -8°C for several hours. Frost damage increases considerably when the relative humidity is low, and the developmental stage of the plant is important with respect to the level of damage, anthesis being the stage most sensitive (Monteros, 2000). Frost resistance is partly controlled by the content of soluble sugars, which decreases the risk of ice formation in the leaves and death by dehydration.

Quinoa may be cultivated in soils of high salinity levels, the most extreme case being in the salt deserts of southern Bolivia, where quinoa is the only crop grown. Quinoa is able to germinate in saline water up to 58 mScm[-1] (Ruiz *et al.*, 1997). Quinoa is much more tolerant to salt than amaranth, which has no specific mechanisms to resist salinity. The variable first affected by salinity in quinoa is plant height.

These characteristics, resistant to adverse abiotic factors, provide potential for cultivation in arid and semi-arid areas, in cold mountain areas and in saline soils where other crops cannot be grown. In addition the quinoa material can be improved by means of an appropriate selection and improvement specifically for these characteristics and for certain geographical regions, in order to expand the agricultural area. The growth period of quinoa ranges from 3 to 8 months, depending on climatic conditions and cultivar.

Regarding the adverse biotic factors, work is carried on with the main disease downy mildew (*Peronospora farinosa*), and the main pest kona-kona (*Eurysacca melanocampta* Meyrick) (Mujica *et al.*, 1998), the objective being to obtaining durable resistance and IPM strategies.

Another aspect of relevance for quinoa is its transformation potential to various agroindustrial products, such as quinoa pops, toasted grain, flakes etc., and concentrated protein from the embryo. Quinoa should be promoted in order to increase consumption, for instance, through governmental programs, to solve the serious problems of malnutrition in South America and elsewhere. From the seeds vegetable milk with exceptional characteristics in flavour and colour can be produced.

The result of the American test of amaranth, which took place few years ago supported by the FAO, shows that this crop has a high production potential, yielding up to 7,900 kg ha[-1]. It was observed that amaranth grows well from sea level in Haiti to 3,710 m in Bolivia, and under a range of precipitations from 176 mm (Argentina) to 1,378 mm (Ecuador), with reasonable yield (Mujica *et al.*, 1999).

The potential for adaptation is higher in quinoa than in amaranth. Jacobsen (1993) observed that quinoa may grow on marginal, dry soils, where irrigation is not possible, and where fertilization and chemical application are restricted or even prohibited, producing up to 3 t ha[-1], harvested with conventional machinery. In Greece quinoa has produced 1.6 and amaranth 2 t ha[-1] (Iliadis *et al.*, 1997), in Sweden up to 2 t ha[-1] (Ohlsson, 1997), and in Finland quinoa and *cañihua* were cultivated with favorable results, with a protein content up to 13% (Kestitalo, 1997). In the Himalayas quinoa associated with potato has yielded 430 kg ha[-1] of quinoa and 12.360 kg ha[-1] of potato (Partap *et al.*, 1998). Quinoa may be considered as a new and promising crop for European agriculture.

With the results of the American and European Test of Quinoa cultivars tested in 25 countries of America and Europe, in addition to Africa and Asia, we will obtain important results with respect to the potential of quinoa for adaptation to different agroclimatic conditions, as well as of its potential for grain and green matter production.

DESIRED CHARACTERS OF QUINOA FOR CULTIVATION IN EUROPE

The ideal variety, or the model plant, of quinoa for seed production in Europe would be uniform and early maturing, which in particular is important for northern Europe, with a maximum growth period of 150 days. Seed yield should be high, of low saponin content, and the plants should be short and simple, that is with no branching, facilitating mechanical harvest. Size, shape and density of the inflorescence could be important for maturing. A large, open inflorescence will probably dry quicker after rain and morning dew than a smaller, compact one, but could also be more prone to seed shattering. The model plant for seed production has been elaborated by Jacobsen and Risi (2000) (Fig. 1).

FIGURE 1. MODEL PLANT OF QUINOA FOR SEED PRODUCTION (JACOBSEN & RISI, 2000).

Forage types should be tall, leafy, of late maturity, with a high green matter yield and low saponin content. Seed propagation for the green type must be conducted in southern Europe.

For many of the examined characters, there exists a considerable variation between cultivars, and it is believed that through selection and breeding it should be possible to combine desired characters in one or a few varieties, which should secure the establishment of quinoa as a new crop for European agriculture.

REFERENCES

Iliadis, C., T. Karyotis and T. Mitsibonas, 1997. Research on quinoa (*Chenopodium quinoa*) and amaranth (*Amaranthus caudatus*) in Greece. In: Crop development for the cool and wet regions of Europe. Spelt and quinoa, Working group Meeting. European Commission COST. 24-25 October. Wageningen, The Netherlands, 85-91.

Jacobsen, S. E., 1993. Quinoa (*Chenopodium quinoa* Willd.) a novel Crop for the European Agriculture. PhD. Thesis. Royal Veterinary and Agricultural University. Copenhagen, Denmark. 145 pp.

Jacobsen, S. E. and J. Risi, 2000. Distribución geográfica de la quinua fuera de los paises andinos. In, Libro de Quinua – FAO (in prep).

Keskitalo, M., 1997. Quinoa (*Chenopodium quinoa*) a new crop for Finland. In: Crop development for the cool and wet regions of Europe. Spelt and quinoa, Working group meeting. European Comission COST. 24-25 October. Wageningen, The Netherlands, 99-102.

Monteros, C., 2000. Tolerancia de la quinua (*Chenopodium quinoa* Willd.) a las bajas temperaturas en diferentes fases fenológicas. M.Sc. Thesis, Universidad Nacional del Altiplano. Puno, Perú. 115 pp.

Mujica, A., 1994. Andean Grains and Legumes. In: Neglected Crop 1492 from a different perspective. FAO. Hernandez Bermejo, J.E. and Leon, J. Editors. Rome, Italy. 131-148.

Mujica, A., and Berty, M., 1997. El Cultivo del Amaranto (*Amaranthus* spp.): Producción, mejoramiento genético y utilización. FAO, UNAP. UDEC. Santiago de Chile. 145 pp.

Mujica, A., S. E. Jacobsen, J. Izquierdo and J. P. Marathee, 1998. Field Book: American and European Test of Quinoa. FAO, UNAP, CIP, CONDESAN. Lima, Perú. 37 pp.

Mujica, A. and S. E. Jacobsen, 1999a. Resistencia de la quinua a la sequía y otros factores adversos y su mejoramiento.En: Fisiología de la resistencia a sequía en Quinua (*Chenopodium quinoa* Willd.). I Curso Internacional. Jacobsen, S.E. and A. Mujica Editores. Proyecto Quinua. CIP-DANIDA-UNAP-INIAP-PROIMPA-KVL .Lima, Perú. 71-78.

Mujica, A. and S. E. Jacobsen, 1999b. Recursos genéticos y mejoramiento de la quinua (*Chenopodium quinoa* Willd.). En: Resúmenes Primer Taller Internacional sobre quinua. Jacobsen, S.E. and A. Valdez Editores. Proyecto Quinua CIP-DANIDA, UNALM,CIP,UNAP. Lima, Perú.

Mujica, A., J. Izquierdo and S. E. Jacobsen, 1999. Prueba Americana de Cultivares de Amaranto (*Amaranthus caudatus L. , A. hipochondriacus L. , A.cruentus L.*). En: Memorias Reunión Técnica y Taller de Formulación de proyecto regional sobre producción y nutrición Humana en Base a Cultivos Andinos. Mujica, A., J. Izquierdo, J. P. Marathee, C. Moron and S. E. Jacobsen, eds. 20-24 de julio de 1998. FAO, UNAP, UNSA, CIP. Arequipa, Perú, 47-53.

Nuñez, N., 1999. Influencia del déficit hídrico en la fisiología y productividad de quinua (*Chenopodium quinoa* Willd.). M.Sc. Thesis, Universidad Nacional del Altiplano. Puno, Perú. 87 pp.

Ohlsson, I., 1997. Quinoa- A potential crop for Sweden. In: Crop development for the cool and wet regions of Europe. Spelt and Quinoa, working group Meeting. European Comission COST. 24-25 october. Wageningen, The Netherlands. 93-97.

Partap,T., B.D. Joshi and N.W. Galwey, 1998. Chenopods. Chenopodium spp. Promoting the conservation and use of underutilized and neglected crop. 22. IPK/ IPGRI. Rome, Italy. 67 pp.

Ruiz-Tapia, E., O. Stolen,J. Christiansenand R. Ortiz, 1997. Assessment of quinoa (*Chenopodium quinoa* Willd.) accessions for tolerance to salinity. In: Crop development for the cool and wet regions of Europe. Spelt and quinoa, Working group Meeting. European Comission COST. 24-25 October. Wageningen, The Netherlands, 69-78.

Spelt (*Triticum spelta* L.), a genetic resource for stress tolerance

J. E. SCHMID[1], S. T. BURGOS[1], M. M. MESSMER[2] AND P. STAMP[1]

[1]*Institute of Plant Sciences, Swiss Federal Institute of Technology, ETH-Zurich
Research Station Eschikon 33, CH-8315 Lindau, Switzerland*
[2]*Swiss Federal Research Station for Agroecology and Agriculture (FAL) Zurich-Reckenholz,
Reckenholzstr. 191, CH-8046 Zurich
Present address: Institute of Pharmaceutical Biology, University of Basel, Benkenstr. 254, CH-
4108 Witterswil, Switzerland*

SUMMARY

Spelt (*Triticum spelta* L.), an alternative cereal, is well adapted to cool and wet pedoclimatic conditions and therefore a valuable genetic resource for stress tolerance. Spelt is a close relative to common wheat (*Triticum aestivum* L.) and thus suitable for exchanging genes by intercrossing with wheat. F_1's of wheat x spelt - intercrosses showed high relative heterosis of 42.1% on average. The analysis of later generations (F_2-F_5) showed a remarkable decrease in relative heterosis, more pronounced than expected form the theoretical models. 226 recombinant inbred lines (RILs) derived from intercrosses between wheat (cv. Forno) and spelt (cv. Oberkulmer) were used to characterise quantitative trait loci (QTL) for lodging resistance and resistance against powdery mildew. Interesting QTL were identified carrying spelt specific traits for abiotic and biotic stress tolerance.

Field and growth chamber experiments were conducted in order to evaluate physiological and genetic parameters responsible for the high adaptation potential of spelt to cool and wet conditions. The identified flooding tolerance of spelt during germination enables spelt to survive better under these unfavourable conditions than wheat. The lower oxygen consumption and the faster growth of the coleoptiles were identified as advantages of spelt avoiding negative effects of flooding. Ten QTL were found for seedling growth after flooding. The importance of chromosome 5A of spelt was again demonstrated for these traits. The investigations confirmed that some spelt varieties could be used as genetic resources to improve stress tolerance in wheat.

*Keywords: flooding tolerance, genetic study, QTL, spelt, stress adaptation, Triticum
spelta L.*

INTRODUCTION

Spelt, a close relative of wheat is used mainly for bread making and livestock feeding. There are few but marked characteristics of spelt that are different from wheat. Spelt plants are taller and have longer ears with tight glumes and a brittle rachis. Spelt grains are long shaped with a high single grain weight. Wheat and spelt are both hexaploid species with three genomes (AABBDD) and seven homologous chromosome groups. Both crops are autogamous but can be crossed with each other. Using RFLP-markers Liu et al. (1990) and Siedler *et al.* (1994) found genetic diversity between spelt and winter wheat genotypes. Genetic studies of crosses between common wheat and spelt were conducted to evaluate possibilities for transferring valuable properties from spelt to wheat and vice versa. (Schmid and Winzeler, 1990). Segregating generations of wheat x spelt crosses were analysed under selective environments (Rimle, 1995; Schmid *et al.*, 1997) and the relative heterosis effects calculated.

For several mapping projects we used a cross between winter wheat (*Triticum aestivum* L.) and winter spelt (*Triticum spelta* L.), both originating from Switzerland. Spelt was chosen as a crossing parent because of the higher level of genetic diversity expected between wheat and spelt than within wheat itself and because of our interest in spelt-specific traits for breeding purposes.

Spelt is usually grown in marginal zones of cereal production with high precipitation, heavy soils and cool temperatures. With respect to common wheat, spelt exhibits more vigorous growth under adverse growth conditions (Rüegger *et al.*, 1990; Schmid *et al.*, 1997). In field trials as well as under controlled environmental conditions the spelt-specific stress tolerance was confirmed. Part of our investigations aimed at detecting physiological parameters mainly involved in the stress tolerance in order to be used for the mapping and characterisation of QTLs.

Genetic studies of crosses between common wheat and spelt

The yield potential and the yield components of the progeny derived from the intercrosses between wheat and spelt varieties were studied in a series of experiments (Schmid and Winzeler, 1990; Schmid *et al.*, 1992; Schmid *et al.*, 1994; Winzeler *et al.*, 1994; Rimle, 1995, Schmid *et al.*, 1997). The Swiss winter wheat varieties Bernina, Forno and Arina were reciprocally crossed with the two spelt cultivars Oberkulmer Rotkorn (Swiss) and Rouquin (Belgium). Grain yield per ear of wheat x spelt crosses (F_1) showed a remarkable relative heterosis of 42.1% on average. All combinations outyielded the higher yielding parent by 24.7% to 45.7%. This rather high heterosis effect was mainly the result of a positive hybrid reaction of the two yield parameters single grain weight and grain number per ear. Single grain weight and the number of grains per ear had similar average relative heterosis values of 18.0% and 19.0%, respectively. The heterosis values for the ear number per plant was markedly lower than for grain number per ear or grain weight. Here, large effects of the varieties were evident. The investigations showed clearly that the use of the distant gene pool spelt opens perspectives to profit from the large potential for heterosis. For practical applications there remain several problems to be solved. Despite the very high heterosis effect the yield potential of spelt needs to be improved, e.g. no short spelt varieties exist at present to produce hybrids short enough for commercial application.

The expression of the heterosis potential of wheat x spelt intercrosses was also studied under wheat and spelt specific pedoclimatic conditions. The relative heterosis of these intercrosses was highest under cool and wet conditions. For grain weight per plant a relative heterosis of 20% resulted under wheat specific growing conditions and under stress (spelt specific conditions) the highest value of 34% was obtained.

The test of the F_2 showed that there is a large reduction of the heterosis effect on yield with a statistically non-significant advantage over the midparent value. The average plant height was shorter than the mean of the parents but due to the large phenotypic variation between the gene pools the F_2 was extremely variable. Therefore it appears not feasible to use a F_2 commercially. The study of the heterosis expression in later generations was conducted by Rimle (1995). He showed that the decrease in relative heterosis from F_1 to F_5 of grain yield and of most other traits was more pronounced than was expected from the theoretical models. In F_3 and later generations the mean values dropped significantly below the level of the parents means. The loss of the parental epistatic effects is considered to be responsible for that reaction.

The genetic studies demonstrated the relevance of the spelt pool for transferring of interesting traits into wheat and for combining wheat and spelt pools in order to use the interesting recombinations and the unexpected high heterosis potential.

Quantitative trait loci for lodging resistance and resistance against powdery mildew in a segregating wheat x spelt population

A genetic map of a cross between the Swiss winter wheat variety Forno and the Swiss winter spelt variety Oberkulmer was constructed (Messmer et al., 1999). 226 recombinant inbred lines (RILs) derived from the intercrosses between theses spelt and wheat varieties were used for mapping and characterising quantitative trait loci (QTLs) for lodging resistance (Keller et al., 1999a) and for resistance against powdery mildew (Keller et al., 1999b). Marker assisted selection (MAS) could become an important tool in breeding for these traits. Concerning lodging resistance investigations, spelt was the susceptible partner but an important element to characterise QTL. For spelt breeding, genes of wheat which increases lodging resistance but with little reduction in the typical long culm of spelt are of special interest. Nine QTL for lodging resistance were detected explaining 63% of the phenotypic variance in a simultaneous fit. Two QTL did not coincide with the QTL for morphological traits therefore it should be possible to introgress lodging resistance genes form wheat into spelt by one or two backcrosses without strongly affecting plant height.

In the QTL study for resistance against powdery mildew the same RILs were used and again spelt was the susceptible crossing parent. With the method of composite interval mapping 18 QTLs for powdery mildew resistance were detected, explaining 77% of the phenotypic variance. Two QTLs with major effects were consistent over all five environments. One of them corresponds to the Pm5 locus derived from Forno on chromosome 7B. The other QTL on 5A was derived from the spelt variety Oberkulmer and did not correspond to any known Pm gene. Again, the spelt chromosome 5A carrying most of the spelt specific characters proved to be an interesting resource for stress tolerance.

Flooding tolerance of spelt compared to wheat - a physiological and genetic approach
Field experiments - reactions to cold and wet conditions

Extensive comparative studies for wheat and spelt were conducted in order to evaluate physiological and genetic parameters responsible for the high adaptation potential of spelt to cold and wet conditions. Reactions of spelt and wheat varieties were investigated with respect to early flooding, a prerequisite for this kind of stress adaptation. Rimle (1995) described spelt cultivars as being more robust than bread wheat during germination and early seedling development, because spelt seeds germinate fast, coleoptiles grow fast and seedlings emerge well despite wet, cool conditions and are winterhardy. The winter wheat variety Forno and the spelt variety Oberkulmer were tested in the field. The stress conditions (cold and wet) were simulated by eight sowing dates from September until January. The temperatures decreased remarkably between the first and the fourth sowing date; for the latest dates temperatures were about constant at 1.5°C. It has to be noted that the soil was covered with snow almost all the time between beginning of November until the end of march, explaining why the soil temperatures remained for a long time at zero degree. The soil was not covered only during two short periods, which allowed the sowing of the 7th and the 8th date. The grain yield of the two genotypes is shown in Fig. 1. For both, wheat and spelt, the late sowing negatively influenced the grain yield. However, at the first sowing date Forno showed a higher yield than Oberkulmer. From the second until the 6th sowing date Oberkulmer yielded significantly more. For the two last dates no difference was found between the two varieties. A multivariable regression conducted with all factors resulted in two main factors explaining the difference in the yield. The first parameter was the number of surviving plants. Oberkulmer showed in all plots more plants m^{-2}, significantly more in the 5th and the 6th sowing date. The second factor was the number of ears m^{-2}. Oberkulmer formed also more ears m^{-2} after the 4th sowing date. The yield was negatively correlated ($r = -0.95$) with the temperature and with the soil water potential. The covering of the soil showed similar reactions with the greatest difference at the 5th and the 6th sowing date. Oberkulmer always germinated faster than Forno. When the conditions were not extremely bad the difference in germination percentage was not significantly different between Oberkulmer and Forno. When the climatic conditions became worse, during the 5th and the 6th sowing dates, this difference increased. Thus, Oberkulmer required a smaller temperature sum to germinate.

Therefore, the sensitive period between sowing and emergence was longer for Forno. This longer emergence period was a real disadvantage if the soil was nearly saturated, as it was the case during the 5th and the 6th sowing date. Rainfalls during this time could lead Forno to suffer more often to a lack of oxygen. Consequently the number of damaged or dead plants was higher for Forno than for Oberkulmer. The loss of plants could be compensated by a higher number of ears plant[-1] but in our study it was not sufficient to avoid the strong yield reduction. Rimle (1995) showed that spelt disposed of better winter hardiness than wheat. Late planting often causes yield depression (Oweis *et al.*, 1998, McLeod *et al.*, 1992). The reasons for this yield decrease could be the death of the plants, the inhomogeneity and the delay of the emergence (Gan *et al.*, 1992), decrease of kernel weight or number of grains per ears (Shah *et al.*, 1994) or problems of desiccation in spring (Janssen, 1929). In our case the low number of plant surviving the winter was the main factor. However, if less plants emerge and if the development of these plants are delayed, the combination of these factors can be reasonably taken as a cause of the low number of plants surviving. The exact reason of the death of the plants is certainly very complex and the study of the main factors affecting the survival could help to give an answer.

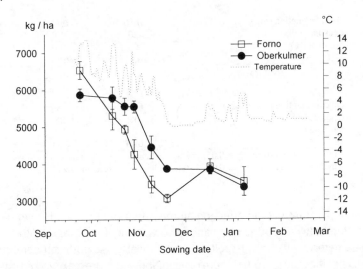

FIGURE 1. GRAIN YIELD (KG / HA) OF FORNO AND OBERKULMER UNDER EIGHT DIFFERENT SOWING DATES. *, **, *** = DIFFERENCE BETWEEN THE TWO GENOTYPES AT P<0.05, 0.01, 0.001 RESPECTIVELY. NS. = NOT SIGNIFICANTLY DIFFERENT.

Evaluation of flooding tolerance of spelt and wheat during germination

Flooding tolerance was identified as a major parameter characterising the spelt-specific growing areas as well as the spelt tolerance to such conditions (Burgos *et al.*, 1999). The aim of this study was to evaluate the capacity of spelt to avoid the negative effects of temporary flooding until the early seedling stage. The experiments were performed in a growth chamber at 10 or 20°C, 75% humidity, and about 300 mmol photons $m^{-2}s^{-1}$ during the photoperiod (16 h). Imbibition was done in the dark. Again, the winter wheat variety Forno and the spelt variety Oberkulmer were used. Without flooding stress, spelt began to germinate faster. It took spelt 24 h (range: 21 and 25 h) to develop 80% of the grains at the stage I and 34 h (range: 30 to 38 h) for wheat. The final percentage of germination was slightly but not significantly higher for spelt. Table 1 shows the comparison between spelt and wheat at 10 and 20°C under flooding stress.

TABLE 1. REACTION OF WHEAT AND SPELT TO TWO DAYS OF FLOODING AT 10 AND 20°C. THE GRAINS WERE FLOODED JUST AFTER IMBIBITION IN AN ERLENMEYER FLASKS. SGI = SUM OF DRY WEIGHT OF THE ROOT AND THE SHOOT DIVIDED BY THE SUM OF THE DRY WEIGHT OF ROOTS, SHOOT, AND REST OF THE ENDOSPERM.

		Wheat (cv. Forno)	Spelt (cv. Oberkulmer)	
10°C				
	†			‡
O2 consumption (mg grain^{-1} d^{-1})		0.16	0.13	*
Leakage (mS)	*	20	13	*
Survival (%)		60	100	*
SGI		0.11	0.14	*
20°C				
	†			‡
O2 consumption (mg grain^{-1} d^{-1})		0.35	0.30	*
Leakage (mS)	*	38	25	*
Survival (%)		2	30	*
SGI		0.07	0.11	*

† indicates a significant ($p < 0.05$) interaction between temperature and genotype.
‡ indicates a significant ($p < 0.01$) difference between wheat and spelt.

The temperature had an effect on all measured parameters. However, there was an interaction between temperature and genotype only for leakage. With regard to the other parameters, wheat and spelt reacted similarly. At both temperatures, wheat consumed significantly ($p < 0.01$) more oxygen, showed more leakage, did not survive as well and showed a smaller seedling growth index. Because there was only a limited exchange of oxygen with the atmosphere, the wheat plants were affected more quickly by a lack of oxygen. Injury to and death of the roots have been attributed to an accumulation of toxic end products of anaerobic metabolism, to a lower metabolism of energy, or to a lack of substrates for respiration. Figure 2a shows the consumption of oxygen of spelt seedlings as percentage of the wheat control. Spelt consumed less oxygen than wheat until 20 hours of imbibition. Thereafter, spelt consumed significantly ($p < 0.05$) more oxygen than wheat. When comparing the three growth stages (Fig. 2b), spelt

476

consumed significantly (p<0.05) less oxygen than wheat. At the beginning of imbibition, spelt consumed 35% less oxygen than wheat. Spelt consumed 20% less oxygen when the roots began to grow, i.e., after 10 h for spelt and 20 h for wheat and 20% less at stage I, i.e., after 24 h for spelt and 34 h for wheat. Spelt survived for a much longer period of flooding without oxygen. The rate of survival was stable and the length of the coleoptile and the biomass of the shoot were less affected than those of wheat. When flooding occurs after the onset of growth, the faster elongation of the coleoptile of spelt was an advantage in avoiding the effect of flooding. Spelt grew better and produced less ethanol under hypoxia, indicating that it was much more tolerant than wheat. Both, the morphological and the metabolic adaptation increase the consistency of early field establishment in flooding prone environments.

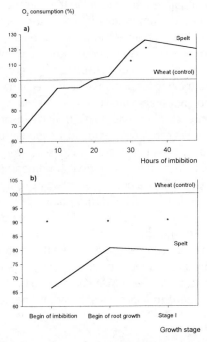

FIGURE 2. OXYGEN CONSUMPTION OF SPELT AS PERCENTAGE OF THE WHEAT CONTROL. A) COMPARISON AFTER DIFFERENT HOURS OF IMBIBITION. B) COMPARISON AT DIFFERENT GROWTH STAGES. THE STAGE "BEGIN OF ROOT GROWTH" OCCURRED AFTER 10 H FOR SPELT AND 20 H FOR WHEAT. STAGE I OCCURRED AFTER 24 H FOR SPELT AND 34 H FOR WHEAT. * INDICATES A SIGNIFICANT (P<0.05) DIFFERENCE BETWEEN WHEAT AND SPELT.

Flooding tolerance of spelt compared to wheat - a genetic approach

This study evaluates the reaction of a wheat x spelt population (F_5 RILs of Forno x Oberkulmer) to flooding stress in the early phase of germination. The tolerance to 48 h flooding just after imbibition was negatively correlated (r=-0.79) with the leakage of metabolites in the soil solution, indicating that the plants which could preserve their membrane integrity survived better. Five QTL (Fig. 3) explaining 40.6% of the phenotypic variance for survival were found, and localized on the chromosomes 2B, 3B, 5A, and 7S. The tolerance to 48 h flooding four days after sowing was best correlated with the mean germination time (r=0.8), indicating that the plants with a fast coleoptile growth during flooding are less susceptible to flooding. Ten QTL were found for seedling growth index after flooding explaining 35.5% of the phenotypic variance. They were localized on chromosomes 2A, 2B, 2D, 3A, 4B, 5A, 5B, 6A, and 7S. The dominant role of the chromosome 5A was again demonstrated. Sixteen of the measured parameters showed a QTL at the location 210 cM. This is the position of the gene q (5A) responsible for the long lax ear of spelt and its hulled kernels. Other loci as well influencing traits such as plant height and flowering time were located in this chromosomal region (Keller et al., 1999; Kato et al., 1999). The importance of chromosome 5A was cited for flooding tolerance (Poysa, 1984), cold tolerance and vernalization requirement (Roberts, 1990), and absicic acid (Quarrie et al., 1997). Because the flooding tolerance of spelt in the second experiment was partly based on the speed of the growth, it is reasonable to find QTL for this trait near to the one for plant height. If selection would be concentrate here upon, this could lead to undesirable high plants with spelt ear type. For this reason it is important to look on other chromosomes for QTL which are not obviously linked to such undesirable traits. Among the chromosomes found for flooding tolerance, the chromosome 2B, 3B, and 6A are known to influence grain yield, seed weight and plant height of the varieties Cheyenne and Wichita under normal conditions (Berke et al., 1992). The chromosomes of the group 2 have a positive effect on flooding tolerance by Thinopyrum elongatum L. (Taeb et al., 1993), and the chromosome 3B influences the winter hardiness (Zemetra and Morris, 1988). The QTL on the chromosome 6A influence also the plant height (Keller et al., 1999). The efficiency of marker assisted selection (MAS) will depend on the genetic parameters and the selection scheme (Lande and Thompson, 1990). This work showed that some spelt varieties could be used as genetic resources to improve flooding tolerance in wheat. The use of MAS could avoid the transmission of undesirable traits. Simple tests and criteria to select wheat breeding lines for flooding tolerance were developed.

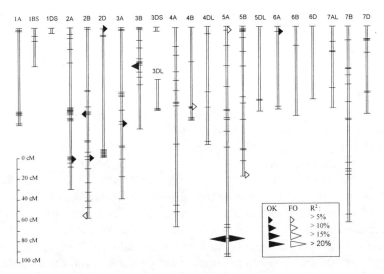

FIGURE 3. POSITION OF SIGNIFICANT (LOD>3.0) QTL ON THE GENETIC MAP OF 204 RILS DERIVED FROM THE CROSS FO X OK. QTL FOR SEEDLING GROWTH INDEX IN FLOODING CONDITIONS AFTER FOUR DAYS GROWTH ARE INDICATED BY TRIANGLES ON THE RIGHT SIDE OF THE CHROMOSOMES. QTL FOR SURVIVAL TO FLOODING JUST AFTER IMBIBITION ARE INDICATED BY TRIANGLES ON THE LEFT SIDE OF THE CHROMOSOMES. THE SIZE OF THE TRIANGLES INDICATES THE EXPLAINED PHENOTYPIC VARIANCE (R²) OF SINGLE QTL. WHITE OR BLACK TRIANGLES INDICATE THAT THE ALLELE FOR IMPROVING FLOODING TOLERANCE WAS INHERITED FROM FORNO OR OBERKULMER, RESPECTIVELY.

REFERENCES

Berke, T. G., P. S. Baenziger and R. Morris, 1992. Chromosomal location of wheat quantitative trait loci affecting stability of six traits, using reciprocal chromosome substitutions. Crop Science, 32: 628-633.

Burgos, St., P. Stamp and J. E. Schmid, 1999. Genetic analysis and early testing of spelt specific stress tolerance. Crop development for the cool and wet regions of Europe; COST 814- workshop, Turku, Finland, 13-15 June 1999. European Commission, 118-126.

Gan, Y., E. H. Stobbe and J. Moes, 1992. Relative date of wheat seedling emergence and ist impact on grain yield. Crop-science, 32: 1275-1281.

Janssen, G., 1929. Effect of date of seeding of winter wheat on plant development and its relationship to winterhardiness. Journal of the American Society of Agronomy, 21: 444-466.

Kato, K., H. Miura and S. Sawada, 1999. QTL mapping of genes controlling ear emergence time and plant height on chromosome 5A of wheat. Theoretical Applied Genetics, 98: 472-477.

Keller, M., Ch. Karutz, J. E. Schmid, P. Stamp, M. Winzeler, B. Keller and M. M. Messmer, 1999a. Quantitative trait loci for lodging resistance in a segregating wheat x spelt population. Theoretical Applied Genetics, 98: 1171-1182.

Keller, M., B. Keller, G. Schachermayr, M. Winzeler, J. E. Schmid, P. Stamp and M. M. Messmer, 1999b. Quantitative trait loci for resistance against powdery mildew in a segregating wheat x spelt population. Theoretical and Applied Genetics 98: 903-912.

Lande, R. and R. Thompson, 1990. Efficiency of marker-assisted selection in the improvement of quantiative traits. Genetics, 124: 743-756.

Liu, Y. G., N. Mori and K. Tsunewaki, 1990. Restriction fragment length polymorphism (RFLP) analysis in wheat. I. Genomic DNA library construction and RFLP analysis in common wheat. Japanese Journal of Genetics, 65: 367-380.

Messmer, M. M., M. Keller, S. Zanetti and B. Keller, 1999. Genetic linkage map of a wheat x spelt cross. Theoretical Applied Genetics, 98: 1163-1170.

McLeod, J. G., C. A. Campbell, F. B. Dyck and C. L. Vera, 1992. Optimum seedling date for winter wheat in southwestern Saskatchewan. Agronomy Journal, 84: 86-90.

Oweis, T., M. Pala and J. Ryan, 1998. Stabilizing rainfed wheat yields with supplemental irrigation and nitrogen in a Mediterranean climate. Agronomy Journal, 90: 672-681.

Poysa, V. W., 1984. The genetic control of low temperature, ice-encasement, and flooding tolerances by chromosomes 5A, 5B, and 5D in wheat. Cereal Research Communication, 12: 135-141.

Quarrie, S. A., D. A. Laurie, J. Zhu, C. Lebreton, A. Semikhodskii, A. Steed, H. Witsenboer and C. Calestani, 1997. QTL analysis to study the association between leaf size and abscisic acid accumulation in droughted rice leaves and comparisons across cereals. Plant molecular biology, 35: 155-165.

Rimle, R., 1995. Agronomische und morphologische Charakterisierung von Weizen (*Triticum aestivum L.*) und Dinkel (*Triticum spelta L.*) sowie von spezifischen Weizen/Dinkel-F1-Hybriden und deren Folgegenerationen von der F2 bis zur F5. Diss ETH Nr. 11242, ETHZ, Zürich.

Roberts, D. W. A., 1990. Identification of loci on chromosome 5A of wheat involved in control of cold hardiness, vernalization, leaf length, rosette growth habit, and height of hardened plants. Genome, 33: 247-259.

Rüegger A., H. Winzeler and J. Nösberger, 1990. Die Ertragsbildung von Dinkel (*Triticum spelta L.*) und Weizen (*Triticum aestivum L.*) unter verschiedenen Umweltbedingungen im Freiland. Journal of Agronomy and Crop Science, 164: 145-152.

Schmid J. E. and H. Winzeler, 1990. Genetic studies of crosses between common wheat (*Triticum aestivum L.*) and spelt (*Triticum spelta L.*). Journal of Genetics and Breeding, 44: 75-80.

Schmid, J. E., H. Winzeler, R. Rimle, A. Rüegger and Ch. Beglinger, 1992. Untersuchungen der Nachkommenschaften aus Weizen x Dinkel-Kreuzungen. Bericht über die 43. Tagung der Vereinigung Oesterr. Pflanzenzüchter: 35-43.

Schmid, J. E., M. Winzeler and H. Winzeler, 1994. Analysis of disease resistance and quality characters of F1 hybrids of crosses between wheat and spelt. Euphytica 75:105-110.

Schmid, J. E., R. Rimle, Ch. Beglinger, M. Messmer, H. Winzeler, A. Rüegger and P. Stamp, 1997. Agronomic and genetic studies with spelt and wheat x spelt crosses. Crop development for the cool and wet regions of Europe; COST 814- workshop, Copenhagen, 22.-24.2.1996. European Commission, 19-30.

Shah, S. A., S. A. Harrison, D. J. Boquet, P. D. Colyer and S. H. Moore, 1994. Management effects on yield and yield components of late-planted wheat. Crop Science, 34: 1298-1303.

Siedler H., M. Messmer, M. Schachermayr, H. Winzeler, M. Winzeler, B. Keller, 1994. Genetic diversity in European wheat and spelt breeding material based on RFLP data. Theoretical Applied Genetics, 88: 994-1003.

Taeb, M., R. M. D. Koebner and B. P. Forster, 1993. Genetic variation for waterlogging tolerance in the Triticeae and the chromosomal location of genes conferring waterlogging tolerance in *Thinopyrum elongatum*. Genome, 36: 825-830.

Winzeler, H., J. E. Schmid and M. Winzeler, 1994. Analysis of the yield potential and yield components of F1 and F2 hybrids of corsses between wheat and spelt. Euphytica, 74: 211-218.

Zemetra, R. S. and R. Morris, 1988. Effects of an intercultivaral chromosome substitution on winterhardiness and vernalization in wheat. Genetics, 119: 453-456.

Small grain cereals and pseudo cereals
Offered papers

What are the mechanisms responsible for frost tolerance in quinoa (Chenopodium quinoa Willd.)?

S. E. JACOBSEN[1], C. MONTEROS[2], J. L. CHRISTIANSEN[3] AND A. MUJICA[4]

[1] International Potato Centre (CIP), Apartado 1558, Lima 12, Peru
[2] Instituto Nacional de Investigaciones Agropecuarias (INIAP), Apartado Postal 17-17-1362, Quito, Ecuador
[3] Dep. Of Agricultural Sciences, Royal Veterinary & Agricultural University, Thorvaldsensvej 40, DK-1871 Frederiksberg C, Denmark
[4] Proyecto Quinua CIP-DANIDA-UNAP, Universidad Nacional del Altiplano, Av. Del Ejercito 329, Puno, Peru

S U M M A R Y

Quinoa (*Chenopodium quinoa* Willd.) is grown in the Andean mountains, traditionally up to an altitude of 4,000 m, where frost is common. The physiological mechanisms responsible for the frost resistance observed in quinoa are barely known. For that reason a laboratory experiment was carried out where frost was applied at increasing intensities and durations, and at various levels of relative humidity, with the objective of determining the physiological response and yield of quinoa to increased levels of frost in three phenological phases.

Quinoa showed to have a supercooling capacity of 5°C, a mechanism which prevents immediate damage by low temperatures. However, the main strategy of quinoa seems to be to tolerate ice formation in the cell walls and the following dehydration of the cells, without suffering irreversible damages. A high content of soluble sugars implied a high level of frost tolerance, and caused a reduction in the freezing temperature and the mean lethal temperature (TL_{50}). Soluble sugars, such as fructans, sucrose and deshydrins, could possibly be good indicators of frost tolerance in breeding material of quinoa.

Keywords: frost tolerance, physiological mechanisms, quinoa, sugars

I N T R O D U C T I O N

The mechanisms responsible for resistance to frost can be divided into evasive and tolerance mechanisms. Evasion is the ability of the plant to avoid ice formation in the tissues, for example by supercooling, while a tolerant plant survives extracellular ice formation and dehydration of tissues without irreversible damage. Frost tolerance can be constitutive, as a genetic character of the species, or induced. Induction may occur when the plant once has been exposed to low temperatures, normally above zero, between 10 and 0°C (Levitt, 1980; Nilsen and Orcutt, 1995; Hardy, 1996).

The thermal analysis, consisting in measurement of temperatures with thermacouples, is suitable to determine supercooling. Under ice formation in the plant a thermal reaction occurs, producing two exotherms. The first exotherm represents ice formation in the apoplast, which means a freezing of extracellular water, while the second exotherm indicates freezing of the intracellular water, which normally occurs one or two degrees below the first exotherm (Hopkins, 1995) (Fig. 1). The nucleation temperature corresponds to the temperature, at which ice formation in the tissue is initiated, corresponding to the second exotherm. The point of freezing of the tissue is the temperature at the first exotherm. The difference between the two exotherms is the supercooling capacity of the tissue (Quamme, 1975).

Quinoa's high level of frost resistance has been known for a long time, but very little is known about the specific mechanisms. The present investigation was planned to identify differences of frost resistance mechanisms in two cultivars of quinoa from different agroecological conditions (valley and altiplano).

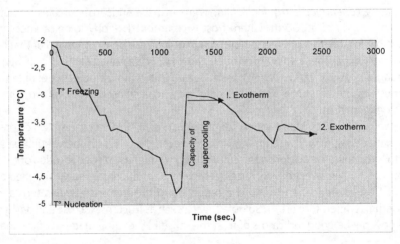

FIGURE 1. THERMAL ANALYSIS IN ORDER TO OBSERVE SUPERCOOLING UNDER CONTROLLED CONDITIONS (QUAMME, 1975; HOPKINS, 1995).

MATERIALS AND METHODS

The investigation was conducted in the Laboratory of Physiology at the University of Concepción, Chile, studying stems and leaves of a valley (Quillohuaman) and an altiplano (Witulla) cultivar, and three acclimatization periods (0.5 and 10 days). The analysis of data was made under a factorial arrangement 2x3x2 with three repetitions. For the variables freezing and nucleation temperatures were utilized 6 repetitions. The experimental unit was one pot of four plants, with 3 kg of soil per pot. The soil was prepared with two parts of mineral soil, one part of compost and one part of sand. For the determinations of sugar and proline stems and leaves from the central third part of the plants were used.

The two quinoa were raised in growth chambers at 20°C. At the 12 true leaves-stage they were transferred to a cultivation chamber BioRef for acclimatization at 4°C during 0.5 or 10 days, respectively. The method for estimating (measuring) average lethal temperature (TL_{50}) consisted in measuring the conductivity of tissues exposed to frost (-2, -4, -8, -12, -16°C) and room temperature (time of exposure), with the rate of tissue death calculated using the following formula:

where

$$Dead\ tissue,\% = \frac{(A/A_1)-(B/B_1)}{1-(B/B_1)}*100$$

A = Conductivity of tissue exposed to frost before ebullition
A_1 = Conductivity of tissue exposed to frost after ebullition
B = Conductivity of tissue exposed to environmental temperature before ebullition
B_1 = Conductivity of tissue exposed to environmental temperature after ebullition

In order to determine the freezing and nucleation temperatures, a freezer was used, connected to a computer with sofware Quilog, which registers the temperature each second.

RESULTS AND DISCUSSION

When the rate of tissue death of the two cultivars for the five temperatures were determined, a logistic curve could be elaborated, defined by the equation:
    where

$$y = \frac{1}{1+e^{a-b(t)}}*100$$

a= -1,943   b= -0,487   for the valley cultivar
a= -3,674   b= -0,590   for the altiplano cultivar
t= temperature (-2, -4, -8, -12, -16 °C)
The a and b were determined from a multiple regression.
For TL_{50}, soluble sugar content, and freezing temperature, highly significant

differences were found between cultivars, plant organs, and acclimatization period, while for nucleation temperature was only observed significant difference between cultivars (Table 1).

TABLE 1. VARIANCE ANALYSIS FOR TL_{50}, FREEZING AND NUCLEATION TEMPERATURES, AND CONTENT OF SOLUBLE SUGAR FOR STEMS AND LEAVES OF TWO QUINOA CULTIVARS AT DIFFERENT ACCLIMATIZATION PERIODS.

	Degrees of freedom (df)	Average lethal temperature (TL_{50})	Soluble sugar content (mg/g dry weight)	Degrees of freedom (df)	Freezing temperature (1. exotherm) (°C)	Nucleation temperature (°C)
		Mean square	Mean square		Mean square	Mean square
Cultivar	1	10.947 **	18.791 **	1	9.05 **	6.619 *
Material	1	3.641 **	17.246 **	1	19.806 **	1.772 ns
Cv. * Mat	1	0.005 ns	0.286 ns	1	0.482 Ns	0.023 ns
Acclimatization	2	14.973 **	326.92 **	2	12.158 **	1.425 ns
Cv. *Aclim	2	0.247 **	6.985 **	2	0.030 Ns	0.714 ns
Mat*Aclim	2	0.132 ns	6.194 **	2	4.7750 **	0.238 ns
Cv. * Mat * A	2	0.242 **	0.205 ns	2	0.044 Ns	0.197 ns
Error	24	0.040	0.235	60	0.203	1.251
Coefficient of variation (%)		4.4	6.5		-15.48	-14.28

ns = Not significant,   * = Significant at the 5% level, ** = Significant at the 1% level

TL_{50} for the valley cultivar Quillohuaman was −3.987°C and for the altiplano cultivar Witulla −5.143°C (Table 2). This indicates a constitutive frost tolerance, with a difference of 1.2°C between the two cultivars even before any exposure to frost. It was observed that the leaves were more susceptible to frost than the stems, with a difference of 1.1°C between the freezing temperature of stems (-3.275°C) and leaves (-2.205°C) (Table 2).

TABLE 2. DATA FOR TL_{50}, FREEZING AND NUCLEATION TEMPERATURE, AND SOLUBLE SUGAR CONTENT FOR STEMS AND LEAVES OF TWO QUINOA CULTIVARS AND DIFFERENT ACCLIMATIZATION PERIODS.

Letters A-C indicate significant differences between treatments (P<0.01)

	Average lethal temperature (TL_{50}) (°C)		Freezing temperature (°C)		Nucleation temperature (°C)		Soluble sugar (mg/g dry weight)	
Cultivar								
Witulla	-5.143	A	-3.084	A	-8.132	A	6.432	A
Quillohuaman	-3.987	B	-2.496	B	-7.525	B	4.993	B
Plant organ								
Stem	-4.910	A	-3.275	A	-7.985	A	6..407	A
Leaf	-4.222	B	-2.205	B	-7.672	A	5.023	B
Acclimatization								
10 days	-5.610	A	-3.514	A	-8.106	A	11.454	A
5 days	-4.629	B	-2.550	B	-7.650	B	4.441	B
0 days	-3.459	C	-2.125	C	-7.729	B	1.250	C

With a longer period of acclimatization, the sugar content increased. Sugar content after 10 days had increased almost ten times, from 1.250 to 11.454 mg of soluble sugar per g dry weight. This indicates that quinoa has the capacity to accumulate sugars under acclimatization. Hardy (1996) mentioned that in barley, after 11 days of acclimatization, the sugar content was increased seven times.

TL_{50} for leaves and stems of the two cultivars declined linearly with days of acclimatization (Figure 2), indicating that during the process of acclimatization, metabolites are accumulated in the plant, causing tolerance to lower temperatures. Stems of the cultivar Witulla had the highest acclimatization capacity. After 10 days TL_{50} fell to 2.1 °C, while for Quillohuaman TL_{50} fell to 1.6°C.

FIGURE 2. TL_{50} FOR LEAVES AND STEMS OF TWO CULTIVARS WITH DIFFERENT PERIOD OF ACCLIMATIZATION.

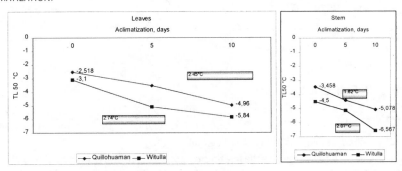

A freezing temperature of the apoplastic water higher than TL_{50} (Table 2, Figs 1,2) indicates, that quinoa plants have the capacity of tolerating extracellular ice formation and dehydration of the tissues, without being irreversibly damaged. Hardy (1996) mentions that plants tolerating ice formation in the tissues have freezing points higher than TL_{50}, as seen in the antarctic species *Deschampia antarctica*, where TL_{50} was -25°C, but the freezing temperature was -7°C.

The nucleation temperatures of Witulla and Quillohuaman were -8.132 and -7.525°C, respectively, while the freezing temperatures were -3.084 and -2.496 °C (Table 2), indicating that in addition to a tolerance to ice formation, which is the principal strategy in relation to frost tolerance, quinoa is able to supercool about 5°C, which is the initial mechanism to prevent immediate damage caused by frost.

For comparison Levitt (1980) mentions that orange-tree can supercool 3°C (temperatures of nucleation and freezing -5 and -2°C, respectively), potatoes can supercool 0.8°C (temperatures of nucleation and freezing -2.4 and -1.9°C, respectively), and winter wheat Aramir can supercool 4.1°C (Bravo, 1996).

The freezing and nucleation temperatures varied according to tissue and cultivar (Figs 1, 2). The bud was more susceptible to low temperatures, with freezing temperatures of -1.7 and -1.1°C for Witulla and Quillohuman, respectively.

The content of soluble sugars were correlated inversely with freezing temperature and TL_{50}. Soluble sugars act as osmoregulators, so that a higher content of dissolved solutes in the intracellular liquid reduces the freezing point, increasing tolerance to cellular freezing. There was significant correlations between freezing temperature and the content of soluble sugars, between freezing temperature and proline, and between TL_{50} and soluble sugars (Table 3). The content of soluble sugar might be utilized as an indicator of frost tolerance.

TABLE 3. CORRELATION BETWEEN FREEZING AND NUCLEATION TEMPERATURES, AND SUGAR AND PROLINE CONTENT.

	Correlation coefficient	Probability	
Temp. Freezing/sugar	- 0,788	0.0001	**
Temp. Freezing/ Proline	-0.468	0.041	*
TL_{500}/ Sugar	- 0,548	0.0005	**
TL_{500}/ Proline	-0.238	0.164	Ns

REFERENCES

Bravo, L. A., 1996. Tolerancia al congelamiento en cebada. Tesis de Doctorado en Ciencias c.m. Biología, Facultad de Ciencias, Universidad de Chile, Santiago.

Hardy, L. A., 1996. Tolerance to the freezing in barley. Doctoral dissertation in Biology Sciences, University of Chile, Santiago.

Hopkins, W., 1995. Introduction to plant physiology. The University of Western Ontario. John Wiley & Sons, INC. New York, 423-443.

Levitt, J., 1980. Responses of Plants to Environmental Stresses. 2nd Edition. Chilling, Freezing, and High Temperature Stresses. Academic Press Inc., New York.

Nilsen, E. and D. Orcutt, 1995. Physiology of plants under stress. Abiotic Factors. Virginia Polytechnic Institute and State University. John Wiley & Sons Inc. New York, 486-511.

Quamme, H. A., 1975. Application of thermal analysis to breeding fruit crops for increased cold hardiness. Horticultural Science, 26: 513-517.

Breeding of quinoa: state of the art

D. MASTEBROEK[1] AND R. VAN LOO[1]

[1] Plant Research International, Wageningen University and Research Centre, P.O. Box 16, 6700 AA Wageningen, The Netherlands

SUMMARY

Quinoa (*Chenopodium quinoa* Willd.) is an ancient seed crop from the Andean region of South America. Over recent decades, quinoa has gained renewed interest because of its high nutritional value. In the early 90's, Plant Research International (formerly CPRO) selected bitter quinoa lines adapted to the north-western European climate with a seed yield of over 4,000 kg ha^{-1} in the Netherlands. Bitterness of quinoa seeds is due to saponins in the seed coat which have to be removed before consumption. This procedure is costly and reduces the seed yield and the content of minerals and vitamins.

This study reports the results of breeding research aimed at the production of high yielding sweet lines, i.e. lines with a very low saponin content. Bitter high yielding CPRO breeding lines were crossed with sweet genotypes with a very low saponin content but adapted to short-day conditions. F2 segregation ratio's confirmed a monogenic dominant inheritance for bitter seeds. F2 population means suggested additive inheritance for plant development and dominant inheritance for high plant height and resistance to downy mildew. Bitterness was not related with early maturity and plant height.

Due to repeated line selection in subsequent generations, several well performing sweet lines were obtained. The mean seed yield of 200 selected lines was 2,370 kg ha^{-1} in 1996 and 1,980 kg ha^{-1} in 1997. In 1997, seed yield was reduced by wet weather conditions. The best performing line showed a seed yield of 3,218 and 2,518 kg ha^{-1} in those two years.

The first sweet genotype 'Atlas', registered for plant breeder's right in 1998, yielded 3,500 kg ha^{-1} in field trials in 1999.

Keywords: Chenopodium quinoa, downy mildew, saponins, sweet quinoa

INTRODUCTION

Quinoa (*Chenopodium quinoa* Willd.) is an ancient seed crop from the Andean region of South America. Quinoa was cultivated by the Incas as a main food crop, but after the Spanish conquest, the crop area declined drastically. Since a few decades, quinoa has gained renewed interest because of its high nutritional value (Koziol, 1992). In the 1980's, quinoa has been adapted to the north-western European climate (Jacobsen *et al.*, 1994 and Risi and Galwey, 1984). Plant Research International (formerly CPRO-DLO) has selected high yielding quinoa lines, which yielded over 4,000 kg ha^{-1} in the Netherlands. These lines are early ripening, have a short plant height and are resistant to sprouting, lodging and seed loss, but contain saponins in the seeds (Mastebroek and Limburg, 1996). Saponins are bitter compounds in the pericarp or seed coat (Villacorta and Talavera, 1976) that reduce the surface tension of water and therefore cause foam when shaken in water. Saponins are toxic if they reach the blood stream, where they disrupt the membranes of red blood cells (Ballón *et al.*, 1976). Therefore, saponins have to be removed by repeated washing and/or abrasion before processing or consumption. However, washing is expensive and abrasion reduces the seed yield. Also the content of minerals and vitamins can be reduced by procedures to remove the saponins (Koziol, 1992), since these substances are also concentrated in the outer layers of the seed (Varriano-Marston and De Francisco, 1984). Therefore, breeding and utilisation of sweet genotypes without saponins in the seed, is desirable. In 1994, Plant Research International started breeding research aiming at the production of high-yielding sweet lines. The results of this programme are presented in this paper.

MATERIALS AND METHODS

Crosses

In 1994, 27 crosses were made between 11 high yielding bitter CPRO breeding lines and four sweet lines (CPRO-66, CPRO-67, CPRO-68 and CPR0-70). The latter were selected from sweet accessions obtained from South America and adapted to a short day length. Hybrid plants were identified on the basis of axil pigmentation (CPRO-66 and CPRO-67) and hypocotyl colouration (CPRO-70) and grown in pots with a diameter of 18 cm in a glasshouse. During the growing period, parents and F1 plants of seven crosses were evaluated for plant development and plant height. Stages of plant development were scored on a decimal scale, developed at Plant Research International (Limburg and Mastebroek, 1996).

Evaluation of F2 plants in the field

During the summer of 1995, 27 populations of 100 F2 plants (two replicates of 50 plants) together with 15 crossing parents were evaluated in a field trial. During the growing season, plants grown in the central square metre of each plot were evaluated for plant development, plant height and infection by downy mildew (*Peronospora farinosa* f. sp. *chenopodii*). Early ripening, short plants with a dense panicle were harvested and their seeds tested for bitterness with a foam test. In two crosses, all F2 plants were harvested and the relation between the saponin characteristic and other characteristics was studied.

Selection

Per selected F2 plant a progeny of 20 F3 plants was raised in a glasshouse during the winter of 1995-1996. Progenies of sweet plants selected in the F3 and subsequent generations were evaluated for agronomic performance in field trials on fertile clay soil in Lelystad, the Netherlands. From F3 until F6 repeated line selection was applied.

R E S U L T S

Evaluation of F1 plants

The variation for plant development and plant height of crossing parents and F1 plants in a glasshouse is presented in Table 1. On the average, plant development of F1 plants was intermediate between that of the parents, but the F1 plants exceeded their parents in plant height.

TABLE 1. VARIATION AND MEAN VALUES FOR PLANT DEVELOPMENT STAGE (DC') AND PLANT HEIGHT OF PARENTS AND F1 PLANTS OF SEVEN CROSSES BETWEEN FIVE BITTER AND THREE SWEET QUINOA GENOTYPES IN A GLASSHOUSE.

		Bitter parents		F1		Sweet parents	
		range	mean	range	mean	range	mean
Plant stage	(19-7-94)	3.5 - 4.3	3.9	3.3 - 3.5	3.4	3.0 - 3.1	3.0
Plant stage	(26-7-94)	3.7 - 4.9	4.3	3.5 - 4.1	3.7	3.1 - 3.3	3.2
Plant height	(19-7-94)	90 - 110	97	110 - 130	116	70 - 110	85

^{1}dc 3.0 to 3.9 = inflorescence development
dc 4.1 to 4.9 = initial flowering to full bloom

F2 evaluation in the field

In Table 2, mid-parent values (MPVs) and F2 means of infection by downy mildew, plant height and plant stage are given of 15 crosses between five bitter lines and three sweet lines. MPVs and population means represent the mean of the five crosses made between five bitter lines and one sweet line. In 1995, there was a severe infection by downy mildew and large variation for infection level was observed. The sweet line CPRO-67 showed a high resistance level, CPRO-66 was moderately infected. On average, crosses with CPRO-67 showed a low infection level for downy mildew, which was lower than calculated for the MPV.

Bitter and sweet parents differed remarkably for plant development on 15 August. At this date, the bitter parents were already in the seed filling stage, whilst the sweet parents were still in the stage of panicle development. On the average, the F2 plants of crosses with CPRO-66 and CPRO-70 were earlier than expected on the basis of the MPV.

The differences for plant height between and sweet parental genotypes were large. Bitter parents were between 120 and 140 cm high, but the sweet parents exceeded 200 cm.

The F2 means for plant height exceeded the MPV in all three groups of crosses.

The relation of bitterness with other characteristics

In the two crosses studied, the number of bitter and sweet F2 plants confirmed a 3:1 segregation. Numbers of bitter and sweet plants were regularly distributed over the different classes of plant development and plant height, except in the extreme classes. No F2 plants were detected which were as late or as early as their parents and sweet genotypes as short as the bitter parents were also lacking. The shortest sweet F2 plants were 160 cm. Several F2 plants were 240 cm high and even exceeded the tall and sweet parent. In the investigated crosses, a significant negative correlation was found between early plant development and plant height (r=- 0.35 and -0.40, respectively).

TABLE 2. MEAN PERFORMANCE IN THE FIELD OF FIVE BITTER AND THREE SWEET PARENTAL QUINOA
GENOTYPES IN COMPARISON TO MPV AND F2 MEANS AVERAGED PER SWEET PARENTAL GENOTYPE.

			5 Bitter parents (P1)	Sweet parents (P2)			Mean MP Value per sweet parent			Mean F2 value per sweet parent		
Characteristic	Range	Mean		66	67	70	66	67	70	66	67	70
Mildew inf.[1]	3 - 9	6.6	6	1	3		6.3	3.8	4.8	6	2.4	4.4
Plant height[2]	116 - 142	155	214	210	220		185	183	188	197	203	197
Earliness[3]	6.4 - 6.9	6.7	3.7	3.4	3.7		5.2	5.0	5.2	5.5	5.1	5.5

[1] 1 = hardly symptoms, 9 = severely infected
[2] measured on 15 August in cm
[3] plant development stage on 15 August, 3.0 to 3.9 = inflorescence development,
5.0 to 5.9 = deflowering, 6.0 to 6.9 = panicle colouration

Selection

In 1995, only 80 sweet F2 plants with an acceptable agronomic performance could be selected out of 2,700 F2 plants. In 20 sweet F3 lines, 10 plants per line were selected for evaluation of their progenies in a field trial in 1996.

Correlation for plant height and early maturity between F3 plants in the glasshouse and F4 lines in the field was not significant.

In 1996, lines resistant to downy mildew, shedding, lodging and pre-harvest sprouting were selected. In 20 F4 lines, again 10 plants were selected for evaluation in 1997.

In 1997, wet weather conditions decreased seed yield, particularly of early maturing genotypes. Mean seed yield was 2,370 kg ha[-1] in 1996 and 1,980 kg ha[-1] in 1997. Maximum seed yields amounted to 3,210 kg ha[-1] in 1996 and 2,520 kg ha[-1] in 1997.

Between the field evaluation in 1996 and 1997, a moderate but significant correlation was found for plant height and early maturity (r=0.60 for both characteristics).

After a final evaluation in 1998, 10 sweet breeding lines were selected for further evaluation, purification and multiplication. One line, called 'Atlas', has been registered for plant breeder's rights. Atlas is a moderately late-ripening variety with light green leaves, white panicles and big white seeds. The plants are moderately high and susceptible to downy mildew. Seed yield of Atlas amounted to 2,500 kg ha[-1] in 1998 and 3,500 kg ha[-1] in 1999 at in field trials. Evaluation of the amino-acids profile of the seed protein of Atlas showed high contents of lysine (6.0%), methionine (2.3%), threonine (4.0%), tryptophan (1.3%) and cystine (2.0%).

DISCUSSION

The segregation ratio of 3:1 found between bitter and sweet F2 plants confirm the conclusion of Gandarillas (1974) that bitterness has a monogenic inheritance. An additive inheritance for earliness was suggested by the finding of an intermediate plant development of F1 plants (Table 1), lack of F2 plants as early or as late as both parents and a normal distribution of numbers of F2 plants over the different classes of plant development.

The findings that F2 means exceeded their MPV for plant height (Table 2) and that F1 plants (Table 1) and several F2 plants exceeded their tallest parent in plant height suggest a dominant inheritance of plant height which agrees with the suggestion of Kenwright (1989) that plant height is depending on dominant genes.

The regular distribution of sweet and bitter F2 plants over the different classes of plant development and plant height suggests that bitterness is not correlated with early plant development and plant height.

The negative correlation between early plant development and plant height found in our study is favourable for the selection of early ripening, short genotypes. However, lack of sweet and early ripening F2 genotypes with a low plant height in the investigated crosses required repeated selection cycles.

The lower mildew infection level of the F2 means in crosses with CPRO-67 than expected on the basis of MPV (Table 2) suggests that the resistance of this parent is dominantly inherited.

Cultivation of the sweet cultivar 'Atlas' in field trials confirmed the seed yield potential achieved in previous experiments. The contents of essential amino acids in the seed protein of 'Atlas' are comparable to those found by Koziol (1992).

Research presented in this paper showed that the breeding programme has been successful and aims have been fulfilled. Further breeding efforts will concentrate on the quality of quinoa for food and feed purposes.

REFERENCES

Ballón, E., W. Tellería and J. Hutton, 1976. Aproximación a la determinación de saponinas por cromatografía de capafina. In: Segunda Convención Internacional de Quenopodiaccas. Universidad Boliviana Tonnás Friás, Comité Departmental de Obras Publicas de Potosi, Instituto Interamericano de Ciencias Agrocolos, Potosi, Bolivia, 89-94.

Gandarillas, H., 1974. Genetica y Origen de la Quinua. Bol. 9 Instituto Nacional de Trigo, Ministeno de Asuntos Compesinos y Agropecuarios, La Paz, Bolivia.

Jacobsen, S. E., I. Jørgensen and O. Stølen, 1994. Cultivation of quinoa (*Chenopodium quinoa*) under temperate climatic conditions in Denmark. Journal of Agricultural Science, Cambridge, 122: 47-52.

Kenwright, P. A., 1989. Breeding the Andean grain crop quinoa (*Chenopodium quinoa*) for cultivation in Britain. PhD thesis, University of Cambridge, England.

Koziol, M. J., 1992. Chemical composition and nutritional evaluation of quinoa (*Chenopodium quinoa* Willd.). Journal Food Composition Analysis, 5: 35-68.

Limburg, H. and H. D. Mastebroek, 1996. Breeding high yielding lines of Chenopodium quinoa Willd. with saponin free seed. In: Stølen, O., K. Bruhn, K. Pithan and J. Hill (Eds.). Small grain cereals and pseudo-cereals. Proceedings of the COST 814 workshop. 22-24 February 1996, Copenhagen, Denmark, 103-114.

Mastebroek, H. D. and H. Limburg, 1996. Breeding for increased harvest security in quinoa (Chenopodium quinoa Willd.). In: Proceedings COST814 Workshop: Small Grain Cereals and Pseudo Cereals. Eds. Stolen, O., K. Bruhn, K. Pithan and H. Hill. Copenhagen, 22-24 February 1996, 79-86.

Risi, J. and N. W. Galwey, 1984. The Chenopodium grains of the Andes: Inca Crops for Modern Agriculture. Advances in Applied Biology, 10: 145-216.

Varriano-Marston, E. and A. de Francisco, 1984. Ultrastructure of quinoa fruit (*Chenopodium quinoa* Willd.). Food Microstructure, 3: 165-173.

Villacorta, S. L. and R. V. Talavera, 1976. Anatomia del grano de quinoa (*Chenopodium quinoa* Willd). Ana. Cient. 14: 39-45.

During late development stages the quinoa crop is not always successful

I. OHLSSON

Swedish University of Agricultural Sciences, Department of Ecology and Crop Production Science, P.O. Box 7043, SE-750 07 Uppsala, Sweden

SUMMARY

The ancient crop from the Andes, quinoa (*Chenopodium quinoa*) has received renewed attention in recent years in European countries due to its frost and drought tolerance.

From studies carried out in Sweden of growing parameters and yield levels of various cultivars from Europe and South America the results have shown promising signs. The relatively short growing season with temperature drop at the end of the season resulted in yield levels of 1,500 to 2,000 kg ha^{-2} from European as well as from south American cultivars.

In 1999, however, the quinoa crop totally failed to develop seeds. In spite of quite normal crop development including flowering no seeds developed. The pollination failed completely and it might be possible that some unknown diseases or metabolite disturbance occurred. Compared to earlier years the climate in 1999 was a little warmer than normal with less and highly uneven distribution of precipitation.

Keywords: drought, frost, pollination, quinoa, seeds

INTRODUCTION

Quinoa (*Chenopodium quinoa*) is an ancient crop from the Andes that has received renewed attention in recent years in European countries due to its frost and drought tolerance. Especially in the north-west region of Europe including Sweden it has become of vital interest to evaluate the quinoa crop. Furthermore, quinoa is a crop of high nutritional value: high protein content, good composition of essential amino acids, good starch characteristics, and no gluten. The latter character is interesting with increasing numbers of young people allergic to gluten.

From studies carried out in Sweden of growing parameters and yield levels of various cultivars from Europe and South America the results have been promising (Ohlsson, 1997; Ohlsson and Dahlstedt, 1999). The relatively short growing season with temperature drop at the end of the season resulted in yield levels of 1,500 to 2,000 kg ha^{-2} from

European as well as from South American cultivars.

With the intention to collect further information and make sure of quinoa adaptation to the growing and environmental conditions in Sweden crop evaluation was carried through to 1999.

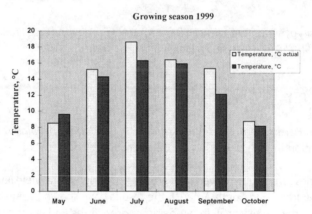

FIGURE 1. TEMPERATURE DURING THE GROWING SEASON.

MATERIALS AND METHODS

The 1999 field experiment was carried out at the University Research Station Stenstugu (57:6 N ; 18:4 E). The genetic material was made up from a limited number of the best yielding cultivars from the 1998 experiment. The cultivars originated from Europe and South America. The sowing took place on May 19 with a row space of 45 cm and a seed rate of 10 kg ha^{-1}. Mechanical hoeing controlled the weeds and no disease attacks on the quinoa crop were observed.

RESULTS AND DISCUSSION

Germination, early development and establishment of the quinoa crop showed that all the cultivars had a normal growth rate. Compared to the conditions of the 1998 crop development the present crop performed well with acceptable response to the environment. It could be noted that a severe attack from weeds was evident a few weeks after emergence. However, it was completely controlled by frequent mechanical hoeing.

This year, however, the quinoa crop totally failed to develop seeds. In spite of quite normal development including flowering no seeds developed. The pollination failed completely and it might be possible that some unknown diseases or metabolite disturbance occurred. Investigations are going on to hopefully clarify the conditions. Compared to earlier years the climate in 1999 was a little warmer than normal with less precipitation

(Figs 1 and 2). From the data presented there is quite good correlation between actual month and average month temperatures at the experimental site. The two months June and July had significant higher temperatures during 1999 compared to average. As regards the climate factor precipitation manifested a great discrepancy from the average monthly precipitation of the months June and July. The June precipitation was double the average for this month. For July the opposite conditions were shown, only 3 mm was obtained. Based on the somewhat extreme conditions at temperature and precipitation at flowering in connection with growing the crop at the northern border of its possible growing area the environment might have negatively influenced pollination or plant hormone status.

Growing period 1999

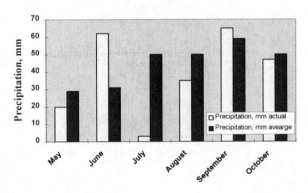

FIGURE 2. PRECIPITATION DURING THE GROWING SEASON.

At present we have no adequate explanation as to why seed development failed. It is well known from crop science that no new crop can be surely evaluated during only two to three years in a new environment. But the evaluation of the quinoa crop will continue in Sweden for some more years. Hopefully, by means of further scientific input and experiments the quinoa crop will become a crop for north European agriculture.

REFERENCES

Ohlsson, I., 1997. Quinoa - a potential crop for Sweden? COST 814 action., European commission. Crop development for cool and wet regions of Europe. Spelt and Quinoa. CPRO-DLO, Wageningen.

Ohlsson, I. and L. Dahlstedt, 1999. Quinoa - potential in Sweden. COST 814: Crop development for the cool and wet regions of Europe. European commission. Alternative crops for sustainable agriculture, Turko, Finland.

The possibilities for spelt growing under Norwegian conditions

M. AASSVEEN, R. ELTUN, O. BJERKE AND H. LINNERUD

The Norwegian Crop Research Institute, Apelsvoll Research Centre, Kapp, Norway

SUMMARY

Based on results from two years' sowing time experiments in the period 1998-99, it appears that spelt can be grown in the inland part of south-eastern Norway, but with varying results. Winter survival seems to be the main problem under Norwegian growing conditions. Both pink snow mould (*Microdochium nivale*) at early sowing, and other winter stress factors at late sowing are reasons for plant destruction during the winter. In the sowing time experiment the spelt varieties Roquin, Ostar and Oberkulmer Rotkorn were compared to the wheat variety Folke, the rye variety Danko and the triticale variety Prego. Spelt yielded much lower than the other species. The spelt varieties had a higher protein content than the wheat, and a sufficient falling number for bread making. The spelt varieties were more susceptible to powdery mildew than the other species. Proper sowing time for spelt seems to be in the first or second week of September.

Keywords: diseases, grain yield, spelt, wheat, winter survival

INTRODUCTION

Spelt (*Triticum spelta* L.) has traditionally not been grown in Norway, and there is very little knowledge about the climatic limitations for spelt growing in this country. In the last few years there has been some interest among organic farmers for growing spelt, but the results have been variable both for grain yield and quality. As part of the SESA programme (Spelt, a recovered crop for the future of sustainable agriculture in Europe), we have investigated the possibilities for growing spelt under Norwegian conditions. Both variety testing and investigation of proper sowing time was part of the project. In this paper, only the results from the sowing time trials will be presented.

MATERIALS AND METHODS

In the years 1998 and 1999 two sowing time experiments were accomplished at Apelsvoll Research Centre. Apelsvoll represents an inland climate of eastern Norway with warm summers and cold winters. Usually there is a snow cover from the middle of November to the middle of April. The average starting date of the growing season (diurnal temperature higher than 6°C) is May 3 and the end date is October 5. The average temperature in the growing period May-September is 12.0°C. The annual precipitation is 600 mm, and more than 50% of this occurs during the growing period. The soil textures are loam and silty sand, with a humus content of 6% in the top soil. The winter cereals are normally sown in early September and harvested a year later.

To investigate the proper sowing time a split-plot experiment with three replications and four sowing times from August 20 to September 20 was undertaken. Three varieties of spelt (Roquin, Ostar and Oberkulmer Rotkorn) were compared to one variety of wheat (Folke), rye (Danko) and triticale (Prego). The trials were carried out on conventionally farmed land, and an amount of 100 kg N ha[-1] compound fertilizer was applied. Except for herbicides no pesticides were used.

RESULTS AND DISCUSSION

The yield level of spelt was in general low in these trials as compared to the other species (Tables 1 and 2). The main reason appears to be serious winter damage caused by pink snow mould (*Microdochium nivale*) at early sowing, and other winter stress factors at late sowing. The spelt varieties were also heavily attacked by powdery mildew during the growing season. The other species were less affected, especially by powdery mildew. Both wheat (Folke), triticale (Prego) and rye (Danko) yielded highest at the second sowing time (September 01). The yield reduction from the second to the third sowing time (September 10) was greatest for wheat. For the wheat we also had a yield reduction from the third to the last sowing time (September 20).

TABLE 1. MAIN EFFECTS OF SOWING TIME AND VARIETIES ON DIFFERENT AGRONOMIC AND QUALITY CHARACTERISTICS. MEAN RESULTS FROM TWO TRIALS AT APELSVOLL RESEARCH CENTRE, 1998 – 99.

	Grain yield		Percentage	Winter	Days to	Snow	Powdery	Sept-	Protein	Falling
	Naked kg/ha	Rel	of kernals	survival, %	heading *	mold	mildew	oria	cont. %	number
Sowing time										
August 20	4230	100	69,8	75	86	4	2	3	12,2	94
September 01	4800	113	71,4	88	85	3	3	2	11,4	103
September 10	4530	107	70,4	90	88	2	3	2	11,7	96
September 20	4550	108	71,2	89	91	1	3	2	12,1	100
Variety										
Roquin	2190	100	71,6	63	93	4	4	3	13,6	226
Ostar	2890	132	70,3	86	94	2	4	2	13,1	238
Oberkulm. Rotk.	2330	106	70,2	84	91	2	4	2	14,6	212
Folke	5190	237		92	93	2	2	2	10,8	257
Prego	7230	330		94	83	2	1	2	9,9	67
Danko	7330	335		95	70	3	1	2	9,1	73

* Days from April 1.

For the spelt varieties Roquin and Oberkulmer Rotkorn there were increases in grain yield from the first to the third sowing time, and Ostar yielded highest at the second sowing time. Roquin had a very low grain yield at the first sowing time (August

20) as compared to the later sowings. The main reason for variation between the spelt varieties in effect of delayed sowing appears to be differences in resistance against pink snow mould.

TABLE 2. COMBINED EFFECTS OF VARIETY AND SOWING TIME ON DIFFERENT AGRONOMIC AND QUALITY CHARACTERISTICS. MEAN RESULTS FROM TWO TRIALS AT APELSVOLL RESEARCH CENTRE 1998 – 99.

Variety	Sowing Time	Grain yield Naked kg/ha	Rel.	Percentage of kernals	Winter survival %	Days to heading*	Snow mold	Powdery mildew	Sept-oria	Protein cont.%	Falling number
Roquin	1	1340	100	71,0	31	91	7	3	3	14,4	217
	2	2460	184	72,1	67	95	5	5	3	12,8	226
	3	2560	191	71,5	76	95	3	5	3	13,1	244
	4	2390	178	71,7	76	96	1	5	2	14,0	217
Ostar	1	2580	100	69,5	79	91	3	4	3	12,9	238
	2	3220	125	70,4	90	91	3	4	2	13,0	244
	3	2850	110	70,1	89	94	2	5	2	13,0	244
	4	2920	113	71,1	86	97	1	4	2	13,6	238
Oberk. Rotk	1	2120	100	69,0	74	88	3	4	3	15,2	165
	2	2380	112	71,7	88	89	2	4	2	14,0	232
	3	2410	114	69,5	89	91	2	4	2	14,7	238
	4	2400	113	70,7	84	96	1	5	2	14,4	244
Folke	1	5140	100		85	92	3	2	3	10,9	250
	2	5780	112		92	88	2	3	2	10,2	232
	3	5120	100		96	95	2	2	2	10,9	272
	4	4730	92		94	97	1	3	2	11,1	264
Prego	1	6890	100		88	83	2	1	2	10,3	65
	2	7520	109		98	82	2	1	2	9,5	69
	3	7070	103		96	83	2	1	2	9,4	65
	4	7430	108		95	85	1	1	2	10,2	68
Danko	1	7300	100		92	69	3	1	2	9,6	71
	2	7420	102		93	69	3	2	2	8,7	77
	3	7140	98		93	70	3	2	2	9,0	73
	4	7440	102		99	71	1	2	2	9,0	73

* Days from April 1.

The sowing time strongly affected the plant development in the autumn, and there is a well known correlation between plant size in the autumn and damage by pink snow mould during the winter. In addition to snow mould it was also found some attack of frit fly (*Oscinella frit* L.) in plots with early sowing. In general delayed sowing reduced the attack of pink snow mould, and at the latest sowing time there was no attack at all (Figs 1 and 2). In spite of this winter survival was not improved after the second sowing time, and the grain yields were reduced. Why is it so? At late sowing, after the middle of September, low temperatures lead to a slow plant development under Norwegian conditions. The small plants do not manage to get prepared for the long winter. Even if they survive, they are too weak in the spring to form enough tillers to make a dense plant stand. Even the Norwegian spring climate does not promote an optimal tillering process because the period from snow melting until full summer is very short. To utilise this short period of time it is essential to have strong plants after the winter.

The protein content and the falling number in the experiments were at a normal level for winter cereals in conventional cropping. The spelt varieties had a considerable higher protein content than winter wheat, and the falling number for the spelt was at a satisfactory level for bread making.

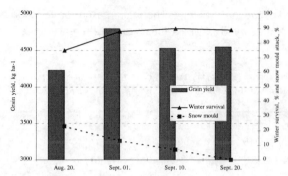

FIGURE 1. GRAIN YIELD, WINTER SURVIVAL AND SNOW MOULD ATTACK AT FOUR DIFFERENT SOWING TIMES. MEAN RESULTS FOR ALL SPECIES, APELSVOLL RESEARCH CENTRE 1998-99.

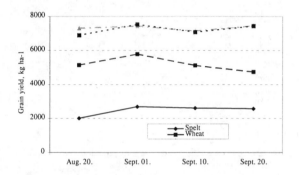

FIGURE 2. GRAIN YIELD AT FOUR SOWING TIMES. MEAN RESULTS FOR EACH SPECIES, APELSVOLL RESEARCH CENTRE 1998-99.

CONCLUSIONS

Based on the sowing time experiments it is clear that spelt can ripen and can be grown in Norway, but the grain yields are much lower than for winter wheat and other winter cereal species. The main problem under Norwegian growing conditions seems to be the winter survival. We have a very narrow space of time for sowing to get an optimal plant development before the winter. Both early and late sowing can lead to plant destruction during winter. At early sowing pink snow mould is the main reason. At later sowing the main problem is that the plants do not reach a growth stage to harden enough before winter sets in. Even if the plants survive, Norwegian spring conditions are not optimal to promote an optimal tillering process if the plants are too weak.

Evaluation of various quinoa varieties (Chenopodium quinoa Willd.) originated from Europe and Latin America

C. ILIADIS[1] AND T. KARYOTIS[2]

[1] N.AG.RE.F - Fodder Crops and Pasture Institute, Larissa Greece
[2] N.AG.RE.F - Map and Soil Classification Institute, Larissa Greece

SUMMARY

Twenty-five quinoa varieties of different geographical origin (Europe - Latin America) were tested for seed yield in central Greece.

Only six European varieties and two Latin American produced seeds while the remaining 17 from Latin American produced only panicles (flowers). This phenomenon could probably be attributed to the extremely high maximum air temperature, higher than 30°C, which prevailed during the flowering period.

The most productive variety was the Danish "E-DK-4 Pocip-Davida-Una" in which the recorded yield was 1,496 kg ha[-1].

Keywords : quinoa, seed yield, varieties

INTRODUCTION

Quinoa (*Chenopodium quinoa* Willd.) introduced into various European countries since early 1980 and although it is not yet commercially cultivated, many research projects have been established in many countries, projects which focused mainly on seed production.

In Greece, the first experiments were established since 1996 at the Fodder Crops and Pasture Institute in Larissa province. Preliminary research focused on the influence of sowing density to optimize yield as well as to find out the appropriate sowing date under xerothermic climatic conditions. Furthermore, after seed harvest, to explore the possibility of using the remaining quinoa stems for energy purposes and for its fibre content (Iliadis *et al.*,1997, 1999).

There has been some disagreement in the literature concerning the type of flowering response exhibited by quinoa. Fuller (1949) found that Bolivian quinoa plants would flower under a broad range of photoperiods and concluded that quinoa is photoperiodically indeterminate, though shorter photoperiods generally favoured the earlier appearance and opening of flowers. Risi (1986) found large differences in flowering date between varieties when had grown at high latitudes in England, possibly due to differences in their sensitivity to long days.

However, other studies showed that several environmental factors affect the ratio of hermaphrodite to female flowers in the genus *Chenopodium* and that temperatures at anthesis determines pollen production (Gandarillas, 1979).

The objective of this study was the evaluation of 25 quinoa varieties of different origin under xerothermic climatic conditions, for adaptation and seed yield.

MATERIALS AND METHODS

Twenty-four varieties which were obtained from Peru (International Centre of Potato) were studied and evaluated for seed yield. The origin of these varieties were from different countries of Europe and Latin America as shown in Table 2. The variety "N° 407" were used as a control.

The experimental design was a randomized complete block with four replications and each experimental plot had a size of 8 m², consisted of four rows with 50 cm distance between rows. Sowing date was the beginning of March and the experiment was fertilized with 80 kg ha⁻¹ of nitrogen . Sowing density of the varieties tested, was 10 kg ha⁻¹. The plots were harvested by hand and seed yield measurements were taken only from the two central rows in each plot.

No herbicide was applied and weeds were uprooted by hand. During the cultivation period four irrigations were applied and a higher quantity of water was regulated during flowering period.

RESULTS AND DISCUSSION

The climatic conditions prevailing during quinoa's cultivation was extremely warm and dry (Table1).

TABLE 1. CLIMATIC CONDITIONS PREVAILED DURING CULTIVATION PERIOD OF THE
  VARIETIES (SPRING 1999).

Months	Air temperature C⁰			Relative humidity %	Solar radiation V/m²	Rainfalls mm
	Mean	Mean maximum	Mean minimum			
March	9,3	14,8	4,4	79,1	3416,5	76,2
April	13,9	20,5	7,4	47,8	5114,9	24,2
May	19,2	26,0	12,1	68,6	5650,5	4,2
June	24,8	31,9	17,1	52,8	6557,5	4,0
July	26,1	32,3	19,6	55,2	6254,3	0,0
August	26,5	33,1	19,5	62,0	6022,7	10,8

Although the experiment was established under an irrigation scheme, extreme air conditions influenced the varieties studied differentially.

It seems that the origin of the varieties played a dominant role. Only 8 among the 25 varieties produced seeds whilst the other 17 produced only panicles and flowers and finally they did not produce seeds. (Table 2).

TABLE 2. EVALUATION OF 25 QUINOA VARIETIES FOR SEED YIELD AND OTHER CHARACTERISTICS, IN LARISSA PROVINCE (AVERAGE OF FOUR REPLICATIONS).

Name of the varieties	Origin	Code Number	Seed Yield (Kg/ha)	Flowering beginning (Days after germination)	Plant's height (cm) at harvest stage	Plant's maturing for harvest (Days after germination)	Dry Stems Weight (Kg/ha)
Cica-127-Cusco	Peru	1	0	68	156	120	6660
Cica-17-Cusco	Peru	2	0	66	141	120	7400
Huariponcno-CRIDER-Puno	Peru	3	0	60	115	118	3320
Kancolla- UNA	Peru	4	0	58	123	122	4730
Narino-INIA-Pasto	Colombia	5	0	77	144	132	2250
Salcedo-INIA-Puno	Peru	6	0	60	113	118	4830
Ratuqui- IBTA	Bolivia	7	0	59	125	118	2600
Kamiri-IBTA	Bolivia	8	0	60	152	121	2880
Real-IBTA	Bolivia	9	0	60	108	120	2530
Juiuy-UNA	Argentina	10	0	60	119	120	4250
Baer-II-U-Conception	Chile	11	302	60	157	110	3670
Ru-2 Pocip-Davida-Una	England	12	794	60	100	100	4810
Ru-5 Pocip-Davida-Una	England	13	1018	60	109	106	3920
NL6-Pocip-Davida-Una	Holland	14	1100	60	90	101	2880
Control " No 407"	Greece	15	812	60	168	116	4500
E-DK-4Pocip-Davida-Una	Denmark	16	1496	59	113	110	3940
G-205-95-Pocip-Davida-Una	Denmark	17	1106	60	118	113	3320
Sayana-IBTA	Bolivia	18	0	62	127	124	2290
Ingapirca-INIAP	Ecuador	19	0	68	113	124	4060
03-21-079BB-Una-Puno	Peru	20	0	68	117	124	4740
03-21- 072RM-Una-Puno	Peru	21	0	63	109	110	3830
Ecu-420-INIAP	Ecuador	22	0	66	118	119	4820
02- Embraba	Brazil	23	459	64	101	102	1630
Canchones- Uap-Iquique	Chile	24	0	0	106	122	180
Illpa-INIA-Puno	Peru	25	0	61	107	120	2180
	$LSD_{0.05}=$		117	1,64		1,44	1150
	$CV=$		15,98	12,40		9,32	12,46

All the tested varieties flowered, with small differences, about 60 days after their germination, although many researchers reported big differences possibly due to their photoperiod-sensitivity to long days (Risi and Galwey, 1984. Risi, 1986). It is assumed that the photoperiod-sensitivity of the varieties was not the main reason in order to argue why some produced seeds, since all flowered at the same time, approximately. The extremely high air temperature, higher than 30°C which prevailed during the anthesis of the varieties in the experiment may be the reason for this differentiation. Further research is needed to find out more precisely the real reason.

Among the varieties which produced seeds the most productive was the variety E-DK-4Pocip-Davida-Una from Denmark (1,496 kg ha⁻¹). The other European varieties exceeded the control variety "N° 407" in yield, while the lowest yields were recorded from the two Latin-American varieties Baer-II-U-Conception (302 kg ha⁻¹) and 02-Embraba (459 kg ha⁻¹), respectively (Table 2).

All the tested varieties, which were grown under irrigation conditions, developed well and matured for harvest about 100-120 days after their germination. Their plants height exceeded 100 cm at harvest stage. The tallest varieties were those with the code number 1, 8, 11 and 15 (Table 2). However, plant height was not correlated with the dry weight of stems after seed harvest. Biomass production was different among the tested varieties. Unfortunately, the varieties with code 1, 2, 6, 20 and 22 gave high biomass production but seeds were not obtained under the xerothermic conditions.

CONCLUSIONS

The origin of the examined varieties was definitely that for seed production, under the warm and dry climatic conditions with long days in which they were grown.

All the European varieties were adapted and produced seeds, whilst the majority of the varieties from Latin American produced only panicles with flowers.

The main reason may be attributed to the extremely increased temperatures >30° C during the flowering period but this needs further investigation because the data of this study are not sufficient

The Danish variety "E-DK-4 Pocip-Davida-Una" was the most productive (1,496 kg ha⁻¹). It became clear that a higher number of potential genotypes of different origin must be evaluated in order that more precise results be obtained.

REFERENCES

Fuller, H. J., 1949. Photoperiodic response of *Chenopodium Quinoa* Willd. and *Amaranthus caudatus*. L. American Journal of Botany, 36: 175-180.

Gandarillas, H., 1979. Genetica y origen. In: Quinoa y Kaniwa Qultivos Andinos (M. E. Tapia, ed.), 45-64. Serie Libros y Materiales Educativos No 49, Instituto Interamericano de Ciencias Agricolas, Bogota, Colombia.

Iliadis, C., Th. Karyotis and Th. Mitsibonas, 1997. Research on Quinoa (Chenopondium quinoa) and Amaranth (Amarantus caudatus) in Greece, In: Proceedings of E.E. Workshop on small grain cereals and pseudosereals. Wageningen 24-28 October 1997. Cost Action 814, 85-91.

Iliadis C., Th. Karyotis and S. Jacobsen, 1999. Effect of sowing date on seed quality and yield of quinoa (Chenopondium quinoa Willd.) in Greece. In: Proceedings of E.E. Workshop on Alternative Crops for Sustainable Agriculture, Turku, Finland 13-15 June 1999. Cost Action 814, 226-231.

Risi, J., 1986. Adaptation of the Andean grain Crop Quinoa (*Chenopodium quinoa* Willd.) for Cultivation in Britain. Ph.D. thesis, University of Cambridge, England.

What are the mechanisms responsible for salt tolerance in quinoa (*Chenopodium quinoa* Willd.)?

S. E. JACOBSEN[1], H. QUISPE[1], J. L. CHRISTIANSEN[2] AND A. MUJICA[3]

[1] *International Potato Centre (CIP), Apartado 1558, Lima 12, Peru*
[2] *Dep. Of Agricultural Sciences, Royal Veterinary & Agricultural University, Thorvaldsensvej 40, DK-1871 Frederiksberg C, Denmark*
[3] *Proyecto Quinua CIP-DANIDA-UNAP, Universidad Nacional del Altiplano, Av. De. Ejercito 329, Puno, Peru*

S U M M A R Y

As soil salinization is seen as an increasing problem in the the future, sal-t tolerance mechanisms were studied in quinoa, which is regarded as a salt tolerant crop species. Two quinoa cultivars were studied, Utusaya, adapted to growth under saline conditions in the salt desert of southern Bolivia, and 03-26-0036 from Puno, Peru (3,800 m above sea level), in addition to a cultivar of amaranth (*Amaranthus caudatus*). The study was conducted in pots in the greenhouse at CIP, Lima.

The amaranth did not show any significant resistance to salt stress. It demonstrated very little ability for regulation of leaf water potential and stomatal conductance, and the plants died at high salinity levels. According to the TS/TC factor (behaviour under drought compared to control treatment), the amaranth was four times more susceptible to salinity than quinoa. Quinoa demonstrated the ability of accumulating salt ions in its tissues in order to adjust leaf water potential. This enabled the plants to maintain cell turgor and limit transpiration, when grown under saline conditions, avoiding physiological drought damage which might have caused death of the plants.

Some of the measured characters, such as leaf area, biomass production, seed yield and harvest index, showed better responses under moderate saline conditions of 10-20 mS cm^{-1}, than with a lower electrical conductance, indicating that quinoa is a facultative halophyte. The cultivar Utusaya was better adapted for grain production under saline conditions than cultivar 03-26-0036, with a higher Medium Lethal Electrical Conductivity (CE_{50}) (24 compared to 22 mS cm^{-1}).

Also it was determined for the two quinoa cultivars that inflorescence size and plant height were the characters most sensitive to salinity. A screening for less susceptibility to these characters might be an avenue to increase seed yield of quinoa in saline soils. It was demonstrated that the two measures of salinity tolerance TC/TS and CE_{50} were suitable for comparison of species and cultivars.

Keywords : amaranth, salt tolerance, stomatal conductance, water potential

INTRODUCTION

Saline soils are a major problem, limiting crop yields. Utilization of these soils requires specific agronomical techniques and cultivation of tolerant species. One of the species, considered tolerant to salinity, is quinoa (*Chenopodium quinoa* Willd.), cultivated in arid and semiarid areas, often with salinity problems (Laboratorio de Suelos de los E.U.A., 1993). Despite the extreme environmental conditions, under which quinoa is grown, very little research has been conducted so far regarding specific mechanisms related to salinity tolerance in quinoa. Recently it was indicated that quinoa is a facultative halophyt (Quispe and Jacobsen, 1999 a, b).

High salt concentrations in the environment induces water deficit in the plants, which must reduce the water potential to survive salinity, normally by synthesizing organic solutes. This is an important physiological characteristic of halophytes, having the ability to accumulate sufficient ions in order to keep growing and avoid water deficit or excess of ions, e.g. Na^+, K^+ and Cl^-, which might provoce toxicity (Flowers and Yeo, 1986; Flowers *et al.*, 1986; Volkmar and Woodbury, 1995; Jacoby, 1998; Poljakoff-Mayber and Lerner, 1998; Prado, 1999). Another physiological response of plants to salinity is diminishing the stomatal conductivity. In this way transpiration is reduced, avoiding physiological drought, and cell turgor is maintained. The reduction of stomatal conductivity implies closing of the stomatas, reducing entrance of CO_2 inhibiting photosynthesis, and reducing the synthesis of photosynthates, causing a reduction of biomass, leaf area and plant height (Bernstein and Hayward, 1958, in Aragón, 1985; Laboratorio de Suelos de los E.U.A., 1993; Porta *et al.*, 1994; Katerji *et al.*, 1994; Srivastava and Kumar, 1995; Reddy and Iyengar, 1998).

MATERIALS AND METHODS

The trial was conducted in a greenhouse at the International Potato Centre (CIP), Lima, from March to July 1999. The plants were growing in pots each containing five kg of substrate. The daily average temperature was from 16.5 (July) to 23.9°C (March), and relative humidity was between 76 (March) and 88% (July).

The quinoa cultivars used were Utusaya from the salt desert of the southern Bolivian altiplano, and 03-21-036 from the genebank of the Universidad Nacional del Altiplano, Puno, Peru, and the amaranth, cultivar Oscar Blanco, from Huancayo, Peru.. The amaranth was included in the study for comparison with quinoa, as it is considered as a crop susceptible to salinity.

The treatments were nine levels of salinity: < 1, 5, 10, 15, 20, 25, 30, 35 and 40 mS/cm of electrical conductance (CE) at 25°C. The salinity gradient was established by the CE of the irrigation water. Drainage water and saturated soil extract were monitored, in order to control the salinity of the substrate and maintain it at the predetermined levels. The substrate consisted of 2 parts of silty soil, 1 part of sand and 1 part of compost. Sea water was utilized as salt source.

Salinization was induced in the plants at the beginning of bud formation, irrigated with diluted sea water to obtain the indicated salinity levels. For the level <1 mS cm⁻¹ household water (300 μS per cm of CE) was utilized. The substrate of the pots was irrigated at 75% of field capacity (FC) to full FC (24%). The experiment was installed in a randomized-block design, with 27 treatments and 5 repetitions. The data were processed under a factorial arrangement 3x9. The analyzed variables were: leaf water potential (MPa), stomatal conductance (cm s⁻¹), leaf area (cm²), plant height (cm), root weight (g), stem weight (g), stem diameter (mm), panicle weight (g), panicle length (cm), seed yield (g pl⁻¹) and harvest index (%). Leaf water potential was measured with a Scholander 80325 pump, Labconco, stomatal conductivity with a AP 4 porometer, Delta–T Devices, and leaf area with a Li-Cor LI 3000, Lamda Institute.

For the analysis of salt tolerance, two factors were used: saline versus control treatment (TS/TC), and average lethal electric conductance (electrical conductance causing 50% death (CE_{50})). For use as the saline treatment (TS) the average of the three most saline treatments were combined, and as control (TC) the average of the three less saline treatments (Royo and Aragües 1995). Values $\geq$ 1 demonstrated tolerance, and values close to 0 susceptibility. For average lethal conductivity, the program Tblcurve, Jandel Corporation, was used to adjust the curves and calculate CE_{50}. Variances were analysed, and the Tukey test was used for comparison of averages (SAS, 1996).

RESULTS AND DISCUSSION

Analysis of saline treatment versus control treatment (TS/TC)

Highly significant differences between cultivars and between the analyzed variables were found for TS/TC indicating that amaranth was most susceptible to salinity (TS/TC = 0.15), followed by Utusaya (TS/TC = 0.59), and 03-26-0036 (TS/TC = 0.70) (Fig. 1).

For amaranth the characters most tolerant to salinity stress were leaf water potential and stomatal conductivity, indicating that amaranth does not adjust its physiological activity to stress, resulting in a low biomass and seed production.

For quinoa, stem diameter and harvest index were most tolerant to salinity, with values for TC/TS close to one, indicating little variation in stem diameter and harvest index with increasing levels of salinity in the environment. Utusaya seems to be most suitable for seed production, because the variables stomatal conductivity and harvest index were higher for Utusaya than for the 03-26-0036, whereas variables associated with biomass production were less affected by salinity for 03-26-0036 than for Utusaya. Accordingly, under conditions of saline stress, Utusaya has higher seed yield, and 03-26-0036 higher biomass production.

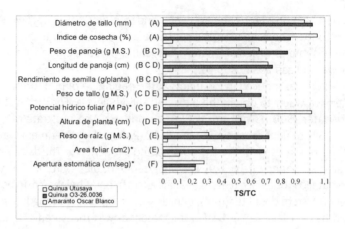

FIGURE 1. SALINITY TOLERANCE ACCORDING TO TS/TC VALUES IN QUINOA CULTIVARS 03-26-0036 AND
UTUSAYA, AND AMARANTH OSCAR BLANCO.
* MEASURED DURING ANTHESIS. LETTERS A-F INDICATE SIGNIFICANT DIFFERENCES ON THE 95% LEVEL.

Stomatal conductivity behaved as the variable least tolerant to salinity. With regard
to the yield components included in this analysis, the order from higher to lower tolerance
in quinoa was:

Stem diameter = Harvest index > Panicle weight >Panicle length = Seed yield
>Stem weight >Plant height.

These results show that the agronomic variables plant height, stem weight and seed
yield are the most sensitive to salinity. In barley (Hordeum vulgare L.), the susceptibility
to salinity was similar (Royo and Aragüez, 1995):

Harvest index > Flowers per spike = Kernels per spike > Heigth = Seed weight >
Grain weight per spike = Spikes per meter > Grain yield = Biomass.

Analysis of average lethal electrical conductance (CE_{50})

The results of the analysis utilizing the parameter of tolerance CE_{50} turned out to be
more consistent for comparison of characters between the two quinoa cultivars, whereas
in comparisons with the amaranth results were not secure. CE_{50} seemed thus to be most
appropriate for comparison of cultivars, not species.

There were highly significant differences between cultivars and between variables.
Utusaya showed to be most tolerant with an average CE_{50} of 20 mS cm^{-1}, while 03-26-
0036 had 18 mS cm^{-1}. This result is different from the result based on TS/TC, because the
high biomass values of Utusaya with a CE of 15 mS cm^{-1} was not taken into consideration
in the former factor.

It was observed that stem weight, seed yield and stem diameter were the most
tolerant to salinity, and stomatal conductance and root weight the least tolerant (Fig. 2).
Seed yield for 03-26-0036 and Utusaya was reduced to 50% with a CE of 22 and 24 mS cm^{-1},

respectively. In barley (Hordeum vulgare L), the reduction occured at a CE of 17 mScm⁻¹ (Subbarao, 1998).

With regard to the yield components CE_{50} gave the following sequence from higher to lower tolerance:

Stem weight = Seed yield = Stem diameter >Harvest index > Panicle weight = Plant heigth > Panicle length.

The agronomic variables panicle length, plant height and panicle weight were the most susceptible to salinity. These characters might be utilized to improve the seed yield of quinoa in a saline environment.

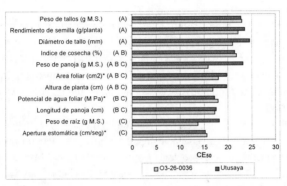

FIGURE 2. TOLERANCE TO THE SALINITY, AS A FUNCTION OF CE_{50}, FOR QUINOA CULTIVARS 03-26-0036 AND UTUSAYA.
*MEASURED DURING ANTHESIS. LETTERS A-F INDICATE SIGNIFICANT DIFFERENCES ON THE 95% LEVEL.

REFERENCES

Aragón, C. M., 1985. Estudio de tolerancia y susceptibilidad del trigo a la salinidad y algunos mecanismos de adaptación. Chapingo. México, 142.

Flowers, T. J., M. A. Hajibacheri and N. J. Clipson, 1986. Halophytes. In: The Quarterly Review of Biology. Vol. 61, N° 3. University of Sussex, 313-337.

Flowers, T. J. and A. R. Yeo, 1986. Ion relations of Plants under Drought an salinity. In: Australian Journal of Scientific Research. Melbourne, Australia, 75-91.

Jacoby, B., 1998. Mechanism involved in salt tolerance of plants. In: Handbook of Plant and Crop Stress. Second edition. Edited by Pessarakli M. Marcel Dekker, Inc., NY. 97, 123.

Katerji, N., J. W. van Hoorn, A. Hamdy, F. Karam and M. Mastrorilli, 1994. Effect of slinity on emergence and on water stress and early seedling growth of sunflower and maize. In: Agricultural Water Management. Elsevier Science, 81-91.

Laboratorio de Salinidad de los E.U.A., 1993. Diagnóstico y Rehabilitación de suelos salinos y sódicos. Ed. Limusa. México DF. México, 172.

Poljakoff-Mayber, A. and H. R. Lerner, 1998. Plants in saline environments. In: Handbook of Plant and Crop Stress. Second edition. Edited by Pessarakli M. Marcel Dekker, Inc., NY, 125-148.

Porta, J., M. López-Acevedo and C. Roquero, 1994. Edafología para la agricultura y el medio ambiente. Edit. Mundi Pres. Madrid. España. 807 pp.

Prado, F., 1999. Fisiología y Bioquímica del estrés: respuestas de las plantas al ambiente. En: Fisiología de la resistencia a sequía en quinua (*Chenopodium quinua* Willd.). 1° Curso internacional. Proyecto quinua, CIP-DANIDA-UNA-INIAP-PROIMPA-KVL. Editores, Jacobsen S., Mujica A. 21 - 29 pp.

Quispe, H. and S. E. Jacobsen, 1999a. Germination of quinoa (*Chenopodium quinoa* Willd.) under saline conditions. In, Proceedings of COST 814-Workshop: Alternative Crops for Sustainable Agriculture, 13-15 June 1999, Turku, Finland, 326-330.

Quispe, H. and S. E. Jacobsen, 1999b. Tolerancia de la quinua (Chenopodium quinoa Willd.) a la salinidad. In: Libro de Resumenes (eds. Jacobsen, S. E. and A. Valdez), Primer Taller Internacional sobre Quinua – Recursos Geneticos y Sistemas de Producción, 10-14 May, UNALM, Lima, Peru, 131.

Reddy, M. and E. Iyengar, 1998. Crop responses to salt stress: Seawater aplication and prospects. In: Handbook of Plant and Crop Stress. Second edition. Edited by Pessarakli M. Marcel Dekker, Inc., NY., 1041-1068.

Royo, A. and R. Aragües, 1995. Efecto de la Salinidad sobre diversos caracteres morfo-fisiológicos y sobre el rendimiento en grano de la cebada. In: Investigación Agraria, Producción y Protección Vegetal. Instituto Nacional de Investigación y Tecnología Agraria y Alimentación. Madrid, España, 71-84.

SAS Institute Inc., 1996. SAS/STAT User's Guide, Release 6.03 Edition. Cary, NC: SAS Institute, 1028.

Srivastava, J.P. and A. Kumar. 1995. current perspectives in water loss from plants and stomatal action. In.: Handbook of Plant and Crop Physiology. Edited by Mohammad Pessarakli. Marcel Dekker, Inc. NY, 45-59.

Subbarao, G. V., 1998. Strategies and scope for improving salinity tolerance in crop plants. In: Handbook of plant and crop stress. Second edition. Edited by Pessarakli M. Marcel Dekker, Inc., NY, 1069-1087.

Volkmar, K. and W. Woodbury, 1995. Plant - Water Relationships. In: Handbook of Plant and Crop Physiology. Edited by Mohammad Pessarakli. Marcel Dekker, Inc. NY, 23-43.

New elaborated products from quinoa: Protein concentrates and colourants

S. E. JACOBSEN[1] AND A. MUJICA[2]

[1] International Potato Centre (CIP), Apartado 1558, Lima 12, Peru
[2] Universidad Nacional del Altiplano, Proyecto Quinua CIP-DANIDA-UNAP, Av. Del Ejercito 329, Puno, Peru

SUMMARY

Quinoa (*Chenopodium quinoa* Willd.) has for more than 7,000 years been one of the major crops of the Andean region, valued for its growth characteristics and its high nutritive value. The protein content of quinoa is high, from 10 to 18%, depending on variety and growth conditions, but most important is its well-balanced composition of amino acids, for instance with a high content of lysine, which often is limiting in food of plant origin.

The main purpose of elaborating new products from quinoa is to promote production and consumption of the crop, for the benefit of the population, many of which live under malnutrition, through nutritional programmes, and to increase income from internal sale and export of the crop. The products of interest are flakes, flour, pops, puf, pasta, breakfast cereals etc.

The highest protein concentration is found in the germ, for which reason this specific fraction should be studied, and its possible use for a quick recovery of children, suffering from malnutrition, nursing mothers etc. It is studied if these proteins can be separated from the grain during the process of dehulling.

Quinoa contains colourants betalains and betaxanthins, which give the plants their different characteristical colours, depending on variety. These colourants have been used domestically for natural cloth and food dyeing.

Keywords : colorants, concentrates, food quality, quinoa

PRODUCTS

Several new products can be elaborated from quinoa, of which protein concentrates and colourants have not been utilized commercially until now.

Protein concentrates

Currently there is a need for obtaining high-quality protein concentrates to solve problems of chronic malnutrition affecting rural and urban populations of the Andean region. Quinoa, in addition to presenting a high protein content, shows an adequate balance of essential amino acids. The protein content in the seeds of quinoa varies from 10 to 22%, depending on genotype. Some genotypes with exceptionally high content of protein in seeds may be selected for the purpose of producing a concentrated protein-rich food supplement.

The protein is mainly concentrated in the embryo of the quinoa seed, which contains up to 45% protein. The embryo can be separated from the rest of the seed through processes of pre-germination or abrasive dehulling. The concentrated embryo can then be utilized directly in the food for children, for instance to obtain a quick recovery of the nutritional level of children suffering from malnutrition, and adults, such as pregnant and breast-feeding women, in a diversity of dishes.

Quinoa genotypes with higher protein content and with a larger proportion of embryo in its seeds should be selected from the wide genetic diversity, including wild species, already existing. Once determined the genotypes most adequate for the acquisition of embryo, seeds should be multiplied by specialized producers, because an inadequate management of fields for seed production will result in problems with impurities due to outcrossing. A processing plant should be built in the rural area in order to facilitate the use of the available labour and to ensure that the added value remains with the producers, whose level of income and access to new markets will improve.

Special emphasis should be put on cleaning procedures, presentation of the product, and declarations, with precise data of the content of protein and essential amino acids. A market analysis including cost-benefit should be carefully performed.

Colourants

The pigments found in plants play important roles in the metabolism and visual attraction in nature. They are also important for humans, attracting our attention and providing us with nutrients. Major plant pigments include carotenoids, anthocyanins and other flavonoids, betalains, and chlorophylls.

Quinoa contains betalains, a natural colourant, which is used traditionally for cloth dyeing and food preparation. Betalains only occur in about 10 plant families, where they are likely to play an important role in attracting animals (Clement et al., 1994). It is difficult to assign a specific function to the betalains within the plants, but the presence in flowers and fruits could indicate a function as attracting pollinators or seed dispersers (Piattelli, 1981). However, its appearance elsewhere in the plant such as the stems and roots may indicate other functions. A defence mechanism against viral infections was suggested (Sosnova, 1970). The colors are red, purple, yellow, pink and pale, present in genotypes that still remain in the gene banks, but are in process of genetic erosion due to reduced use and substitution by synthetic dyes. The natural colourants present in the quinoa plant can be utilized in foods, for instance, those similar to which are currently extracted from cochinilla obtained from *Opuntia ficus*. It is necessary to select for this character, and to optimize the extraction techniques.

The betalain pigments, present in the entire plant, are composed of nitrogenous derivatives of betalamic acid, ranging in colour from yellow to orange, red and violet (Piattelli, 1981). Chemically the betalains can be divided into two groups: Betacyanins (red-violet) with maximum peak of absorption 480 nm, and betaxantins (yellow-orange) with maximum peak close to 540 nm. The betalains may be used in the food industry for yogurt, wine, and cheese (von Elbe *et al.*, 1974). In the Andean area its use is quite frequent as cloth dye. Historical data reveal that the betalains were an important source of colour for cosmetics from before the Tsin dynasti in China (Laufer, 1919, in Sosnova, 1970). The beet (*Beta vulgaris*) may be an appropriate source of betalains; however, the climatic requirements of beet are very different from those of quinoa, so that quinoa colourants may be a new source of income for the small-scale farmers of the Andean mountains, through a sustainable production of quinoa.

Research is required on the content of pigments present in different plant organs, the phenological stage of highest content of pigments, denaturation of betalain, composition of the pigments, and identification of genotypes of high content and persistance of colourants. Studies should also be conducted on their potential uses in food products, regarding flavour and possible degradation during cooking and preparation.

Future prospects

Both the production of concentrated protein and colourants from quinoa present very promising prospects for the rural agroindustry of the Andes, which can produce new products that differ from what is currently known with comparative and competitive advantages for the benefit of the producer and the consumer, obtaining healthy, natural, and highly nutritive products.

REFERENCES

Clement, J. S., T. J. Mabry, H. Wyler and A. S. Dreiding, 1994. Chemical review and evolutionary significance of the betalains. In, Caryophyllales: evolution and systematics (Behnke, H.D. and T.J. Mabry, eds.). Springer Verlag, 247-261.

Elbe, J. H. von, J. H. Pasch and J. P. Adams, 1974. Betalains and foods colorants. Proceedings of the IV International Congress of Food Science and Technology, 1: 485-492.

Piattelli, M., 1981. The Betalains: Structure, biosynthesis, and chemical taxomomic in Biochemistry of Plants. Vol. 7: 557-573. Ed. E. E. Conn. Academic Press Inc.

Sosnova, V., 1970. Reproduction of sugar beet mosaic and tobacco mosaic viruses in anthocynized beet plants. Biol. Plant. 12: 424-427.

Quinoa milk: A new promising product

A. MUJICA[1], R. ORTIZ[1], V. APAZA[2] AND S. E. JACOBSEN[3]

[1] Universidad Nacional del Altiplano, Proyecto Quinua CIP-DANIDA-UNAP, Av. Del Ejército 329, Puno, Peru
[2] Instituto Nacional de Investigaciones Agrarias (INIA), EE. Illpa, Puno, Peru
[3] International Potato Center (CIP), Apartado 1558, Lima 12, Peru

SUMMARY

Quinoa, an Andean grain crop of high nutritive value and world-wide adaptability, may be used in the production of healthy and nutritive food, rich in high quality proteins with an adequate balance of essential amino acids, and a high content of important vitamins and minerals. Aiming at the European market, however, new processed products need promotion and marketing, as only little is known about the crop and the preparation of it.

As the consumers in general are interested in new, healthy and delicious foods, several products based on quinoa have been considered, one of them being quinoa milk. It is expected that this way of consuming vegetal proteins will have a potential demand, as an alternative to soymilk, which is facing problems on some markets.

It has been demonstrated, that it is possible to extract milk of high nutritive value from cooked quinoa grains, with the desired taste and colour, differing according to genotype. The product made from quinoa milk can be used immediately, or can be used in further agroindustrial food products. Using less liquid while grinding the seeds, the milk will be a paste suitable for jellies and sauces.

Keywords : nutritive value, quinoa milk

INTRODUCTION

Quinoa is an Andean grain of high nutritional value, with an outstanding protein quality and a capacity to be transformed into a large range of products. Among them are vegetable milk, which may have a potential for consumption by children and adults, directly as milk or in other dairy produces, for alleviation of problems with malnutrition in South America. It is estimated that in Peru 48% of the school children suffer from chronic malnutrition, and in the rural areas the percentage is as high as 67 (Ministerio de Educación, 1994). The areas most affected in Peru are Puno, Junín, Ancash, Cusco, Ayacucho, Cajamarca, Apurímac and Huancavelica.

Quinoa milk

The preparation of quinoa milk is a relatively simple process which does not require expensive equipment. There is a large genetic variability existing in quinoa in the genebanks of South America, which makes it possible to identify genotypes, adapted to this type of transformation; however, it will be necessary to perform selections to identify the material most suitable to milk production, obtaining a product of desired colour, flavour, and nutritive value.

The first step in the production of milk is to eliminate the saponins by dehulling and washing the seeds, carefully in order not to remove the embryo. As soon as the quinoa seeds are free from saponins, they are boiled in water, in a well-defined quantity and duration, important for the quality of the final product. The milling is carried out to obtain a homogeneous mass, permitting that its solid components can be separated from the liquids, followed by a separation of the liquid phase. The liquid is homogenized and pasteurized, and if needed natural flavours and colourants can be added, followed by canning. The quinoa milk is then ready for human consumption.

As this is a completely new product, so far only produced in the laboratory of the Universidad Nacional del Altiplano, Puno, the entire production process should be optimized, including homogenization, pasteurization, and packaging of the milk in such a way that the product is maintained nutritive, attractive, and economic for the consumer and the producer.

Vegetable quinoa milk and the solid part which remains after the milk is produced, may be utilized by children and adults, and especially by people having problems with consumption of meat protein, and in regions of problems with malnutrition. Quinoa could be a basic element for protein intake in schools, hospitals and other places, with the purpose of improving the general nutritive level of the population. The solid residue may be consumed directly in soups etc., or transformed into other products such as desserts, cooked dishes, gelatins, flans, or dried for obtaining precooked flour. The use of both the main product, milk, and the residue, contributes to the total income of quinoa for the farmer and the agroindustry.

Future prospects

Quinoa milk may, in the near future, be of significance for consumption, as a high-quality, nutritive and healthy product, of easy digestion for the school children of the high Andean region, who suffer from malnutrition. It will be necessary to extend the production areas of cultivars for milk production, and to promote instalment of processing plants for milk production in areas of quinoa production, in such a way that rural agroindustries are benefiting from the production.

An aspect of great importance will be the motivation and dissemination of the use and utilization of this highly nutritive and tasty product among the consumers, who may be adult consumers and people unable to uptake animal lactose or casein. Quinoa milk might be an alternative to the most common vegetable milk, produced from soybean.

REFERENCES

Ministerio de Educación, 1994. I Censo Nacional de Talla en Escolares 1993. Ministerio de Educación, UNICEF, PMA, and FONCODES, Lima, Perú, 19-25.

Adaptation of maca (*Lepidium meyenii* Walpers) to different agroecosystems

A. MUJICA[1], V. APAZA[2], A. CANAHUA[3] AND S. E. JACOBSEN[4]

[1] *Universidad Nacional del Altiplano, Proyecto Quinua CIP-DANIDA-UNAP, Av. Del Ejercito 329, Puno, Peru*
[2] *Instituto Nacional de Investigaciones Agrarias (INIA), EE. Illpa, Puno, Peru*
[3] *Proyecto Waru Waru, CARE, Puno, Peru*
[4] *International Potato Centre (CIP), Apartado 1558, Lima 12, Peru*

SUMMARY

Maca (*Lepidium meyenii* Walpers), an Andean root crop, was, in historic time, grown or collected on the high plateaus of Peru, Bolivia and Ecuador. However, it disappeared as a cultivated crop, only leaving a wild, related species without edible roots. During the last years, the maca has experienced an extraordinary success in Peru. In 1980 the cultivated area of maca was 15 ha, its growth region limited to the high plateau of Junìn, 3,900 m asl, but the area increased during the 1990s until a provisional culmination in 1999, where 2,000 ha was sown, apart from Junìn, also in Puno, Cusco and Arequipa. This significant increase in production is explained by an increased demand and new products on the market.

Previously it was believed that maca only could grow under cold conditions in high altitudes, but this has shown not to be true, as maca can be adapted to different altitudes and agroclimatic conditions. Maca has a high content of vitamins and minerals, but the main effect of the root crop, which has increased demand for export, is its qualitative characteristics of improving sexual vigour and fertility, both with men and women.

Keywords : cold conditions, maca, qualitative value

INTRODUCTION

In the past it was believed that maca (*Lepidium meyenii* Walpers) could only be grown in conditions of high altitudes and with intensive cold. It was cultivated or at least present in the Bolivian altiplano (Oruro), in Peru in the high zones of Junín, Huancavelica, Apurímac, Ayacucho, Arequipa, Cusco, Moquegua, Tacna and Puno, and in cold areas of Ecuador and Argentina (Tello *et al.*, 1991; Rea, 1992). However, maca disappeared in its cultivated form, and only remained a wild relative called chichira, chichicara or mata conejo (*Lepidium chichicara*), which does not form edible roots.

Searches for the cultivated species have been conducted in the altiplano of Puno, having found other edible roots of maca in proces of genetic erosion, such as ichuru or chijuru (*Stangea rhizonta*), and llama llama, ccapaso or mauka (*Mirabilis expanza*), whose large production of botanical seed is of good germinative capacity when cultivated in greenhouse.

It is known that maca is adapted to the high altitudes of the Andean region, but may also be sown in other latitudes of better climatic conditions. Maca is considered of increasing importance in human consumption, not only in the Andean region, but also among the urban population where there is a demand for natural and nutritive diets. In addition maca has other nutritional qualities, such as a high content of vitamins and minerals, and medicinal properties (Garay, 1992). The nutritional value shows future prospects for use to satisfy demands of healthy, natural, and highly nutritive food (Table 1).

TABLE 1. AVERAGE COMPOSITION OF DRY MACA ROOTS.

Protein, %	18.25	Na, mg/100g	40
Fat, %	2.2	Cu, mg/100g	5.9
Fiber, %	8.5	Zn, mg/100g	6.1
Ca, mg/100g	650	Mn, mg/100g	0.8
P, mg/100g	329	Fe, mg/100g	24
Mg, mg/100g	114	Se, mg/100g	0.3
K, mg/100g	2050	B, mg/100g	26

In addition maca contains carotene (vit. A), thiamine (vit. B), riboflavin (Vit. B2), ascorbic acid (vit. C), and niacin (Inade-Pelt-Cosude, 1999).

Present situation

In Puno investigations have been conducted with maca since 1988 by INIA and the Universidad Nacional del Altiplano, Puno (UNAP), initially in greenhouses, then in small wooden boxes put in the field, and in experimental fields in Salcedo, Camacani and Illpa. Currently it is calculated that is sown nearly 200 ha in Puno, in the areas of Macusani, Crucero and Raya, situated at 4,000 m, and more than 2,000 ha in the traditional growth area of Junín.

Promising results have been obtained in Ayaviri, 3,850 m, with 770 mm of precipitation and 7°C of mean temperature, with yields of fresh roots of 10 t ha⁻¹ in small plots. Seed was broadcast, with 10 t ha⁻¹ animal manure. In Camacani of UNA, Puno, 3,828 m, maca was tested sown directly, mixed with animal manure, utilizing small high-beds. The installation was not optimal, and the water supply, which is obligatory for securing an acceptable germination and establishment of the crop, was insufficient, so yield was only 7 t ha⁻¹. In Illpa of UNA, Puno, it was found that it is an advantage to sow on virgin land. Animal manure must be decomposed before application, otherwise the presence of weeds and larvae is increased. These are acting as pests, yet not determined, attacking the hypocotyledons, reducing yield significantly. An early weeding is also important, because maca is very susceptible to competition from weeds. The maximum distance of the high-beds should be 1.20 m, which facilitates various tasks of labour and harvest. In the Experimental Station La Raya of the UNA, Puno, there has been obtained an excellent quality and yields of fresh roots exceeding 15 t ha^{-1}, in humid highlands with deep soils rich in organic matter.

A trial for the production of botanical seeds has been conducted, with the treatments of darkness, diffuse light and direct light, during emergence of the hypocotyledons before planting, resulting in the best response with the treatment of darkness, and obtaining more vigorous plants as well as a larger seed production.

In the experimental station of Salcedo, INIA, Puno (3,825 m), was transplanting of maca evaluated with good results. The process of transplanting is sensitive, as the radicle must be placed perpendicularly in the soil, after making a hole and avoiding that root damage. The radicle is placed in the hole and then stamped in order to secure direct contact with the soil, followed by a heavy irrigation.

In San Camilo, Arequipa (2,300 m), maca was tested both by transplanting and direct sowing, with a satisfactory establishment; however, the production of hypocotyledons was inferior resulting in very small roots and a yield of 5 t ha^{-1}. There was observed downy mildew (*Peronospora parasitica*), forming small spots in the field, which may be a disease of importance in the future in favourable conditions in Arequipa (Quiros and Aliaga, 1997), aphids (*Aphis* sp.) and *Empoasca* sp., which were controlled. In the Colca valley, Arequipa, where maca was possibly produced in the past, because there not only exists a village by this name, but its wild relative (*Lepidium chichicara*) has been found abundantly in the fields of the region.

This year maca has been broadcast sown in various locations of the altiplano of Puno, in Quinsachata (4,300 m), Azangaro (3,890 m), Illpa (3,845 m), Ayaviri (3,850 m) and Ilave (3,835 m), using the same technology as recommended for the crop in the central Andes of Junìn, utilizing as seed the *charpos* (seeds mixed with animal manure) from the seed suppliers of Cerro de Pasco and Huancayo, in which is observed a mixture of ecotypes with hypocotyledons of different colours, such as white, yellow, purple, grey, and black, and of different forms (Solis, 1997). Preliminary test harvest has indicated yields of 8-10 t ha^{-1} of regular to small-sized hypocotyledons. It is believed that these maca will be easily conserved as the farmers are experienced in the preparation of chuño (potato), oca, olluco and mashua.

There has been observed problems with the Andean potato weevil (*Premnotrypes solani*), attacking the roots and hypocotyledons of the maca, which may constitute an important pest in the future, and attacks of birds, damaging the young hypocotyledons significantly.

In the growing season 1998/1999 CARE-Peru initiated intensive work on maca, with experiments in Illpa (3,845 m) and in Quinsachata (4,300 m), representing the conditions of lake (circunlacustre) and Suni (high zone distant from the lake). The preliminary results were:

a) Due to lack of precipitation in the period of establishment yields were only 650-7,300 kg ha^{-1}.

b) The crop prefers flat areas, even if temperature may decline to -10°C.

c) Maca prefers silty soils of high organic matter content. Animal manure is present in Puno, which is a livestock area.

d) Maca is very susceptible to drought, especially during germination and establishment.

e) Various pests have been observed:

- In the establishment and formation of the hypocotyledon, *Dipterous* larvae attack the root, diminishing plant density.

- In maturation there may be a significant attack of noctuideos larvae (*Feltia* spp.) and Andean potato weevil, which may cause losses of up to 80%. The problem is of less importance in fallow soils and in high altitude areas. Other pests were aphids.

- In the high areas as Quinsachata, attacks of rodents have been seen.

- Downy mildew (*Peronospora parasitica*) was observed, especially in humid environments, and also *Rhizoctonia* spp.

Based on actual experience on the cultivation of maca in Puno it can be concluded that the preferred conditions for the cultivation of this root crop is humid highland with deep soils rich in organic matter.

The future of maca

a) Puno and other parts of the Andean region present favorable agroecological conditions for the reintroduction and development of maca, especially in the extensive, high plains of the agroecological zone called Suni, where 200,000 of the total 500,000 ha are under irrigation, and the limiting factor for other crops, except for forage grasses, are frost.

b) In order to secure the success of the maca, the market should be ensured, based on the development of an appropriate technology.

d) It will be necessary to establish collaboration and strategic alliances between public and private institutions, devoted to research, promotion, marketing and credit.

REFERENCES

Garay, C., 1992. Cultivo de la Maca. Serie Divulgativa: 16-92. INIAA, Proyecto TTA. Lima, Perú, 28.

INADE/PELT-COSUDE, 1999. Investigaciones sobre Maca en el Altiplano de Puno. Tomo I. Programa Institucional de Waru-Waru, PELT. Puno, Peru, 194.

Quiros, C. F. and C. R. Aliaga, 1997. Maca (*Lepidium meyenii* Walp.). In: Andean Roots and Tubers: Ahipa, Arracacha, Maca and Yacon. Promoting the conservation and use of underutilized and neglected crops 21. Hermann, M. and J. Heller, eds. CIP, IPK, IPGRI. Roma, Italia, 182-191.

Rea, J., 1992. Raíces Andinas: Maca. In: Cultivos Marginados, Otra Perspectiva de 1942. J. E. Fernández Bermejo and J. E. León, eds. FAO. Roma, Italia, 163-166.

Solis, E. R., 1997. Producción de Maca en la Meseta de Bombom. Imprenta Ríos. Huancayo, Perú, 27-36.

Tello, J., M. Hermann and A. Calderón, 1991. La maca (*Lepidium meyenii* Walpers): Cultivo alimenticio potencial para las zonas altoandinas. VII Congreso Internacional sobre Cultivos Andinos, 4-9 febrero 1991. La Paz, Bolivia.

Adaptive traits of emmer wheat (*Triticum turgidum ssp. dicoccum*) to low-input agriculture

F. MICELI, G. TASSAN MAZZOCCO, L. MARCHIOL AND M. BALDINI

Dept. Crop Production and Agricultural Technology, University of Udine, Udine (Italy)

SUMMARY

Emmer wheat is currently grown on approximately 3,000 ha in Italy, generally under low-input conditions. Adaptation, yield formation processes and whole-plant responses to low-input conditions were analysed in Udine (NE Italy) relative to durum wheat as control, in semi-controlled and field experiments. Short stems and high harvest index (HI) of modern durum varieties, compared to 'old' architecture of emmer wheat landraces, may inherently limit tolerance to severe N and/or water stresses. Grain yields of emmer were only marginally affected by severe post-anthesis drought in drainage lysimeters, while under low-input field conditions, emmer landraces showed significantly higher yields, notwithstanding lower HI. Emmer wheat is an interesting minor cereal for low-fertility agroecosystems; the future of the crop outside typical areas will be driven by consistently high prices on the speciality markets.

Keywords: emmer, low-input agriculture, stress tolerance, Triticum turgidum ssp. dicoccum

INTRODUCTION

Cultivated hulled wheats - einkorn, emmer and spelt - in Italy are known under the common name of 'farro' (Perrino and Laghetti, 1994). Until a few years ago, emmer (*Triticum turgidum* ssp. *dicoccum* Schrank ex Schubler) was a relict crop, representing at least in part the direct descendant of the Etruscan and Roman farro (D'Antuono, 1994). Then, organic food habits and EU policies fostered emmer crops. Emmer occupies niches in traditional farming systems, where less fertile environments represent a serious constraint for bread and durum wheats (Vazzana, 1996); recently its total area has been estimated at about 3,000 ha, mostly in Central and Southern Italy (Porfiri *et al.*, 1998). Within emmer populations, large morphological variation can easily be observed (for instance, awn length in 'Garfagnana' population). However, relative to modern durum cultivars, they all share an 'old' canopy structure: taller culms, longer and thinner leaves, lower harvest index. Such architecture, largely inadequate to high-input agriculture, may confer adaptation to stressful environments, as larger stem reserves facilitate assimilate translocation under stress (Blum, 1998). Most emmer production, from low-input or 'organic' agriculture, is currently placed on the market at reasonably high prices. In Friuli (NE Italy) where emmer is not cultivated, the humid climate (approx. 1,450 mm rainfalls year[-1] in Udine) is frequently associated with very permeable soils, and drought conditions usually span a few weeks in summer. Heavy N fertilisations and irrigations are still popular, and nitrate leaching is a real concern. The adaptation to low-input and rainfed agriculture of two emmer landraces, with emphasis on plant tolerance to post-anthesis drought, was assessed here by comparison with modern durum cultivars.

MATERIALS AND METHODS

Selected tetraploid wheats were grown in semi-controlled (drainage lysimeters - 1996/97) and field (1998/99) conditions. Nitrogen was supplied at 50-80 kg ha[-1] and crop management, where applicable, was comparable to that locally in use for winter cereals. Two emmer landraces (Molise and Potenza) and two commercial durum varieties (Ofanto and Adamello) were grown in 1996/97 in lysimeters (0.8 m^2 x 0.7 m soil depth) under a rain shelter. Soil water content was measured 3 times a week by a TDR system; water was uniformly restored to field capacity up to anthesis, then irrigation was discontinued on half lysimeters and two water treatments were imposed. Uppermost leaf chlorophyll (SPAD-502, Minolta) and soil water content were monitored weekly; flag leaf CO_2 exchange rate (CER) (LiCor 6400), leaf and culm area indexes (LAI and CAI), biomass and grain yield were assessed on selected dates. The 1998/99 field experiment, arranged in a RCB design with 4 replicates, was carried out in Udine on a low-fertility soil (Typic Udifluvents). Nitrogen was supplied at 80 kg ha[-1]. Flag leaf traits, biomass accumulation, grain yield and harvest index were assessed on two emmer landraces (Molise and Potenza), a durum variety (Neodur) and an emmer x durum variety (Davide).

RESULTS AND DISCUSSION

a) Lysimeters experiment - 1996/97
Above-ground biomass accumulation at anthesis (GS 60) and at harvest (GS 90), was higher in emmer wheats. They exceeded durum wheats also for green area index, flag leaf area and length at anthesis; conversely, lower leaf chlorophyll content (SPAD values) and leaf thickness were recorded in top-canopy leaves throughout the season. At harvest, similar grain yields were obtained among wheats in well watered (WW) conditions. Interestingly, post-anthesis water shortage (WS) caused a larger yield reduction on durum (average 30%), compared to dicoccum (average 9%). Indeed, HI in durum dropped in WS conditions while yield remained fairly stable in dicoccum.

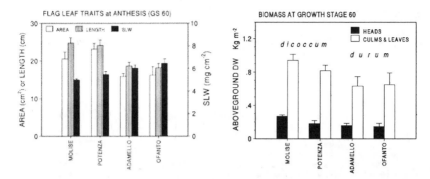

FIGURE 1. LYSIMETERS 1996/97. FLAG LEAF TRAITS, BIOMASS ACCUMULATION AND GRAIN YIELDS IN DICOCCUM (MOLISE AND POTENZA) AND DURUM (ADAMELLO AND OFANTO), UNDER WELL WATERED (WW) AND POST-ANTHESIS WATER STRESS (WS) CONDITIONS.

Emmer flag leaves initiated senescence close to anthesis, while fully-green tissues were maintained approximately two weeks more in durum. A session of flag leaf photosynthesis (carried out at GS 70 in each subspecies) showed low photosynthetic capacity in dicoccum relative to durum. Different photosynthetic responses to water shortage between emmer landraces were also detected. Apparently, post-anthesis crop photosynthesis may have a lower impact on yield formation in emmer wheats, compared to modern semi-dwarf durum varieties. Pre-anthesis photosyntates, accumulated in longer stems (and roots) of emmer, could play a key role in assimilate relocation when a final stress emerges. Stem reserves' contribution to yield formation are being currently (1999/00) examined.

b) Field Experiment - 1998/99

In general, grain yields in emmer and durum wheats were in the low range, even for the Italian standards (Table 1). Limited soil depth (0.4-0.6 m) and N inputs (80 kg ha⁻¹) were also associated to unusually high temperatures at grain-filling stages (Porfiri *et al.*, 1999). However, such conditions can be seen as an excellent environment for testing tetraploid wheat performance under a low-input system. At anthesis, the durum variety Neodur had the highest SPAD index, but the absolute values confirmed a low N status for all tetraploid wheats. Emmer landraces had higher LAI (and CAI, culm area index; data not shown); such growth indexes were associated with ample above ground biomass accumulation at anthesis and at harvest, and finally to resonable yields. We had no data about weed presence; however large emmer biomass and stature represent an indirect positive feature about crop capture of nutrients and sunlight. Growth, DM accumulation and grain yield of Davide (durum x dicoccum line) were poor, probably because of overwintering problems in our northern Italy location. In general, emmer grain yields were significantly lower than conventional wheat and barley crops of our area. However, on the five-year average 1992-97, emmer grain in Italy was marketed at about 2-3 times the price of durum grain (Chiorri and De Filippis, 1999).

TABLE 1. LOW-INPUT FIELD EXPERIMENT, UDINE 1998/99. LEAF INDEXES, ABOVEGROUND BIOMASS AND
GRAIN YIELDS FOR TWO EMMER LANDRACES (MOLISE AND POTENZA), A DURUM VARIETY (NEODUR) AND
AN EMMER X DURUM VARIETY (DAVIDE).
LETTERS INDICATE DIFFERENCES AMONG MEANS (SNK TEST AT $P_{0.1}$).

	Anthesis			*Harvest*		
	Flag Leaf SPAD-502	Leaf Area Index	Aboveground DM g m^{-2}	Aboveground DM g m^{-2}	Grain Yield Mg ha^{-1}	Harvest Index %
MOLISE	28.7 b	2.61 ab	825 a	838 a	2.92 a	32.0 b
POTENZA	31.5 ab	2.95 a	766 a	913 a	2.69 a	35.2 b
NEODUR	34.3 a	1.72 bc	491 a	615 b	2.09 b	45.3 a
DAVIDE	28.7 b	1.31 c	641 a	580 b	1.98 b	35.6 b

CONCLUSIONS

Compared to modern durum varieties, in emmer landraces yield formation processes appeared dependent on pre-anthesis photosynthesis. At later stages, flag leaf contribution to crop photosynthesis is lower, taking into account the early start of leaf senescence. Large vegetative biomass of emmer facilitates photosynthate storage and mobilisation under drought conditions, as indirectly shown by the fact that yields were only marginally affected by a severe post-anthesis drought. Relative to modern durum wheat, emmer is an interesting crop for marginal, low-fertility environments, were nitrogen and water resources are scarce and/or incostant. Additional work is needed to fully exploit emmer potential in low-input agroecosystems.

REFERENCES

Blum, A., 1998. Improving wheat grain filling under stress by stem reserve mobilisation. Euphytica, 100: 77-83.

Chiorri M. and R. De Filippis, 1999. Aspetti tecnico-economici della coltivazione biologica del farro. L'Informatore Agrario, 44: 27-29.

D'Antuono L. F., 1994. Obsolete wheats in Italy: an overview on cultivation, use and perpectives for their conservation. In: Report of the IPGRI workshop on conservation and use of underutilized Mediterranean species, Valenzano, Bari, Italy 28-30 March 1994 (S. Padulosi, H. Ager and E. Frison, eds.). IPGRI, Rome.

Perrino P. and G. Laghetti, 1994. Il farro: cenni storici ed aspetti agronomici. In: Il farro, un cereale della salute. (Perrino P., D. Semeraro and G. Laghetti, eds.). Atti del Convegno, Potenza 18 giugno 1994.

Porfiri O., L. F. D'Antuono, B. Borghi, P. Codianni, M. Corbellini, L. Mazza and R. Castagna,

1998. Genetic variability of a hulled wheats collection evaluated in different agronomic environments in Italy. Proc. Third International Triticeae Symposium, 4-8 May 1997, Aleppo, Syria.

Vazzana C., 1996. The role of farmers' associations in safeguarding endangered populations of farro in Italy. In: Hulled wheats. Promoting the conservation and use of underutilized and neglected crops. (Padulosi S., K. Hammer and J. Heller, eds.) Proc. First International Workshop on Hulled Wheats, 21-22 July 1995, Castelvecchio Pascoli, Tuscany, Italy. IPGRI, Rome.

Isolation and characterization of saponins and other minor components in quinoa (Chenopodium quinoa Willd.)

S. E. JACOBSEN[1], I. DINI[2], O. SCHETTINO[3], T. SIMIOLI[2], G. C. TENORE[2] AND A. DINI[2]

[1] International Potato Centre (CIP), Apartado 1558, Lima 12, Peru
[2] Dipartimento di Chimica delle Sostanze Naturali, Universita Federico II, Via Domenico Montesano 49-80131, Napoli, Italy
[3] Dipartimento di Chimica Farmaceutica e Tossicologica, Universita Federico II, Via Domenico Montesano 49-80131, Napoli, Italy

SUMMARY

The purpose of the work presented was to study minor components of quinoa for their chemical and biological properties. Isolation and characterization of biologically active compounds are essential for pharmacological and dietary studies, in order to evaluate the possible uses of a crop species.

Minor or secondary components in plants, such as saponins, have importance for taste and nutritional value. Saponins, which are soapy compounds of an amphiphilic nature, are constituted of a lipid, soluble moiety, which is a triterpenoid or a steroid derivative, in various positions substituted with sugar or acid residues, creating a wide and complex group of compounds. Such structural variety indicates differences in biological, chemical, toxicological and flavour properties. Quinoa saponins, present in the seed hull, are considered as antinutritional factors for their bitter taste and their haemolytic capacity, and for that reason they have to be eliminated before consuming. Recent studies on saponins from legumes, however, have demonstrated benefical effects such as hypocholesterolemic, antiinflammatory, antiallergic, antiviral, antidiabetic, antimycotic and immune-stimulatory properties, the latter of which may prevent colon cancer. In this study saponin compounds have been isolated and characterized through a screening of two cultivars of quinoa, a bitter and a sweet, that is, with a high and low level of saponins, respectively. The saponins reported have not previously been found in quinoa.

Quinoa seeds contain also flavonol glycosides. Flavonoids in foods are considered important as antioxidants, and in reducing the risk of cancer and arteriosclerosis.

Keywords : chemical and biological properties, quinoa, saponins

INTRODUCTION

Quinoa, originating from the Andean region of South America, constitutes a staple food for millions of native inhabitants. Quinoa has been introduced into Europe, where it has been studied in many countries, including Italy, but one problem of the quinoa is the content of a bitter-tasting compound in the seed hull, saponins, for which reason quinoa seeds have to be processed before consumption. Apart from seeds leaves also are used as a nutritious and tasty vegetable, like spinach. Quinoa seeds range in diameter from 1.0 to 2.5 mm and in seed weight from 1.9 to 4.3 g per 1,000 seeds (Alvarez *et al.*, 1990). Previously, attention has been focusing primarily on the content and quality of the proteins and lipids in quinoa, that is, the profile of essential amino acids and fatty acids. However, the presence in foods of some minor constituents, together with carbohydrates, lipids, proteins and vitamins, may be of significance for the plant. Recent epidemiological studies have revealed the importance of these compounds, the reason being the difficulties in isolating and characterising them, and to study their beneficial effects. The progress of modern techniques for analysing natural substances shows that the beneficial effect of some foods may be due to triterpenoids and flavonoids. These compounds, constituents of quinoa grains (De Simone *et al.*,1990; Mizui *et al.* 1988, 1990), show a complex chemical structure with a wide variability of functionality, in nature sometimes linked with a variable number of different sugar units. Structural or functional chemical differences or differences in sugar content can result in important variations in physical, chemical, and biochemical properties of these compounds. Also nutritional and taste properties of the food containing saponins or flavonoids vary, causing a bitter or sweet taste, due to the flavonoids and their fine structural variations. Flavonoids in food are considered to have many beneficial effects on human health. Saponins are regarded as the main antinutritional factor found in legumes and quinoa. The toxicity of saponins, ascribed to their cytotoxic and surfactant properties, depends upon their type, method of absorption, and target organism. Quinoa can be classified according to its saponin concentrations as either sweet (saponin-free or less than 0.11% saponins on a fresh weight basis) or bitter (containing more than 0.11% saponins).

The saponin concentration in food products depends on cultivar and the processing method. The method consists in a removal by abrasive dehulling of the outer layers of the seed, where they are concentrated, and by washing the seeds in water. Recently, there has been a pharmacological interest in saponins related to their ability to induce changes in intestinal permeability, which may help in the absorption of particular drugs, and their hypocholesterolemic effects. As the saponins in quinoa have been relatively little studied their potential commercial uses remain unknown.

MATERIALS AND METHODS

This work studied a commercial quinoa cultivar from Mascorona, sold as washed quinoa, where the saponins have been washed out, and kancolla with a high saponin content. The saponins in quinoa are triterpenoid glycosides (Mizui *et al.*, 1988, 1990). Normally the sapogenins contnent is analysed by acid hydrolysis, however; in this way it is not possible to know the exact nature of the products present in the plant, and to correlate structure-taste and structure-biological activity. Using appropriate recent sophisticated separation techniques, we isolated whole saponins and analysed the exact structure by spectroscopic techniques such as uv, ir, mass and ¹H NMR, ¹³C NMR, with bidimensional correlations to characterise fine structural differences.

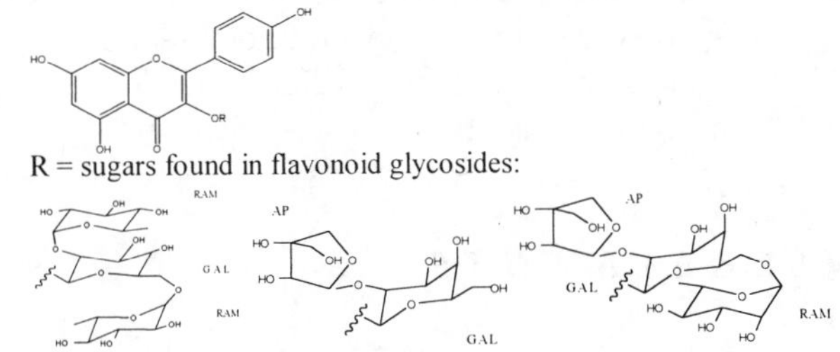

R = sugars found in flavonoid glycosides:

FIGURE 1. QUINOA AGLYCONE OF FLAVONOID GLYCOSIDES.

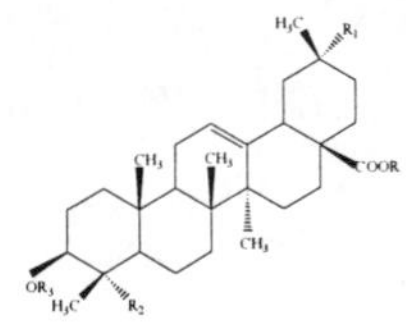

NAME	R	R₁	R₂
Phytolaccagenic acid	Glc	COOCH₃	CH₂OH
Oleanolic acid	Glc	CH₃	CH₃
Spergulagenic acid	Glc	COOCH₃	CH₃
Hederagenin	Glc	CH₃	CH₂OH

R₃ = Sugars found in triterpene saponins of *Chenopodium quinoa* seeds:

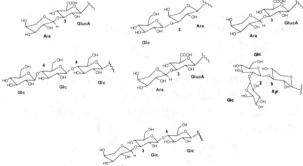

FIGURE 2. SAPOGENINS OF TRITERPENE SAPONINS IN *CHENOPODIUM QUINOA* SEEDS.

RESULTS AND DISCUSSION

Three flavonol glycosides were isolated, with the kaempferol as aglycon moiety, and three saccharide moieties, one disaccharide and two trisaccharides, including apiose, rhamnose and galactose as the monosaccharide unities (Fig. 1).

In the washed quinoa there were still seven saponins, some of which not isolated previously in quinoa. Four sapogenins, oleanolic, phytolaccagenic, spergulagenic acids and hederagenin, were isolated. The sugar moieties were linked to C-28 and C-3 of the aglycons. In every saponin in COO-28 a O-b-D-glucopyranosyl- moiety was found. Differences in sugars linked to C-3 were in number (two or three), sequence, composition of monosaccharid units (glucose, arabinose and glucuronic acid), in nature of interglycosidic linkages (a or b), and the aglycon (Fig. 2).

ACKNOWLEDGEMENTS

The work was supported by a grant of Programma Operativo Plurifondo 1994-1999; Sottoprogramma 5 - Misura 5.4; Azione 5.4.2; Centri Pubblici di Ricerca; Bando di gara annualita' 1997; Progetto di ricerca sottoposto alla valutazione per il finanziamento da parte della Regione Campania ai sensi della l.r. 31.12.96, n°10738 pubblicato sul B.U.R.C. n.3 del 16 gennaio 1997 modificato ed integrato il 5/3/1997 (delibera n.919 B.U.R.C. n.13 del 10/3/1997).

REFERENCES

Alvarez, M., J. Pavón and S. von Rütte, 1990. Caracterización, 5-30. In: Ch. Wahli (ed.). Quinua: hacia su coltivo omercial. Latinreco S.A., Casilla 17-110-6053, Quito, Ecuador.

De Simone, F., A. Dini, C. Pizza, P. Saturnino and O. Schettino, 1990. Two flavonol glycosides from *Chenopodium quinoa*. Phytochemistry, 29: 3690-3692.

Mizui, F., R. Kasai, K. Ohtani and O. Tanaka, 1988. Saponins from brans of quinoa, *Chenopodium quinoa* Willd., I. Chemical. Pharmaceutical. Bulletin 36: 1415-1418.

Mizui, F., R. Kasai, K. Ohtani and O. Tanaka, 1990. Saponins from brans of quinoa, *Chenopodium quinoa* Willd., II. Chemical. Pharmaceutical. Bulletin. 38: 375-377.

Agronomic and physiological response of quinoa (*Chenopodium quinoa* Willd.) to frost at three phenological stages

S. E. JACOBSEN[1], C. MONTEROS[2], J.L. CHRISTIANSEN[3] AND A. MUJICA[4]

[1] *International Potato Centre (CIP), Apartado 1558, Lima 12, Peru*
[2] *Instituto Nacional de Investigaciones Agropecuarias (INIAP), Apartado Postal 17-17-1362, Quito, Ecuador*
[3] *Dep. Of Agricultural Sciences, Royal Veterinary & Agricultural University, Thorvaldsensvej 40, DK-1871 FrederiksbergC, Denmark*
[4] *Proyecto Quinua CIP-DANIDA-UNAP, Universidad Nacional del Altiplano, Av. De. Ejercito 329, Puno, Peru*

SUMMARY

The capacity of frost resistance in quinoa is well known, but very little investigation has been made. Considering that quinoa is a valuable genetic resource, experiments were carried out to determine the response of quinoa to different intensities and durations of frost under different relative humidities, and to determine the variation of yield and content of sugar, proline, and protein related to frost, with the purpose of developing criteria for selection of frost-resistant varieties.

On the basis of results from greenhouse and phytotron experiments it was concluded that in the two true leaves-stage the cultivars from the altiplano of Peru tolerated temperatures of -8°C for 4 hours, while the Interandean valley cultivar tolerated -8°C only for 2 hours. At temperatures of -4°C and 60% relative humidity the percentage of dead plants was 56, while at the same temperature, but at 90% of relative humidity, there was only 25% dead plants. At -4°C, in two true leaves-stage, yields were diminished by 9.2% compared to the control without frost, while at the 12 true leaves and flowering-stage the yield reductions were 50.7 and 65.7%, respectively. An increased level of soluble sugars implied a greater tolerance to frost, resulting in improved yields.

Keywords : frost, physiology, quinoa

INTRODUCTION

The presence of frost is one of the principal limiting factors for agricultural production in the high Andean region, where one of the most important grain crops is quinoa

(*Chenopodium quinoa* Willd.), which generally is less affected by frost than most other crop species. Frost normally occurs in the Andean region between 12 p.m. and 6 a.m., with a duration from 1 to 6 hours (Grace, 1985; Capelo, 1993). The two most common types of frost are the radioactive and connective frosts, which are known as white and black frost, respectively. White frost, which causes relatively little damage in nature (Ruiz, 1995), occurs under a high relative humidity. With this type of frost water vapour is condensed and frozen on the leaf surface, a physical change which causes the release of heat and a slow cooling of the environment.

Black frost occurs when the air is dry and the dew temperature is not reached. Water vapour does not freeze; instead the water in the leaf tissue freezes. Air temperature falls rapidly because there is no atmospheric vapour to attenuate this phenomenon. When the sun begins to shine in the morning, the ice evaporates rapidly, causing necrotic spots in the foliage (Ruiz, 1995).

The present experiment had the objectives to: 1. Determine the damage in quinoa, caused by different intensities and duration of frost under different relative humidities, and 2. Determine the effects on seed yield and the content of sugar, proline, and protein, in two cultivars of quinoa, with different frost intensities at different phenological phases.

MATERIALS AND METHODS

The first study was carried out in greenhouse and phytotron conditions at the International Potato Centre (CIP), Lima, Peru. A Peruvian valley cultivar (Quillohuaman), and four cultivars from the altiplano of Peru (Wariponcho, LP-4B, Witulla, Ayara), were studied at different relative humidities (60 and 90%), temperatures (-2, -4, -8°C) and frost duration (2, 4, 6 h). A random design was used, with three replications, and the data were analyzed as a factorial arrangement 5x3x3 and 2x2x2x3.

In the second study the same valley cultivar and one of the cultivars of the altiplano (Witulla) were used, in three phenological phases (two true leaves, 12 true leaves and anthesis), and three temperatures (-2, -4 and 19°C (control)). A random design with 24 treatments and 3 replicates was used, and the data were analyzed as a factorial arrangement 2x3x3.

The experimental units were made up of 8 plants (two pots with 4 plants in each), each pot containing 5 kg of soil. The soil was prepared with 2 parts of mineral soil, 1 part of compost and 1 part of sand. The soil humidity was kept at 75% of field capacity. Plant death and yield in kg ha^{-1} was calculated according to plant density, estimating 1,280 plants ha^{-1}.

RESULTS AND DISCUSSION

There were highly significant differences for the studied variables: cultivar, phenological phase, relative humidity, duration and intensity of frost.

The risk of cellular tissue death by ice formation and dehydration of the tissue increases with longer frost periods and lower temperatures. In the phenological phase of two true leaves, the five cultivars were not damaged when they were exposed to temperatures of -2 and -4°C of 2, 4 and 6 hours duration (no dead plants), while at temperatures of -8°C the proportion of dead plants was 5.0, 11.7 and 21.7%, for 2, 4 and 6 hours of frost exposure, respectively (Table 1). This is in accordance with Limache (1992), who indicated that in the phenological phase of six true leaves, 16 ecotypes had a damage rate from 2.7 to 26.5%.

TABLE 1. NUMBER AND PERCENTAGE OF DEAD PLANTS UNDER DIFFERENT COMBINATIONS OF TEMPERATURE AND DURATION, IN TWO TRUE LEAF STAGE.
THE LETTERS A-D INDICATE SIGNIFICANT DIFFERENCES BETWEEN TREATMENTS (P<0.01).

Temp., °C	Duration, hours	Dead plants (number)	Dead plants (%)	
-2		0.000	0.000	D
	2	0.000	0.000	D
	4	0.000	0.000	D
-4	6	0.000	0.000	D
	2	0.000	0.000	D
	4	0.000	0.000	D
	6			
-8	2	0.400	5.000	C
	4	0.933	11.667	B
	6	1.733	21.667	A

The susceptibility to frost depended on cultivar, indicating that the genetic constitution plays a role for the level of frost resistance. In the phenological phase of two true leaves, the cultivars from the altiplano tolerated temperatures of -8°C for 4 hours, with a rate of dead plants from 4 to 13%, while the valley cultivar at the same temperature, -8°C, reached the same level after only 2 hours (Fig. 1).

The rate of damage and plant death, which must be caused by extracellular ice formation and dehydration of the tissue, is seen in Table 2. At a temperature of -4°C and 60% relative humidity, the rate of dead plants was 56%, while at the same temperature, but with high relative humidity the rate of dead plants was only 25%. With 60% relative humidity and 6 hours duration, the rate of dead plants was 46%, while with 90% relative humidity and the same duration, the rate was 27% (Table 2).

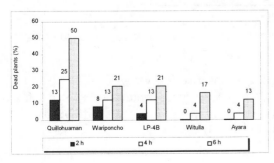

FIGURE 1. PERCENTAGE OF DEAD PLANTS IN FIVE CULTIVARS EXPOSED TO -8°C OF DIFFERENT DURATION.

TABLE 2. DEAD PLANTS WITH DIFFERENT COMBINATIONS OF RELATIVE HUMIDITY, TEMPERATURE, AND FROST DURATION.
THE LETTERS A-E INDICATE SIGNIFICANT DIFFERENCES BETWEEN TREATMENTS (P<0.01).

Rel. hum., %	Temp., °C	Dead plants (number)	Dead plants (%)		Rel. hum., %	Duration, hours	Dead plants (number)	Dead plants (%)	
60	-2	0.944	11.806	C	60	2	1.417	17.708	D
60	-4	4.500	56.250	A	60	4	3.083	38.542	B
90	-2	0.444	5.556	D	60	6	3.667	45.833	A
90	-4	2.000	25.000	B	90	2	0.167	2.083	E
					90	4	1.333	16.667	D
					90	6	2.167	27.083	C

The phenological stage seems to be important, as plants at two true leaves-stage were only little affected by temperatures of -4°C, with a significant seed yield decrease of 9.2% compared to the control grown at 19°C, while yield of plants exposed to frost of -4°C at the 12 true leaves-stage and at anthesis decreased 50.7 and 65.7%, respectively (Fig. 2). This result is in accordance with results of Canahua and Rea (1979), who found that quinoa in the cotyledoneous leaf-stage, and in two and five true leaves stage, behaved as tolerant with no damage by low temperatures, while frost during bud formation and anthesis seriously affected the quinoa. Limache (1992) concluded that quinoa resists frost without major damage before the bud formation phase, but is very susceptible to frost during anthesis. Monteros and Jacobsen (1999) showed that quinoa was most tolerant to frost in the 12 leaf stage, and most frost sensitive in anthesis.

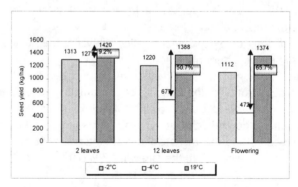

FIGURE 2. SEED YIELD (KG/HA) AT -2, -4 AND 19°C IN THREE PHENOLOGICAL PHASES.
THE BAR AND THE ARROWS REPRESENT THE DIFFERENCE BETWEEN YIELD AT -4°C COMPARED TO THE CONTROL.

A temperature of -4°C seriously affected the valley cultivar, which yielded 0.6 t ha⁻¹, representing a yield decrease of 56.2% compared with the control, not exposed to frost. Cultivar Witulla of the altiplano was less affected, yielding 1.0 t ha⁻¹, corresponding to a 26.7% decrease compared to the control (Fig. 3).

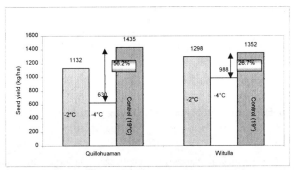

FIGURE 3. SEED YIELD (KG HA⁻¹) OF TWO CULTIVARS OF QUINOA EXPOSED TO -2, -4 AND 19°C.
THE BAR AND THE ARROWS REPRESENT THE DIFFERENCE BETWEEN YIELD AT -4°C COMPARED TO THE
CONTROL.

The variation in frost tolerance between the two cultivars of quinoa may be due to the content of soluble sugars. The cultivar of the altiplano (Witulla) presented higher content of soluble sugars than the valley cultivar (Quillohuman). At the 12 true leaf-stage Witulla had a sugar content of 3,215 mg g⁻¹ dry weight, while Quillohuaman had 2,853 mg g⁻¹ dry weight (Table 3). Lancer (1995) and Stone (1993), cited by Hardy (1996), mention that the frost tolerance may be related to high content of solutes, which are responsible for protection and support of the cellular structures under frost stress. Exposed to frost, the two cultivars accumulate soluble sugars, and it is seen that at −4 °C Witulla and Quillohuman had higher content of sugar (3,310 and 3,096 mg/g dry weight), respectively), than at 19°C (2,648 and 2,381 mg g⁻¹ dry weight), respectively.

TABLE 3. CONTENT OF SOLUBLE SUGARS, WITH DIFFERENT COMBINATIONS OF PHASE AND
TEMPERATURE, IN TWO CULTIVARS OF QUINOA.

Phenological phase	Cultivar	Soluble sugar (mg/g dry weight)		Temp. °C	Cultivar	Soluble sugar (mg/g dry weight)	
12 true leaves	Quilloh.	2.853	B	-4	Quillohuaman	3.096	B
	Witulla	3.215	A		Witulla	3.310	A
Flowering	Quilloh.	2.624	C	19	Quillohuaman	2.381	D
	Witulla	2.743	BC		Witulla	2.648	C

CONCLUSION

The content of soluble sugars was positively correlated to yield (r = 0.688), for which reason it is concluded that the level of soluble sugar may be utilized as indicator of frost tolerance.

REFERENCES

Canahua, A. and J. Rea, 1979. Quinuas resistentes a heladas. En, II Congreso Internacional de Cultivos Andinos, Junio 4-8. ESPOCH. Riobamba. 143-150.

Capelo, G., 1993. Respuesta de 36 clones promisorios de melloco al efecto de heladas en dos provincias de la Sierra Ecuatoriana, Riobamba, Ecuador.

Grace, B., 1985. El clima de Puno, Puno, Perú, 180.

Hardy, L. A., 1996. Tolerance to the freezing in barley. Doctoral dissertation in Biology Sciences, University of Chile, Santiago.

Limache, J., 1992. Tolerancia a heladas de 14 ecotipos y 2 variedades de quinua (Chenopodium quinoa Willd.), en Waru-Waru de Caritamaya-Acora. Tesis Ingeniero Agrónomo. Universidad Nacional del Altiplano. Puno, Perú,180.

Monteros, C. and S. E. Jacobsen, 1999. Resistance of quinoa (Chenopodium quinoa Willd.) to frost. In, Proceedings of COST 814-Workshop: Alternative Crops for Sustainable Agriculture, 13-15 June 1999, Turku, Finland, 319-325.

Ruiz, E., 1995. Agrometeorología. Universidad Autónoma Agraria Antonio Narro. Primera edición, México, 81-101.

Potential for Chenopodium quinoa (Willd.) acclimatisation in Poland

K. GÊSIÑSKI

Department of Botany and Ecology, Faculty of Agriculture of the University of Technology and Agriculture in Bydgoszcz, ul. Prof. S. Kaliskiego 7, 85-796 Bydgoszcz, Poland

S U M M A R Y

The quinoa cultivation research in 1998-1999 in Poland. The research was an attempt to evaluate the potential for acclimatisation of the cultivars of *Chenopodium quinoa* as well their production potential. Special attention was paid to the possibilities of using the species for green mass and seed production. Similarly detailed analyses were carried out to define the contents of ashes, protein, crude fibre and crude fat in the dry matter. *Chenopodium quinoa* is the richest in nutrients of all the cereals, most importantly, in quality protein, hence a very good composition of aminoacids, specifically exogenous amino acids. The results show specific differences between the cultivars, some of which are adapted to Polish climate and soil conditions.

Keywords : acclimatisation, green mass, quinoa, seed production

I N T R O D U C T I O N

The economic and social transformation taking place in Poland has brought about numerous changes in agricultural production. They are a result of a production simplification system, and especially a search for a decrease in production costs. To solve the problem, new species of dicotyledons are being introduced which, at low costs and with a good crop value, would be promising in crop-rotation. *Chenopodium quinoa* could be used here (Carlsson R., 1989; Gêsiñski K., Kwiatkowska B., 1999; Jacobsen S. E., *et al.*, 1994; Nalborczyk E., 1995; Risi J., Galwey N. W., 1989; 1991).

Lately an interest in *Chenopodium quinoa* has increased with discoveries of its agricultural potential, namely, a positive reaction to fertilisation and flooding, high reproductive potential, resistance to pathogens and weeds and very good nutritive properties.

Chenopodium quinoa is the richest in nutrients of all the cereals, most importantly, in quality protein, hence a very good composition of amino acids, specifically exogenous amino acids (Gêsiñski K., Kwiatkowska B., 1999 a, b; Nalborczyk E., 1995;1996).

The present paper presents the results of some elements of the investigation for the 5P06B 04914 research project, currently realised, financed by the State Committee for Scientific Research in Poland.

MATERIALS AND METHODS

The experimental plots were established in the village of Chrzastowo near the town of Naklo in the north-western Poland. The soil was treated appropriately and fertilised with 75:53.5:53.5 kg of NPK ha[-1] (Grochowski Z., 1996; Jahnson D. L., 1993; Risi J., Galwey N. W., 1989).

Three cultivars of quinoa were cultivated. The quinoa was sown in a randomised complete block with four replications. The total area of a single plot was 16 m^2, while the harvest area was 12 m^2. The quantity of seeds m^{-2} amounted to 1.7 g. The sowing depth was 1.5 cm (Grochowski Z., 1996). The sowing date was May 7th 1998 and 1999. Before the experiment was set up, the chemical analyses of soils were conducted to define acidity, organic carbon content, done with the Tiurin method, and the humus percentage. The type of soil, contents of phosphorus and potassium, with Egner-Riehm method, and magnesium with Schachtschabel method were defined.

During the study the following were taken into consideration: germination, flowering, milky ripeness, yellow maturity, seed yield and the field stand. Special attention was paid to the possibilities of using the species for green mass and seed production. Similarly detailed analyses were carried out to define the contents of ashes, protein, crude fibre and crude fat in the dry matter.

During the growing season, *Lygus nugulipensis*, which occurred sporadically, was destroyed with the Decis 2.5 EC preparation. The results were statistically analysed with the Tukey Test (P=95%).

TABLE 1. RAINFALL AND SUN EXPOSURE.

Features	May	June	July	August	September	October	Σ
Rainfall (mm) 1998	57.8	93.0	100.6	83.1	89.0	57.6	481.1
Rainfall (mm) 1999	45.6	53.6	36.8	35.3	13.3	30.2	214.8
sun exposure (hour/day)1998	7.0	6.0	6.8	6.2	4.6	2.8	1024.8
sun exposure (hour/day)1999	9.6	6.1	9.5	8.3	7.1	3.2	1341.4

RESULTS

Chemical analyses showed that the experiment was carried out on brown soil on light clay with the content of more than 26% of silt.

The soil reaction was 6.85, the humus content amounted to 1.76%, while the phosphorus content was high and amounted to 26.6 mg of P_2O_5 per 100 g of the soil, similarly to the content of potassium which amounted to 25.9 mg of K_2O per 100 g of the soil, and magnesium, 4.3 mg per 100 g of the soil.

TABLE 2. TEMPERATURE (C^0).

Temperature	May	June	July	August	September	October
monthly mean (1998)	15.2	18.9	17.9	16.7	14.4	7.9
monthly mean (1999)	14.0	17.7	21.5	19.0	17.4	8.6
maximum monthly mean (1998)	19.2	21.7	21.8	21.6	17.9	10.3
maximum monthly mean (1999)	18.4	21.3	26.3	23.7	22.4	12.0
minimum monthly mean (1998)	7.9	-	-	11.7	9.6	4.4
minimum monthly mean (1999)	7.1	11.9	14.8	12.3	11.4	5.0

The vegetation periods over 1998-1999 differed considerably; the rainfall over respective months of 1998 was higher than the corresponding values observed in 1999. The rainfall over the vegetation period in 1998 exceeded by more than two-folds the rainfall of 1999 (Table 1). In 1999 the sun exposure was significantly higher than in the previous year and the sum of the sunshine hours hours over the vegetation exceeded by over 30% the respective number of 1998. Similarly the air temperature was higher in 1999 (Table 2), while the length of the vegetation period of the cultivars analysed did not differ within years and amounted to 150 days in 1998 and about 116-118 days in 1999 (Table 3).

TABLE 3. DEVELOPMENT STAGES; NUMBER OF DAYS (1999).

Cultivars	Full germination	Inflorescence	Beginning of flowering	End of flowering	Milky maturity	Full maturity
Faro	4	41	53	79	92	118
Sandowal	4	40	52	78	88	117
Olav	4	40	52	78	92	116

The weather conditions considerably influenced the seed yield; in 1998 it was over two-fold higher than the one the following year, while the highest significant seed yield over the years analysed was observed in 'Faro' which in 1998 amounted to 3.589 t ha^{-1} (Fig. 1). Similar relationships over the years analysed were noted for green mass yield which in 1998 was much higher. Out of all the cultivars analysed, the highest values were also observed for Faro (Fig. 2).

The seed chemical composition was, as follows; the share of the dry matter was 89% in all the cultivars and did not differ significantly. The crude ash content was highest in Faro and it differed by about 1% from the values observed for the other cultivars (Table 4). The crude protein content showed highest in Olav yet only by 0.32% but it differed significantly .

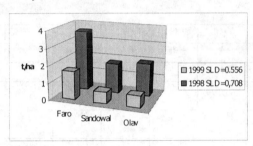

FIGURE 1. SEED YIELD (T HA⁻¹).

The fat content in Faro exceeded that in the other cultivars by 1%. The fibre content in respective cultivars was observed to be from 4.4 to 5.8%, while the lowest was observed in Olav. The chemical composition of green mass showed that the dry matter content in respective cultivars did not show significant differences; similarly the crude ash content across cultivars amounted from 11.2 to 11.8%, hence considering crude ash content, the quinoa green mass remains of a comparable value with green mass of other crops in Poland.

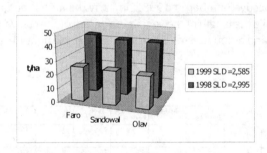

FIGURE 2. GREEN MASS YIELD (T HA⁻¹).

The cultivars researched did not differ significantly in their protein content and remained similar to other species. No significant differences were observed across cultivars in their crude fat content; mean value amounted to 3.2%; here the quinoa green mass was poorer by about 1% than that of those of the other species. The crude fibre, as a nutrient influencing digestibility is of great importance; here again no significant differences were observed across cultivars. Mean values amounted from 26.7% (Olav) to 27% (Faro). The content of crude fibre in the green mass of the crop researched was only slightly lower than those of popular mixtures of grasses with leguminous crops. Such similar relationships are present when we compare the chemical composition of quinoa green mass with the first cuts of the other plant species, while comparing with further cuts, the chemical composition of the quinoa green mass is more favourable. The contents of nutrients in quinoa seeds and in green mass did not differ considerably over the research years analysed, except the percentage of crude protein which in 1999 increased by 30%.

The present research evaluated the potential for acclimatisation of the cultivars of *Chenopodium quinoa* researched as well production potential. *Chenopodium quinoa* green mass remains of similar and, in some cases, higher quality than that of popular mixtures of grasses with leguminous crops and, quinoa seeds are richest in nutrients, as compared with all the cereals reported in literature.

The results of the research presented show some differences between the cultivars which adapted to Polish climate and soil conditions.

TABLE 4. CONTENTS OF ASHES, PROTEIN, CRUDE FIBRE AND CRUDE FAT IN DRY MATTER (%).

Cultivars	Dry matter Seeds / Green mass		Crude ashes Seeds / Green mass		Crude fat Seeds / Green mass		Crude fibre Seeds / Green mass		Crude protein Seeds / Green mass	
Faro	89.4	90.8	4.9	11.2	5.9	16.0	5.8	27.0	7.5	3.2
Sandowal	89.1	90.7	4.0	11.8	4.5	17.5	5.0	26.9	7.7	3.4
Olav	89.4	91.2	3.9	11.4	4.8	15.0	4.4	26.7	7.8	3.3

CONCLUSIONS

1. The results presented showed a potential for cultivation of the cultivars analysed.
2. The cultivars researched showed varied seed yields and similar green mass yields.
3. The highest seed yield was observed in Faro.
4. The percentages of crude protein, crude fibre, ashes and crude fat across the *Chenopodium quinoa* cultivars were similar both for seeds and green mass, respectively.
5. The weather conditions were the basic factor determining seed and green mass yields; and despite extremely dry and moist research years, *Chenopodium quinoa* adapted to such conditions and gave satisfactory yields, Faro being the best variety.

REFERENCES

Carlsson, R., 1989. Green biomas of native plants and new, cultivated crops for multiple use: food, fodder, fuel, fibre, for industry, phytochemical products and medicine. In: New Crops for Food and Industry (eds. Wickens G., Haq N., Day), 223-234, 15, London.

Gêsiñski, K. and B. Kwiatkowska, 1999a. Justification for the introduction of *Chenopodium quinoa* Willd. Part one. Cultivation potential; phenology and morphology. Miedzynarodowa

Konferencja Naukowa "Biologiczne, agrotechniczne i ekonomiczne uwarunkowania plonowania roslin uprawnych" Bydgoszcz 1998.

Gêsiñski, K., B. Kwiatkowska, 1999b. Justification for the introduction of Chenopodium quinoa (Willd.). Part two. Yielding on light soil. Miedzynarodowa Konferencja Naukowa "Biologiczne, agrotechniczne i ekonomiczne uwarunkowania plonowania roslin uprawnych" Bydgoszcz 1998.

Grochowski, Z., 1996. Komaosa ryzowa- *Chenopodium quinoa* Willd. in: Nowe rosliny uprawne na cele spozywcze, przemyslowe i jako odnawialne zródla energii, 44-59, SGGW Warszawa.

Grochowski, Z., 1998. Biologia, uprawa i wykorzystanie komosy ryzowej w Polsce (*Chenopodium quinoa* Willd). W: Hodowla Roslin i Nasiennictwo, Nr 2, 21-26.

Jacobsen, S. E., I. Jorgensen, O. Stolen, 1994. Cultivation of quinoa (*Chenopodium quinoa*) under temperate climatic conditions in Denmark. Journal of Agricultural Science,122: 47-52.

Jahnson, D. L., S. M. Ward, 1993. Quinoa. In: New Crops (eds. John Wiley and Sons), 222-227, ref., New York; USA.

Nalborczyk, E., 1995. Znaczenie zachowania zasobów genowych roslin dla srodowiska i rolnictwa. W: "Problemy róznorodnosci biologicznej", Komitet Naukowy "Czlowiek i Srodowisko", 19-29. Oficyna Wydawnicza IE PAN.

Nalborczyk, E., 1996. Potencjalne mozliwosci plonowania i poprawy jakosci roslin uprawnych. Przemysl Spozywczy, 50.

Risi, J., N. W. Galwey, 1989. Chenopodium quinoa of the Andes: a crop for temperate latitudes. in: New Crop for Food and Industry (eds Wickens G., Haq N., Day P.), 21; London.

Risi, J., N. W. Galwey, 1991. Genotype x Environment Interaction in the Andean Grain Crop Quinoa (*Chenopodium quinoa*) in Temperate Environments. Plant Breeding,107: 141-147.

Alternative fibre crops
Invited papers

Research and development of fibre crops in cool season regions of Canada

R. SAMSON[1], P. DUXBURY[1] AND L. MULKINS[1]

[1]Resource Efficient Agricultural Production-Canada, Box 125, Sainte Anne de Bellevue, Quebec, Canada, H9X 3V9

SUMMARY

Both annual and perennial agri-fibre crops are being developed in Canada as fibre crop species. Annual crops are primarily being targeted as crops for higher value land and smaller, but higher value markets. Research studies on hemp and flax examine the adaptation of European varieties to Canadian growing conditions, and investigate cultural practices and their impact on fibre quality. Additionally, increasing area of short-statured grain hemp varieties may provide a by-product for some fibre applications.

Perennial grasses are being developed for marginal lands and larger, but generally lower value, fibre and energy market applications. The main grass under biomass development is switchgrass. In the wetter and cooler regions of Canada, other more chilling-tolerant C_4 grasses such as prairie cordgrass have potential as an alternative species to reed canarygrass. The main advantages of C_4 grasses over C_3 grasses are their lower silica and nutrient contents, high water use efficiency, and their ability to be harvested more easily using the delayed harvesting system.

Fibre markets for perennial grasses currently include their use for livestock bedding, "straw bale" housing, and as a compost substrate for mushroom production. Promising future markets include the pulp and paper and composite industries as well as energy industries. Commercial plantings of switchgrass were made in 1999 for a demonstration cellulosic ethanol plant. Processing of switchgrass as a pelletized feedstock has a strong net energy balance and appears a promising means to use the material for space heating or composite applications.

Keywords: fibre crops, flax, hemp, markets, reed canarygrass, switchgrass

INTRODUCTION

There is a growing interest in Canada in the development of agricultural sources of fibre for non-food markets such as pulp and paper, fibreboard, composites and biofuels. Food-related opportunities include their use as a horticultural mulch, for livestock bedding applications, and as a compost substrate for mushroom production. Many factors suggest Canada could become an important producer of agri-fibres in the cooler temperate zones of the world. It has a large agricultural land base, an excellent transportation infrastructure, is a relatively low cost commodity producer and has a strong research and production infrastructure from its wood-based fibre industries. This overview will emphasize opportunities for perennial fibre crops as: 1) Canadian production experience is limited with annual fibre crops in comparison to other cool, temperate regions and 2) larger opportunities for agri-fibre utilization in industrial applications are likely to be realized from perennial fibre crops such as switchgrass and reed canarygrass that have a lower cost of production and are more widely adapted to marginal farm land than annual crops.

Annual Fibre Crops

Hemp (*Cannabis sativa*) is a dedicated annual fibre crop that appears to be well suited to Canada's climatic conditions. Recent legislative changes by the Canadian government have made it possible for farmers to grow this crop once again. Most production research to redevelop the crop has been addressing the suitability of European fibre hemp varieties, seeding dates and rates, and time and method of harvest. The overall goal is to optimize fibre quality and yield of the various products while minimizing harvesting costs and easing harvesting problems. Recently there has been increased effort to introduce and develop some shorter statured dual grain and fibre hemp varieties, which may produce a more economical fibre for use as a co-product in industrial applications. The 1999 growing season in Canada saw a sharp increase in hemp production with 12,500 hectares planted. However, the hemp industry is experiencing some growing pains as one of the main processors of the production from this acreage recently went bankrupt. As a result, the land area planted to hemp in the year 2000 is expected to be reduced to about 6,000-8,000 ha. Despite this set back to the Canadian industry, a plant-breeding program has been initiated in southern Ontario to develop hemp varieties specifically adapted to this region. The main target markets for hemp are non-woven fibre applications (such as a reinforcing agent for manufacturing automobile panels) and seed for various food products.

Fibre flax (*Linum usitatissimum* L.) production in Canada was virtually eliminated in the period following World War II, due to the loss of government financial assistance, competition from newly developed synthetic fibres, and technological advancements promoting the adoption of various other natural fibres. Although currently most popular in Western Europe, where production systems have benefited from investment in breeding programmes, government subsidies, and technological advances, fibre flax is being re-established in Canadian markets for woven applications. Canada appears to be an ideal location for fibre flax production because of its abundance of land, advanced production systems of other crops, an agricultural history that includes fibre flax, and the development of technologies that enable the blending of different types of fibres. Since most of the cultivation of fibre flax has been based in Western Europe, an expanded research effort is required to successfully reintroduce the crop into eastern Canada. Preliminary research conducted on the adaptability of modern European cultivars to eastern Canadian growing conditions suggests that most fibre flax varieties grown in eastern Canada have very high biomass production relative to those grown in Western Europe (Couture, 1999). However, since the sole Canadian fibre flax plant recently went bankrupt, the most significant challenge facing the reintroduction of the crop into Canada may be restoring the confidence of farmers. Fortunately, the plant is now under new ownership and 500-600 ha will be planted in the year 2000, with production of 3,000 ha anticipated by 2003.

Perennial Grasses as Biomass Crops

Fast-growing perennial grasses are ideal candidates for fibre production as they have lower maintenance costs and are more efficient at collecting solar radiation during the growing season than annual crops. Perennial grasses are also better adapted to marginal soils, which have low opportunity costs for agricultural production. Grasses are categorized into two broad groups, cool and warm season, based on their photosynthetic cycle. Cool season grasses utilize the C_3 metabolic pathway and are most common in wet regions with cool nightime temperatures. Reed canarygrass is perhaps the most promising perennial grass crop in these wet cool regions for biomass applications. In zones with somewhat higher temperatures, warm season (C_4) grasses such as switchgrass (*Panicum virgatum*) and miscanthus (*Miscanthus sinensis*), which have moderate chilling tolerance, may be more productive. C_4 plants use only one half as much water per tonne of biomass produced, which contributes to their higher yield potential than C_3 species such as reed canarygrass. In North America, miscanthus has not been extensively evaluated as there are concerns about the species escaping into natural areas, and more productive native C_4 grasses are available. Nonetheless, more chilling-tolerant C_4 grasses will likely need to be developed for more northerly areas. Presently, the main areas of switchgrass production are confined to those regions suitable for silage maize production. Other native C_4 grasses are better adapted than switchgrass to cooler regions and to more extreme soil moisture conditions. Prairie cordgrass (*Spartina pectinata*) and prairie sandreed (*Calamovilfa longifolia*) are most likely the two highest priority native C_4 grasses to be developed. Prairie sandreed is better adapted to the drier (>40 cm annual precipitation) and cooler prairie regions of western Canada. Performance data on unimproved stands of prairie sandreed in western Canada (Stumberg *et al.*, 1998) and the U.S. Great Plains (Jacobson *et al.*, 1986) indicate that the species has good potential if seedling vigour problems can be overcome. Prairie cordgrass has more significant seed establishment problems than prairie sandreed. However, prairie cordgrass has greater yield potential than switchgrass in wetter, cooler environments as it has a longer period of leaf area duration (Madakadze *et al.*, 1998). Big bluestem (*Andropogon gerardii*) is another potential biomass species. It has a similar native range to switchgrass, but has a higher stem to leaf ratio, and merits further investigation as a fibre crop.

Perennial Grasses for Fibre Utilization

The main advantage of perennial grasses is that they can produce more fibre per hectare than hardwood trees in most of North America and they can be harvested each and every year. In eastern Canada, annual yields from 6 to 13 oven-dry tonnes (ODT) ha⁻¹yr⁻¹ (depending on the harvesting regime) can be achieved with current switchgrass cultivars. Fall-harvested reed canarygrass usually produces between 7-12 ODT ha⁻¹yr⁻¹ and its productivity is frequently moisture limited. Perennial grasses cannot replace softwood fibre, but usually have better pulping properties than cereal straws. For pulp and paper production, the preferred harvest period at present for both reed canarygrass and switchgrass is the spring harvest. According to this technique, the crops are not cut in the fall but rather left in the field to overwinter and are harvested in early spring prior to spring regrowth (Hemming *et al.*,1994). With the delayed harvesting system, translocation and leaching of nutrients to the soil recycles nutrients for the next growing season. This reduces the ash content of the feedstock, which subsequently minimizes black liquor treatment problems in the pulp mills.

The Silica Issue and its Impacts on Agri-fibre Utilization

Silica is the main quality barrier preventing perennial grasses and straw from being more widely utilized in both the pulp and paper industry and the energy sector. Silica, which is the single largest component of ash in perennial grasses, varies greatly in quantity between species. In the pulp and paper industry, silica-rich feedstocks complicate the recycling of chemicals from recovery boilers, and increase maintenance costs while shortening the lifespan of machinery. Developing lower ash feedstocks will facilitate the entry of agri-fibres such as perennial grasses into the pulp and paper industry.

There are two principal ways in which silica comes into contact with biomass feedstocks: i) through surface deposition by soil contamination, and ii) internally through water uptake by passive water flow and/or metabolic processes (Samson and Mehdi, 1998). In perennial grasses, the major mechanism of silica entry is through the uptake of monosilicic acid in water. Crop residues, such as corn and straw, are generally higher in silica than dedicated feedstocks, as these residues are more exposed to wind erosion during the production cycle, and to soil contamination during harvesting.

The main difference in silica contents between perennial grass species is often related to the photosynthetic mechanism of the grass, and to the amount of water being transpired by the plant. As warm season (C_4) grasses, on average, use half as much water as C_3 grasses per tonne of biomass produced (Black, 1971), the decreased water usage reduces the uptake of monosilicic acid resulting in a lower ash content of the plant. This effect was demonstrated in an analysis of various feedstocks collected by REAP-Canada for analysis by the pulp and paper industry (Table 1). The C_3 species (reed canarygrass and phragmites) were found to have more than twice as much ash content as the C_4 species (prairie cordgrass, switchgrass, big bluestem, prairie sandreed, and miscanthus). Wheat straw was found to have a higher ash content than other C_3 species because it was also grown on a clay soil (to be discussed), and the residue is prone to silica deposition during the production and harvesting processes.

Prairie cordgrass *(Spartina pectinata)*	C_4 perennial	1.6%
Switchgrass *(Panicum virgatum)*	C_4 perennial	1.7%
Big bluestem *(Andropogon gerardii)*	C_4 perennial	1.8%
Prairie sandreed *(Calamovilfa longifolia)*	C_4 perennial	1.9%
Miscanthus *(Miscanthus sinensis)*	C_4 perennial	2.0%
Reed canarygrass *(Phalaris arundinacea)*	C_3 perennial	6.3%
Phragmites *(Phragmites communis)*	C_3 perennial	7.5%
Wheat straw	C_3 annual	11.1%

Within species, the water use efficiency will fluctuate depending on the region in which the crops are grown, and on the soil type. Water use per tonne of biomass produced is highest in regions which have a low rainfall to evaporation ratio, and where biomass crops are grown on marginal soils (Samson and Chen, 1995). A combination of these conditions may explain some of the higher values obtained by a U.S. survey reporting switchgrass ash contents of 2.8%-7.6% (McGlaughlin *et al.*, 1996).

The translocation and deposition of silica in plants is also heavily influenced by the soluble silica levels in the soil, which is present as monosilicic acid; $Si(OH)_4$ (Jones and Handreck, 1967). Clay soils have higher monosilicic acid levels than sandy soils, and therefore produce feedstocks with higher silica levels. A Scandinavian study found silica levels in reed canarygrass to be highly influenced by soil type; reed canarygrass had silica levels of 1.3%, 1.9% and 4.9% on sandy, organic, and clay soils, respectively (Pahkala *et al.*, 1996). In Denmark, high silica contents in wheat straw were strongly correlated to clay soils as well (Sander, 1997). Silica is mainly deposited in the leaves, leaf sheaths and inflorescences of plants. Lanning and Eleuterius (1987) found switchgrass silica contents to be 1.03%, 3.85%, 3.41% and 5.04% in stems, leaf sheaths, leaf blades and inflorescences, respectively, in Kansas prairie stands. Due to the low stem silica content, the overall silica concentration of the grass decreases as the stem content increases.

Commercialization Opportunities for Perennial Grasses in the Pulp and Paper industry

To improve quality for the pulp and paper industry, one of the strategies being developed as a means to increase the stem content is to reduce the leaf content by overwintering. Pulping studies have found that the stem component of grasses, followed by the sheaths and then the leaves, has the highest pulp yield, fibre length, and brightness (Goel *et al.*, 1998). However, with increasing stem content, biomass yields are reduced. Spring-harvested switchgrass yields were found to be approximately 24% lower in south-western Quebec than that of fall harvested switchgrass (Radiotis *et al.*, 1996). Higher losses may be experienced during mild winters. This loss of biomass is due to both the late season translocation of materials to the root system in winter (Parrish and Wolf, 1992), and the physical loss of leaves and seed heads during winter (Radiotis *et al.*, 1996). This lower yield increases the cost of spring-harvested relative to fall-harvested switchgrass by approximately 17% (Girouard *et al.*, 1999b).

Selecting less brittle switchgrass varieties and plants with higher stem to leaf ratios will improve the economics of spring harvesting. However, long -term fall harvesting of switchgrass in more northerly regions requires further field testing to evaluate yield sustainability. With additional research in plant breeding, reducing yield and cost differences between fall and spring harvested material is achievable. Fractionation of the stem and leaf components for utilization in agri-fibre and energy markets respectively may expand opportunities for utilization of fall-harvested crops for pulp and paper applications. In regions such as eastern Canada, where hardwood chips are generally delivered to pulp mills for $80-$100 per ODT, switchgrass provides a cost advantage at the mill gate – an advantage that will grow as wood fibre supplies tighten. The most recent economic analysis of switchgrass production in eastern Canada for use as a spring-harvested crop for pulp utilization estimates costs to be $61 to $81 t^{-1} (Girouard et al., 1999a). Estimates are mostly influenced by achievable yields and land opportunity costs.

By planting switchgrass on marginal land, the farm economy would be strengthened through additional farm receipts. For instance, it has been estimated that adding 15% switchgrass pulp to the fine paper and hardwood market pulp currently produced in eastern Ontario and southwestern Quebec would require less than 5% of the agricultural land base and provide new farm receipts of $20-40 million a year (Fox et al., 1998). Overall, most of the traditional supply problems with using agri-fibre crops are now largely resolved (Table 2). The main barrier to the use of perennial grasses in the pulp and paper industry at present is the low economic return from the pulp and paper industry, which is preventing the major capital investment necessary to utilize the material in the industry.

TABLE 2. TRADITIONAL SUPPLY BARRIERS TO THE USE OF AGRI-FIBRES IN CANADA (GIROUARD AND SAMSON, 2000; SAMSON, 2000).

Barrier	Solution
• Infrastructure set to handle wood	Integrate agri-fibre lines into existing mills.
• Security of supply	Emphasize drought tolerant perennial fibre crops instead of residues.
• Low cost fibre does not always translate into low fibre cost pulp	Use higher cellulose content sources like perennial grasses.
• High ash and silica content	Use species with intrinsically lower contents, overwinter material, source material from sandy soils and avoid soil contamination by using perennials.
• Logistics of supply systems/material bulkiness	Grow high yielding crops within a short distance of a mill, use high density square balers and new fabric covered outdoor buildings for on-farm storage; use leading-edge digester technology to reduce the impact of bulkiness on throughput.
• Short fibre length	Blend agri-fibres with wood fibres and improve fibre characteristics through investing in plant breeding

Other Fibre Applications of Perennial Grasses

Other Fibre Applications of Perennial Grasses

A number of other smaller fibre applications have been attracting grower and industry interest in switchgrass. There is interest in eastern Canada in switchgrass as a livestock bedding because cereal straw is scarce. As well, switchgrass is proving to be a promising feedstock for compost production for mushroom cultivation. At present, mushroom-producing companies in eastern Canada and the north-eastern United States have to transport winter wheat straw over 500 km to supply their needs. Winter wheat is favored because it has a relatively long straw with a hollow structure that produces a well-structured and aerated compost. Commercial trials of mushroom compost from switchgrass have been successful and it appears to be a suitable substitute for winter wheat straw, particularly because it contains fewer weeds. This could be a relatively high value market for switchgrass, as winter wheat straw is being purchased at approximately $100 t^{-1} (Cdn). In the year 2000, several straw bale houses will also be constructed in Quebec using switchgrass. This material is being sold at $120 t^{-1} in small bales. The low nitrogen content and dry nature of spring harvested switchgrass make it less prone to decomposition than cereal straw for this application.

Biomass Energy Applications for Perennial Grasses

Undoubtedly the fibre applications of perennial grasses will also frequently be coupled with their use in the biomass energy industry in the future. As mentioned earlier, high value components such as stems may be fractionated and utilized for fibre, while other lower quality fibre components may be used for energy. Recent biomass energy developments in Canada are having an impact on the commercialization of perennial grass biomass crops and could help improve their economics for use as fibre crops. The first of these developments has been the construction of a cellulose-derived ethanol production demonstration facility that will use agricultural feedstocks for its supply, including cereal straw, corn stalks and switchgrass. Approximately 125 ha of switchgrass were planted in the spring of 1999 in Ontario's Ottawa valley for this plant. The project is a joint venture between Iogen Corporation, a Canadian enzyme manufacturer, and Petro Canada, one of Canada's largest oil companies. The plant is a $25 million investment and it will use approximately 60 tonnes of biomass per day when it begins operation in August 2000. If the technology proves successful, larger facilities will be built to operate at capacities in the order of 1,000 tonnes per day.

A second emerging biomass energy market opportunity is that of densified biomass fuels. Presently, approximately 100,000 tonnes of pelletized wood residues are being exported annually into Scandinavia from Canada. This may also create market opportunities for perennial grasses. The use of perennial grasses for pelletizing purposes has been facilitated by the recent development of new, close-coupled gasifier, pellet stove technology (www.pelletstove.com). It has burned switchgrass fuel pellets with a combustion efficiency of 82-84% (Samson *et al.*, 2000). An economic analysis found switchgrass to be a promising feedstock for pellet production as it required minimal drying inputs and had a higher throughput potential than wood (Table 3). The pellets could have market applications for both energy and composite applications.

TABLE 3. SUMMARY OF PRELIMINARY PELLET PRODUCTION COSTS (CDN$ PER TONNE).
FEEDSTOCK COST FOR SHORT ROTATION WILLOW AND SWITCHGRASS BASED ON GIROUARD ET AL., 1999B,
FOR $U.S. DIVIDE BY 1.5. PRODUCTION RATES BASED ON 30 LBS HP^{-1} FOR WOOD RESIDUES, 45-70 LBS HP^{-1}
FOR SWITCHGRASS AND 35-45 LBS HP^{-1} FOR SHORT ROTATION WILLOW.

	Wood Industry Survey	Switchgrass	Short Rotation Willow
Feedstock	$ 34.35	$46-$68	$58-$85
Drying	$11.93	$0	$15.00
Direct Pelleting Costs	$59.00	$25.26-39.33	$39.33-$50.57
Bagging	$19.25	$19.25	$19.25
Total cost	$124.53	$93.51-$129.58	$131.58-$169.82

Energy Costs Associated with Switchgrass Pellet Production

An analysis of the energy costs associated with switchgrass fuel pelleting is important in identifying the greenhouse gas offset potential of the technology. The energy costs associated with switchgrass production and delivery to a large industrial user have been estimated to be approximately 0.91 GJ t^{-1} for an 8 t^{-1} yield (Girouard et al., 1999b). In the case of pellet production, the hauling distance would be reduced from an average of 60 km to 20 km, as the pellet conversion facility is much smaller than a pulp and paper industry. This reduces the energy cost to 0.79GJ t^{-1} and creates an energy output to input ratio for the crop (assuming an energy content of the crop to be 18.5 GJ t^{-1}) of 23:1 (Samson et al., 2000). This high level of energy output to input compares favourably to grain production, which is typically in the 4-6:1 range.

Additional energy is required for pre-processing, pelletizing, marketing and delivery of switchgrass for use as a pelletized product. The energy costs associated with switchgrass fuel pellet production is estimated to be 1.27 GJt^{-1} (Table 4). Surprisingly, production and delivery of switchgrass represents 62% of the energy required in the entire switchgrass fuel pellet production chain from field to delivery to the consumer. This is largely due to the energy associated with fertilizer use and application which represents 36% of the total energy cost. Nonetheless the net energy output to input ratio is 14.6:1 (assuming an energy content of 18.5GJt^{-1} in the feedstock). Considering that this material can be used quite conveniently as a substitute for fuel oil heating, it appears an excellent strategy to maximize the energy output from a hectare of land. By comparison, the energy balance of switchgrass fuel pellet production appears to be in the order of 3-4 times higher than cellulosic ethanol (Bull et al., 1992), and about ten times higher than corn ethanol (Shapouri et al., 1995). It is evident that fuel pellet production from switchgrass is an efficient land use strategy to displace oil use compared to alternative cropping and energy end use applications which have much less favourable energy production and energy output to input ratios. As well, it bodes well for switchgrass pellets to be a sustainable feedstock to replace plastics in composite applications.

TABLE 4. ENERGY ASSOCIATED WITH SWITCHGRASS PELLETS.

Activity	GJ/tonne
Switchgrass establishment	0.028
Switchgrass fertilization and application	0.460
Switchgrass harvesting	0.231
Switchgrass transportation	0.072
Pellet mill construction	0.043
Pellet mill operation	0.244
Management, sales and billing	0.027
Delivery of pellets	0.166
Total input energy	1.271
Total output energy	18.50
Energy output/input ratio	14.6

ACKNOWLEDGEMENTS

REAP-Canada's work on biomass feedstock development has been funded since 1992 by the Bioenergy Development Program of Natural Resources Canada through the Federal Panel on Energy Research and Development (PERD). Research support on switchgrass fibre crop development has been provided by the Agricultural Adaptation Council of Ontario, the University of Guelph, Guelph, Ontario and Domtar Inc. and Noranda Inc.

REFERENCES

Black, C.C., 1971. Ecological implications of dividing plants into groups with distinct photosynthetic production capacities. Advanced Ecological Resources, 7: 87-114.

Bull, S.R., C.J. Riley, K.S. Tyson and R. Costello, 1992. Total fuel cycle emissions analysis of biomass to ethanol production. In Proceedings of the XVI Conference on Energy and Biomass from Wastes, Orlando, Florida, 1-18.

Couture, S.J., 1999. Agronomic aspects of fibre flax production in Quebec. MSc. Thesis, Macdonald Campus of McGill University, Ste Anne de Bellevue, Quebec, Canada.

Fox, G., P. Girouard and Y. Syaukat, 1998. An Economic Analysis of the Financial Viability of Switchgrass as a Raw Material for Pulp Production in Eastern Ontario. Biomass and Bioenergy, 16: 1-12.

Girouard, P. and R. Samson, 2000. The Potential Role of Perennial Grasses in the Pulp and Paper Industry. Pulp and Paper Canada Magazine. PAPTEC, Montreal, Canada (submitted).

Girouard, P., M. Walsh and D. Becker, 1999a. "Biocost-Canada: a new tool to evaluate the economic, energy, and carbon balances of perennial energy crops". Proceedings of the 4th Biomass Conference of the Americas. Oakland, California, 85-89.

Girouard, P., C. Zan, B. Mehdi and R. Samson, 1999b. Economics and Carbon Offset Potential of Biomass Fuels. Final Report. Study performed for the Federal Panel on Energy R&D (PERD), Natural Resources Canada, Ottawa. 96 pp.

Goel,K., R. Eisner, G. Sherson, T. Radiotis and J. Li, 1998. Switchgrass: a Potential Pulp Fibre Source. In Proceedings of the 84th Annual Meeting, Technical Section, Canadian Pulp and Paper Association. Montreal, January, 1998. B109-B114.

Hemming, M.S., M. Jarbvenpa and T. Mauna, 1994. "On-farm handling techniques for reed canarygrass to be used as a raw material in the pulp industry". PIRA International/Silsoe Research Institute Joint Conference, Non-wood fibres for industry. 23-24 March, Silsoe, UK., Vol.1. Paper 12, 11 pp.

Jacobson, E.T., D.A. Tober, R.J. Hass and D.C. Darris, 1986. The performance of selected cultivars of warm season grasses in the northern prairie and plains states. In: Proceedings of the Ninth North American Prairie Conference. Edited by G.L Clambey and R.H. Pemble. Tri-College Center for Environmental Studies, Moorhead, Minnesota. 215-221.

Jones, L.H.P. and K.A. Handreck, 1967. Silica in soils, plants and animals. Advances in Agronomy. 19: 107-149.

Lanning, F.C. and L.N. Eleuterius, 1987. Silica and ash in native plants of the central and southeastern regions of the United States. Annals of Botany 60: 361-375.

Madakadze, I.C., B.E. Coulman, A.R. McElroy, K.A. Stewart and D.L. Smith, 1998. Evaluation of selected warm-season grasses for biomass production in areas with a short growing season. Bioresource Technology 65: 1-12.

Mclaughlin, S.B., R. Samson, D. Bransby and A. Wiselogel, 1996. Evaluating physical, chemical, and energetic properties of perennial grasses as biofuels, Proceedings of the Seventh National Bioenergy Conference. Volume 2. September 15-20, Nashville. Tennessee, 1-8.

Pahkala, K., T. Mela, H. Hakkola, A. Jarvi and P. Virajari, 1996. Production and Use of Agrofibre in Finland. Final report of the study. Part 1. Production of agrofibre crops: agronomy and varieties, 84 pp.

Parrish, D.J. and D.D. Wolf, 1992. Managing switchgrass for sustainable biomass production. In Liquid fuels from renewable resources. American Society of Agricultural Engineers, St Joseph. Michigan. 34-39.

Radiotis, T. J. Li, K. Goel and R. Eisner, 1996. Fiber characteristics, pulpability, and bleachability studies of switchgrass. Proceedings of the 1996 TAPPI Pulping conference, 371-376.

Samson, R. and Y. Chen, 1995. Short-rotation forestry and the water problem; Proceedings of the Canadian Energy Plantation Workshop, Natural Resources Canada, Ottawa Ontario; 43-49.

Samson, R., P. Duxbury, M. Drisdell and C. Lapointe, 2000. Assessment of Pelletized Biofuels, PERD Program, Natural Resources Canada, Ottawa, Ontario, Contract 23348-8-3145/001/SQ; April 2000.

Samson, R.A. and B. Mehdi, 1998. Strategies to reduce the ash content in perennial grasses. Proceedings of Bioenergy 98: Expanding Bioenergy Partnerships, 1124-1131.

Sander, B, 1997. Properties of Danish biofuels and the requirements for power production. Biomass and Bioenergy 12 (3) 177-183.

Shapouri, H., J. Duffield and M. S. Grabonski, 1995. Estimating the net energy value of corn-ethanol. Second Biomass conference of the America's, Portland, Oregon. 976-985.

Stumborg, M., J. G. McLeod, P. G. Jefferson, G. E. Timbers, J. P. Dubuc, R. Michaud, and R. Samson, 1998. The Potential Production of Agricultural Biomass for Fuel Ethanol in Canada. In Proceedings of the Renewable Energy Technologies in Cold Climates '98 Conference. Montreal. Canada. May 4-6,1998. 79-84.

Alternative fibre crops and sustainable development in agriculture

N. EL BASSAM

Institute of Crop and Grassland science, Federal Agricultural Research Centre (FAL), Braunschweig, Germany

SUMMARY

Sustainable development has been defined by the World Commission on Environment and Development as a strategy that meets the needs of present without compromising the ability of further generations to achieve their own requirements. The key concept is to promote the conservation and the sustainable use of natural resources, which allow long-term economical growth and enhancement of productive capacity, along with being equitable and environmentally acceptable.

A sustainable agriculture system is that which over the long term enhances environmental quality and resource base on which agriculture depends, meets basic human food and fibre requirement and is economically viable as well.

Sustainable agriculture should, therefore, ensure conservation and augmentation of the natural resources and improve the environmental quality. The main indicators for such a system are the volumes of inputs of nutrients, water and chemicals, erosion index, energetic output-input ratios as well as the possible influence on the environment. Several C_3 and C_4 fibre and non-fibre crops have been investigated and compared in this context. Most sustainable production system could be achieved by miscanthus and reed canary grass followed by hemp and flax in comparison to other food crops.

C_4 fibre crops in general species posse high yield potential and the perennial C_4 species indicate lower erosion-index, before CO_2 reduction rates and needs less fertiliser, water and chemicals.

Keywords: environmental conservation, fibre crops, food, fuels, natural resources, sustainability

INTRODUCTION

The concept of sustainability of production system is increasingly becoming a requirement for maintaining the basis of human life. The sustainable management of natural resources both in industry and in agriculture involves a strategy which, while taking into account the interests of the present, preserves the preconditions for future generations to have all the necessary conditions available to them for satisfying their needs. The key concept consists in fostering the sustainable use of natural resources and the protection of the environment. Applying this principle contributes to long-term economic growth under conditions which are acceptable for production which is environmentally sound and economic with resources.

The system of sustainability management plays a special part in agriculture, since numerous complex factors form the basis of production in this field. The key elements of sustainability in agriculture are:
- Political strategies and management, including the economic, social, cultural and population policy framework conditions, and also strategies for research and development.
- Energy and inputs, among other things plant protection, nutrients, ecological land cultivation, machinery and technology.
- Genetic resources: identification, evaluation and utilisation of phytogenetic resources by breeding and bio and genetic technology.
- Factors of climate and their impact.
- Soil and water.

Scientific results and increasing environment-consciousness are reinforcing the realisation that the exploitation of fossil energy sources and other non-renewable raw materials are among the causes of climate change. It is precisely in the discussion about the greenhouse effect that becomes clear how they can influence the sustainability of natural production systems. The use of renewable and regenerative raw materials in the industrial sectors, however, closes the cycle of a sustainable mode of production.

In order to apply the principle of sustainable management in reality, a highly complex way of looking at the problem is required, involving various disciplines of agricultural production systems.

Before the introduction of synthetic fibres, many are derived from chemicals produced from fossil fuel sources such as oil and natural gas, man relied on natural fibres of plant or animal origins for clothing. Concern over environmental issues, such as sustainability and the depletion of non-renewable resources, has brought about renewed activity and interest in plant fibres as sources of industrial raw materials: pulp and paper, automobile industry, panels and for clothing.

The aim of this paper is to investigate the interaction between the fibre crops and different constraints of sustainable development in agriculture production systems.

Targets of Sustainable agriculture

Sustainable development includes three main dimensions: environmental, social and economical components.

The basic targets of a sustainable agriculture could be described as follows:
· Intragenerational and intergenerational equity: Future generations should have the same chances as present.
· Socio-economical dimension: Access to food for all.
· Resource management: Maintaining the structure and patterns of production constraints

of natural resources – utilisation not be greater than the regeneration potential.
· Bio-diversity: Conservation of the natural habitat – flora and fauna.
· Ecological dimensions: Avoidance of ecological disturbances and disasters.
· Global responsibility: Equal standards and scales. One earth – One humanity.

DETERMINANT FACTORS

The determination of sustainability in production of fibre from alternative crops depends on their productivity potentials which are genetically fixed and can be influenced by different measures, their requirements and impact on the environment and climate:

Key Factors:
Yield
· potential
· productivity

Requirements:
· Climate
· Soils
· Inputs
· Energy

Impact
· Environment
Soils, Water, Flora, Fauna, Air ....
· Climate

RESULTS AND DISCUSSION

Wide utilisation of plant raw materials for fibre production offer the chance to reorganise the cultivation patterns towards an environmentally consistent system through increasing the number of plant species, reintroducing traditional crops and introducing alternative species. This will lead to the production of different fibre feedstocks with greater outputs and lower environmental inputs. It will lead also to diversification, reducing the inputs, such as fertilisers, herbicides, fungicides, fuels, etc. This can be achieved by careful selection of fibre plant species.

Table 1 reflects the main agro-technical requirements of some fibre crops. Table 2 and 3 indicate the achieved yields of fibre crops at different regions of Europe. Miscanthus and switch grass are very producible in the UK while sorghum, kenaf and hemp in Spain. Also the energy balance was very positive especially for sorghum (Table 3). Environmental and ecological indicators are summarised in the Tables 4 and 5. Perennial fibre crops have very low erosion index and low herbicide and nutrient application rates. Table 5 gives detailed information regarding ecological indicators of several fibre crops in comparison to other field crops.

TABLE 1. AGRO-TECHNICAL ASPECTS OF FIBRE CROPS.

	yield	N	P	K
Miscanthus	14.3	0.58	0.042	0.69
switch grass	15.1	0.54	0.067	0.17
reed canary-grass	6.6	0.61	0.39	0.18
reed	10.7	-	-	-

TABLE 2. YIELD (T DM HA⁻¹, 1997) AND NPK CONCENTRATION (%) (CHRISTIAN, D. ET AL., 1999).

plant species	seed requirements, density	time of sowing or planting	sowing depth (cm)	nitrogen fertilisation	basic fertilisation P K Mg
hemp	35-40 kg/ha	mid-April/ mid-May	2-3	80-100	80 160 40
Miscanthus	1-2 plants/m²	May-beginning of June	8-10	1.year 50 foll. years 80-100	100 120 80
reed canary grass	10-15 kg/ha	March/April or July/August	1-2	60-80	50- 150- 70 200

TABLE 3. MEAN PRODUCTIONS OF THE DIFFERENT TREATMENTS AND ENERGY BALANCE (MEAN VALUES) FOR EACH CROPS.

crop	hemp	*Sorghum*	kenaf
harvesting (days after seeding)	86	130	157
DM (kg /ha)	12359	21463	16388
"energy profit account" (Mcal/ha)	41827	81824	51055
"energy production efficiency"	8,04	14,95	9,59

TABLE 4. FERTILISER AND HERBICIDE APPLICATION AND SOIL EROSION RATES.

cropping system	N-P-K application rate (kg/ha/year)	herbicide application rate (kg/ha/year)	soil erosion rate (tonnes/ha/year)
annual crops			
corn	135-60-80	3.06	21.8
soybeans	20-45-70	1.83	40.9
perennial crops			
herbaceous	50-60-60	0.25	0.2
short-rotation woods	60-15-15	0.39	2.0

TABLE 5. ECOLOGICAL INDICATORS OF VARIOUS CROPING PATTERNS.

	mobile nutrients	erosion	diseases	pests	weeds
hemp	++	0	+	+	+
rape seed	++	++	0	-	-
linseed	++	0	+	++	-
sunflower	++	0	-	+	-
wheat	-	+	-	0	-
rye	0	+	0	+	-
seed corn	0	0	+	0	-
potato	0	0	++	+	+
sugar beet	0	0	-	-	--
Miscanthus C4, per.	++	++	++	++	0
reed canary grass C3, per.	++	++	+	-	++

Scale: ++ very positive effect; + positive effect; 0 fair; - negative effect; -- very negative effect

The growth and productivity of crops depends on their genetic potential. The degree of realisation of this potential is closely related to the environmental factors dominating in the region and the external inputs. Yields achieved in field experiments do not represent the physiological limits of the present cultivars, but only demonstrate that portion of the genetic potential which is realised by optimal utilisation of present means of cultivation and levels of inputs. Yield and response of cultivars to environmental conditions and inputs is under genetic control and therefore an improved response is accessible via screening, selection and breeding.

Considering all aspects influencing sustainability system, perennial C4 plant species offer the best chance to achieve sustainability i.e. miscanthus and switch grass, followed by reed canarygrass, fibre sorghum, hemp and flax. It should be also indicated that some fibre crops like hemp and fibre sorghum can serve as "4F" crops for food, fodder, fuel and fibre.

REFERENCES

El Bassam, N., 1998. Energy plant species. James & james Publishers, London.

Christian, D.G., A.B. Ricde and N.E. Yates, 1999. Evaluation of herbaceous grasses. Alternative Crops for Sustainable Agriculture, EUR 19227 en.

Alternative fibre crops
Offered papers

Prospects for fibre hemp production in Scotland

B. R. TAYLOR[1], F. MILNE[2] AND K. C. WALKER[1]

[1]SAC, Plant and Crop Science Division, Ferguson Building, Craibstone Estate, Bucksburn, Aberdeen AB21 9YA, UK
[2]SAC Plant and Crop Science Division, Bush Estate, Penicuik, Midlothian, EH26 0PH, UK

SUMMARY

Fibre hemp (*Cannabis sativa*) is suited to cool temperate climates and requires relatively simple management. Field trials on hemp from 1994 to 1997 near Aberdeen in Scotland indicated that for maximum stem yield seed rates of 40 to 60 kg ha[-1] may be required, higher than further south due to poorer establishment, and that hemp responds to nitrogen application rates up to 150 kg ha[-1]. No variety was clearly best. No serious pest problems were observed but crops suffered stem damage from *Botrytis* spp. Soil conditions at sowing were critical for vigorous early growth and weed suppression. Where early growth was slow, herbicides appeared to have advantages. For the crop to be viable in the UK it is estimated that farm yields should exceed 7.5 t ha[-1] of field-retted stems at 85% dry matter. In trials yields of dry stems ranged from 3 to 10 t ha[-1] for different treatments, with plants growing to over 2m in height in 100 days. Field-scale observation plots in 1998 and 1999 yielded 5 t ha[-1] of dry stems and highlighted the practical difficulties of converting a standing green crop of hemp into retted, storable material with good quality fibre. The time of harvesting is critical in achieving maximum yield whilst giving the crop an opportunity to ret and dry in the field. New methods of harvesting and storage without drying are being investigated in Scotland.

Keywords: fibre hemp, harvest, nitrogen, seed rate

INTRODUCTION

Interest in fibre hemp (*Cannabis sativa*) has increased in the UK in recent years as the area of the crop has expanded from 600ha in 1993, when the first licences to grow hemp in the UK were issued, to around 1,600ha in 1999. Hemp stems contain 20-30% fibre (Van der Werf, 1994), traditionally used for rope, canvas, textiles and oil products (Bocsa and Karus, 1996); with renewed interest in the crop a wide range of uses is once more being developed, including quality paper-making (Judt, 1995), woven textiles (Kozlowski, 1998), composites, moulded products and combinations with other materials (Rowell, 1994).

Fibre hemp is an annual, spring-sown crop suited to the cool temperate climates of Europe (Bocsa and Karus, 1996). For the crop to be viable in the UK it is estimated that farm yields of 7.5 t ha^{-1} of dried stems are required to give gross margins comparable to the major combinable crops (Nix, 1998). Yields of 12-18 tonnes ha^{-1} of dried stems have been recorded in trials in Holland (Van der Werf, 1994), 9-12 t ha^{-1} in France, 7-8 t ha^{-1} in Germany and 7-9 t ha^{-1} in the UK (Hoppner and Menge-Hartmann, 1999). Hemp can be used as a break crop in cereal rotations and may benefit soil aeration and drainage due its deep tap root (Eavis and Walker, 1996). The work reported here assessed potential yields, agronomic practices and practical difficulties of growing hemp in Scotland.

MATERIALS AND METHODS

Replicated factorial trials were carried out on sandy loam soils at Craibstone, near Aberdeen, north east Scotland. Plots were 10m x 2m sown in 12cm rows. Fertiliser to supply 75 kg ha^{-1} N and 23-33 kg ha^{-1} P and 44-62 kg ha^{-1} K according to soil analysis was applied before sowing. Treatments were: 1994, 2 varieties (F34, F56) x 2 rates of N top dressing (0, 50kg ha^{-1}) x 2 swathing dates (23 September, 24 October) x 2 replicates, sown on 10 May; 1995, 3 varieties (F19, F34, Kompolti) x 3 seed rates (40, 60, 80 kg ha^{-1}) x 2 rates of N top dressing (0, 75kg ha^{-1}) x 3 replicates, sown on 17 May and swathed on 30 August; 1996, 3 varieties (F12, F34, Kompolti) x 3 seed rates (40, 60, 80 kg ha^{-1}) x 2 rates of N top dressing (0, 75kg ha^{-1}) x 3 replicates, sown on 8 May and swathed on 24 October; 1997, 2 seed rates (40, 80 kg ha^{-1}) x 3 N top dressings (0, 75 kg ha^{-1} at sowing, 75 kg ha^{-1} when the crop was 30 cm tall) x 3 replicates, sown with F19 on 28 May and swathed on 2 October. Swathing was carried out with a reciprocating mower. Except in 1994 when yield was measured after field retting and drying, stems with remaining leaves were weighed at swathing and samples taken for oven dry matter determination.

Observation plots in which commercial machinery could be used were sown with F19 at Craibstone on 13 May 1998 and 12 May 1999. In 1998 harvest dates and methods were compared: cutting with a Shelbourne-Reynoldsswather on 25 August, 16 September and 8 October and baling after field retting and drying; and desiccating with diquat (3 l ha^{-1} Reglone) on 25 September and cutting and baling after drying as a standing crop. Fibre strength assessments were made on samples taken at the time of cutting or 10 days after desiccation. In 1999 seed rates of 36 kg ha^{-1} (170 viable seeds m^{-2}) and 60 kg ha^{-1} (284 viable seeds m^{-2}) with and without herbicide (4.5 l ha^{-1} Gramonol 5) were compared.

RESULTS AND DISCUSSION

Yields of dry stems ranged from over 3 to nearly 10 t ha^{-1}, with plants growing to over 2m in height in 100 days. Plant establishment appeared to be affected by soil conditions at sowing. In good conditions in 1994, F34 and F56 established 221 plants m^{-2} and 163 plants m^{-2} respectively. In the 1995, 1996 and 1997 trials, despite crops being sown into good 'cereal' seed beds, variation in soil conditions resulted in slow emergence, poor establishment and competition from weeds in some plots, resulting in high coefficients of variation for dry stem yields (15 to 29%). The main effects of variety, seed rate and nitrogen fertiliser on stem yields in the field trials are shown in Tables 1 to 3 respectively.

TABLE 1. STEM YIELDS OF VARIETIES IN TRIAL (T HA⁻¹ DM).

			Variety			
Year	F12	F19	F34	F56	Kompolti	S.E.D.
1994			7.33	6.62		0.418
1995	6.58		6.65		6.98	0.325
1996		5.08	5.33		3.09	0.389

TABLE 2. EFFECT OF SEED RATE ON STEM YIELD (T HA⁻¹ DM).

	Seed rate (kg ha⁻¹)			
Year	40	60	80	S.E.D.
1995	6.89	6.88	6.44	0.325
1996	3.86	4.32	5.32	0.389
1997	9.05		8.10	1.155

TABLE 3. EFFECT OF NITROGEN TOP-DRESSING ON STEM YIELD (T HA⁻¹ DM).

	Nitrogen top-dressing			
Year	none	75 kg ha⁻¹ at sowing	50/75 kg ha⁻¹ at 30 cm	S.E.D.
1994	7.05		6.91	0.418
1995	6.51		6.96	0.325
1996	3.46		5.54	0.389
1997	6.46	9.84	9.42	1.415

TABLE 4. STEM YIELD AND QUALITY IN THE 1998 OBSERVATION PLOT.

Harvest [a]	Date of baling	% DM of bales	Yield of bales t ha⁻¹ DM	Tensile strength of fibres MPa
24 Aug (S)	25 Sep	89.6	4.36	1022 [b]
16 Sep (S)	15 Oct	86.9	5.07	
2 Oct (S)	29 Oct	80.6	5.42	1040 [b]
25 Sep (D)	11 Nov	80.5	5.19	1239 [c]

[a] S = swathed and field dried; D = chemically desiccated
[b] at cutting, [c] 10 days after desiccation

Varieties differed significantly in stem yield only in 1996; the medium-early variety F34 (Hoppner and Menge-Hartmann, 1999) yielded well in all years, whilst the later Kompolti gave the highest yield in 1995 but the lowest in 1996 due to low plant numbers.

Seed rates above 40 kg ha⁻¹ gave significant increases in stem yield only in 1996. In England, Cromack (1998) found little response to seed rates above 35-40 kg ha⁻¹ provided that densities of 100 stems m^{-2} were attained. The 1995 trial averaged 176 stems m^{-2} in August, seed rate having no significant effect on numbers due to self thinning. Populations were less in 1996 with seed rate having a significant effect on July plant numbers (42, 61 and 86 plants m^{-2} from seed rates of 40, 60 and 80 kg ha^{-1} respectively). In 1997 July populations were 56 and 115 plants m^{-2} from the 40 and 80 kg ha^{-1} seed rates respectively. These results suggest that seed rates of 40-60 kg ha^{-1} are required in Scottish conditions in order to avoid yield loss from low plant numbers.

Except in the 1994 trial which followed potatoes on a soil of 10% organic matter, stem yields responded to N top-dressing applied when the crop was about 30cm tall; the 1997 trial indicated that there was no loss in yield when the N top-dressing was applied at sowing.

The date of cutting is likely to affect both hemp stem yield and fibre quality. Stem yields in the 1994 trial were significantly higher when cut on 23 September (7.50 t ha^{-1}) than on 24 October (6.45 t ha^{-1}). Data from the 1998 observations (Table 4) show that the crop was difficult to dry if cut after mid-September. However, fibre strength in the lower stems at the August and October cuts and the desiccated crop 10 days after chemical application, compared favourably with accepted values for whole stems of 690 MPa obtained by Bledzki *et al.* (1996), and implies that Scotland is well suited to producing high quality fibre.

Yields of baled hemp from the 1998 and 1999 observation plots averaged 5.01 and 4.89t ha^{-1}; they were probably low because of stem breakage and loss during turning in the field and problems in correctly setting machines in a new crop; sample cuts taken at the time of swathing gave dry stem yields double those calculated from the baled crop.

Hemp normally requires no chemical inputs (Struik *et al.*, 1999). The present trials had no apparent pest problems but suffered stem damage from *Botrytis* spp. Where soil conditions at sowing are favourable, the vigorous early growth of hemp allows it to compete with weeds, but in cooler Scottish conditions removal of weeds before the start of rapid growth may be beneficial and a herbicide justified.

ACKNOWLEDGEMENTS

SAC receives financial support from the Scottish Executive Rural Affairs Department.

REFERENCES

Bocsa, I. and M. Karus, 1996. The Cultivation of Hemp. Hemptech, Sebastopol, California, 184pp.

Cromack, H.T.H., 1998. The effect of cultivar and seed density on the production and fibre content of Cannabis sativa in southern England. Industrial Crops and Products, 7: 205-210.

Eavis, R. M. and K. C. Walker, 1996. Implications of new crops and new crop types on rotational cropping systems. Aspects of Applied Biology, 47: 19-26.

Hoppner, F. and U. Menge-Hartmann, 1999. Evaluation of different European hemp cultivars. In 6th Symposium on Renewable Resources and 4th Symposium on Industrial Crops and Products, Bonn, Germany, 23-25 March 1999, 368-372.

Judt, M., 1995. Hemp (*Cannabis sativa* L) - Salvation for the earth and for the papermakers? Agro-Food-Industry Hi-Tech July/August, 1995: 35-37.

Kozlowski, R., 1998. Bast fibrous plants as a source of raw material for diversified areas of application. In European Conference on Renewable Raw Materials, Crops for Industry, Gmunden, Austria 6-8 October 1998, 77-90.

Nix, J., 1997. Farm Management Pocketbook 28th edition. University of London, 24.

Rowell, R. M., 1994. Market Potential for the Use of Natural Fibres in Composite Materials. Report to the Food and Agriculture Organisation of the United Nations.

Struik, P. C., S. Amaducci, M. J. Bullard, N. C. Stutterheim, G. Venturi and H. T. H. Cromack, 1999. Agronomy of fibre hemp (*Cannabis sativa* L.) in Europe. In 6th Symposium on Renewable Resources and 4th Symposium on Industrial Crops and Products, Bonn, Germany, 23-25 March 1999, 318-323.

Van der Werf, H. M. G., 1994. Crop physiology of fibre hemp (*Cannabis sativa* L.). Doctoral thesis, Wageningen Agricultural university, Wageningen, the Netherlands, 152 pp.

Effect of hemp (*Cannabis sativa, L*) in a crop rotation hemp-wheat in the humid cool areas of North-eastern of Spain

G. GORCHS[1], J. LLOVERAS[2] AND J. COMAS

[1] ESAB-UPC- Escola Superior d'Agricultura de Barcelona – UPC. Barcelona, Spain
[2] UdL-IRTA- Universitat de Lleida – IRTA. Lleida, Spain

SUMMARY

Hemp was reintroduced in Spain (south Pyrenean area, 400 to 800 m above sea level and 707 mm average annual rainfall) for pulp paper manufacturing in 1972 where it has been showing a good adaptation. At present it is also grown because it is considered an excellent precedent for wheat in the rotation hemp-wheat. To study the effect of hemp in the subsequent wheat in a hemp-wheat rotation an experiment was conducted from 1994 to 1997. The treatments compared were: 1) wheat monoculture, 2) wheat rotation with fertilized hemp, 3) wheat rotation with unfertilized hemp, 4) two-year wheat after fertilized hemp and 5) two-year wheat after unfertilized hemp. Initial results of two years of wheat in rotation with hemp are presented (1996 and 1997).

The results show that hemp is a good precedent for wheat in the humid areas of N.E. Spain (southern Pyrenees), because wheat grain after hemp yields at least 1,350 kg ha^{-1} higher than wheat in monoculture (4,374 kg ha^{-1} vs 2,789 kg ha^{-1}). This increase came from increases in ears m^{-2}, and number of grains per ear. The second year of wheat after hemp still gave higher yields than wheat grown in monoculture although without statistical differences. Soil parameters do not show clear differences between crop rotations. The direct cause of the rotation effect is not still known and the plant and soil parameters measured in this study do not offer a whole explanation of the effect of the hemp.

Keywords: grain yield, rotation effect, soil NO$_3$-N content, soil physical properties

INTRODUCTION

Hemp has been a traditional crop in some areas of Spain, but after 1960 almost disappeared. The crop, considered a renewable and environmentally friendly resource of industrial products, was reintroduced for pulp paper manufacturing in 1972 in the south Pyrenean area, where it has been expanding in these cool winter and humid areas of Spain (1,600 ha in 1999) because of its good adaptation to the growing conditions and cropping systems of this area (708 mm average annual rainfall; 400 to 900 m above sea level) (Gorchs and Lloveras, 1998). Hemp is an excellent plant to use in a crop rotation and fulfils all the requirements for making cropping systems more sustainable (Ranalli, 1999) since it helps to improve soil structure, suppresses weeds, and reduces the use of biocides and disease incidence on current crop rotations (Van de Werf *et al.*, 1995). Wheat grain yield increase as a result of the use of hemp as a preceding crop are reported by an increases number of farmers in different crop cultivation areas (Gorchs and Lloveras, 1998; Bocsa, 1998). However, there is little information about the quantification of the beneficial effect of hemp in the subsequent wheat. The main objective of the present research is to study the quantification of the rotation effect of hemp as a cultural precedent to wheat in north-eastern Spain.

MATERIALS AND METHODS

An experiment was conducted from 1994 to 1997 in southern Pyrenees (Merlès, 110 km North of Barcelona; 42° N, 1° 99'E) in an area where hemp and wheat are traditionally grown in rotation. Soils are normally loamy and basic, with a pH of 8.2 and organic matter contents of 1.7%. The experimental design was a fully randomised-block design with four replications (10 m long and 5 m wide plots). The treatments were: 1) wheat monoculture, 2) wheat rotation with fertilized hemp, 3) wheat rotation with unfertilized hemp, 4) two-year wheat after fertilized hemp and 5) two-year wheat after unfertilized hemp. The wheat cultivar used was 'Soissons'.

The rotation layout until 1997 is presented on Figure 1. The data available are two years of the three first treatments and one year (1997) for the rotations of two-year wheat after hemp.

Previous Year	Wheat	Wheat	Wheat	Wheat	Wheat
1995 (94/95)	Wheat	Fertilized hemp	Unfertilized hemp	Wheat	Wheat
1996 (95/96)	Wheat	Wheat	Wheat	Fertilized hemp	Unfertilized hemp
1997 (96/97)	Wheat	Wheat	Wheat	Wheat	Wheat
Keys used to the wheat Treatments in 1997	Wheat monoculture	Wheat/wheat/ fert. hemp	Wheat/ wheat/ unfert. hemp	Wheat/fert. hemp	Wheat/unfert. hemp

FIGURE 1. GENERAL FIELD LAYOUT OF THE CROP ROTATION STUDY FOR WHEAT TREATMENTS.

The wheat parameters studied were: a) Yield and yield components (grain, straw and harvest index, ears m^{-2}, grains m^{-2} and 1,000-grain weight), b) Grain quality (specific weight, protein and moisture content) and c) Crop phenology, plant height and nitrate content at two nodes, in the base of stem, weeds and pests. The determinations of soil parameters were: a) Soil nitrate content at tillering and at harvest and b) Organic matter at 0-30 cm, bulk density, soil aggregates and penetration strength at harvest.

The 1996 and 1997 growing seasons were warmer than the average (Table 1) and precipitation were much higher, although in both years there was no rain from February to the end of April affecting the yields of wheat.

	Nov	Dec	Jan	Feb	March	April	May	June	Year
Mean air temperature	5.9	2.9	2.6	4.3	6.4	8.1	12.8	17.3	7.5
1996	+1.6	+2.9	+3.6	+2.6	+0.9	+2.5	+0.8	+1.1	+2.0
1997	+2.0	+0.7	+2.4	+1.8	+3.2	+3.7	+2.6	+1.6	+2.2
Mean rainfall	38	43	29	37	51	60	91	84	433
1996	+58	+51	+129	-21	-17	+28	-10	+39	+257
1997	+25	+82	+76	-34	-51	-21	-39	+34	+73

TABLE 1. AVERAGE OF MONTHLY MEAN AIR TEMPERATURE (0ºC) AND RAINFALL (MM) AND DEVIATION FROM THE LONG-TERM AVERAGE (1941-1980) IN 1996 AND 1997, AT MERLÈS.

RESULTS

The results of both years are presented in Figs 2 to 3 and Table 2. Wheat grain and above ground dry matter yields are presented in Figure 2, while yield components are presented in Figure 3. Soil properties under different crop rotations are presented in Table 2. The results suggest the following initial conclusions:

1. Hemp is a good precedent for wheat in the humid area of N.E. Spain (southern Pyrenees). Wheat grain and above-ground dry matter yields after hemp are respectively, 1.35 and 2.5 Mg ha^{-1} higher and statiscally different than wheat after wheat. This increase in yield came from increases in yield components.

2. Second year wheat after hemp yielded sligthly higher than wheat monoculture although no statistical differences were found .

3. Soil determinations do not show clear differences among crop rotations: Soil NO$_3$-N content at wheat tillering and at wheat harvest and penetration strength at first 0-10 cm and 10-20 cm for wheat rotation treatments tend to be lower for wheat after hemp, in

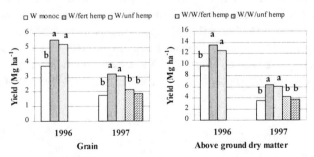

FIGURE 2. WHEAT GRAIN PRODUCTION AND ABOVE GROUND DRY MATTER YIELD UNDER DIFFERENT WHEAT HEMP ROTATIONS. WITHIN YEARS, MEANS WITH SAME LETTER ARE NOT DIFFERENT (SNK TEST, P<0.05). W=WHEAT; MONOC=MONOCULTURE; FERT=FERTILIZED; UNF=UNFERTILIZED.

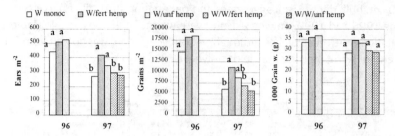

FIGURE 3. WHEAT YIELD COMPONENTS UNDER DIFFERENT CROP ROTATIONS. WITHIN YEARS, MEANS WITH SAME LETTER ARE NOT DIFFERENT (SNK TEST, P<0.05). W=WHEAT; MONOC=MONOCULTURE; FERT=FERTILIZED; UNF=UNFERTILIZED.

TABLE 2. EFFECT OF CROP ROTATION ON SOIL PROPERTIES IN WHEAT. WITHIN YEARS, MEANS WITH SAME LETTER ARE NOT DIFFERENT (SNK TEST, P<0.05).

	NO₃-N at tillering (ppm)		NO₃-N at harvest (ppm)		Organic matter (%)		Aggregates (%)		Bulk density (gr/cm³)	
Rotation	96	97	96	97	96	97	96	97	96	97
Wheat monoculture	11.4 b	12.3 a	23.1 b	27.5 a	1.13 a	1.68 a	32.21 a	36.34 a	1.44 a	1.81 a
Wheat/fert. Hemp[1]	12.0 b	8.5 a	16.3 b	25.2 a	1.17 a	1.60 a	31.54 a	34.05 a	1.47 a	1.78 a
Wheat/unfert. hemp	21.4 a	9.0 a	17.2 b	22.9 a	1.17 a	1.55 a	35.24 a	34.94 a	1.46 a	1.77 a
Mean	13.36	11.2	18.38	28.17	1.15	1.63	32.99	35.84	1.46	1.78
C. V. (%)	67.31	58.59	36.76	52.08	11.39	7.7	4.64	2.67	8.59	8.97

1. fert.=fertilezed; unfert.=unfertilized. Within years, means with same letter are not different (SNK test, P<0.05).

agreement with the farmers general knowledge that hemp improves soil structure (Bocsa, 1998; Gorchs and Lloveras, 1998).

CONCLUSIONS

The preliminary results of this study show that hemp can be an excellent precedent for wheat, and wheat grain yields after hemp increased by 40%, which is double the yield increases reported by Bocsa (1998). As a consequence, hemp may play an important agricultural role in the humid south Pyrenean areas of North-eastern of Spain. However the direct cause of the rotation effect is not well known and the plant and soil parameters measured in this study do not offer a whole explanation of the effect of the hemp.

ACKNOWLEDGEMENTS

The practical assistance of M. Martínez, X. Nisa and X.Recasens are gratefully acknowledged.

REFERENCES

Bócsa, I. and M. Karus, 1998. The cultivation of hemp: botany, varieties, cultivation and harvesting. Hemptech, Sebastopol, CA (USA). 184 pp.

Gorchs, G. and J. Lloveras, 1998. Hemp production in Spain: present situation and future perspectives. Alternative fibre crops meeting (COST WG 814-II), Barcelona, June 5-6: 6 -9.

Gorchs, G. and J. Lloveras, 1998. Effect of cultural techniques on fibre hemp (*Cannabis sativa, L.*) production in humid areas of North-eastern of Spain. Alternative fibre crops meeting (COST WG 814-II), Barcelona, June 5-6: 10-15.

Ranalli, P., 1999. Agronomical and physiological advances in hemp crops. In: P. Ranalli (Ed.) Advances in Hemp Research. Food Products Press, New York London: 61-80.

Werf, H. M. G. van der, W. C. A. van Geel, L. J. C. van Gils and M. Wijlhuizen, 1995. Agronomic research on hemp (*Cannabis sativa* L.) in Netherlands, 1987-1993. Book abstracts of Symposium on hemp, Frankfurt, March 2-5, 1995.

Reed canarygrass maintained its productivity for eight years

K. PAHKALA AND T. MELA

Agricultural Research Centre of Finland, FIN-31600 Jokioinen, Finland

SUMMARY

The effect of stand age on dry matter (DM) yield and the proportion of plant parts was studied in a reed canarygrass (*Phalaris arundinacea* L.) trial sown in 1990. The experimental years were 1991-1998. The trial comprised two fertiliser rates (100 and 200 kg N ha^{-1}) and two harvesting times (seed stage in autumn and delayed harvesting in the following spring). When reed canary grass was harvested in spring, the number of the production years did not affect significantly the harvested DM yield after the first year, and the DM yield was 6-9 t ha^{-1} throughout the rest of the experiment (2nd-8th grass year). In autumn, the yields depended more on the weather conditions and fertiliser rate than the yields harvested in spring. The proportion of stems in harvested biomass ranged from 39% to 76% being highest in spring and in the older stands.

Keywords: harvesting time, Phalaris arundinacea, plant parts, yield

INTRODUCTION

Reed canarygrass (*Phalaris arundinacea* L.) is grown as a winterhardy forage crop all over the northern hemisphere. It has been studied for energy purposes and for raw material of pulp and paper since 1990 at the Agricultural Research Centre of Finland. When reed canarygrass is grown for industrial purposes, the number of production years is a critical factor for the profitable production of grass. The persistence of a forage grass stand is normally 4-5 years in Finland. However, in many trials reed canarygrass stayed productive for more than 5 years especially, when the trials were harvested in spring and the grass canopy was totally dry.

From plant parts, the stem fraction is the most suitable for paper making since it has the highest fibre content and the lowest mineral content (Pahkala *et al.*, 1999; Pahkala and Pihala, 2000). The present study concerns the effect of grass age and harvesting time on DM yield at the first eight harvests and the proportion of plant parts at seven harvests of reed canarygrass sown in 1990.

MATERIALS AND METHODS

The effect of the age of reed canarygrass was studied on a farm-scale field of sandy loam with pH values 6.3. Reed canarygrass (cv. Venture, Peterson Seed) was sown in 1990 and harvested according to the harvesting programme presented in Table 1. The plot size was 15 m². The field experiment was arranged as split-plot design with 3 replicates. Two fertiliser rates (100 and 200 kg N ha⁻¹) were completely randomised into blocks using commercial NPK (20-5-4) fertiliser applied annually in May after the spring harvesting. The fertilisation treatments combined with two harvesting times. Dry matter yields were obtained in both harvests from the ley years 1 to 8.

For analysing the plant fractions, a sample of 25 x 50 cm (consisting about 100 - 120 plants) was taken from each plot, cutting the plants near the soil surface. Plant fractions (stem, leaf sheath, leaf blade, panicle) were analysed from 2nd to 8th harvesting years. For differences, the analysis of variance was done for DM yield, stem proportion and stem yield. The effect of ley year was used as a repeated factor when variables were analysed.

TABLE 1. THE HARVESTING DATES (FROM 1991 TO SPRING 1999) OF REED CANARY GRASS SOWN IN 1990.

Ley year	Harvesting dates	
	Seed stage	Delayed harvest
1	16.9. 1991	5.5. 1992
2	24.7. 1992	27.4. 1993
3	29.7. 1993	25.4. 1994
4	3.8. 1994	11.5. 1995
5	25.7. 1995	8.5. 1996
6	16.8. 1996	12.5. 1997
7	16.8. 1997	11.5. 1998
8	12.8. 1998	5.5. 1999

RESULTS

The effect of grass stand age on dry matter yield depended very significantly on harvesting time (Fig. 1). The lowest DM yields were harvested in the beginning of the experiment in 1991 (spring) and 1992 (autumn) (Fig. 1). Later the yields were significantly higher ranging between 6 and 9 t ha⁻¹ on an average. At spring harvesting, the age of the grass did not affect significantly the harvested DM yield at the lower fertiliser rate, and the yield remained constant throughout the period between 1992 and 1998. Among the autumn yields, only in 1992 the yield was significantly lower than the yields in the rest of the years. The DM yields varied greatly at the higher fertiliser rate and the highest yields were more than 9 t ha⁻¹ at both harvesting times in 1997 (Fig.1). When the years 1-3 were compared to the years 6-8, no significant decrease or increase in yield was observed during the experiment years either in the autumn or in the spring yields.

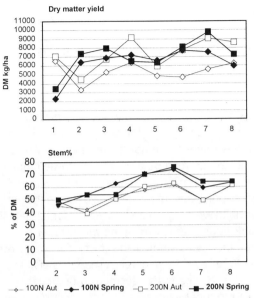

FIGURE 1. DRY MATTER YIELD (KG HA⁻¹) OF REED CANARY GRASS FROM LEY YEAR 1 TO 8 AND THE PROPORTION OF STEMS IN HARVESTED BIOMASS FROM LEY YEAR 2 TO 8.

The proportion of stem fraction was significantly higher in spring (61.8%) than at the autumn harvest (53.1%) (Fig. 1). The proportion varied depending on the harvesting year being lowest in 1992 (spring yield) or in 1993 (autumn yield) and increasing in the older stands. Fertiliser rate had a small effect on stem proportion. The stem yield (kg ha⁻¹) varied yearly more than stem proportion (Fig. 2). The mean stem yields in spring were 1200 kg ha⁻¹ higher than yields harvested in autumn. Stem yields increased in older stands and the higher fertiliser rate resulted 880 kg ha⁻¹ higher amounts of stems. The proportion of leaf blades averaged 27.1% in autumn and 19.4% in spring, leaf sheaths 16.9% and 18.8% of the DM yield, respectively. Panicles were found only at seed stage in autumn when their proportion was 2.9% of the DM yield (Fig. 2).

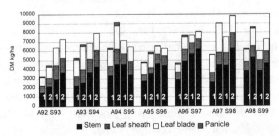

FIGURE 2. THE TOTAL DRY MATTER YIELD AND PLANT PARTS OF REED CANARY GRASS AUTUMN 1992 (A92) TO SPRING 1999 (S99) (FROM LEY YEAR 2 TO 8). THE NUMBERS ON COLUMNS: 1= FERTILISER RATE 100 KG N HA⁻¹, 2= 200 KG HA⁻¹.

DISCUSSION

When reed canarygrass is grown for industrial purposes (for paper pulp or bioenergy), the number of production years is important factor for economic reasons. After emergence the development of reed canary grass sward seems to take at least 2 years to the full growth and yield. The slow development of a reed canarygrass stand is reported also in Swedish studies (Landström *et al.*, 1996). However, according to the experiment the dry matter yields can increase and stay high for several years, even to the age of 8 years.

In northern countries where the temperatures are below 0°C in winter, and snow covers fields for several months, reed canarygrass is harvested for industrial purposes in spring time before the new growth is too tall (Landström *et al.*, 1996; Pahkala, 1998). In the study, the harvest in spring gave more stem yield due to the high stem percentages. The proportion of stem in harvested biomass was high in spring yield since the proportion of leaf blades and panicles decreased during the winter time.

From the two fertiliser rates studied the lower one was closer to the practical fertilisation level, 70-100 kg N ha^{-1} used for reed canarygrass (Pahkala, 1999; Landström, 1999). The fertiliser rate 200 kg N ha^{-1} seemed to be unnecessary high at least for spring harvesting since it did not gave a significant increase in the DM yield or in the proportion of stem fraction.

ACKNOWLEDGEMENTS

The authors wish to thank the Ministry of Agriculture and Forestry and the Agricultural Research Centre of Finland for financing this study as a part of the projects "Production and use of agrofibre in Finland" and "Biomass production for fibre and energy".

REFERENCES

Landström, S., 1999. Sustainability of reed canary grass in cold climate. In: Alternative Crops for Sustainable Agriculture. COST 814 Workshop, June 13-15, 1999, Turku, Finland. European communities, Luxembourg. EUR 19227 EN. 194-197.

Landström, S., L. Lomakka and S. Andersson, 1996. Harvest in spring improves yield and quality of reed canary grass as a bioenergy crop. Biomass and Bioenergy, 11: 333-341.

Pahkala, K. A., 1998. The timing and stubble height of delayed harvest of reed canary grass grown for energy and fibre use in Finland. In: Biomass for Energy and Industry. Proceedings of the International Conference. Würzburg, Germany, 8-11 June 1998. C.A.R.M.E.N., 204-206.

Pahkala, K., 1999. Cultivation methods of reed canary grass grown in Northern Europe. In: BioBase : European Energy Crops InterNetwork: Archive. DocumentID B10504. (Elelectronic publication, HTML).

Pahkala, K. A., M. Eurola and A. Varhimo, 1999. Effect of genotype and growing conditions on fibre and mineral composition of reed canary grass (*Phalaris arundinacea* L.). COST 814 Workshop, June 13-15, 1999, Turku, Finland. European communities, Luxembourg. EUR 19227 EN. 29-42.

Pahkala, K. and M. Pihala, 2000. Different plant parts as raw material for fuel and pulp production. Industrial Crops and Products, 11: 119-128.

Screening trials with new breeding lines of Reed canarygrass (Phalaris arundinaceae) under development for varieties for energy and industrial use in Northern Europe

R. OLSSON[1] AND S. LANDSRÖM[2]

[1] Swedish University of Agricultural Sciences, Department of Agricultural Research for Northern
[2] Sweden, Laboratory for Chemistry and Biomass, Umeå, Sweden

SUMMARY

New breeding lines of reed canarygrass, RCG, deriving from Sweden (north and south parts), Finland and Germany have been evaluated in eight countries of Northern Europe for growth, quality and possibilities to use the delayed harvesting method. In total, there were 14 breeding lines tested and compared with the available forage variety Palaton from North America.

The plants were established from seeds in glasshouses and then planted out in split plot trials in field. 1995 and harvested until 1998. Two harvesting times : late summer and spring were tested.

The trials were located in Finland (Jokioinen and Sotkamo), Germany (Braunschweig), Denmark (Foulum), Sweden (Svalöv and Röbäcksdalen), Ireland (Dublin), Wales (Aberystwyth), England (Rothmstead) and Scotland (Dundee).

The trials have demonstrated a good potential for developing new industrial varieties with higher yield and quality than available forage varieties originating from North America. The best line has at all places given yields about 20% higher than in the forage variety.

The tested varieties have given good quality in both north and south regions but poorer quality in western regions where the shoots never died off. The quality for use in energy production and pulp and paper industry was thus poor with these lines in the maritime region. New breeding lines adapted to the mild winter climate in the maritime areas are thus needed .

Keywords: delayed harvest, plant breeding materials, reed canarygrass, screening trials

INTRODUCTION

Reedcanary grass (RCG) *(Phalaris arundinaceae)* has been used as a forage crop in to a minor extent in Europe and North America. The grass has mostly been used on less drained soils where traditional forage grasses are less suitable. The reason for this has been the large amount of rhizomes, which have given the soil good bearing capacity for grazing animals and machines.

The potential of RCG for biomass production was first recognised in Sweden in the Project Agrobioenergi . The highest yielding crops investigated for biofuel use were RCG and willow (Andersson, 1989). At that time forage varieties and conventional harvesting systems were used. This gave high production costs for the biomass to be competitive as fuel or pulp raw material.

A new production system, spring harvest or delayed harvest, was presented in 1991 (Olsson *et al.*, 1991) and plant breeding research for industrial and energy varieties was also initiated by Svalöf-Weibull AB.

The delayed harvested method has since that been evaluated and accepted as possible all over Sweden. (Hadders and Olsson, 1997). Besides better production economy the new harvesting method has also given a better quality for pulp as well as for energy purposes (Landström *et al.,* 1996).Early plant breeding materials were also tested and showed a good potential for increased biomass yield (Lindvall,1996).

Evaluations of new plant breeding materials from Sweden, Finland and Germany for growing and use with the delayed harvesting method in north European conditions were initiated in 1995 in the AIR programme.

MATERIALS AND METHODS

The screening experiments consist of 15 populations ("varieties"): 11 from Sweden, 1 from USA, 2 from Germany and 1 from Finland. Palaton (no. 12) was the best commercial variety and has been used as standard for evaluation of other new populations in these field trials. The 11 trial sites (in Sweden and Finland more than one site) were located geographically as showed by the map in Figure 1.

Because of small amounts of seed available, plants were raised in greenhouses and planted in the field by hand in the early summer 1995. The plot size was 1,25 x 2,25 m, with 60 plants in each plot and the distance between plants was 25 cm. The trials were arranged in a randomised-block system with six replicates. Three replicates were harvested at each harvest time. All 15 populations of the breeding material were harvested both in late summer/autumn and early spring (delayed harvest) for comparison of dry matter yield, fractional and chemical composition. At some sites the grass was harvested manually, but at most sites with a Haldrup forage plot harvester.

FIGURE 1. THE LOCATIONS FOR SCREENING TRIALS.

Climatic conditions at the trial sites during the project period varied a lot in mean temperature and precipitation during the experimental period. Some sites had both unusual warm and cold temperatures. There were also very big variations in precipitation with both unusual dry and wet conditions.

Fertilisation of the field trials varied between different sites due to different soil fertility. On average the yearly nitrogen supply was about 90 kg N ha^{-1}. Phosphorus and potassium fertilisation was adjusted to meet the need at each site.

RESULTS

Most of the populations were taller at northern than southern sites. On average population no. 10 was tallest (about 170 cm). Lodging or tendency to bending down of the straws occurred to some degree in all the varieties, beginning already at the end of summer in the south and west regions. The proportion stem/leaf varied a little between the populations but was on average 75% stem in the spring harvest and about 10% lower in autumn.

The yields are average values of the three years' results and they are presented as mean values (and standard deviation) for three geographical regions due to different climatic conditions at the sites.

North = cold and dry; Röb.(SE), Sot.,(FIN), Yli.,(FIN), Jok.,(FIN).
South = warm and dry; Sval.(SE), Foul.(DK), Braun.(GE).
West = warm and vet; Roth.(UK), Aber.(UK), Dund.(UK), Tipp.(IRL).

Due to rather small field plots the actual yield figures can be a bit uncertain, but the relations between the populations are adequate.

Yields in the delayed harvest in early spring were unexpectedly a bit higher in the west than in the north region (Fig. 2). This could be due to the fact that in UK and Ireland the grass did not die off completely during the unusual warm winters. Therefore it was also difficult to reach the desired high dry matter content (85%) in the grass. The dry matter content at these sites was often only about 70% (irrespectively of population), and that is not satisfactory for storage and fuel quality. In the north and the south regions the dry matter content at spring harvest were mostly about 85%. The differences between the RCG populations follow the same pattern as in the late summer harvest, i.e. population no. 10 was the best.

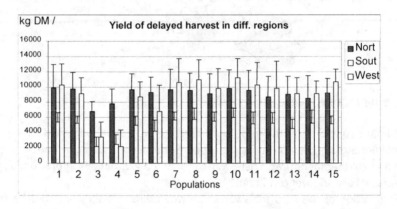

FIGURE 2. YIELD OF DIFFERENT POPULATIONS IN SCREENING TRIALS WITH BREEDING MATERIAL OF REED CANARY GRASS IN DIFFERENT GEOGRAPHICAL REGIONS. MEAN AND STANDARD DEVIATION FOR DELAYED HARVEST (EARLY SPRING) DURING 3 YEARS OF LEY.

DISCUSSION AND CONCLUSIONS

The results from the screening trials obtained during 1998 resemble and verify the results obtained in 1997. It is also obvious that there are differences in the results from different sites. Population numbers 7, 10 and 15 has in almost all countries given the highest yield, and two populations (numbers 3 and 4) gave poor yield in the southern region. Other characters such as height, stem/leaf ratio and date of flowering have also been of high importance for ongoing breeding programmes for reed canarygrass. The screening trials have given valuable information on significant differences between the included populations.

By delaying the harvest from autumn to spring the yield decreased to about 3/4 of the autumn level, but the DM content increased to about 85% at the northern sites. However, at the sites in south-west (in England, Wales, Scotland and Ireland) the problem with low DM content and continuous green shoots during winter is detrimental to the use of a delayed harvest system in early spring. The main advantage with the delayed harvest system is that quality of the crop as a biofuel or for use in paper pulping will increase considerably due to the decrease in the mineral content by leaching during winter; the decrease in content of Si, K and Cl is especially beneficial.

ACKNOWLEDGEMENTS

This project has been carried out with financial support from the Commission of the European Communities, Agriculture and Fisheries RTD programme AIR3-CT94-2465.

REFERENCES

Andersson S., 1989. Gräs för produktion av energiråvara. Art, kvävegödsling, skördetid (Grass for energy purpose. Species, nitrogen fertilisation and harvest time). Ny åkeranvändning inom skogslänen. Swedish University of Agricultural Sciences, 5-6 December 1989, Umeå.

Hadders, G. and R. Olsson,1997. Harvest of grass for combustion in late summer and spring. Biomass and Bioenergy,12: 171-175.

Landström, S., L. Lomakka and S. Andersson, 1996. Harvest in spring improves yield and quality in reed canary grass as bioenergy crop. Biomass and Bioenergy, 12: 333-341.

Lindvall,E.,1996. Breeding reed canarygrass as an energy or fibre crop, potential yield capacity and variation in quality characters in locally collected ecotypes.Proceedings of the 20th Meeting of EUCARPA, Fodder crops and Amenity, Grasses section, Radzikow Poland, 7-10 October,1996.

Olsson, R., 1991. Vårskördad rörflen-Konsekvenser för kvaliteten (Spring harvested grass-Consequences for quality). Konferens: Rörflen för massa och bränsle. 10-11 september 1991, Karlstad.

Utilisation possibilities of selected alternative grasses in reclamation of fallow and waste lands in Poland

W. MAJTKOWSKI

Plant Breeding and Acclimatization Institute, Botanical Garden, Bydgoszcz, Poland

SUMMARY

Structural changes in Polish agriculture and development of about 1.8 M ha of fallow land and another 3.5 M ha of industrially contaminated areas probably will be very important before integration with the European Union. This problem may be solved by afforestation and cultivation of alternative crops, as a source of renewable biomass for energy, pulp and paper or other uses. Possibilities of cultivation of tall perennial C_4 grasses in Poland were evaluated on the basis of observations in the Botanical Garden in Bydgoszcz and in experimental fields: around the Nitrogen Plant (Pulawy), on the coal-mining dump (Bieruń near Katowice) and on deposit of lime (Jeziórko near Tarnobrzeg). Basing on growing and winter hardiness observations the most promising crops for this purposes were perennial C-4 grasses: *Andropogon gerardi* Vitm., *Miscanthus giganteus* J.M. Greef & M. Deuter, *M. sacchariflorus* (Maxim.) Hack., *Panicum virgatum* L., *Sorghastrum mutans* (L.) Nash and *Spartina pectinata* Link. Above species were well adapted to the Polish climatic conditions and should be used as potential alternative crops for cultivation in Poland. Introduction of these new crops must be preceded by studies of their propagation, soil and climatic requirements, technology of cultivation and processing.

Keywords: biomass, C_4 grasses, energy crops, reclamation

INTRODUCTION

Rapid economic and civilisation development during last century resulted in serious threats to living conditions on our planet. One of the most serious threats is global climate warming as the effect of increase of atmospheric concentration of greenhouse gases. The Rio de Janeiro Convention obligates us to undertake activities to reduce emission of the above gases. All programmes on reduction of CO_2 emission base on need for increase of renewable energy use - wind, water, sun, geothermal and biomass. According to plans made by European Union up to year 2010 approximately 12% of total energy will be obtained from renewable sources. All activities will be financially supported by the Common Agricultural Policy through usage of agricultural and forestry waste and cultivation of energetic plants.

In Poland the energy from renewable sources only reaches 2% now. Last year The Parliament of Republic of Poland in a review of necessary changes in energy policy undertook a resolution to increase renewable energy sources.

MATERIALS AND METHODS

In the grass collection of the Botanical Garden of Plant Breeding and Acclimatization Institute (IHAR) for 1993 numerous observation on growth and development of perennial C_4 grass species were undertaken.

Under conditions of extensive cultivation of the grass collection in Bydgoszcz the following traits were evaluated:
- general aspect - visual evaluation, in 1-9 scale (9 - the best, 1 - dead plants),
- green matter yield (kg m^{-2}),
- some morphological traits (height of plants etc.).

Grass species were also evaluated in some recultivation experiments on the following destroyed areas:
· Pulawy - around the Nitrogen Plant (poor, dry sandy soil and high chemical compounds emission, e.g. ammonia etc.), under roots compost was added to increase the soil sorption capacity,
· Bieruń near Katowice (Silesia Region) on a coal-mining dump,
· Jeziórko near Tarnobrzeg - on deposit of lime after sulphur extraction (flotation method).

Chemical composition of soil from experimental plots were shown in Table 1.

TABLE 1. CHEMICAL COMPOSITION OF SOIL FROM EXPERIMENTAL PLOTS.

Trait	Localization of experiment			
	Bydgszcz	Puławy	Bieruń*	Jeziórko
soil type	lessive brown-gray	podozolic	coal-mining dump	lime depository
salinity [μS/cm]	100	50-250	100-250	2400
pH in H$_2$O	5,6-6,6	4,7-4,9	7,9-8,1	7.3
N-NO3 [mg/l]	20	<10	<10	<10
P [mg/l]	35-66	10 - 15	40-55	36
K [mg/l]	82-108	6 - 20	180-210	20
Na [mg/l]	-	38 - 39	650-800	60
Mg [mg/l]	13-40	4 - 6	400-500	97
Ca [mg/l]	442-643	80-180	830-1600	4600

* - values before the experiment started, after 4 years pH decreased to 4,5

RESULTS

Observation on the development of C_4 grass species resulted in the conclusion that there are good conditions for cultivation of them in Poland (Table 2). High yielding ability of Miscanthus x giganteus was confirmed. Two-year old experimental plots of the mentioned species yielded the same as four-years old plots of *Andropogon gerardi*, *Panicum virgatum* and *Spartina pectinata*. However, the problem of susceptibility of *Miscanthus giganteus* under low temperatures (especially young plants) need to be further examined.

In recultivation experiments *Spartina pectinata* showed the highest resistance for different site conditions. It had the best persistence, the best root system and yield. Development of *Spartina pectinata* on destroyed areas was normal, and was not different from taht observed in Bydgoszcz. *Andropogon gerardi*, *Miscanthus sacchariflorus*, *Panicum virgatum* and *Spartina pectinata* were suitable for park-like reclamation of post-mining waste areas in Bieruñ.

TABLE 2. RESULTS OF EVALUATION OF SELECTED GRASS SPECIES IN BOTANICAL GARDEN OF IHAR AND IN RECULTIVATION EXPERIMENTS.

Evaluated traits	Species	Experiments location:			
		Bydgoszcz	Puławy *	Bieruń	Jeziórko
General aspect [scale 1-9]	A.g.	9	-	8	-
	M.g.	9	-	-	-
	M.s.	9	7	8	9
	P.v.	9	-	5	-
	S.n.	9	-	-	-
	S.p.	9	9	9	9
Plant height [cm]	A.g.	238	-	163	-
	M.g.	337	-	-	-
	M.s.	209	91,2	116	153
	P.v.	134	-	73	-
	S.n.	180	-	-	-
	S.p.	234	173,6	155	170
Green matter yield [kg/m²]	A.g.	11.4	-	-	-
	M.g.	21.9	-	-	-
	M.s.	4.7	0.7	-	-
	S.p.	7.2	1.7	-	-

*- addition of compost to increase the soil sorption capacity
A.g. - *Andropogon gerardi*, M.g. - *Miscanthus giganteus*, M.s. - *Miscanthus sacchariflorus*,
P.v. - *Panicum virgatum*, S.n. - *Sorghastrum mutans*, S.p. - *Spartina pectinata*

DISCUSSION AND CONCLUSIONS

Experiments on alternative crops were undertaken for several years in numerous West European countries, USA and Canada. In Sweden *Phalaris arundinacea* L. as well as *Salix purpurea* L. are used for combustion as substitutes for coal or wood. The above species are cultivated in regions not suitable for agricultural production. Local populations of *Phalaris arundinacea* L. are also good material for paper pulp production (Lindvall, 1997). Tall grass C_4 species are considered to have higher light conversion efficiency and productivity than C_3 plants resulting in higher yields, especially during hot summers (Beale and Long, 1995). A very promising species in Germany is *Miscanthus giganteus*, while in Canada and USA *Andropogon gerardi*, *Panicum virgatum* and *Sorghastrum mutans* are expected to cover road sides and waste areas (Greef, 1996, Lewandowski and Kicherer, 1997, McLaughlin, 1997, Noyd et al., 1997, Skeel and Gibson, 1996, Speller, 1993).

The US Department of Energy took *Panicum virgatum* into research programmes on energy crops for central and north-eastern regions in the 90's (Sanderson *et al.* .1997). In Spain and Portugal *Arundo donax* L., a 4 m high grass species is a good source of biomass for paper pulp and energy purposes. *Spartina pectinata* and *S. cynosuroides* Roth are taken into account as potential energy crops for north-western England (Beale and Long, 1995). In some regions of Asia *Miscanthus sacchariflorus* is used as an anti-erosive plant for its intensive heavy metals uptake from soil (Hsu and Chou, 1992).

Structural changes in Polish agriculture focused on energy crops are not possible without support from government, as for example in West European countries. From 1988 to 1995 programmes such as: ECLAIR and FLAIR (development of new technologies with new species), CAMAR (adaptation of new species for market) and AIR (agricultural and technological research) were founded with 670 M ECU.

There is no tall, perennial grass species in the Polish flora that will be suitable for cultivation on light soil so it is worthwhile to undertake relevant research.

REFERENCES

Beale, C. V. and S. P. Long, 1995. Can perennial C_4 grasses attain high efficiencies of radiant energy conversion in cool climates? Plant Cell and Environment, 18 (6): 641-650.

Greef, J. M., 1996. Etablierung und Biomassebildung von Miscanthus x giganteus. Cuvillier Verlag Gottingen: 1-162.

Hsu, F. H. and C. H. Chou, 1992. Inhibitory effects of heavy metals on seed germination and seedling growth of Miscanthus species. Botanical Bull. of Academia Sinica, 33 (4): 335-342.

Lewandowski, I. and A. Kicherer, 1997. Combustion quality of biomass: practical relevance and experiments to modify the biomass guality of *Miscanthus giganteus*. European Journal of Agronomy, 6: 163-177.

Lindvall, E., 1997. Breeding reed canarygrass as an energy or fibre crop potential yield capacity and variation in quality characters in locally collected ecotypes. Procc. of 20-th EUCARPIA Meeting Fodder Crops and Amenity Grasses Section "Ecological aspect of breeding fodder crops and amenity grasses", Radzików, 7-10.10.1996: 117-120.

McLaughlin, S. B., 1997. Forage crops as bioenergy fuels: evaluating the status and potential. Procc. of the XVIII Intern. Grassland Congress, Winnipeg & Saskatoon, Canada: 61-68.

Noyd, R. K., F. L. Pfleger, M. R. Norland and D. L. Hall, 1997. Native plant productivity and litter decomposition in reclamation of taconite iron ore tailing. Journal of Environmental Quality, 26 (3): 682-687.

Sanderson, M. A. and R. L. Reed, 1997. Switchgrass management for a biomass energy feedstock in Texas. Procc. of the XVIII Intern. Grassland Congress, Winnipeg & Saskatoon, Canada: 19-5-19-6.

Skeel, V. A. and D. J. Gibson, 1996. Physiological performance of *Andropogon gerardi, Panicum virgatum* and *Sorghastrum mutans* on reclaimed mine spoil. Restoration Ecology, 4 (4): 355-367.

Speller, C. S., 1993. The potential for growing biomass crops for fuel on surplus land in the UK. Outlook on Agriculture, 22 (1): 23-29.

Trials with industrial hemp, Denmark 1998-1999

P. FLENGMARK

Danish Institute of Agricultural Sciences, Department of Plant Biology, Flakkebjerg, Denmark

S U M M A R Y

The aim was to examine the potential yield of dry matter and crude fibre in five varieties of hemp grown at different plant densities and different row spacing, and to evaluate their seed production capacity. Six experiments have been carried out at Flakkebjerg Research Center and Roenhave Experimental Station.

The varieties used in these trials were the French varieties Fedora, Fedrina, Felina and Futura, and the German variety Fasamo. All varieties had a low content of cannabinol.

Total dry matter varied from 8 to 12 t ha^{-1} in the French varieties, but was somewhat lower in the early German variety Fasamo.

Plant density varied from 8 kg ha^{-1} to 64 kg ha^{-1}, this means from about 30 plants m^{-2} to 240 plant m^{-2}.

Except for a slight decrease at low seed rate, no influence was observed in dry matter stem yield.

Row distance had no effect on dry matter stem yield.

Crude fibre yield varied in the French varieties from 2.5 to 4.7 t ha^{-1} and somewhat lower in the German variety Fasamo. In general, the yield of fibre was a little lower at a sowing rate of 8 kg ha^{-1} than at higher rates.

There was a marked difference in yield between Flakkebjerg and Roenhave 1998, Flakkebjerg having a lower yield. In 1999 however, the sites were equal and high in yield.

Seed yields 1998 varied depending on variety from 300 to 600 kg seed ha^{-1}. Some bird damage was noted. The quality was poor with many unripe seeds. In 1999 the quality was more even. With Fasamo, seed yields of 1,100 kg ha^{-1} was obtained independent of seed rates. With the French varieties best yield was obtained at low seed rate and decreased markedly at higher rates.

Keywords: dry matter yield, fiber yield, hemp, row spacing, sowing rates, varieties

I N T R O D U C T I O N

Due to abandoning by law in 1961 of growing hemp in Denmark, very little knowledge of the potential of newer low, cannabinoic (THC) varieties is available.

Hemp varieties of low THC have primarily been grown as "border rows"to sugar beet varieties for seed production by the firm Danisco.

An intensive campaign for allowance to grow hemp opened up per mission in 1998 under the control of Ministry of Food, Fisheries and Agriculture.

From 1998 DIAS has been partners in a scientific programme with hemp directed by the Centrer for Plant Fibre Technology at The Royal Agricultural and Veterinary University and with partners from Danish Technical University , Risoe Research Center, Aalborg University and the Farmers Union Org.

MATERIALS AND METHODS

Six experiments were carried out at Flakkebjerg Research Centre and Roenhave Experimental Station during 1998 and 1999 with the French varieties Fedora, Fedrina, Felina and Futura, and with the German variety Fasamo. The varieties were established with different sowing rates: 8, 16, 32 and 64 kg ha^{-1} and with two row distances of 24 and 48 cm. The layout of the trials were randomized-block design. At Flakkebjerg, five varieties were combined with four sowing rates and with four replicates-in total 80 plots. At Roenhave one experiment with Futura were established with four sowing rates and two row distances and with four replicates-in total 32 plots. Another trial was with the four French varieties at two row distances and with four replicates-in total 32 plots.

In 1998, the weather were good during the growing season with sufficient amounts of rain, but the autumn season was cold and wet and caused prolonged growing of the hemp and a low dry matter content in the stem at harvest-average 35%. Excess of precipitation was +150mm.

In 1999 the weather was normal in May, but very wet in June. The summer period was warm, above normal, specially in September. Excess of precipitation was + 99mm.

RESULTS AND DISCUSSION

Plant density and row spacing, Roenhave

Stem dry matter yield varied from 10.6 to 12.6 t ha^{-1}. Best results were with row distance 24 cm and with 32 kg ha^{-1} of seed. Year 1998 was a little better than 1999. Yield of leaves and seed varied from 1.8 to 2.9 t DM ha^{-1}. Best results were with 8 kg ha^{-1}, 1998. No difference was observed between the two row distances. Fibre yield varied from 3.4 to 4.3 t ha^{-1}. Row distance of 24 cm and with 32 kg seed ha^{-1} was the highest yielding. In general, 24 cm was better than 48 cm row distance. The fibre content was a little higher in 1999 than in 1998. The only difference in plant height was seen in seeding rate. The lower seeding rate, the taller the plant!

Varieties and row spacing, Roenhave

Stem dry matter yield varied from 7.8 to 12.3 t ha⁻¹. Best yield was obtained with Futura and lowest with Felina. Generally 24 cm was better than 48 cm row distances. Yield of leaves and seed varied from 1.6 to 3.0 t ha⁻¹. 1998 was remarkably better than 1999. No big differences between the two row spacings or the varieties. Fibre yield varied from 2.7 to 4.4 t ha⁻¹ with the highest yield in Futura. Lowest yielding was Felina. There was a decrease in fibre yield at row distance of 48 cm. There was a quite uniform content in Fedrina and Futura opposite to Fedora and Felina, but no clear explanation to this variation is found. Plant height. Futura was the tallest variety.

Varieties and seeding rates with hemp, Flakkebjerg

Fedora, Fedrina, Felina, Futura and Fasamo were tested at four sowing rates: 8, 16, 32 and 64 kg ha⁻¹. Stem dry matter yield varied within the French varieties from 8.0 to 12.9 t DM ha⁻¹, and with the German variety Fasamo (low, early) from 4.8 to 7.9 t DM. Highest yield was obtained with Fedrina and Futura. A slight decrease was seen at the lowest seeding rate. Yield of leaves and seed varied within the five varieties from 2.0 to 4.2 t DM ha⁻¹. The year 1998 was remarkably lower than 1999, and generally there was a decrease in yield at higher plant densities. Lowest fibre yield was found in Fasamo and highest yield in Fedrina, a variation from 1.4 to 4.6 t ha⁻¹. In 1998 the yield was generally lower than in 1999 and generally the fibre yield increased at higher sowing rates. Percent of fiber was lower in 1998 than in 1999 and generally the percent increased at higher sowing rates. Fasamo and Futura were lower in fibre percent than the other varieties. Fasamo was the shortest variety-a little below 2 meters and Futura the highest. Generally the plant height decreased at higher plant densities.

In 1998 the harvested material of leaves and seed were trashed out for seed yield determination. There was a tendency to lower yield at high seeding rates except for the variety Fasamo, which showed the best yield at the highest seeding rate. Fedora gave the highest seed yield, about 600 kg ha⁻¹ and Fasamo the lowest with about 300 kg ha⁻¹. Some bird damage was seen in the plots. In 1999 the plots for seed production were covered by net. Highest seed yield was measured in Fedrina and Fasamo (1,145 kg ha⁻¹), but while Fedrina and the other French varieties showed a remarkably decrease in seed yields at higher sowing rates, Fasamo remained constant in seed yield.

The harvested material was differentiated in four seed sizes: > 2.8mm, 2.5-2.8mm, 2.2-2-4mm and < 2.2mm and given a character for intensity of brown colour, 0-9, where 9 is mostly brown. The smallest seed size was green and unripe and Futura had the most part of green seeds. Compared to the sown seed, the harvested seed was smaller in seed size, about 3 g/1,000 seed. Fasamo had the smallest seeds and Futura the biggest seeds.

No major difference was seen between the varieties in fatty acid composition.

DISCUSSION AND CONCLUSIONS

A decision by law opened up the growing of industrial hemp and field inspections during the growing season by officials takes place. Samples from the fields are examined for content of THC.

Some knowledge have been built up during the two years of trials and are supported by former results in Denmark and by local trials by the farmers union. Trials from the northern part of Europe are useful for comparison as well. Diseases are rarely seen and only with *Sclerotinia*. Only traditional harvest methods are available on big scale: swathing, dew retting and baling.

New processes for fibre removal are in progress all over Europe. Hemp is a promising species for industrial use of fibres for a wide range of composites.

Has a high dry matter and fibre yield per ha and has potential for use of both fibre and seed.

Can be used in non-pesticide or organic farming systems.

REFERENCES

Bagge, H. and A. Larsen, 1951. Forsög med Spindehamp 1941-1948. Tidsskrift for Planteavl, 54. Bind, 628-685.

Larsen, A., 1963. Stammeforsög med Spindehamp 1957-1961. Tidsskrift for Planteavl, 67. Bind 3. Hæfte, 435-443.

Menge Hartmann, U. and F. Höppner, 1995. Insfluss variierter Anbaubedingungen auf die Faserausbildung zweier Faserhanfsorten. Landbauforschung Völkenrode, 45. Jahrgang, Heft 4, 168-176.

Vries, F. P. de, M. J. F. Hendriks and E. Dronkers, 1997. "1000 tonnes of Dutch hemp produces by Hemp-Flax B. V."Stationsweg 22, Ressen, The Netherlands.

Closing session

Highlights and perspectives of European co-operation within the framework of COST Action 814

PETER STAMP

Institute of Plant Sciences, ETH Zentrum, Universitätstrasse 2, 8092 Zürich, Switzerland

INTRODUCTION

Much of northern and western Europe as well as many upland regions in eastern, central and southern Europe are characterised by a cool, wet climate for most or part of the year. In former times, various types of subsistence farming were established, based on a few low-yielding crops such as spring barley as well as on cattle grazing. Modern methods of trade have reached even remote corners of Europe, thus reducing, at least for the time being, farming activities in these marginal regions. Furthermore, the type and range of economically feasible agricultural activity is severely limited compared to regions with more favourable conditions. One way to solve this problem is to concentrate on the cultivation of the few crops and farming systems which are adapted to such conditions. However, the quantity and quality of produce quantity are not particularly stable, inducing farmers to minimise economic risks by using, sometimes inefficiently, more fertilisers and agrochemicals, leading to an increasing number of environmental hazards (e.g. agrochemical pollution, run-off and leaching).

A productive and sustainable production of food and raw material is necessary in these regions, so it is also important to consider the comparative advantages of these marginal areas. The main climatic problem, high and evenly distributed rainfall, can also be regarded as an advantage, because a lack of water is the main limiting factor for crop production in many parts of the world. The physiology of many plants enables them to produce considerable amounts of biomass under permanently cool conditions if enough water is available. For this reason, the challenge in many European countries was perceived to be the identification of promising common, neglected or new plant species for traditional and new systems of farming, species that would profit instead of suffer from the conditions in cool, wet regions if major weaknesses could be got rid of in their overall adaptation. During the 1980s an ideal situation presented itself when basic plant scientists developed powerful physiological and molecular biological tools to identify and analyse reliable single components of adaptation; there was a new generation of agronomists, who had the know-how and training to engage in intensive co-operation with basic plant scientists. This was understood as an outstanding opportunity for improving the tolerance of plant species to abiotic stress, such as excess water and low temperatures, necessary as long as the environmental stress situation persists whereas tolerance to biotic stress (e.g.

pests and disease) is short-lived, because biotic stresses are in constant state of change. In several countries in northwestern Europe, the climate of which is influenced by the Gulf Stream, many groups were working, individually, on improving tolerance to cool, wet conditions, and producing excellent results; in the late 1980s it was decided that these studies should become the topic of intensive, collaborative projects.

Although the integration of improved crops into diversified sustainable agro-ecosystems is the task of national and regional extension services, the initial discussions among basic plant scientists and agronomists led to insights into major weaknesses of agro-ecosystems, which could be eliminated by improving crop species. Many farming systems in cool, wet regions are based on cattle. Thus, a first important step was perceived to be the improvement of pasture quality. Grasses, a major component of pastures, do well with a considerable input of fertilisers. To improve the quality of theses pastures and to reduce the input of fertilisers, it was crucial to introduce a legume like white clover into pastures. It was important to gain greater insight into the long-term persistence of white clover under very variable maritime winter conditions, with the goal of adapting breeding strategies and management systems.

A further opportunity for minimising the influx of external resources in cattle-based farming systems is local production of energy and protein fodder with crops of outstanding quality like maize and soybean. Although these are thermophilic crops they can, in principle, be adapted to cultivation in many cool, wet regions, because the production of high-quality seeds can be outsourced to favourable regions. It became a major goal to increase our knowledge of the most sensitive biochemical and physiological life processes of such thermophilic crops in order to understand and eliminate the major obstacles to increased yield consistency and high sustainability of such crops.

Many countries saw an economic risk in basing farming systems exclusively on cattle. This led to the identification of two other major areas of activity which were, however, included only recently in this COST Action, because the necessary expertise had to be gained. First, arable crops such as spelt wheat and quinoa have been neglected or are relatively new, respectively; both do very well in cool, wet regions and are a source of non-allergic food with interesting quality aspects. However, they are not well adapted to modern farming practices and increased soil fertility; these problems must be solved by goal-oriented breeding programs.

Furthermore, some fibre crops do particularly well in wet climates (e.g. hemp, miscanthus and reed canarygrass). Miscanthus is partially thermophilic, and an advantage was seen in linking its improvement with progress in the breeding of maize and soybean. Knowledge of reed canarygrass could be linked to our growing understanding of winter survival and cutting strategies in the production of white clover. Thus it was decided to include these crops in research programmes as being potentially high-quality industrial products.

Finally, from the beginning of this project the ecological threat of nitrate leaching could not be overlooked in our effort to maintain the cool, wet regions of Europe at a competitive, productive level. During the first few years, progress made in improving strategies for nitrogen-efficient farming systems was followed up by workshops. These activities were intensified by bringing together scientists who are on the right path for genetically improving the capacity of several target crops to use nitrogen more efficiently.

It would be unrealistic to expect drastic changes in crop adaptation only within eight years when it has taken farmers eight thousand years to change wild plants into reliable crops and modern plant breeders took eight decades to breed high yielding crop varieties. Nevertheless, we could make the most of the eight years allotted to us to solve a number of crucial problems related to the adaptation of crops to cool, wet regions.

Our goals and achievements

During Round I, it was our goal to gain a understanding of the mechanisms involved in overwintering of an important pasture species such as *Trifolium repens* L., (white clover). Our network of experimental sites grew to include regions from Italy to northern Norway and Iceland. Another approach was to conduct complementary laboratory tests for an improved definition of selection criteria for chilling-tolerant maize and soybeans. The working group which carried out these tests benefited from the financial support given by Brussels to three excellent laboratories in Poland and Slovakia. During this first round an intensive analysis was made within the scope of the Technical Annex how to determine and how to expand our investigations to new or neglected alternative crops. During intensive discussions at the Management Committee Meetings and assisted by highly qualified external experts, further promising areas of interest for new working groups were identified: "Small grain cereals and pseudocereals", "Alternative fibre crops" and "Nitrogen use efficiency".

Overwintering and Spring Growth of White Clover

Cattle farming continues to be a reliable activity in cold and wet regions. COST 814 has been determined to increase economic competitiveness in this area, too. It was concluded that plant adaptation is a major factor in the establishment of pasture systems with a high and stable proportion of white clover (*Trifolium repens*). This legume is a native European plant and improves the fodder quality and, thus, the productivity of cattle. It grows well with reduced input of external mineral nitrogen in contrast to grasses. However, a major drawback for productive cattle farms is that white clover is unpredictable as far as overwintering is concerned. The proportion of white clover fluctuates from season to season. As a first step it was decided to screen for white clover cultivars with contrasting characteristics with respect to winter hardiness and productivity, which are normally difficult to combine. Thereafter, a common protocol was set up for a network of field experiments in which overwintering and cold adaptation of these two contrasting model cultivars were compared. This approach proved to be extremely successful. Started by a few central European laboratories, it soon attracted 12 laboratories in ten countries, from the Friulian Alps of Italy to Iceland and northern Norway. Until them, scientific investigations of this important topic had been carried out at a national level. Through COST 814, a fast and efficient exchange of expertise led to clear, uniform protocols according to which cold adaptation and overwintering of white clover would be evaluated in future collaborative studies. Above all, it was deemed necessary to characterise precisely the conditions in winter which range from moderately cold winters in Ireland, with a scarcely interrupted growing season, to Scandinavian winters, subjecting the plants to very stressful situations, ranging from a thick and persistent snow cover to returning ice encasement in Iceland and Finland. Thus an extremely valuable data set was collected within the scope of the COST 814 program, requiring the collaboration of a number of laboratories. In order to process this unique set of data, financial support was applied for and granted by COST 814 for the purpose of appointing an outstanding scientist for a period of one year. In close contact with all participants, this expert analysed and modelled the patterns of overwintering of white clover, an unprecedented way to predict the best adapted white clover cultivars and to manage them to ensure their endurance. During Round II, further investigations were initiated in a collaboration with selected laboratories. Their aim was to achieve well-adapted, clover-based grassland systems which had been deemed to be necessary from the ongoing network study. This includes competition among clover and grass varieties which can be predeterminant for overwintering and the nitrogen and carbon economy under low temperature; it was also necessary to study the symbiotic *Rhizobium* partner. Genetic shifts in the white clover population were observed at an early stage; plants that survived under extremely harsh conditions were selected to launch specific genetic studies on genetic shifts, including molecular tools, but which can be directly used as valuable new germplasm by those scientists who are involved in white clover breeding.

Some of these results were published annually in detailed reports (1993 to 1999), supplemented by a workshop at the Conference of the European Grassland Federation in 1996 in Grado, Italy and in a workshop at Pamplona in 1998 (Publ. 8). This led to the formulation of valuable internal guidelines, but a major manual will be a refereed publication which will lay down the new standards for the successful establishment of white clover, which requires the selection and development of the most suitable genetic material for requirements. The importance of publishing these achievements is demonstrated by the agreement reached with the renowned journal, Annals of Botany, which will publish them in a special issue in 2001 (Publ. 11).

Adaptation of Thermophilic Crops

During the preparation of COST 814, it was clearly perceived that the maintenance of agricultural activities in marginal areas cannot be based exclusively on perennial grassland species. Looking at the history of most of the arable crops, they migrated slowly from southern parts of the old world to central, western and northern Europe. The success of farmers in achieving plant adaptation to climate is poorly documented with the exception of a few, famous examples such as grapes, which initially performed badly in the early days of the Roman empire. Today, however, high-quality wine is produced in Burgundy and the Rhine-Mosel valley! Today, too, we can find long-season thermophilic field crops such as maize, soybean and sunflower in cool temperate climates because of the desired superiority of their products. It was decided that COST 814 should concentrate on the basic improvement of the chilling tolerance of such target crops to achieve the following long-term goals:

a. enhancement of yield consistency, making these crops acceptable to farmers because of the small risk of failure;

b. reduced input and protection level, because vigorous crops become more suitable for sustainable cropping systems;

c. increase in the biodiversity at the field level by a larger choice between climatically well adapted crops.

COST provides a flexible platform for initiating, expanding, and, if necessary, changing the direction of a scientific approach. Within a short period of time, many excellent laboratories from all over Europe combined their expertise, which ranged from the analysis of growth processes to the understanding of physiological limitations such as nutrient assimilation at the root level and to the disturbance of photosynthetic processes within chloroplasts. These interactions among breeders, agronomists, plant physiologists and, especially during Round II, molecular biologists, proved to be extremely successful in fine-tuning the goals and the best conditions to attain them within a complementary research program. Before, a large number of laboratory experiments on chilling tolerance was concentrated on seedlings after a temperature drop from about 20°C to almost 0°C for a few hours or days; a multitude of such results have been published in renowned international journals. Within the COST 814 co-operation it was soon demonstrated that such situations rarely occur in cool, wet regions in Europe during the early seedling stage! Thus, protocols were established which brought attention that the best simulation to field condition was achieved by a long-term adaptation to sub-optimal temperatures in the range of about 14°C. These conditions were very similar to conditions in the glass-house where vegetables such as tomatoes were produced at a lower temperature for economic reasons. This proved to be very fruitful, because links were quickly established to researchers in The Netherlands, who have considerable experience in the chilling tolerance of tomatoes.

Remarkable progress was already made by the end of Round I in that a clear protocol was established for morphological selection criteria in cold-tolerant soybeans. It was proven that, contrary to most other thermophilic crops, the flowering stage is the most sensitive period for a high and consistent yield. Defining temperature thresholds for productive soybean varieties provides guidelines for farmers and extension services. In Austria, France and Switzerland, high yielding, extremely early, and cold-tolerant soybean varieties are now available. In order to appreciate the level of these achievements, one has to understand that in a major soybean producing country like the United States soybean varieties are classed from 0 to 10, according to whether they are early or late varieties. In Europe, it was necessary to establish new classes for earliness and triple zero (000) varieties are now available! Unfortunately the low world market prices may endanger work on adaptation in Europe; a breeding programme solely for our cool, wet regions may be stopped soon for economic reasons.

Major physiological processes that occur in the root and leaf are well understood because of the intensive collaboration of the COST 814 scientists. We demonstrated clearly that a well branched root system in cool soils is a prerequisite for maize genotypes to adapt to cool, wet regions; however, interdependent processes also occur between the shoot system and the soil, because a well functioning supply of carbohydrates to the root is essential for keeping these developmental processes well balanced. In former years, it was reported that photosynthetic efficiency played the smallest role in the chilling tolerance of maize. Collaborative research, carried out within COST 814, brought very convincing evidence to light, revealing that, at relevant cool temperatures (see above), combined with a high light intensity, photo-oxidative damage is actually a very important cause of the poor performance of maize seedlings at low temperatures. The tremendous progress made in understanding critical bottlenecks has been due to a considerable extent to methodological improvements such as high resolution chlorophyll fluorescence imaging techniques, a very powerful tool for detecting the sites of early stress effects and enabling molecular analysis of those sites.

Molecular studies were initiated as early as Round II, because it cannot be feasible for breeders to select directly for an improved root morphology, for example. These investigations must be carefully planned. At the moment marker populations are established between laboratories which hopefully will lead to suitable Quantitative Trait Loci (QTL) for breeders within a few years. A direct consequence of our high level of knowledge about photo-thermic damage to leaves were experimental breeding studies for improving germplasm, which is presently being tested by a private breeder, and the development of molecular markers at CIMMYT in Mexico. These studies should make it easier to introgress such traits into yield-consistent maize varieties for marginal cool, wet regions in Europe.

Due to the necessity of an exchange of expertise among disciplines, it was decided at the beginning of COST 814 to invite many leading scientists to participate in progress discussions and COST instituted supporting workshops for this purpose. Four of these workshops were devoted, at least in part, to cold tolerance of agricultural crops and provided an excellent platform for the exchange of new ideas. All the major achievements outlined above are fully documented in four preceeding volumes (Publs. 2, 4, 7, 8).

Alternative Crops

During the initial discussions about the Action "Crop development for the cool and wet regions", it was regarded as an important mandate to identify alternative crops which might be suitable because they had adapted to climatic conditions, have a low requirement for external inputs and results in particularly interesting products for regional and/or international markets. Throughout Round I we profited from experts on the Management Committee who assisted in identifying a large number of likely crops, culminating in a workshop in Wageningen in 1994, which was attended by many scientists (Publ. 3). Thereafter, it was decided to concentrate on a few crops with a number of the attributes outlined above in Round II.

Small grain cereals and pseudocereals

Within this group the main focus was on two species, both of which are already well adapted to cool, wet regions and are excellent, alternative food of high quality. Spelt wheat can be considered to be a neglected, traditional species which was extremely important in cool, wet mountainous regions of Europe. Interest in this close relative of bread wheat was revived because of its low demand for soil nitrate and its use in producing a range of bakery products which are low in allergic gluten components. During recent years, major advantage and disadvantages of this crop were defined. Its specific product quality has been recognised, and for this reason European breeders have become aware that improving agronomic characters such as lodging resistance, important in cool, wet regions, by the introgression of bread wheat is feasible only when the essential quality traits of spelt are monitored and maintained. Otherwise laborious efforts to re-establish an ecologically valuable crop in cool, wet regions would be futile, because industry refuses to accept an expensive product from a plant which looks like spelt but is "masked" bread wheat. The working group has made considerable progress identifying the most important traits for high seedling vigour of spelt, which is often sown in cold, wet soil in autumn. The traits were grouped together as tolerance and avoidance mechanisms when there is a lack of oxygen (hypoxia) during germination and early seedling growth. Molecular markers have been developed for such traits; thus, it will be possible in the future to use spelt as an alternative source of genes, which may improve the adaptation of bread wheat to cool, wet regions!

Quinoa, a new crop in Europe , has a long tradition in South America. The crop does extremely well on poor soil. Many different ecotypes exist in South America, and it is, therefore, a considerable challenge to determine the most suitable ideotypes for cool, wet regions. Quinoa can be considered to be a multipurpose crop, which can be used for human consumption and animal feed because of it high nutritional value. The recent development of saponine-free cultivars in The Netherlands offers several new forms of human and animal nutrition (e.g., several forms of vegetarian and baby food, grains which are toasted or ground into flour and green pellets are used as animal feed). Quinoa can also be utilised as an industrial crop because of its starch content (about 60%). The starch granules are uniformly small in size (1 to 4mm) and make quinoa starch different from the starch of other plant species with several potential industrial applications. Similar to a neglected, traditional crop such as spelt, the agronomic traits that determine productivity (e.g., seed quality, germination in cool soil, early and synchronous flowering) have to be defined and improved. The main outcome of the collaboration in recent years can be briefly summarised as a clear definition of the agronomic procedures that lead to safe crop management and settling priorities in selecting breeding goals such as photo-periodic insensitivity, tolerance to germination in cold soils and early maturity. These efforts will be continued in the next years, because quinoa products are making it an increasingly important commodity in Europe; it is paving the way to biodiverse agriculture in cool, wet regions. The main achievements are documented in two proceedings (Publs. 6, 10).

Alternative fibre crops

Quite a number of crops that grow under the temperate conditions in Europe provide fibres of varying quality. Such crops may be particularly suitable for cool, wet regions because the availability of sufficient water is a prerequisite for a high biomass production. This was recognised and discussed in sub-group meetings of COST 814 during Round I. Such crops offer the chance to produce a widely marketable commodity instead of niche products. Thus, they are a valuable means to an important source of income of marginal regions. On the other hand, they must compete with imported fibre crops on the world market as well as with regional forestry products. For these reasons, it was deemed necessary to first determine whether priority should be given to quality fibre products rather than to alternative crops. It was decided by the The Management Committee of COST 814, however, to focus primarily on the climatic and agronomic adaptation of potential crops, because this offers the best opportunity to refer to existing crops. At the beginning of Round II, a number of crops were analysed for their potential suitability, traditional crops such as flax, hemp, nettle as well as new crops like *Phalaris arundinacea* (reed canarygrass) and *Miscanthus sinensis* (miscanthus).

Many European countries have shown great interest in miscanthus, a very productive fibre crop from East Asia. It was perceived to be a real challenge to concentrate on a variety of aspects ranging from nutrient efficiency, good overwintering and rapid regrowth of this C4 plant. Although it is a reasonably winter hardy crop, it tends to be susceptible to low temperatures during early spring growth. This gave rise to an intensive collaboration among research groups working on the adaptation of thermophilic plants such as maize. The development of molecular markers for chilling-stable photosynthesis in maize will make it possible to transfer this knowledge to miscanthus. However, the yield consistency and profitability of this crop will also depend on the ability of this crop to overwinter.

This is true as well for the second potential fibre crop, reed canarygrass. An indigenous crop, well-adapted to the rather wet, cool conditions of northern and western Europe, it is a reliable source of short fibres which augments the long fibres produced by trees. In spite of its origin, not all strains of this grass species are as suitable for producing high-quality fibre. For this reason, much effort was put into testing and selecting of productive, well adapted varieties which can tolerate harsh winter conditions in the north. We drew on experience with the overwintering of white clover, because similar unique winter stress situations (e.g., ice encasement of plants) have to be withstood.

Miscanthus and reed canarygrass have a similar ecological advantage that is linked to the harvest at the end of winter. At this time most nutrients such as nitrogen, phosphorous and potassium have returned to the soil or soil cover which puts such cultivation systems at a considerable advantage in ecologically vulnerable cool, wet regions.

With regard to hemp, an annual crop, its suitability in cool, wet regions with, at least in part, high summer temperatures was generally accepted. Breeding priorities were defined: e.g., low THC content and a rapid early and late growth. Furthermore, the focus was placed on factors related to high-quality fibre, especially the quantification of cell wall contents, to ensure a competitive market sector for this neglected old crop.

The results of these activities were presented in detail at several, well-documented working group meetings and at a final workshop in Turku, Finland in 1999, which was dedicated to alternative crops for a sustainable agriculture in the cool, wet regions of Europe (Publ. 10). It is to be hoped that new platforms for intensive research activities will be established; in close contact with other working groups, it became increasingly clear that the establishment of these crops requires long-term scientific study, based on the progress made with better known related crops.

Nitrogen Use Efficiency

The modernisation of agricultural systems has always been accompanied by considerable environmental hazards such as erosion when the soil is bare, run-off of nutrients and pesticides into water systems and leaching of unwanted substances into ground water. All these hazards are, of course, aggravated by cool conditions when poorly adapted crops develop slowly and have sub optimal root systems. At the beginning of Round I, the Management Committee decided to concentrate on an environmental problem which is of importance in all the cool, wet regions of Europe, in lowlands as well as in hilly and mountainous regions: the nitrogen use efficiency of crops and cropping systems. In 1992 and 1995, workshops were dedicated to this theme with the goal of gathering together the most competent experts and focusing research activities on the general goal of plant adaptation (Publs. 1, 5). Considerable effort was put into developing a better understanding of nitrogen cycling in arable cropping systems, and grassland systems, resulting in sound knowledge on how and when the synchronisation of nitrogen availability and plant demand could be reached. During these workshops and at subsequent Management Committee meetings, considerable progress was made in modelling the N demand of target crops of the COST 814 Action: these included maize and especially the development of systems which include dead and living cover crops in association with maize cultivation in cool, wet regions. It was acknowledged, however, that the approach being taken was still too broad to be followed up in detail within the scope of the Action, which was expressly dedicated to crop adaptation. For this reason, N-supply strategies, and cropping systems at the farm level were no longer at the core of these activities.

It was agreed that nitrogen efficiency is a major attribute for well-adapted crops. Thus, the Working Group on nitrogen use efficiency was established in Round II. As soon as collaborative research began, it became evident that important scientific terms, such as N-efficiency, definitions of the major scientific expressions, N-utilisation and N-uptake had to be clearly defined before breeding goals could be decided upon. The initial investigations concentrated on determining the plant attributes that are important for superior genotypes with regard to morphology and physiology and their subsequent utilization as selection markers. In line with the other working groups, special attention was paid to the introduction of molecular markers into the breeding process, because it is difficult to screen for nitrogen use efficiency under highly variable cool, wet conditions.

A crop of maize proved to enhance nitrogen losses when the soil was bare in spring; great progress was made in identifying breeding germplasm which performs well under low availability of nitrogen in the soil, a very important attribute both for ecologically-adapted management with a low early input of fertiliser and for the cropping systems defined in Round I in which cover crops reduce the early availability of nitrogen for maize! Furthermore, Quantitative Trait Loci (QTL) were identified for the nitrogen use efficiency in maize under conditions of low availability. These QTL have to be developed further for molecular marker assisted maize breeding.

For other arable crops, such as bread wheat and especially spelt wheat, private breeding companies were successful in determining simple seedling traits as a first step towards selecting for nitrogen use efficiency; further steps must be taken to achieve marker-assisted breeding.

Very promising approaches have been followed in defining nitrogen use efficiency criteria for fodder grasses. Especially for perennial ryegrass, one of the most important crop species in cool and wet pastures, large-scale cooperation has been established among six European laboratories to establish marker-assisted breeding strategies to improve nitrogen use efficiency with the final aim of increasing milk and meat production and reducing nitrogen input. These studies can be broadened to include new germplasm for the overwintering of white clover, which will further reduce the input of nitrogen inputs while the quality of fodder continues to improve.

Finally, some of the work being done on finding QTL will be extended beyond the scope of this Action with the goal of sequencing genes for nitrogen use. Considering the rapid progress made in molecular biology, such as understanding the syntheny among related genomes, genetic traits for nitrogen use efficiency of one crop can be efficiently transferred to other crop species of interest in the cool, wet regions of Europe. The major outcome of the collaborative work can be found in the proceedings of the workshop from Ghent, Belgium in 1999 (Publ. 9).

Our perspectives

The multidisciplinary approach of COST 814 gave rise to working group meetings and workshops which proved to be excellent platforms for disseminating ideas that had been intensively discussed and developed by the Management Committee. Overlapping interests with goals from Framework IV of the EU led for example to a widely joined SECO programme on the development of spelt wheat. Some important topis could not, in spite of some overlap, be integrated within the present Action. Seed quality, for example, was also a major goal of COST 814, but finally a specific new COST Action was proposed by Hungary on seed quality, approved as COST Action 828.

Although COST 814 concentrated on crop development in cool, wet regions in Europe, the general approaches – from the gene to the crop – are also of interest to the international scientific community. All members were encouraged by the Management Committee to publish the results of the collaborative research in renowned international journals.

One of the major strengths of COST 814 was its broad, multidisciplinary approach which lead to collaboration among outstanding researchers in Europe. These researchers from many disciplines opened the door to consulting with experts world-wide. It can be regarded as a proof of the importance of this Action as a multidisciplinary platform for the exchange and development of scientific ideas that renowned experts from North and South Americas and from East Asia were motivated to participate in the workshops. A Japanese Scientist, for example, was so impressed by the Cost Action that he pleaded for the development of similar platforms for East and South-East Asia!

Involving private breeders in COST 814 proved to be difficult, contrary to our initial expectations. In general, this was due to reluctance to invest in breeding goals which do not lead immediately to a highly and widely marketable product. In contrast, the principal objective of COST 814 was to develop crops specifically adapted to marginal regions. Governmental funding is mandatory if the breeding of alternative new crops and the improvement of neglected crops such as small grains and pseudocereals, very early soybean cultivars and newly cultivated fibre crops (e.g. reed canarygrass) are to continue. Before these crops are well established in all regions, private breeders are increasingly reluctant to invest in activities that concentrate on marginal regions. The Management Committee reached the conclusion that, together with scientific studies, European governments must become involved if the biodiversity of crops is to be pursued on a long-term basis.

Understandably, private breeders showed much more interest when the tolerance of widely distributed crops such as maize was the focus of our investigations. Adaptation to a cool, wet spring climate is crucial in cool, wet regions, but it is also a valuable asset for improving early vigour in more favourable regions. Several contacts were established with maize breeding companies in Europe and North America, concerning the development of molecular markers for cold tolerance. As mentioned above, a joint project between a participating laboratory and a private company has begun this year.

The benefits of a multidisciplinary approach to a broad topic like "Crop Development for the Cool and Wet Regions of Europe" were widely acknowledged, and it became clear that it will to take a long time to find solutions for marginal regions. Nevertheless, the Management Committee recommended new, specific Actions which would quickly implement the newly developed molecular tools. On a personal note, three of the five highly competent group leaders will have retired by the end of this year. They and the Management Committee have encouraged a new generation of European scientists to take responsibility for future work in this area. Two new Actions have been proposed, which have partly grown out of the two working groups on the overwintering of white clover and the low temperature tolerance of thermophilic crops. They will both focus on general adaptation mechanisms to sub optimal growth conditions without specific regional aspects.

Our suggestions

We are proud that we were able to motivate new experts in Europe to participate in our workshops. Unfortunately, we had to draw the line – within the scope of this project for Europe – at allowing non-European scientists to join specific Working Groups. These workshops were also very valuable for an integrating new partners from central and east European countries like Hungary, Poland and Slovakia. Above all, we are grateful that the Working Group meetings were always hosted by those members who had access to the facilities of research stations and universities and this helped to keep the costs low. This was extremely important for young collaborators who were keen to participate. Only two officially funded scientists were allowed to participate, too few, especially for larger member countries.

It proved difficult to find adequate funding for the collaborative projects in all the member countries. This revealed the necessity of contacting and motivating national funding agencies to take into their consideration an expert review, organised and approved by the Management Committee as an added value of a national project application. This would be a advantage benefit for the individual co-ordination of activities at the right time, which could be a comparative advantage instead of a disadvantage to STD programs with a rigid start of all research groups at a prefixed date.

During Round I, scientific exchange and the training of scientists already profited from the excellent instrument of Scientific Short Term Missions. The Management Committee stressed that the scientific benefits and the importance of more efficient co-operation was extremely high in comparison to the low expenses for single missions. Financial support was generally given to our young colleagues, often from central and eastern Europe. The maximum period of training time of 30 days. We wish to express our gratitude to all member institutions who contributed inexpensive accommodation, etc., thus making training possible. The Management Committee strongly recommended that the Commission in Brussels should increase the length of these short-term scientific projects to three months in justified cases.

ACKNOWLEDGEMENTS

From the beginning of Round I COST 814 profited from a Management Committee which included experts from fields of basic plant physiology to applied agronomy. The enormous task of defining the most urgent goals for plant adaptation to cool, wet regions and to meet these goals by making the best use of expertise in the participating laboratories as well as motivating new laboratories to participate in could never have been achieved without the ability of the Management Committee to engage in fruitful discussions and make appropriate decisions. It was a great advantage that many countries were represented by one member from applied science and one from the basic sciences. Progress was accelerated by the willingness of the Management Committee to devote time to organising workshops for the core tasks, assisted by members from all the participating countries. Furthermore, the Management Committee succeeded in motivating the best international experts to participate in the workshops and shore their views with us on the work of COST 814. Special thanks go to those institutions which made substantial financial contributions as well as making their facilities available for enabling them to be conducted these workshops, at the level of the best international conferences on specialised topics. All the contributions to these workshops have been published as full papers in proceedings of the workshops.

Above all we gratefully acknowledge the assistance and support of the Commission in Brussels in publishing the proceedings of COST 814.

We are proud that our collaborative work was successfully and remained harmonious for such a long period. We are sure that many of our achievements will serve directly and indirectly as the basis for sustainable and productive agriculture in the cool, wet regions of Europe.

COST 814 PUBLICATIONS

1- Proceedings: Workshop on "Nitrogen Cycling & Leaching in Cool & Wet Regions of Europe", Gembloux (B), 22/23 Sep 1992 (ISBN 2-87263-089-9)

2- Proceedings: Workshop on "Crop Adaptation to Cool, Wet, Climates", Aberystwyth (UK), 23/24 Mar 1993 (ISBN 2-87263-102-X)

3- Proceedings: Workshop on "Alternative Oilseed and Fibre Crops for Cool & Wet Regions of Europe, Wageningen (NL), 7/8 Apr 1994 (ISBN 2-87263-119-4)

4- Proceedings: Workshop on "Crop Adaptation to Cool Climates", Hamburg (D), 13/14 Oct 1994 (ISBN 2-87263-147-X)

5- Proceedings: Workshop on "Nitrogen Supply and Nitrogen Fixation of Crops for Cool and Wet Climates", Tromsö (N), 7/9 Sep 1995 (ISBN 92-827-5346-8)

6- Proceedings: Workshop on "Small Cereals and Pseudo Cereals" Copenhagen (DK), 22/24 Feb 1996 (ISBN 92-827-8733-8)

7- Proceedings: Workshop on „Crop Development for the Cool and Wet Regions of Europe", Warsaw (PL), 15/17 Mar 1997 (ISBN 92-828-1810-1)

8- Proceedings: Workshop on „Crop Development for Cool and Wet Climate of Europe", Pamplona (E), 19/21 Oct 1998 (ISBN 92-828-6947-4)

9- Proceedings: Workshop on „N-use Efficiency", Melle (B), 2/5 Jun 1999 (ISBN 92-8 2 8 - 8670-0)

10 -Proceedings: Workshop on „Alternative Crops for Sustainable Agriculture", Turku (FIN), 13/15 Jun 1999 (ISBN 92-828-7831-7)

11- Special issue of Annals of Botany, appearance date July 2001: "Overwintering and Dynamics of White Clover (Trifolium repens L.)", (Scientific results of COST 814)

INDEX OF AUTHORS

European Commission

EUR 19683 — COST Action 814 — Crop development for the cool and wet regions of Europe

Edited by G. Parente and J. Frame

Luxembourg: Office for Official Publications of the European Communities

2000 — 628 pp. — 16.2 x 22.9 cm

ISBN 92-894-0227-X

Price (excluding VAT) in Luxembourg: EUR 93.50